A2-Level Mathematics

A2 Maths is seriously tricky — no question about that.
To do well, you're going to need to revise properly and practise hard.

This book has thorough notes on everything in modules C3, C4, S2 and M2.
It'll help you learn the stuff you need and take you step-by-step through loads of examples.

It's got practice questions... lots of them. For every topic there are warm-up and exam-style questions. Plus there are two full practice exams at the end of each module.

And of course, we've done our best to make the whole thing vaguely entertaining for you.

Complete Revision and Practice

Exam Board: OCR

Contents

Core Mathematics C3

C3 Section 1 — Algebra and Functions
Functions and Mappings 1
Composite Functions 2
Inverse Functions 3
Modulus 4
Transformations of Graphs 7
Practice Questions 8

C3 Section 2 — Exponentials and Logarithms
e^x, ln x and Graphs 10
Using e^x and ln x — Solving Equations 11
Practice Questions 13

C3 Section 3 — Trigonometry
Sin^{-1}, Cos^{-1} and Tan^{-1} 15
Secant, Cosecant and Cotangent 16
Using Trigonometric Identities 17
The Addition Formulas 18
The Double Angle Formulas 19
The R Addition Formulas 20
More Trigonometry Stuff 21
Practice Questions 22

C3 Section 4 — Differentiation and Integration
Chain Rule 24
Differentiation of e^x and ln x 25
Product Rule 26
Quotient Rule 27
More Differentiation 28
Relating Rates of Change 29
Integration of e^x and $1/x$ 30
Volumes of Revolution 31
Practice Questions 32

C3 Section 5 — Numerical Methods
Location of Roots 34
Iterative Methods 35
Numerical Integration 37
Practice Questions 38

C3 Practice Exams
C3 — Practice Exam One 40
C3 — Practice Exam Two 43

Core Mathematics C4

C4 Section 1 — Algebra and Functions
Simplifying Expressions 46
Algebraic Division 47
Partial Fractions 49
Practice Questions 51

C4 Section 2 — Parametric Equations
Parametric Equations of Curves 53
Using Parametric Equations 54
Parametric and Cartesian Equations 55
Practice Questions 56

C4 Section 3 — Binomial Expansions
Basic Binomial Expansions 58
Trickier Expansions 59
Approximating with Binomial Expansions 61
Practice Questions 62

C4 Section 4 — Differentiation
Differentiation of Sin, Cos and Tan 64
More Trig Differentiation 65
Differentiation with Parametric Equations 66
Implicit Differentiation 67
Practice Questions 69

C4 Section 5 — Integration
Integration of Sin and Cos 71
Integration of $f'(x)/f(x)$ 72
Integration Using the Chain Rule Backwards 73
Integrating Trig Things Using Trig Identities 74
Integration by Substitution 75
Integration by Parts 76
Tough Integrals 77
Differential Equations 78
Practice Questions 80

C4 Section 6 — Vectors
Vectors 82
Vector Equations of Lines 85
Scalar Product 86
Practice Questions 89

C4 Practice Exams
C4 — Practice Exam One 91
C4 — Practice Exam Two 93

Contents

Statistics S2

S2 Section 1 — The Poisson Distribution

The Poisson Distribution ... 95
The Poisson Parameter ... 96
Using Poisson Tables ... 97
Po(λ) as an Approximation to B(n, p) ... 98
Worked Problems ... 99
Practice Questions ... 100

S2 Section 2 — Continuous Random Variables

Probability Density Functions ... 102
Mean and Variance ... 104
More on Continuous Random Variables ... 105
Practice Questions ... 106

S2 Section 3 — The Normal Distribution

Normal Distributions ... 108
The Standard Normal Distribution, Z ... 109
Normal Distributions and Z-Tables ... 110
Normal Approximation to B(n, p) ... 112
Normal Approximation to Po(λ) ... 114
More About Approximations ... 115
Practice Questions ... 116

S2 Section 4 — Sampling and Hypothesis Tests

Sampling ... 118
Sampling Distribution of $\overline{X}$ ... 119
Estimation ... 120
Null and Alternative Hypotheses ... 121
Significance Levels and Critical Regions ... 122
Hypothesis Tests and Normal Distributions ... 123
Hypothesis Tests and Binomial Distributions ... 125
Hypothesis Tests and Poisson Distributions ... 127
Practice Questions ... 128

S2 Practice Exams

S2 — Practice Exam One ... 130
S2 — Practice Exam Two ... 133

Statistical Tables ... 136

Mechanics M2

M2 Section 1 — Centres of Mass

Discrete Groups of Particles in 1 Dimension ... 146
Discrete Groups of Particles in 2 Dimensions ... 147
Standard Uniform Laminas ... 148
Composite Shapes ... 149
Centres of Mass in 3 Dimensions ... 150
Laminas in Equilibrium ... 151
Practice Questions ... 152

M2 Section 2 — Statics of Rigid Bodies

Moments ... 154
Rigid Bodies ... 156
Rigid Bodies and Friction ... 157
Laminas and Moments ... 159
Practice Questions ... 160

M2 Section 3 — Projectiles

Projectiles ... 162
Practice Questions ... 165

M2 Section 4 — Uniform Circular Motion

Circular Motion ... 166
Conical Pendulums ... 167
Practice Questions ... 168

M2 Section 5 — Energy, Work and Power

Work Done ... 170
Kinetic and Potential Energy ... 171
The Work-Energy Principle ... 173
Power ... 175
Practice Questions ... 177

M2 Section 6 — Collisions

Impulse ... 180
Collisions ... 182
Complex Collisions ... 184
Collisions and Energy ... 185
Practice Questions ... 186

M2 Practice Exams

M2 — Practice Exam One ... 188
M2 — Practice Exam Two ... 191

C3 — Answers ... 194
C4 — Answers ... 208
S2 — Answers ... 226
M2 — Answers ... 237

Index ... 255

Contributors:
Andy Ballard, Mary Falkner, Paul Jordin, Sharon Keeley-Holden, Simon Little, Sam Norman, Ali Palin, Andy Park, David Ryan, Lyn Setchell, Caley Simpson, Jane Towle, Jonathan Wray, Dawn Wright

Proofreaders:
Mona Allen, Vicky Daniel, Janet Dickinson, Glenn Rogers

Published by CGP

ISBN: 978 1 84762 586 1

Groovy Website: www.cgpbooks.co.uk

Printed by Elanders Ltd, Newcastle upon Tyne.

Based on the classic CGP style created by Richard Parsons.

Functions and Mappings

In A2 maths, your teacher might ask you to draw a mapping diagram. Sadly, they don't want you to draw an exciting map with rivers, mountains, caves and secret tunnels on it — they want you to draw a boring diagram. Shame.

Values in the Domain are Mapped to values in the Range

1) A mapping is an operation that takes one number and transforms it into another. E.g. 'multiply by 5', 'square root' and 'divide by 7' are all mappings.
2) The set of numbers you can start with is called the domain, and the set of numbers they can become is called the range. Mappings can be drawn as diagrams like this: You can also draw mappings as graphs (see below).
3) The domain and / or range will often be the set of real numbers, $\mathbb{R}$ (a real number is any positive or negative number (or 0) — fractions, decimals, integers, surds). If x can take any real value, it's usually written as $x \in \mathbb{R}$.
4) You might have to work out the range of a mapping from the domain you're given. For example, $y = x^2$, $x \in \mathbb{R}$ has the range $f(x) \geq 0$, as all square real numbers are positive (or zero).

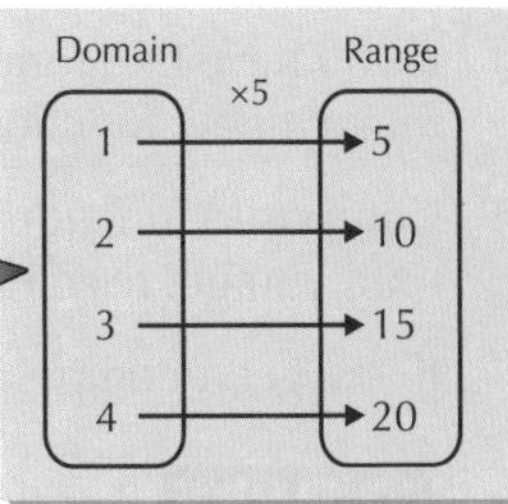

Other sets of numbers include $\mathbb{Z}$, the set of integers, $\mathbb{N}$, the set of natural numbers (positive integers, not including 0) and $\mathbb{C}$, the complex numbers (made up of 'imaginary' numbers — you don't meet these in C3 or C4).

A Function is a type of Mapping

1) Some mappings take every number in the domain to only one number in the range. These mappings are called functions. If a mapping takes a number from the domain to more than one number in the range (or if it isn't mapped to any number in the range), it's not a function.

Functions (e.g. x^2) are usually written as $f(x) = x^2$ or $f : x \rightarrow x^2$.

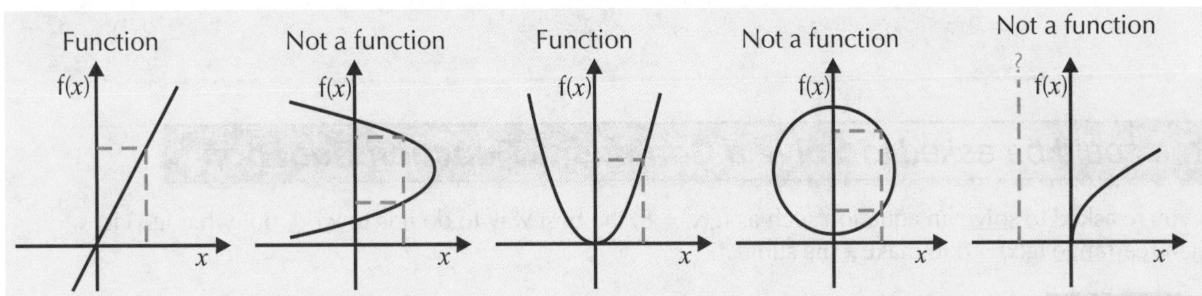

2) For the graphs above, the first and third are functions because each value of x is mapped to a single value of $f(x)$. The second and fourth aren't functions because the values of x are mapped to two different values of $f(x)$. The fifth also isn't a function, this time because $f(x)$ is not defined for $x < 0$.
3) Some mappings that aren't functions can be turned into functions by restricting their domain. For example, the mapping $y = \frac{1}{x-1}$ for $x \in \mathbb{R}$ is not a function, because it's not defined at $x = 1$ (draw the graph if you're not convinced). But if you change the domain to $x > 1$, the mapping is now a function.

Functions can be One-to-One or Many-to-One

1) A one-to-one (or one-one) function maps one element in the domain to one element in the range — e.g. $f(x) = 2x$, $x \in \mathbb{R}$ is one-to-one, as every x is mapped to a unique value in the range (the range is also $\mathbb{R}$). So only 3 in the domain is mapped to 6 in the range.
2) A many-to-one (or many-one) function maps more than one element in the domain to one element in the range (remember that no element in the domain can map to more than one element in the range, otherwise it wouldn't be a function). $f(x) = x^2$, $x \in \mathbb{R}$ is a many-to-one function, as two elements in the domain map to the same element in the range — e.g. both 3 and –3 map to 9.

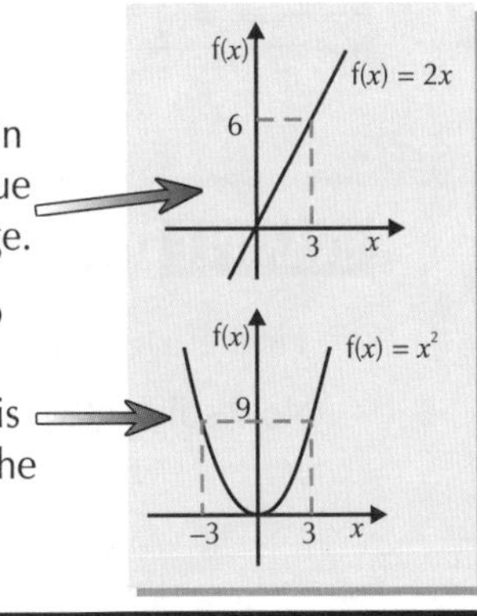

Welcome to my domain...

When you're drawing a function or a mapping, you should draw a mapping diagram if you're given a discrete set of numbers (e.g. $x \in \{0,1,2,3\}$), but you should draw a graph if the domain is continuous (e.g. $x \in \mathbb{R}$).

Composite Functions

You're not done with functions yet. Oh no. You need to know what happens if you put two (or more) functions together. There's only one way to find out...

Functions can be Combined to make a Composite Function

1) If you have two functions f and g, you can combine them (do one followed by the other) to make a new function. This is called a composite function.
2) Composite functions are written fg(x) — this means do g first, then f. If it helps, put brackets in until you get used to it, so fg(x) = f(g(x)). The order is really important — usually fg(x) ≠ gf(x).
3) If you get a composite function that's written $f^2(x)$, it means ff(x) — you do f twice.

Composite functions made up of three or more functions work in exactly the same way.

EXAMPLE For the functions $f(x) = 2x^3$ $\{x \in \mathbb{R}\}$ and $g(x) = x - 3$ $\{x \in \mathbb{R}\}$, find:

a) fg(4) b) fg(0) c) gf(0) d) fg(x) e) gf(x) f) $f^2(x)$.

a) $fg(4) = f(g(4)) = f(4-3) = f(1) = 2 \times 1^3 = 2$

b) $fg(0) = f(g(0)) = f(0-3) = f(-3) = 2 \times (-3)^3 = 2 \times -27 = -54$

c) $gf(0) = g(f(0)) = g(2 \times 0^3) = g(0) = 0 - 3 = -3$

From parts b) and c) you can see that fg(x) ≠ gf(x).

d) $fg(x) = f(g(x)) = f(x-3) = 2(x-3)^3$

e) $gf(x) = g(f(x)) = g(2x^3) = 2x^3 - 3$

f) $f^2(x) = f(f(x)) = f(2x^3) = 2(2x^3)^3 = 16x^9$

You could be asked to Solve a Composite Function Equation

If you're asked to solve an equation such as fg(x) = 8, the best way to do it is to work out what fg(x) is, then rearrange fg(x) = 8 to make x the subject.

EXAMPLE For the functions $f(x) = \sqrt{x}$ with domain $\{x \geq 0\}$ and $g(x) = \frac{1}{x-1}$ with domain $\{x > 1\}$, solve the equation fg(x) = ½. Also, state the range of fg(x).

First, find fg(x): $fg(x) = f\left(\frac{1}{x-1}\right) = \sqrt{\frac{1}{x-1}} = \frac{1}{\sqrt{x-1}}$

So $\frac{1}{\sqrt{x-1}} = \frac{1}{2}$

Rearrange this equation to find x:

$$\frac{1}{\sqrt{x-1}} = \frac{1}{2} \Rightarrow \sqrt{x-1} = 2 \Rightarrow x - 1 = 4 \Rightarrow x = 5$$

To find the range, it's often helpful to draw the graph of fg(x):

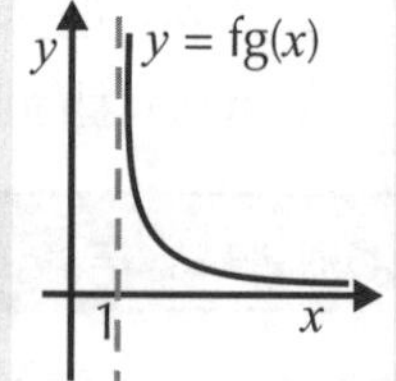

The domain of fg(x) is $x > 1$ (though the question doesn't ask for this) and the range is fg(x) > 0.

Be careful with the domains and ranges of composite functions.

EXAMPLE For the functions $f(x) = 2x + 1$ $\{x \in \mathbb{R}\}$ and $g(x) = x^2$ $\{x \in \mathbb{R}\}$, solve gf(x) = 16.

Find gf(x): $gf(x) = g(2x+1) = (2x+1)^2$.

Now solve gf(x) = 16: $(2x+1)^2 = 16 \Rightarrow 4x^2 + 4x + 1 = 16$
$\Rightarrow 4x^2 + 4x - 15 = 0$
$\Rightarrow (2x-3)(2x+5) = 0$ so $x = \frac{3}{2}$ or $x = -\frac{5}{2}$

You could have solved $(2x + 1)^2 = 16$ by taking square roots of both sides.

Compose a concerto for f(x) and orchestra...

The most important thing to remember on this page is the order you do the functions in — for fg(x) you always do g first as g is next to x. It's like getting dressed — you wouldn't put your shoes on before your socks, as your socks go next to your feet.

Inverse Functions

Just when you'd got your head around functions, ranges, domains and composite functions, they go and turn it all back to front by introducing inverses.

Only One-to-One Functions have Inverses

1) An inverse function does the opposite to the function. So if the function was '+ 1', the inverse would be '– 1', if the function was '× 2', the inverse would be '÷ 2' etc. The inverse for a function f(x) is written $f^{-1}(x)$.
2) An inverse function maps an element in the range to an element in the domain — the opposite of a function. This means that only one-to-one functions have inverses, as the inverse of a many-to-one function would be one-to-many, which isn't a function (see p.1).
3) For any inverse $f^{-1}(x)$,

Doing the function and then the inverse...

$$f^{-1}f(x) = x = ff^{-1}(x)$$

...is the same as doing the inverse then doing the function — both just give you x.

4) The domain of the inverse is the range of the function, and the range of the inverse is the domain of the function.

EXAMPLE The function $f(x) = x + 7$ with domain $x \geq 0$ and range $f(x) \geq 7$ is one-to-one, so it has an inverse.

The inverse of + 7 is – 7, so $f^{-1}(x) = x - 7$. $f^{-1}(x)$ has domain $x \geq 7$ and range $f^{-1}(x) \geq 0$.

Work out the Inverse using Algebra

For simple functions (like the one in the example above), it's easy to work out what the inverse is just by looking at it. But for more complex functions, you need to rearrange the original function to change the subject.

Finding the Inverse

1) **Replace f(x) with y to get an equation for y in terms of x.**
2) **Rearrange the equation to make x the subject.**
3) **Replace x with $f^{-1}(x)$ and y with x — this is the inverse function.**
4) **Swap round the domain and range of the function.**

EXAMPLE Find the inverse of the function $f(x) = 3x^2 + 2$ with domain $x \geq 0$, and state its domain and range.

1) First, replace f(x) with y: $y = 3x^2 + 2$.
2) Rearrange the equation to make x the subject:

$$y - 2 = 3x^2 \Rightarrow \frac{y-2}{3} = x^2 \Rightarrow \sqrt{\frac{y-2}{3}} = x$$

$x \geq 0$ so you don't need the negative square root.

It's easier to work with y than f(x).

3) Replace x with $f^{-1}(x)$ and y with x:

$$f^{-1}(x) = \sqrt{\frac{x-2}{3}}$$

4) Swap the domain and range: the range of f(x) is $f(x) \geq 2$, so $f^{-1}(x)$ has domain $x \geq 2$ and range $f^{-1}(x) \geq 0$.

You might have to Draw the Graph of the Inverse

The inverse of a function is its reflection in the line $y = x$.

EXAMPLE Sketch the graph of the inverse of the function $f(x) = x^2 - 8$ with domain $x \geq 0$.

It's easy to see what the domains and ranges are from the graph — f(x) has domain $x \geq 0$ and range $f(x) \geq -8$, and $f^{-1}(x)$ has domain $x \geq -8$ and range $f^{-1}(x) \geq 0$.

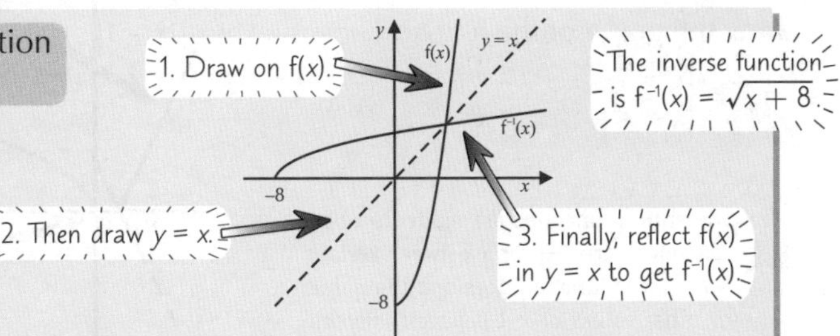

Line y = x on the wall — who is the fairest of them all...

I think I've got the hang of this inverse stuff now — so the inverse of walking to the shops and buying some milk would be taking the money out the till, putting the milk back on the shelf, leaving the shop and walking home backwards. Sorted.

Modulus

The modulus of a number is really useful if you don't care whether something's positive or negative — like if you were finding the difference between two numbers (e.g. 7 and 12). It doesn't matter which way round you do the subtraction (i.e. 12 – 7 or 7 – 12) — the difference between them is still 5.

Modulus is the Size of a number

1) The modulus of a number is its size — it doesn't matter if it's positive or negative. So for a positive number, the modulus is just the same as the number itself, but for a negative number, the modulus is its positive value. For example, the modulus of 8 is 8, and the modulus of –8 is also 8.

2) The modulus of a number, x, is written $|x|$. So the example above would be written $|8| = |-8| = 8$.

The modulus is sometimes called the absolute value.

3) In general terms, for $x \geq 0$, $|x| = x$ and for $x < 0$, $|x| = -x$.

4) Functions can have a modulus too — the modulus of a function f(x) is its positive value. Suppose f(x) = –6, then $|f(x)| = 6$. In general terms,

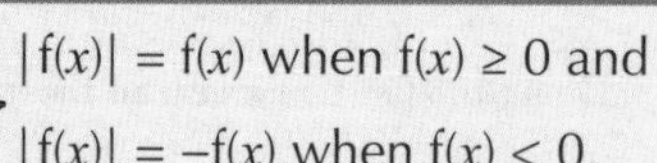

$|f(x)| = f(x)$ when $f(x) \geq 0$ and

$|f(x)| = -f(x)$ when $f(x) < 0$.

5) If the modulus is inside the brackets in the form $f(|x|)$, then you make the x-value positive before applying the function. So $f(|-2|) = f(2)$.

The Graphs of |f(x)| and f(|x|) are Different

You'll probably have to draw the graph of a modulus function — and there are two different types.

1) For the graph of $y = |f(x)|$, any negative values of f(x) are made positive by reflecting them in the x-axis. This restricts the range of the modulus function to $|f(x)| \geq 0$ (or some subset within $|f(x)| \geq 0$, e.g. $|f(x)| \geq 1$).

2) For the graph of $y = f(|x|)$, the negative x-values produce the same result as the corresponding positive x-values. So the graph of f(x) for $x \geq 0$ is reflected in the y-axis for the negative x-values.

3) The easiest way to draw these graphs is to draw f(x) (ignoring the modulus for now), then reflect it in the appropriate axis. This will probably make more sense when you've had a look at a couple of examples:

EXAMPLE Draw the graphs of $y = |f(x)|$ and $y = f(|x|)$ for the functions $f(x) = 5x - 5$ and $f(x) = x^2 - 4x$.

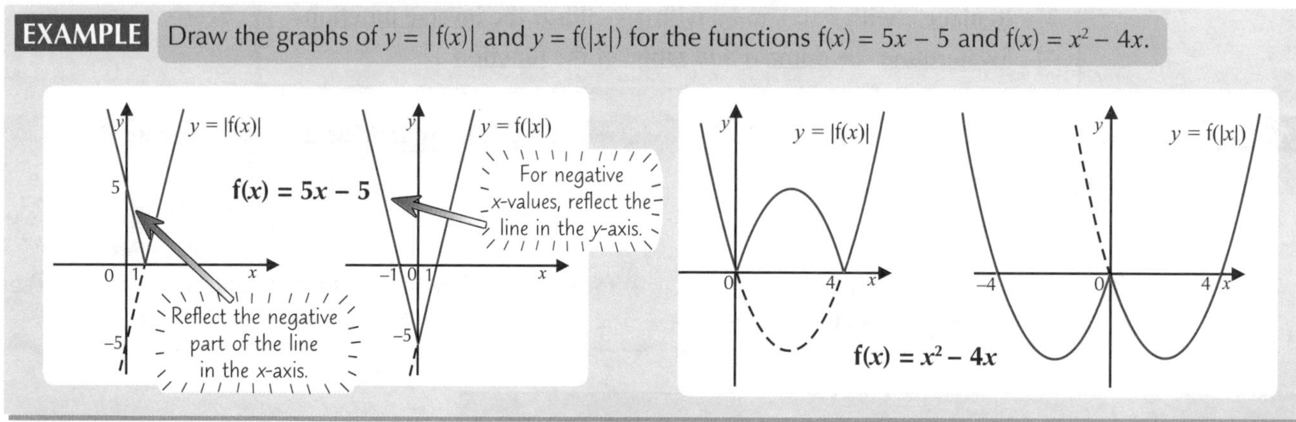

EXAMPLE

Draw the graph of the function $f(x) = \begin{cases} |2x+1| & x < 0 \\ \sqrt{x} & x \geq 0 \end{cases}$.

Sometimes functions are made up of two or more parts — for x between certain values, the function does one thing, but for other values of x it behaves differently.

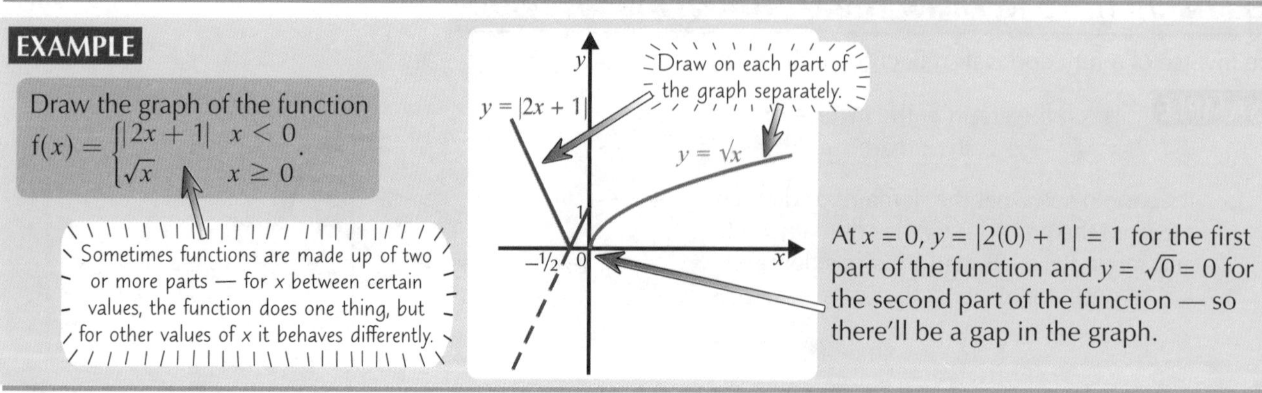

At $x = 0$, $y = |2(0) + 1| = 1$ for the first part of the function and $y = \sqrt{0} = 0$ for the second part of the function — so there'll be a gap in the graph.

Modulus built the city of Mode...

You might have to draw modulus graphs for functions like f(x) = ax + b from scratch. You could be asked for trig graphs and exponentials too. For harder graphs, you'll often be given a graph which you can use as a starting point for the modulus.

Modulus

An exam question might ask you to solve an equation like '$|f(x)| = n$' (for a constant n) or '$|f(x)| = g(x)$' for a function g. I admit, it would be more exciting to solve a crime, but I'm afraid modulus functions must come first...

Solving modulus functions usually produces More Than One solution

Here comes the method for solving '$|f(x)| = n$'. Solving '$|f(x)| = g(x)$' is exactly the same — just replace n with $g(x)$.

Solving Modulus Equations of the form |f(x)| = n

1) **First, sketch the functions $y = |f(x)|$ and $y = n$, on the same axes.** ← The solutions you're trying to find are where they intersect.
2) **From the graph, work out the ranges of x for which $f(x) \geq 0$ and $f(x) < 0$:**
   E.g. $f(x) \geq 0$ for $x \leq a$ or $x \geq b$ and $f(x) < 0$ for $a < x < b$ ← These ranges should 'fit together' to cover all possible x values.
3) **Use this to write two new equations, one true for each range of x...**
   (1) $f(x) = n$ for $x \leq a$ or $x \geq b$ ← The original equation '$|f(x)| = n$' becomes '$f(x) = n$' in the range where $f(x) \geq 0$...
   (2) $-f(x) = n$ for $a < x < b$ ← ...and it becomes '$-f(x) = n$' in the range where $f(x) < 0$.
4) **Now just solve each equation and check that any solutions are valid — get rid of any solutions outside the range of x you've got for that equation.**
5) **Look at the graph and check that your solutions look right.**

Sketch the Graph to see How Many Solutions there are

EXAMPLE Solve $|x^2 - 9| = 7$.

1) First off, sketch the graphs of $y = |x^2 - 9|$ and $y = 7$. They cross at 4 different points, so there should be 4 solutions.

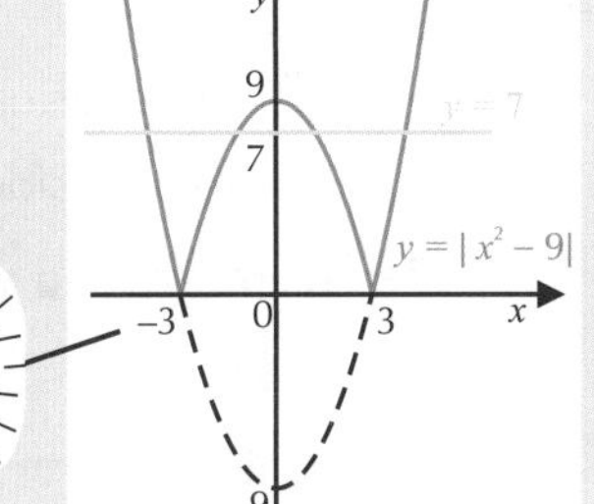

2) Now find out where $f(x) \geq 0$ and $f(x) < 0$:
   $x^2 - 9 \geq 0$ for $x \leq -3$ or $x \geq 3$, and $x^2 - 9 < 0$ for $-3 < x < 3$

   $x^2 - 9 = (x + 3)(x - 3)$, so curve crosses x-axis at 3 and −3.

3) Form two equations for the different ranges of x:
   (1) $x^2 - 9 = 7$ for $x \leq -3$ or $x \geq 3$
   (2) $-(x^2 - 9) = 7$ for $-3 < x < 3$
4) Solving (1) gives: $x^2 = 16 \Rightarrow x = 4, x = -4$
   Check they're valid: $x = -4$ is in '$x \leq -3$' and $x = 4$ is in '$x \geq 3$' — so they're both valid.
   Solving (2) gives: $x^2 - 2 = 0 \Rightarrow x^2 = 2$ so $x = \sqrt{2}, x = -\sqrt{2}$.
   Check they're valid: $x = \sqrt{2}$ and $x = -\sqrt{2}$ are both within $-3 < x < 3$ — so they're also both valid.
5) Check back against the graphs — we've found four solutions and they're in the right places. Nice.

EXAMPLE Solve $|x^2 - 2x - 3| = 1 - x$.

1) Sketch $y = |x^2 - 2x - 3|$ and $y = 1 - x$. The graphs cross twice.

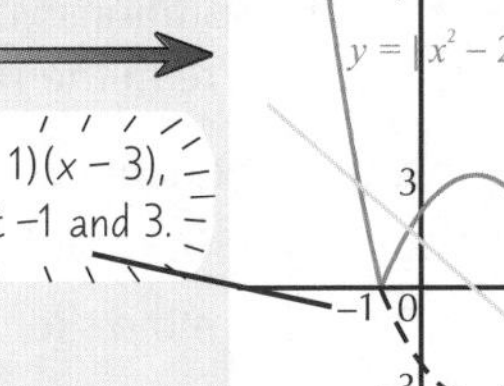

2) Looking at where $f(x) \geq 0$ and where $f(x) < 0$ gives...

   $x^2 - 2x - 3 = (x + 1)(x - 3)$, so it crosses axis at −1 and 3.

3) (1) $x^2 - 2x - 3 = 1 - x$ for $x \leq -1$ or $x \geq 3$
   (2) $-(x^2 - 2x - 3) = 1 - x$ for $-1 < x < 3$.
4) Solving (1) using the quadratic formula gives $x = 2.562$, $x = -1.562$.
   $x \leq -1$ or $x \geq 3$, so this solution is not valid... ...but this one is.
   Solving (2) using the quadratic formula gives $x = 3.562$, $x = -0.562$.
   $-1 < x < 3$, so this solution is not valid... ...but this one is.
5) Checking against the graph, there are two solutions and they're where we expected. El coolio.

How very interesting...

So if the effect of the modulus is to make a negative positive, I guess that means that |exam followed by detention followed by getting splashed by a car on the way home| = sleep-in followed by picnic followed by date with Hugh Jackman. I wish.

Modulus

Three whole pages on modulus might seem a bit excessive, but it's a tricky little topic that can easily trip you up if you're not careful. It's better to be safe than sorry, as my Auntie Marjorie would say — and believe me, she would know.

You might come across a modulus in an **Equation** or an **Inequality**

You saw how to solve modulus equations on the previous page, but there are a few more useful relations you can use.

1) If you have $|a| = |b|$, this means that $a^2 = b^2$ (as $-a$ and a are the same when squared). This comes in really handy when you have to solve equations of the form $|f(x)| = |g(x)|$ (see below).
2) Inequalities that have a modulus in them can be really nasty — unfortunately you can't just leave the modulus in there. $|x| < 5$ means that $-5 < x < 5$.

   This is because $|x| < 5$ means that $x < 5$ and $-x < 5$, and $-x < 5$ is the same as $x > -5$. You can then put the two inequalities together to get $-5 < x < 5$.
3) Using this, you can rearrange more complicated inequalities like $|x - a| \leq b$. From the method above, this means that $-b \leq x - a \leq b$, so adding a to each bit of the inequality gives $a - b \leq x \leq a + b$.

EXAMPLE Solve $|x - 4| < 7$.

As $|x - 4| < 7$, this means that $-7 < x - 4 < 7$. Adding 4 to each bit gives $-3 < x < 11$.

Solve a modulus equation by **Squaring Both Sides**

If you have an equation of the form $|f(x)| = |g(x)|$, you can solve it using the method on the previous page, but it can get a bit messy with all the modulus signs flying all over the place. Instead, you can use the fact that if $|a| = |b|$ then $a^2 = b^2$ and square both sides of the equation. You'll end up with a quadratic to solve, but that should be a doddle.

EXAMPLE By squaring both sides, solve $|x + 3| = |2x + 5|$.

First, square both sides: $x^2 + 6x + 9 = 4x^2 + 20x + 25$

Then rearrange and solve: $0 = 3x^2 + 14x + 16$

$= (3x + 8)(x + 2)$ So $x = -\frac{8}{3}$ or $x = -2$.

You could also have solved it by sketching the graphs like you did on the previous page:

EXAMPLE
a) By sketching the graphs, solve $|x + 3| = |2x + 5|$.
b) Hence solve the inequality $|x + 3| < |2x + 5|$.

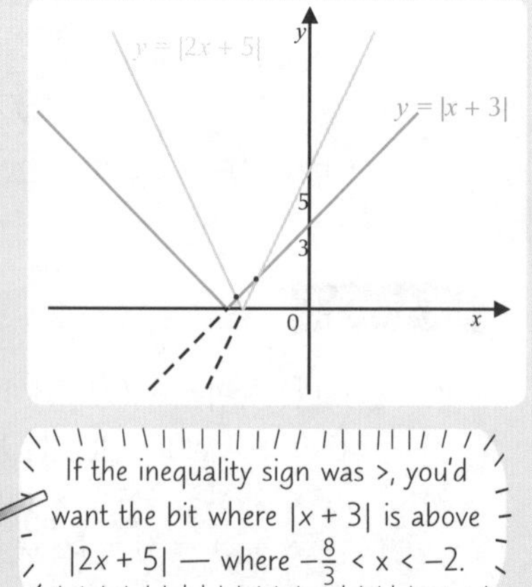

a) Sketch $y = |x + 3|$ and $y = |2x + 5|$. The graphs cross twice.

From the graph, you can see that there's one solution where $x + 3 = 2x + 5$, and another where $x + 3 = -(2x + 5) = -2x - 5$.

Solving $x + 3 = 2x + 5$ gives $x = -2$ and solving $x + 3 = -2x - 5$ gives $x = -\frac{8}{3}$ (these are the solutions you found above — and you can see from the graph that they're in the right places).

b) To solve the inequality $|x + 3| < |2x + 5|$, you have to look at the graphs and work out where the graph of $|x + 3|$ is underneath the graph of $|2x + 5|$: you can see from the sketch that this is true when $x < -\frac{8}{3}$ and when $x > -2$.

If the inequality sign was >, you'd want the bit where $|x + 3|$ is above $|2x + 5|$ — where $-\frac{8}{3} < x < -2$.

If you'd tried to solve $-(x + 3) = -(2x + 5)$ and $-(x + 3) = 2x + 5$, you would have just got the same pair of solutions. This is true for any equation of the form $|f(x)| = |g(x)|$ — it might look more complicated than $|f(x)| = n$ or $|f(x)| = g(x)$, but it's actually a bit easier. You can either square both sides or, if you don't want to, you only have to solve two equations: $f(x) = g(x)$ and $-f(x) = g(x)$.

Be there or b^2...

Personally, I think squaring both sides is a bit easier (but then again, I'm a sucker for a quadratic equation). You'll get the same answer whichever way you do it, so it's up to you. By the way, please don't mention penguins to Auntie Marjorie.

Transformations of Graphs

Back in C1, you came across transformations of graphs — vertical and horizontal translations, stretches and reflections. In C2, you saw stretches on trig graphs. As if that wasn't enough for you, you now need to be able to do combinations of transformations — more than one applied to the same graph.

There are Four main Transformations

The transformations you met in C1 and C2 are translations (adding things — a vertical or horizontal shift), stretches or squeezes (either vertical or horizontal) and reflections in the x- or y- axis. Here's a quick reminder of what each one does:

$y = f(x + c)$

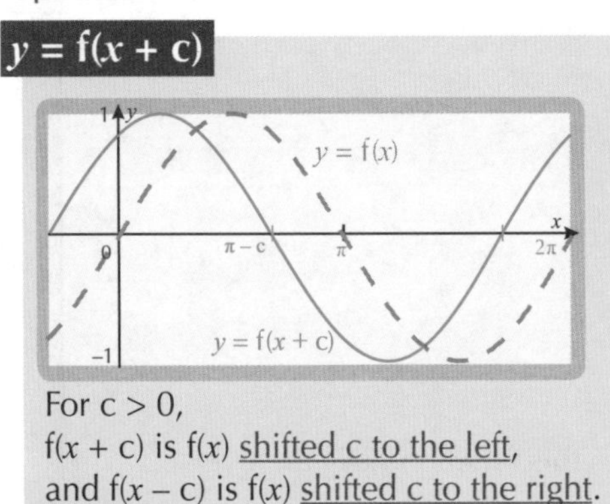

For $c > 0$,
$f(x + c)$ is $f(x)$ shifted c to the left,
and $f(x - c)$ is $f(x)$ shifted c to the right.

$y = f(x) + c$

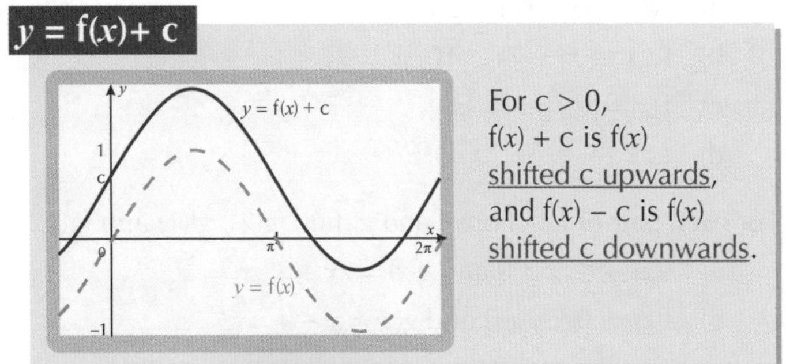

For $c > 0$,
$f(x) + c$ is $f(x)$ shifted c upwards,
and $f(x) - c$ is $f(x)$ shifted c downwards.

All these graphs use $f(x) = \sin x$.

$y = af(x)$

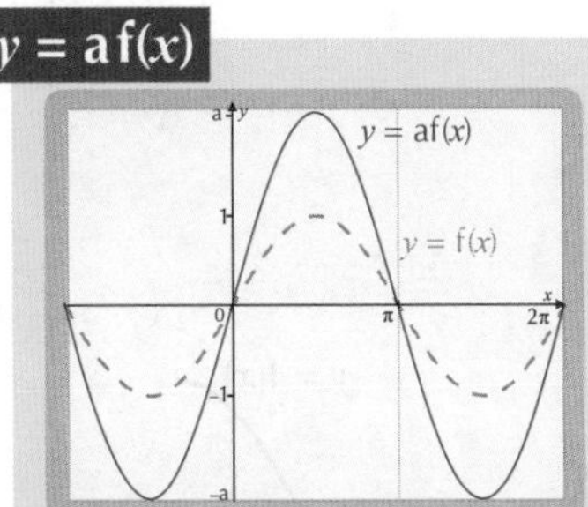

If $a > 1$, the graph of $af(x)$ is $f(x)$ stretched vertically by a factor of a.

If $0 < a < 1$, the graph is squashed.

And if $a < 0$, the graph is also reflected in the x-axis.

Remember that a squash by a factor of a is really a stretch by a factor of $1/a$.

$y = f(ax)$

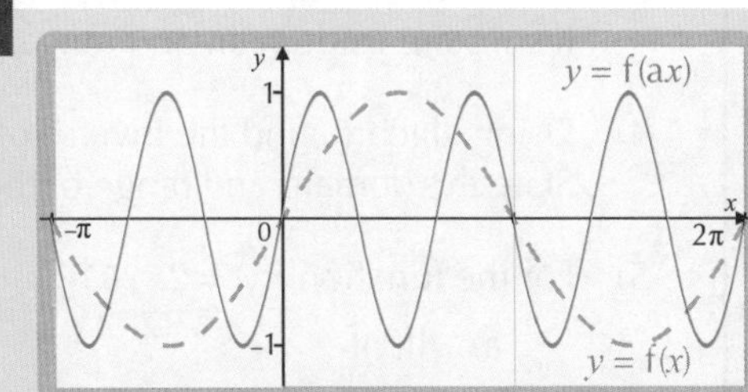

If $a > 1$, the graph of $f(ax)$ is $f(x)$ squashed horizontally by a factor of a.

If $0 < a < 1$, the graph is stretched horizontally.

And if $a < 0$, the graph is also reflected in the y-axis.

Do Combinations of Transformations One at a Time

Combinations of transformations can look a bit tricky, but if you take them one step at a time they're not too bad. Don't try to do all the transformations at once — break it up into separate bits (as above) and draw a graph for each stage.

EXAMPLE The graph shows the function $y = f(x)$. Draw the graph of $y = 3f(x + 2)$, showing the coordinates of the turning points.

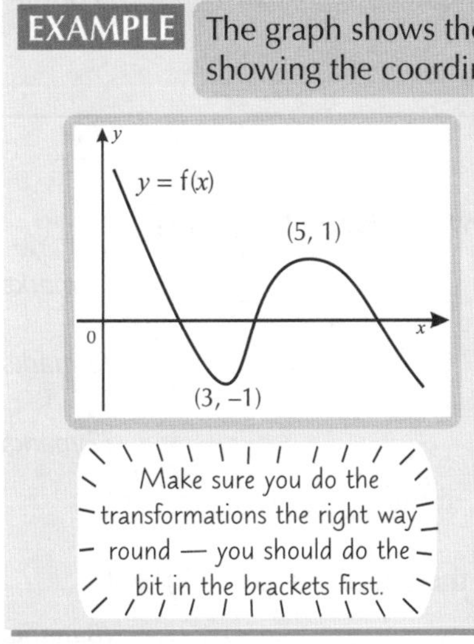

Don't try to do everything at once. First draw the graph of $y = f(x + 2)$ and work out the coordinates of the turning points.

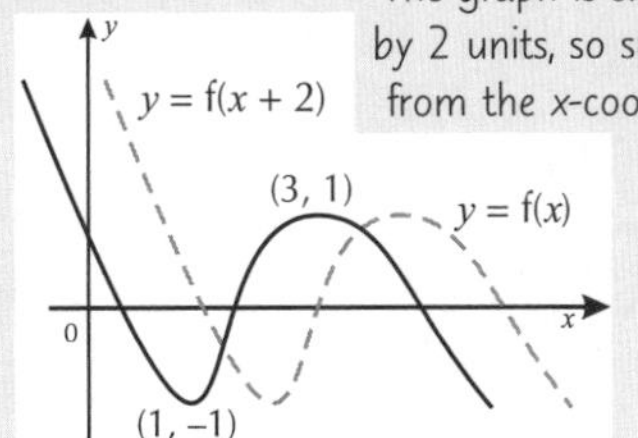

The graph is shifted left by 2 units, so subtract 2 from the x-coordinates.

Now use your graph of $y = f(x + 2)$ to draw the graph of $y = 3f(x + 2)$.

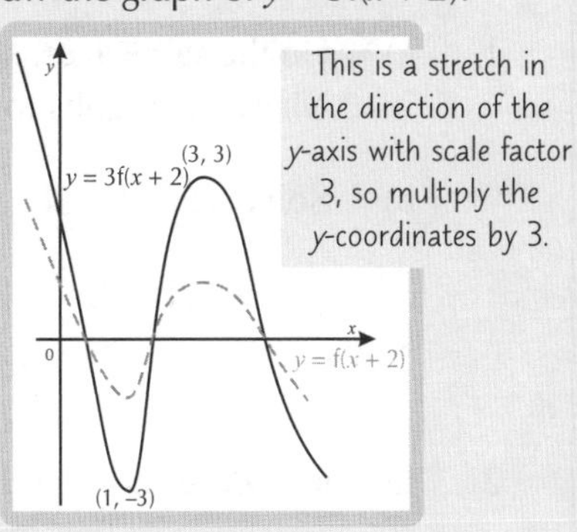

This is a stretch in the direction of the y-axis with scale factor 3, so multiply the y-coordinates by 3.

Tea and cake — the perfect combination...

Working out coordinates can be a bit tricky. The easiest way to do it is to work out what you're doing to the graph, then think about what that does to each point. Have a look at your transformed graph and check that the new coordinates make sense.

C3 Section 1 — Practice Questions

Well, that's the first section over and done with, and what better way to round it off than with some lovely questions. Have a go at these warm-up questions to get you in the mood.

Warm-up Questions

1) For the following mappings, state the range and say whether or not the mapping is a function. If not, explain why, and if so, say whether the function is one-to-one or many-to-one.
   a) $f(x) = x^2 - 16,\ x \geq 0$
   b) $f : x \to x^2 - 7x + 10,\ x \in \mathbb{R}$
   c) $f(x) = \sqrt{x},\ x \in \mathbb{R}$
   d) $f : x \to \frac{1}{x-2},\ x \in \mathbb{R}$

2) For each pair of functions f and g, find fg(2), gf(1) and fg(x).
   a) $f(x) = \frac{3}{x},\ x > 0$ and $g(x) = 2x + 3,\ x \in \mathbb{R}$
   b) $f(x) = 3x^2,\ x \geq 0$ and $g(x) = x + 4,\ x \in \mathbb{R}$

3) A one-to-one function f has domain $x \in \mathbb{R}$ and range $f(x) \geq 3$. Does this function have an inverse? If so, state its domain and range.

4) Using algebra, find the inverse of the function $f(x) = \sqrt{2x-4},\ x \geq 2$. State the domain and range of the inverse.

5) For the function $f(x) = 2x - 1\ \{x \in \mathbb{R}\}$, sketch the graphs of:
   a) $|f(x)|$
   b) $f(|x|)$

6) Use your graph from part 5) a) to help you solve the equation $|2x - 1| = 5$.

7) Solve the equation $|2x + 1| = |x + 4|$.

8) The function $y = f(x)$ is shown on the graph on the right. Draw the graph of $y = 2f(x) + 1$.

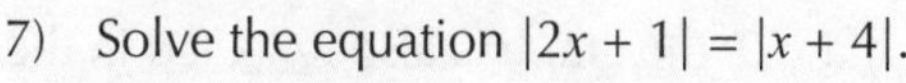

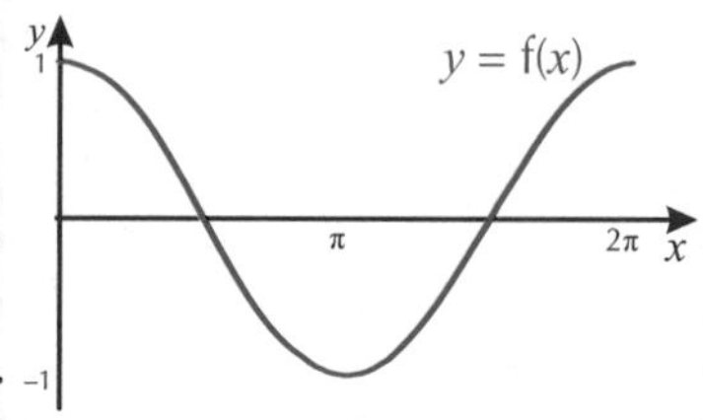

Now that you're in the algebra and functions zone (not to be confused with the twilight zone or the phantom zone), I think you're ready to have a go at some exam-style questions.

Exam Questions

1 a) On the same axes, sketch the graphs of $y = |2x|$ and $y = |x - 1|$, showing clearly the points where the graphs touch the x- and y- axes.

(3 marks)

b) Solve $|2x| = |x - 1|$.

(3 marks)

c) Hence solve $|2x| \leq |x - 1|$.

(2 marks)

2 In words, describe what happens to the curve $y = x^3$ to transform it into the curve $y = 2(x - 1)^3 + 4$.

(6 marks)

C3 Section 1 — Practice Questions

They were nice questions to ease you in gently. I have to warn you, they get a bit harder on this page. It's nothing you can't handle though. Just arm yourself with a mosquito net, an invisibility cloak and some algebraic knowledge and you'll be fine.

3 The functions f and g are given by: $f(x) = x^2 - 3,\ x \in \mathbb{R}$ and $g(x) = \frac{1}{x},\ x \in \mathbb{R}, x \neq 0$.

a) Find an expression for $gf(x)$. *(2 marks)*

b) Solve $gf(x) = \frac{1}{6}$. *(3 marks)*

4 For the functions f and g, where

$$f(x) = 2^x,\ x \in \mathbb{R} \qquad \text{and} \qquad g(x) = \sqrt{3x-2},\ x \geq \tfrac{2}{3},$$

find:

a) $fg(6)$ *(2 marks)*

b) $gf(2)$ *(2 marks)*

c) (i) $g^{-1}(x)$ *(2 marks)*

(ii) $fg^{-1}(x)$ *(2 marks)*

5 The function f(x) is defined as follows: $f : x \to \frac{1}{x+5}$, domain $x > -5$.

a) State the range of $f(x)$. *(1 mark)*

b) (i) Find the inverse function, $f^{-1}(x)$. *(3 marks)*

(ii) State the domain and range of $f^{-1}(x)$. *(2 marks)*

c) On the same axes, sketch the graphs of $y = f(x)$ and $y = f^{-1}(x)$. *(2 marks)*

6 The graph below shows the curve $y = f(x)$, and the intercepts of the curve with the x- and y-axes.

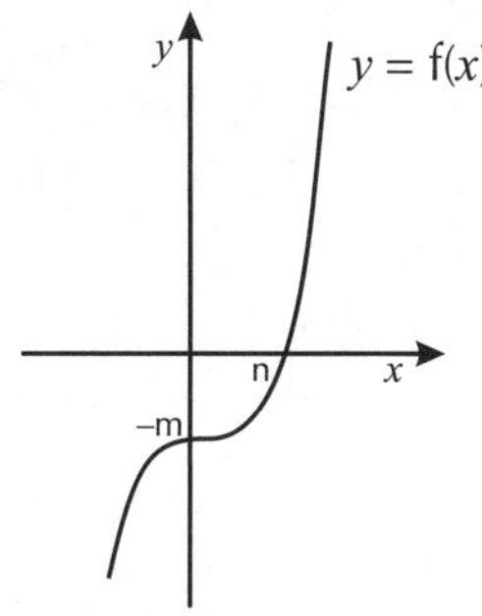

Sketch the graphs of the following transformations on separate axes, clearly labelling the points of intersection with the x- and y-axes in terms of m and n.

a) $y = |f(x)|$ *(2 marks)*

b) $y = -3f(x)$ *(2 marks)*

c) $y = f(|x|)$ *(2 marks)*

e^x, ln x and Graphs

Exponentials are useful 'cos lots of 'real' things increase (or decrease) exponentially — student debts, horrible diseases... We'll start off with a quick recap of some things from C2, then I'll introduce you to some very special functions...

Graphs of $y = a^x$ and $y = a^{-x}$ show Exponential Growth and Decay

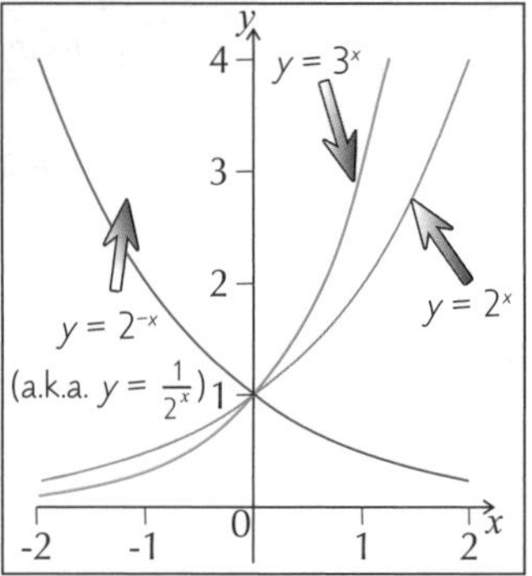

You should be familiar with these graphs from C2.
The main feature of exponential growth / decay is that the rate of increase / decrease of the function is proportional to the function itself.
So if we plotted the gradient of $y = a^x$, it would have the same shape as $y = a^x$.

The main points to remember for $y = a^x$ functions ($a > 0$) are:

1) As $x \to \infty$, $y \to \infty$ (and the gradient also $\to \infty$).
2) As $x \to -\infty$, $y \to 0$ (which means that a^x is always positive).
3) When $x = 0$, $y = 1$ (so they all pass through (0, 1) on the y-axis).

$\to$ means 'tends to'.

The Gradient of the Exponential Function $y = e^x$ is e^x

There is a value of 'a' for which the gradient of $y = a^x$ is exactly the same as a^x. That value is known as e, an irrational number around 2.7183 (it's stored in your calculator just like π). Because e is just a number, the graph of $y = e^x$ has all the properties of $y = a^x$...

1) $y = e^x$ cuts the y-axis at (0, 1).
2) As $x \to \infty$, $e^x \to \infty$ and as $x \to -\infty$, $e^x \to 0$.
3) $y = e^x$ does not exist for $y \leq 0$ (i.e. e^x can't be zero or –ve).

The disturbingly interesting fact that e^x doesn't change when you differentiate is used lots in the differentiation section — see p.25.

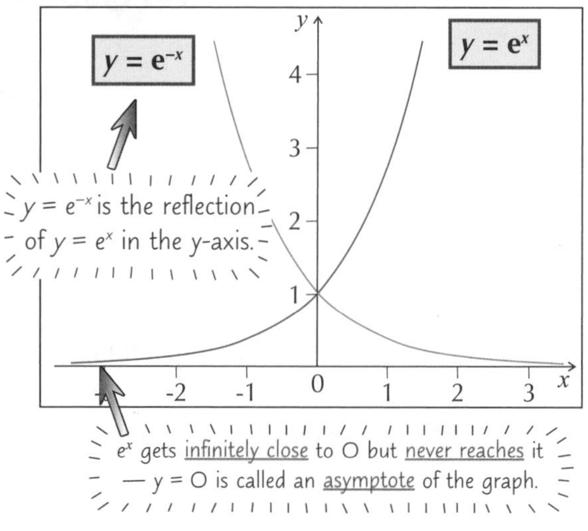

e^x gets infinitely close to 0 but never reaches it — $y = 0$ is called an asymptote of the graph.

ln x is the Inverse Function of e^x

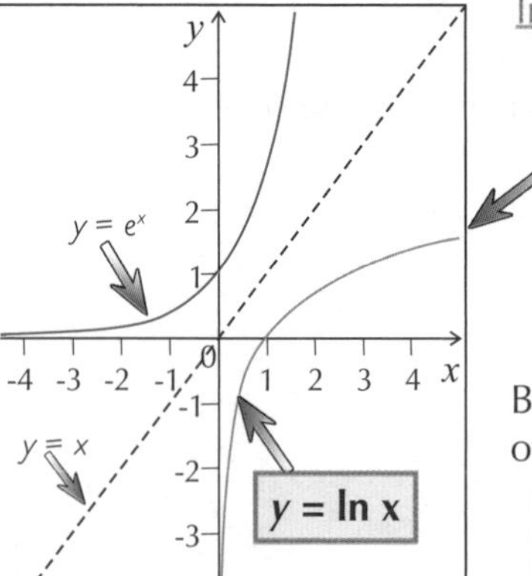

$y = \ln x$ has an asymptote at $x = 0$.

ln x (also known as $\log_e x$, or 'natural log'*) is the inverse function of e^x (see p.3):

1) $y = \ln x$ is the reflection of $y = e^x$ in the line $y = x$.
2) It cuts the x-axis at (1, 0) (so $\ln 1 = 0$).
3) As $x \to \infty$, $\ln x \to \infty$ (but 'slowly'), and as $x \to 0$, $\ln x \to -\infty$.
4) $\ln x$ does not exist for $x \leq 0$ (i.e. x can't be zero or negative).

Because ln x is a logarithmic function and the inverse of e^x, we get these juicy formulas and log laws...

$$e^{\ln x} = x$$
$$\ln(e^x) = x$$

i.e. doing one function then the other to x takes you back to x.

These formulas are extremely useful for dealing with equations containing 'e^x's or 'ln x's, as you'll see on the next page...

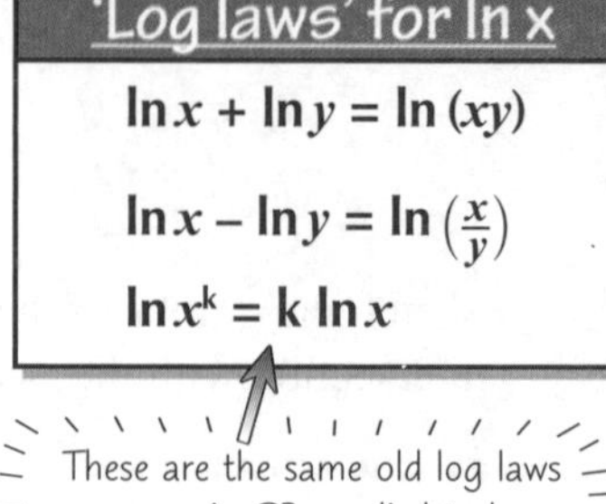

'Log laws' for ln x

$$\ln x + \ln y = \ln(xy)$$
$$\ln x - \ln y = \ln\left(\frac{x}{y}\right)$$
$$\ln x^k = k \ln x$$

These are the same old log laws you saw in C2, applied to ln x.

*Certified organic

'e' is for exponential, but also for easy exam questions — no excuses...

When it comes to logs, I prefer the natural look. Remember the limits of $y = e^x$, $y = e^{-x}$ and $y = \ln x$ from the graphs, and polish up your skills with the log laws from C2, and the rest of the topic should be a breeze. Naturally.

Using e^x and ln x — Solving Equations

Now what makes e^x and ln x so clever is that you can use one to cancel out the other, which comes in very handy for solving equations. You'll need all those fruity formulas from the previous page to get through this one...

Use the *Inverse Functions* and *Log Laws* to Solve Equations

EXAMPLES a) Solve the equation $2\ln x - \ln 2x = 6$, giving your answer as an exact value of x.

1) Use the log laws (see previous page) to simplify $2\ln x - \ln 2x = 6$ into:
   $\ln x^2 - \ln 2x = 6 \Rightarrow \ln (x^2 \div 2x) = 6 \Rightarrow \ln (\frac{x}{2}) = 6$.
2) Now apply the inverse function e^x to both sides — this will remove the ln $(\frac{x}{2})$:
   $e^{\ln (\frac{x}{2})} = e^6 \Rightarrow \frac{x}{2} = e^6 \Rightarrow x = 2e^6$. And since we need an exact value, leave it as that.

Using $e^{\ln x} = x$ from the last page

b) Find the exact solutions of the equation $e^x + 5e^{-x} = 6$.

1) A big clue here is that you're asked for more than one solution. Think quadratics...
2) Multiply each part of the equation by e^x to get rid of that e^{-x}:
   $e^x + 5e^{-x} = 6 \Rightarrow e^{2x} + 5 = 6e^x \Rightarrow e^{2x} - 6e^x + 5 = 0$.
3) It starts to look a bit nicer if you substitute y for e^x: $y^2 - 6y + 5 = 0$.
4) Since we're asked for exact solutions, it will probably factorise:
   $(y - 1)(y - 5) = 0 \Rightarrow y = 1$ and $y = 5$.
5) Put e^x back in: $e^x = 1$ and $e^x = 5$.
6) Take 'ln' of both sides to solve: $\ln e^x = \ln 1 \Rightarrow x = \ln 1 = 0$ and $\ln e^x = \ln 5 \Rightarrow x = \ln 5$.

Basic power laws — $(e^x)^2 = e^{2x}$ and $e^{-x} \times e^x = e^0 = 1$.

Using $\ln e^x = x$

Real-Life functions look like $y = e^{ax+b} + c$ and $y = \ln (ax + b)$

You should be familiar with the shape of the bog-standard exponential graphs, but most exponential functions will be transformed in some way. You need to know how the key features of the graph change depending on the function.

EXAMPLES Sketch the graphs of the following functions, labelling any key points and stating the value of 'a':
a) $y = e^{-7x+1} - 5$ ($x \in \mathbb{R}, y > a$) and b) $y = \ln (2x + 4)$ ($x \in \mathbb{R}, x > a$).

$y = e^{-7x+1} - 5$

1) 'Key points' usually means where the graph crosses the axes, i.e. where x and y are 0:
   When $x = 0$, $y = e^1 - 5 = -2.28$. When $y = 0$, $e^{-7x+1} = 5 \Rightarrow -7x + 1 = \ln 5 \Rightarrow x = -0.0871$.
2) Next see what happens as x goes to $\pm\infty$ to find any asymptotes:
   As $x \to \infty$, $e^{-7x+1} \to 0$, so $y \to -5$. As $x \to -\infty$, $e^{-7x+1} \to \infty$, so $y \to \infty$.
3) Now use this information to sketch out a graph. y can't go below -5, so if $y > a$, $a = -5$.

This tells you the range of values for the function (see p.1).

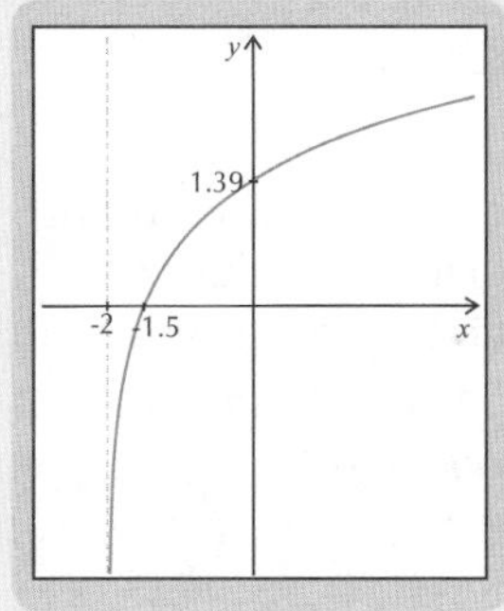

$y = \ln (2x + 4)$

1) First the intercepts: When $x = 0$, $y = \ln 4 = 1.39$. When $y = 0$, $2x + 4 = e^0 = 1 \Rightarrow x = -1.5$.
2) As $x \to \infty$, $y \to \infty$ (gradually).
3) As $x \to -\infty$, y decreases up to the point where $2x + 4 = 0$, at which it can no longer exist (since ln x can only exist for $x > 0$). This gives an asymptote at $2x + 4 = 0$, i.e. $x = -2$.
4) Sketch the graph using this information. x can't go below -2, so if $x > a$, $a = -2$.

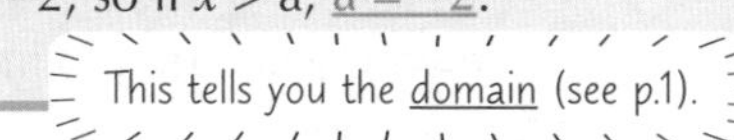

No problems — only solutions...

All the individual steps to solving these equations are easy — the hard bit is spotting what combination of things to try. A good thing to look for is hidden quadratics, so try and substitute for e^x or ln x to make things look a bit nicer. The sketches get easier with practice, so you'd best get cracking.

Using e^x and ln x — Solving Equations

This page is all about models. Except they're modelling exponential growth and decay in real-world applications rather than the Chanel Autumn/Winter collection. Sorry.

Use the Exponential Functions to Model real-life Growth and Decay

In the exam you'll usually be given a background story to an exponential equation.
They may then ask you to find some values, work out a missing part of the equation, or even sketch a graph.
There's nothing here you haven't seen before — you just need to know how to deal with all the wordy bits.

EXAMPLE The exponential growth of a colony of bacteria can be modelled by the equation $B = 60e^{0.03t}$, where B is the number of bacteria, and t is the time in hours from the point at which the colony is first monitored ($t \geq 0$). Use the model to predict:

a) the number of bacteria after 4 hours.

You need to find B when $t = 4$, so put the numbers into the equation:

$B = 60 \times e^{(0.03 \times 4)}$
$= 60 \times 1.1274...$
$= 67.6498...$

So $B = 67$ bacteria.

You shouldn't round up here — there are only 67 whole bacteria, not 68.

b) the time taken for the colony to grow to 1000.

1) You need to find t when B = 1000, so put the numbers into the equation:
$1000 = 60e^{0.03t} \Rightarrow e^{0.03t} = 1000 \div 60 = 16.6666...$

2) Now take 'ln' of both sides as usual:
$\ln e^{0.03t} = \ln (16.6666...) \Rightarrow 0.03t = 2.8134...$
$\Rightarrow t = 2.8134... \div 0.03 =$ 93.8 hours to 3 s.f.

EXAMPLE The concentration (C) of a drug in the bloodstream, t hours after taking an initial dose, decreases exponentially according to $C = Ae^{-kt}$, where k is a constant. If the initial concentration is 0.72, and this halves after 5 hours, find the values of A and k and sketch a graph of C against t.

1) The 'initial concentration' is 0.72 when $t = 0$, so put this information in the equation to find the missing constant A: $0.72 = A \times e^0 \Rightarrow 0.72 = A \times 1 \Rightarrow A = 0.72$.

2) The question also says that when $t = 5$ hours, C is half of 0.72. So using the value for A found above: $C = 0.72e^{-kt}$
$0.72 \div 2 = 0.72 \times e^{(-k \times 5)}$
$\Rightarrow 0.36 = 0.72 \times e^{-5k} \Rightarrow 0.36 = \frac{0.72}{e^{5k}} \Rightarrow e^{5k} = \frac{0.72}{0.36} = 2.$

3) Now take 'ln' of both sides to solve:
$\ln e^{5k} = \ln 2 \Rightarrow 5k = \ln 2 \Rightarrow k = \ln 2 \div 5 = 0.139$ to 3 s.f.

4) So the equation is $C = 0.72e^{-0.139t}$.
You still need to do a sketch though, so find the intercepts and asymptotes as you did on page 11:
When $t = 0$, $C = 0.72$. As $t \to \infty$, $e^{-0.139t} \to 0$, so $C \to 0$.

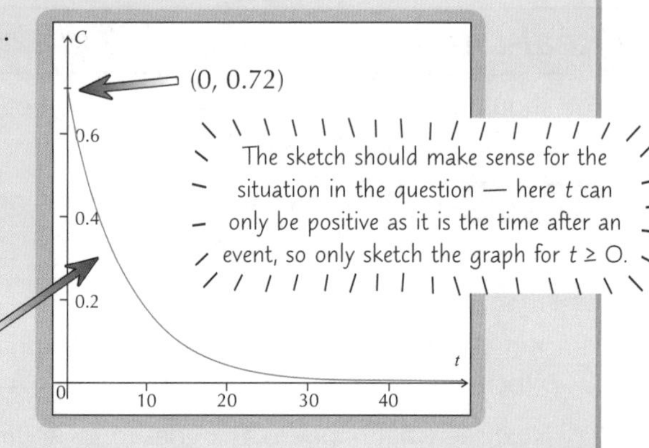

The sketch should make sense for the situation in the question — here t can only be positive as it is the time after an event, so only sketch the graph for $t \geq 0$.

It might not always be e

Sometimes the examiners will try to confuse you by giving you a model that doesn't use e (e.g. $Z = Ak^t$).
These are pretty much the same as the ones above, but they might ask you to find k as well.

EXAMPLE The value of a painting, V, is increasing according to the model $V = Ak^t$, where t is the time in years and A and k are constants. Its initial value is £300, and after 3 years it is worth £500. Find the values of A and k, and work out how long it will take for the value of the painting to triple (to the nearest year).

1) To find A, just put the values you're given into the equation (remembering that $t = 0$ at the initial value). So $300 = Ak^0 \Rightarrow A = 300$ (as $k^0 = 1$).

2) Use your value of A to find k:
$500 = 300k^3 \Rightarrow \frac{5}{3} = k^3 \Rightarrow k = \sqrt[3]{\frac{5}{3}}$ or 1.185...

3) When the value has tripled, $V = 900$. Using this value and your values of A and k, find t:
$900 = 300(1.185...)^t \Rightarrow 3 = (1.185...)^t$.
Take ln of both sides:
$\ln 3 = \ln (1.185...)^t = t\ln (1.185...) \Rightarrow t = 6.45$ (3 s.f.).
So it will take 6 years for the value to triple.

Learn this and watch your knowledge grow exponentially...

For these wordy problems the key is just to extract the relevant information and solve them like you did on the last page. The more you practise, the more familiar they'll become — fortunately there's a fair bit of practice on the next two pages.

C3 Section 2 — Practice Questions

Well that section was short and sweet, rather like that lovely Richard Hammond.
While it's all fresh in your mind, have a go at these little hamsters...

Warm-up Questions

1) Plot the following graphs on the same axes, for $-2 \leq x \leq 2$:
   a) $y = 4e^x$ b) $y = 4e^{-x}$ c) $y = 4 \ln x$ d) $y = \ln 4x$.

2) Find the value of x, to 4 decimal places, when:
   a) $e^{2x} = 6$ b) $\ln (x + 3) = 0.75$ c) $3e^{-4x+1} = 5$ d) $\ln x + \ln 5 = \ln 4$.

3) Solve the following equations, giving your solutions as exact values:
   a) $\ln (2x - 7) + \ln 4 = -3$ b) $2e^{2x} + e^x = 3$.

4) Sketch graphs of the following, labelling key points and asymptotes:
   a) $y = 2 - e^{x+1}$ b) $y = 5e^{0.5x} + 5$ c) $y = \ln (2x) + 1$ d) $y = \ln (x + 5)$

5) The value of a motorbike (£V) varies with age (in t years from new) according to $V = 7500k^{-0.2t}$.
   a) How much did it originally cost?
   b) After 5 years, its value is £3,000. What is the value of k?
   c) What is its value after 10 years?
   d) After how many years will the motorbike's value have fallen below £500?

Feeling confident? Thought so.
Let's see how you handle these exam-style problems — they're a wee bit more problematic...

Exam Questions

1 a) Given that $6e^x = 3$, find the exact value of x. *(2 marks)*

b) Find the exact solutions to the equation:

$$e^{2x} - 8e^x + 7 = 0.$$

(4 marks)

c) Given that $4 \ln x = 3$, find the exact value of x. *(2 marks)*

d) Solve the equation:

$$\ln x + \frac{24}{\ln x} = 10$$

giving your answers as exact values of x. *(4 marks)*

2 The sketch below shows the function $y = e^{ax} + b$, where a and b are constants.

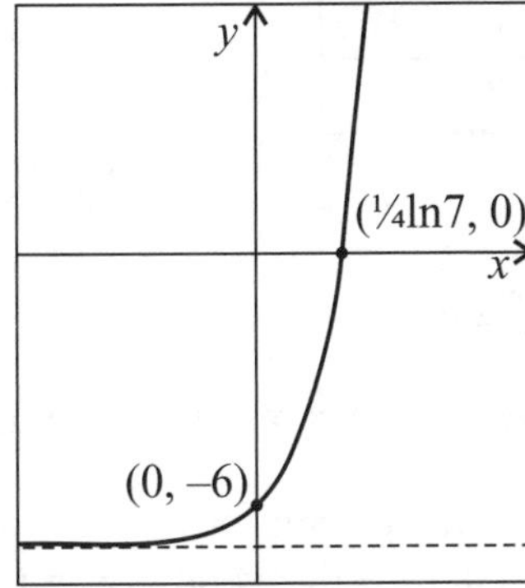

Find the values of a and b, and the equation of the asymptote shown on the sketch. *(5 marks)*

C3 Section 2 — Practice Questions

3 A breed of mink is introduced to a new habitat.
The number of mink, M, after t years in the habitat, is modelled by:

$$M = 74e^{0.6t} \quad (t \geq 0)$$

a) State the number of mink that were introduced to the new habitat originally. *(1 mark)*

b) Predict the number of mink after 3 years in the habitat. *(2 marks)*

c) Predict the number of complete years it would take for the population of mink to exceed 10 000. *(2 marks)*

d) Sketch a graph to show how the mink population varies with time in the new habitat. *(2 marks)*

4 A curve has the equation $y = \ln(4x - 3)$.

a) The point A with coordinate $(a, 1)$ lies on the curve. Find a to 2 decimal places. *(2 marks)*

b) The curve is only defined for $x > b$. State the value of b. *(2 marks)*

c) Sketch the curve, labelling any important points. *(2 marks)*

5 Solve the following equations, giving your answers as exact values of x.

a) $2e^x + 18e^{-x} = 20$ *(4 marks)*

b) $2 \ln x - \ln 3 = \ln 12$ *(3 marks)*

6 A radioactive substance decays exponentially so that its activity, A, can be modelled by

$$A = Be^{-kt}$$

where t is the time in days, and $t \geq 0$. Some experimental data is shown below.

t	0	5	10
A	50	42	

a) State the value of B. *(1 mark)*

b) Find the value of k, to 3 significant figures. *(2 marks)*

c) Find the missing value from the table, to the nearest whole number. *(2 marks)*

d) The half-life of a substance is the time it takes for the activity to halve.
Find the half-life of this substance, in days. Give your answer to the nearest day. *(3 marks)*

$\sin^{-1}$, $\cos^{-1}$ and $\tan^{-1}$

So here we go, forging deep into the mathematical jungle that is trigonometry.
Up first it's inverse trig functions — you need to know what they are, and what their graphs look like...

$\sin^{-1}$, $\cos^{-1}$ and $\tan^{-1}$ are the Inverses of Sin, Cos and Tan

In Section 1 you saw that some functions have inverses, which reverse the effect of the function. The trig functions have inverses too.

SIN^{-1} is the inverse of sine. It's also known as arcsine (or arcsin).

COS^{-1} is the inverse of cosine. It's also known as arccosine (or arccos).

TAN^{-1} is the inverse of tangent. It's also known as arctangent (or arctan).

You should have buttons for doing $\sin^{-1}$, $\cos^{-1}$ and $\tan^{-1}$ on your calculator.

The inverse trig functions reverse the effect of sin, cos and tan.
For example, $\sin 30° = 0.5$, so $\sin^{-1} 0.5 = 30°$.

To Graph the Inverse Functions you need to Restrict their Domains

1) The functions sine, cosine and tangent are NOT one-to-one mappings (see p.1) — lots of values of x give the same value for $\sin x$, $\cos x$ or $\tan x$. For example: $\cos 0 = \cos 2\pi = \cos 4\pi = 1$, and $\tan 0 = \tan \pi = \tan 2\pi = 0$.
2) Only one-to-one functions have inverses, so for the inverse to be a function you have to restrict the domain of the trig function to make it one-to-one (see graphs below). This means that you only plot the graphs between certain x values, so that for each x value, you end up with one y value.
3) As the graphs are inverse functions, they're also reflections of the sin, cos and tan functions in the line $y = x$.

SIN^{-1}

For $\sin^{-1}$, limit the domain of $\sin x$ to $-\frac{\pi}{2} \le x \le \frac{\pi}{2}$ (the range of $\sin x$ is still $-1 \le \sin x \le 1$).

This means the domain of $\sin^{-1} x$ is $-1 \le x \le 1$ and its range is $-\frac{\pi}{2} \le \sin^{-1} x \le \frac{\pi}{2}$.

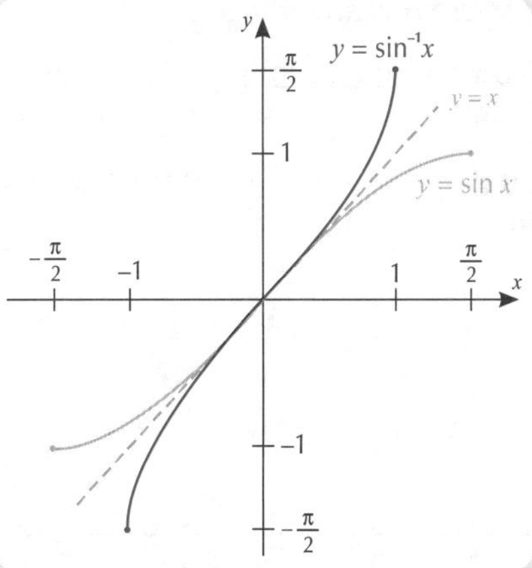

This graph goes through the origin.

The coordinates of its endpoints are $(1, \frac{\pi}{2})$ and $(-1, -\frac{\pi}{2})$.

COS^{-1}

For $\cos^{-1}$, limit the domain of $\cos x$ to $0 \le x \le \pi$ (the range of $\cos x$ is still $-1 \le \cos x \le 1$).

This means the domain of $\cos^{-1} x$ is $-1 \le x \le 1$ and its range is $0 \le \cos^{-1} x \le \pi$.

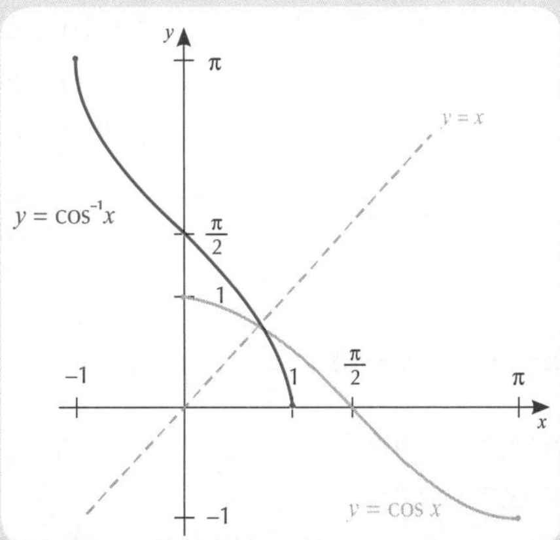

This graph crosses the y-axis at $(0, \frac{\pi}{2})$.

The coordinates of its endpoints are $(-1, \pi)$ and $(1, 0)$.

TAN^{-1}

For $\tan^{-1}$, limit the domain of $\tan x$ to $-\frac{\pi}{2} \le x \le \frac{\pi}{2}$ (this doesn't limit the range of $\tan x$).

This means that the domain of $\tan^{-1} x$ isn't limited, but the range of $\tan^{-1} x$ is limited to $-\frac{\pi}{2} \le \tan^{-1} x \le \frac{\pi}{2}$.

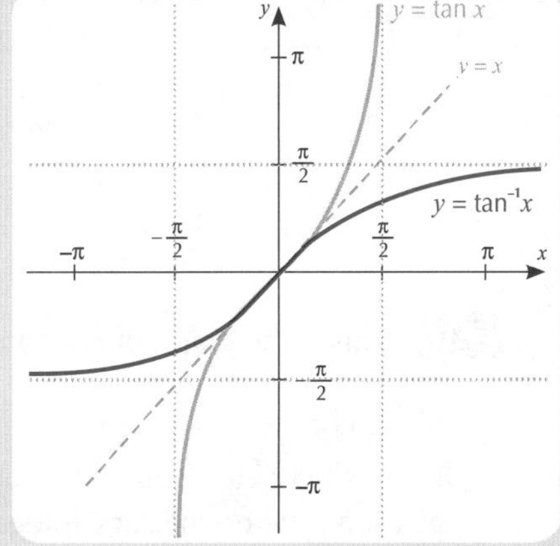

This graph goes through the origin.

It has asymptotes at $y = \frac{\pi}{2}$ and $y = -\frac{\pi}{2}$.

So applying the inverse function reverses everything...

It's really important that you can recognise the graphs of the inverse trig functions — you need to know what shape they are, what restricted domains you need to use to draw them, and any significant points, like where they end or where they cross the axes. You can check the graph by reflecting the curve in the line $y = x$ and seeing if you get the trig function you want.

Secant, Cosecant and Cotangent

Just when you thought you'd seen all the functions that trigonometry could throw at you, here come three more. These ones are pretty important — they'll come in really handy when you're solving trig equations.

Cosec, Sec and Cot are the Reciprocals of Sin, Cos and Tan

When you take the reciprocal of the three main trig functions, sin, cos and tan, you get three new trig functions — cosecant (or cosec), secant (or sec) and cotangent (or cot).

$$\operatorname{cosec} \theta \equiv \frac{1}{\sin\theta} \qquad \sec \theta \equiv \frac{1}{\cos\theta} \qquad \cot \theta \equiv \frac{1}{\tan\theta}$$

The trick for remembering which is which is to look at the third letter — co**s**ec (1/**s**in), se**c** (1/**c**os) and co**t** (1/**t**an).

Since $\tan\theta = \frac{\sin\theta}{\cos\theta}$, you can also think of cot θ as being $\frac{\cos\theta}{\sin\theta}$.

Graphing Cosec, Sec and Cot

COSEC This is the graph of $y = \operatorname{cosec} x$.

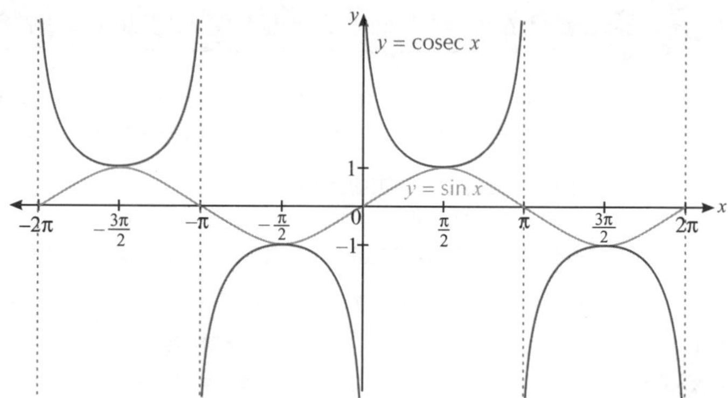

1) Since $\operatorname{cosec} x = \frac{1}{\sin x}$, $y = \operatorname{cosec} x$ is undefined at any point where $\sin x = 0$. So cosec x has asymptotes at $x = n\pi$ (where n is any integer).
2) The graph of cosec x has minimum points at $y = 1$ (wherever the graph of sin x has a maximum).
3) It has maximum points at $y = -1$ (wherever sin x has a minimum).

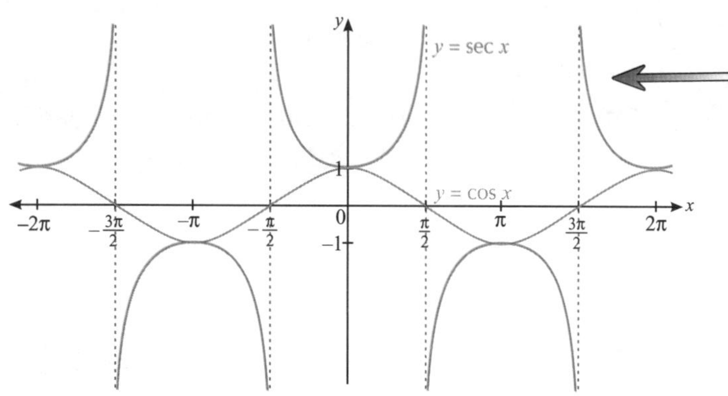

SEC This is the graph of $y = \sec x$.

1) As $\sec x = \frac{1}{\cos x}$, $y = \sec x$ is undefined at any point where $\cos x = 0$. So sec x has asymptotes at $x = \left(n\pi + \frac{\pi}{2}\right)$ (where n is any integer).
2) The graph of sec x has minimum points at $y = 1$ (wherever the graph of cos x has a maximum).
3) It has maximum points at $y = -1$ (wherever cos x has a minimum).

COT This is the graph of $y = \cot x$.

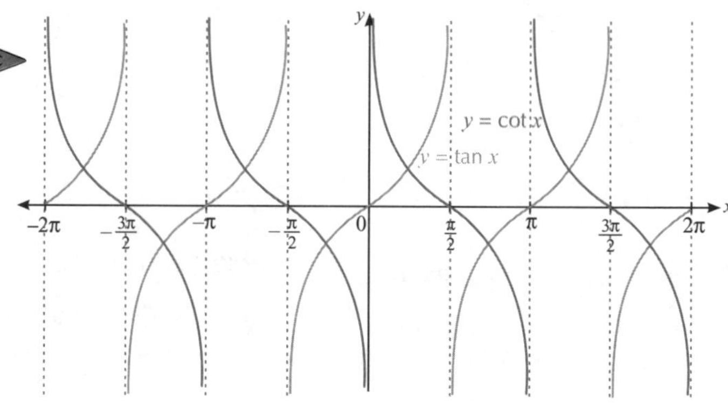

1) Since $\cot x = \frac{1}{\tan x}$, $y = \cot x$ is undefined at any point where $\tan x = 0$. So cot x has asymptotes at $x = n\pi$ (where n is any integer).
2) $y = \cot x$ crosses the x-axis at every place where the graph of tan x has an asymptote — this is any point with the coordinates $\left(\left(n\pi + \frac{\pi}{2}\right), 0\right)$.

Why did I multiply cot x by sin x? Just 'cos...

Remember to look at the third letter to work out which trig function it's the reciprocal of. I'm afraid you do need to be able to sketch the three graphs from memory. Someone in examiner world clearly has a bit of a graph-sketching obsession. You might have to transform a trig graph too — you use the same method as you would for other graphs (see p.7).

Using Trigonometric Identities

Ahh, trig identities. More useful than a monkey wrench, and more fun than rice pudding. Probably.

Learn these Three Trig Identities

Hopefully you remember using this handy little trig identity before: **IDENTITY 1:** $\cos^2\theta + \sin^2\theta \equiv 1$

The $\equiv$ sign tells you that this is true for all values of θ, rather than just certain values.

You can use it to produce a couple of other identities that you need to know about...

IDENTITY 2: $\sec^2\theta \equiv 1 + \tan^2\theta$

To get this, you just take everything in Identity 1, and divide it by $\cos^2\theta$:

$$\frac{\cos^2\theta}{\cos^2\theta} + \frac{\sin^2\theta}{\cos^2\theta} \equiv \frac{1}{\cos^2\theta}$$
$$1 + \tan^2\theta \equiv \sec^2\theta$$

Remember that $\cos^2\theta = (\cos\theta)^2$.

IDENTITY 3: $\mathrm{cosec}^2\theta \equiv 1 + \cot^2\theta$

You get this one by dividing everything in Identity 1 by $\sin^2\theta$:

$$\frac{\cos^2\theta}{\sin^2\theta} + \frac{\sin^2\theta}{\sin^2\theta} \equiv \frac{1}{\sin^2\theta}$$
$$\cot^2\theta + 1 \equiv \mathrm{cosec}^2\theta$$

Use the Trig Identities to Simplify Equations...

You can use identities to get rid of any trig functions that are making an equation difficult to solve.

EXAMPLE Solve the equation $\cot^2 x + 5 = 4\,\mathrm{cosec}\,x$ in the interval $0° \le x \le 360°$.

You can't solve this while it has both cot and cosec in it, so use Identity 3 to swap $\cot^2 x$ for $\mathrm{cosec}^2 x - 1$.

$$\mathrm{cosec}^2 x - 1 + 5 = 4\,\mathrm{cosec}\,x$$

Now rearranging the equation gives: $\mathrm{cosec}^2 x + 4 = 4\,\mathrm{cosec}\,x \Rightarrow \mathrm{cosec}^2 x - 4\,\mathrm{cosec}\,x + 4 = 0$

So you've got a quadratic in cosec x — factorise it like you would any other quadratic equation.

$$\mathrm{cosec}^2 x - 4\,\mathrm{cosec}\,x + 4 = 0$$
$$(\mathrm{cosec}\,x - 2)(\mathrm{cosec}\,x - 2) = 0$$

If it helps, think of this as $y^2 - 4y + 4 = 0$. Factorise it, and then replace the y with cosec x.

One of the brackets must be equal to zero — here they're both the same, so you only get one equation:

$$(\mathrm{cosec}\,x - 2) = 0 \Rightarrow \mathrm{cosec}\,x = 2$$

Now you can convert this into sin x, and solve it easily:

$$\mathrm{cosec}\,x = 2 \Rightarrow \sin x = \tfrac{1}{2}$$
$$x = 30° \text{ or } x = 150°$$

To find the other values of x, draw a quick sketch of the sin curve: From the graph, you can see that sin x takes the value of ½ twice in the given interval, once at $x = 30°$ and once at $x = 180 - 30 = 150°$.

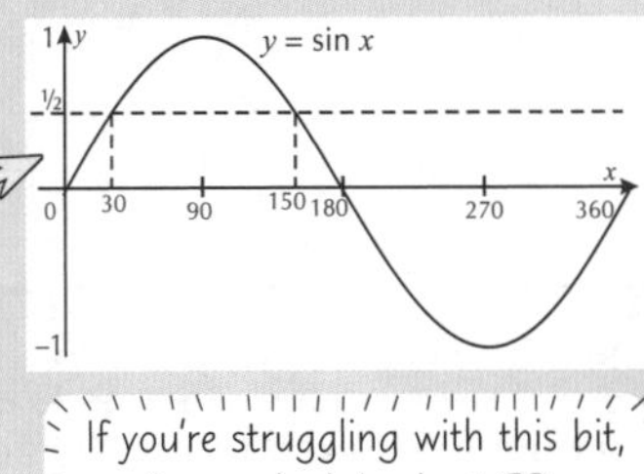

If you're struggling with this bit, have a look back at C2.

...or to Prove that two things are The Same

You can also use identities to prove that two trig expressions are the same, like this:

EXAMPLE Show that $\frac{\tan^2 x}{\sec x} \equiv \sec x - \cos x$.

You need to take one side of the identity and play about with it until you get the other side. ⟹ Left-hand side: $\frac{\tan^2 x}{\sec x}$.

Try replacing $\tan^2 x$ with $\sec^2 x - 1$: $\equiv \frac{\sec^2 x - 1}{\sec x} \equiv \frac{\sec^2 x}{\sec x} - \frac{1}{\sec x} \equiv \sec x - \cos x$ ...which is the right-hand side.

The Addition Formulas

You might have noticed that there are quite a lot of formulas lurking in this here trigonometry jungle. There are some more coming up on this page I'm afraid, so brace yourself — they're all about adding and subtracting angles...

You can use the *Addition Formulas* to find *Sums of Angles*

You can use the addition formulas to find the sin, cos or tan of the sum or difference of two angles.
When you have an expression like sin $(x + 60°)$ or cos $(n - \frac{\pi}{2})$, you can use these formulas to expand the brackets.

These formulas are given to you on the formula sheet.

$$\sin(A \pm B) \equiv \sin A \cos B \pm \cos A \sin B$$

$$\cos(A \pm B) \equiv \cos A \cos B \mp \sin A \sin B$$

$$\tan(A \pm B) \equiv \frac{\tan A \pm \tan B}{1 \mp \tan A \tan B}$$

Watch out for the ± and ∓ signs in the formulas — especially for cos and tan. If you use the sign on the top on the RHS, you have to use the sign on the top on the left-hand side too — so $\cos(A + B) = \cos A \cos B - \sin A \sin B$.

Use the *Formulas* to find the *Exact Value* of trig expressions

1) You should know the value of sin, cos and tan for common angles (in degrees and radians). These values come from using Pythagoras on right-angled triangles — you did it in C2.

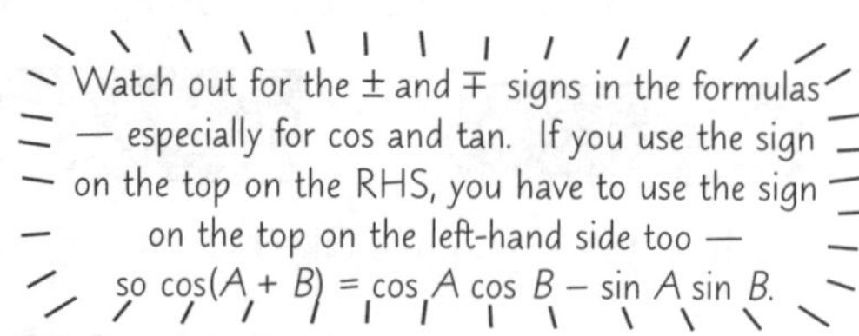

	0°	30°	45°	60°	90°
	0	$\frac{\pi}{6}$	$\frac{\pi}{4}$	$\frac{\pi}{3}$	$\frac{\pi}{2}$
sin	0	$\frac{1}{2}$	$\frac{1}{\sqrt{2}}$	$\frac{\sqrt{3}}{2}$	1
cos	1	$\frac{\sqrt{3}}{2}$	$\frac{1}{\sqrt{2}}$	$\frac{1}{2}$	0
tan	0	$\frac{1}{\sqrt{3}}$	1	$\sqrt{3}$	n/a

2) In the exam you might be asked to calculate the exact value of sin, cos or tan for another angle using your knowledge of those angles and the addition formulas.
3) Find a pair of angles from the table which add or subtract to give the angle you're after. Then plug them into the addition formula, and work it through.

EXAMPLE Using the addition formula for tangent, show that $\tan 15° = 2 - \sqrt{3}$.

Pick two angles that add or subtract to give 15°, and put them into the tan addition formula.
It's easiest to use tan 60° and tan 45° here, since neither of them are fractions.

$$\tan 15° = \tan(60° - 45°) = \frac{\tan 60° - \tan 45°}{1 + \tan 60° \tan 45°}$$

Using $\tan(A - B) = \frac{\tan A - \tan B}{1 + \tan A \tan B}$

Substitute the values for tan 60° and tan 45° into the equation:

$$= \frac{\sqrt{3} - 1}{1 + (\sqrt{3} \times 1)} = \frac{\sqrt{3} - 1}{\sqrt{3} + 1}$$

Now rationalise the denominator of the fraction to get rid of the $\sqrt{3}$.

$$\frac{\sqrt{3} - 1}{\sqrt{3} + 1} \times \frac{\sqrt{3} - 1}{\sqrt{3} - 1} = \frac{3 - 2\sqrt{3} + 1}{3 - \sqrt{3} + \sqrt{3} - 1}$$

If you can't remember how to rationalise the denominator have a peek at your C1 notes.

Simplify the expression... $= \frac{4 - 2\sqrt{3}}{2} = 2 - \sqrt{3}$ ...and there's the right-hand side.

You can use these formulas to *Prove Identities* too

You might be asked to use the addition formulas to prove an identity. All you need to do is put the numbers and variables from the left-hand side into the addition formulas and simplify until you get the expression you're after.

EXAMPLE Prove that $\cos(a + 60°) + \sin(a + 30°) \equiv \cos a$

Put the numbers from the question into the addition formulas:

Be careful with the + and – signs here.

$$\cos(a + 60°) + \sin(a + 30°) \equiv (\cos a \cos 60° - \sin a \sin 60°) + (\sin a \cos 30° + \cos a \sin 30°)$$

Now substitute in any sin and cos values that you know...

$$= \frac{1}{2}\cos a - \frac{\sqrt{3}}{2}\sin a + \frac{\sqrt{3}}{2}\sin a + \frac{1}{2}\cos a$$

..and simplify:

$$= \frac{1}{2}\cos a + \frac{1}{2}\cos a = \cos a$$

This section's got more identities than Clark Kent...

I was devastated when my secret identity was revealed — I'd been masquerading as a mysterious caped criminal mastermind with an army of minions and a hidden underground lair. It was great fun, but I had to give it all up and write about trig.

The Double Angle Formulas

Whenever you see a trig expression with an even multiple of x in it, like $\sin 2x$, you can use one of the double angle formulas to prune it back to an expression just in terms of a single x.

There's a **Double Angle Formula** for **Each Trig Function**

Double angle formulas are just a slightly different kind of identity. They're called "double angle" formulas because they turn any tricky $2x$ type terms in trig expressions back into plain x terms.

You need to know the double angle formulas for sin, cos and tan:

$$\sin 2A \equiv 2\sin A\cos A$$

$$\cos 2A \equiv \cos^2 A - \sin^2 A$$
or $\equiv 2\cos^2 A - 1$
or $\equiv 1 - 2\sin^2 A$

$$\tan 2A \equiv \frac{2\tan A}{1 - \tan^2 A}$$

You can use the identity $\cos^2 A + \sin^2 A \equiv 1$ to get the other versions of the cos $2A$ formula.

You get these formulas by writing $2A$ as $A + A$ and using the addition formulas from the previous page.

Use the **Double Angle Formulas** to **Simplify** and **Solve Equations**

If an equation has a mixture of $\sin x$ and $\sin 2x$ terms in it, there's not much that you can do with it in this form. So that you can simplify it, and then solve it, you have to use one of the double angle formulas.

EXAMPLE Solve the equation $\cos 2x - 5\cos x = 2$ in the interval $0 \le x \le 2\pi$.

First use the double angle formula $\cos 2A \equiv 2\cos^2 A - 1$ to get rid of $\cos 2x$ (use this version so that you don't end up with a mix of sin and cos terms).

$2\cos^2 x - 1 - 5\cos x = 2$

Simplify so you have zero on one side...
...then factorise and solve the quadratic that you've made:

$2\cos^2 x - 5\cos x - 3 = 0$
$(2\cos x + 1)(\cos x - 3) = 0$
So $(2\cos x + 1) = 0$ or $(\cos x - 3) = 0$

The second bracket gives you $\cos x = 3$, which has no solutions since $-1 \le \cos x \le 1$.

So all that's left is to solve the first bracket to find x:

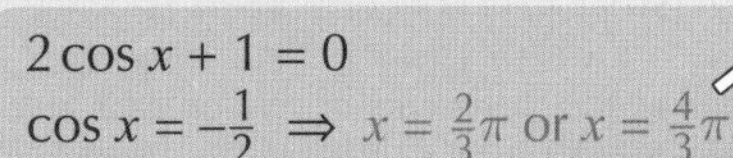

$2\cos x + 1 = 0$
$\cos x = -\frac{1}{2} \Rightarrow x = \frac{2}{3}\pi$ or $x = \frac{4}{3}\pi$.

Sketch the graph of $\cos x$ to find all values of x in the given interval: $\cos x = -½$ twice, once at $\frac{2}{3}\pi$ and once at $2\pi - \frac{2}{3}\pi = \frac{4}{3}\pi$.

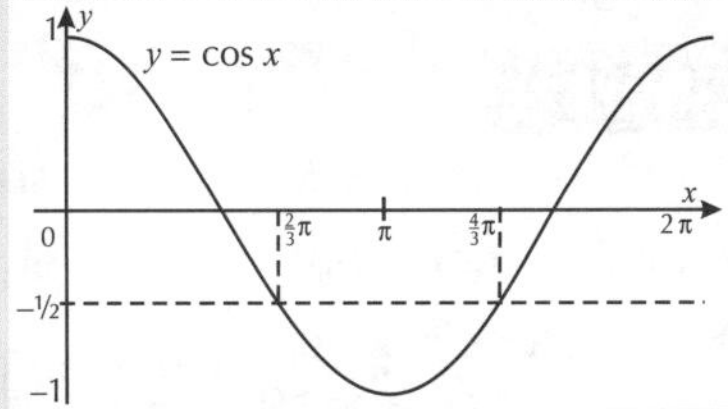

You can use a **Double Angle Formula** even when the x term **Isn't 2x**

Whenever you have an expression that contains any angle that's twice the size of another, you can use the double angle formulas — whether it's $\sin x$ and $\sin 2x$, $\cos 2x$ and $\cos 4x$ or $\tan x$ and $\tan \frac{x}{2}$.

EXAMPLE Prove that $2\cot\frac{x}{2}(1 - \cos^2\frac{x}{2}) \equiv \sin x$

Use the identity $\sin^2\theta + \cos^2\theta \equiv 1$ to replace $1 - \cos^2\frac{x}{2}$ on the left-hand side:

Left-hand side: $2\cot\frac{x}{2}\sin^2\frac{x}{2}$

Now write $\cot\theta$ as $\frac{\cos\theta}{\sin\theta}$:

$2\frac{\cos\frac{x}{2}}{\sin\frac{x}{2}}\sin^2\frac{x}{2} \equiv 2\cos\frac{x}{2}\sin\frac{x}{2}$

Now you can use the sin $2A$ double angle formula to write $\sin x \equiv 2\sin\frac{x}{2}\cos\frac{x}{2}$ (using $A = \frac{x}{2}$).

So using the sin double angle formula... $\equiv \sin x$ ...you get the right-hand side.

You can work out half-angle formulas for cos and tan from the double angle formulas. This example uses the one for sin.

Double the angles, double the fun...

You definitely need to know the double angle formulas off by heart, because they won't be on the exam formula sheet. So it's a case of the old "learn 'em, write 'em out, and keep going until you can do all three perfectly" strategy. And don't forget to be on the lookout for sneaky questions that want you to use a double angle formula but don't contain a "2x" bit.

The R Addition Formulas

A different kind of addition formula this time — one that lets you go from an expanded expression to one with brackets...

Use the R Formulas when you've got a Mix of Sin and Cos

If you're solving an equation that contains both sin θ and cos θ terms, e.g. $3\sin\theta + 4\cos\theta = 1$, you need to rewrite it so that it only contains one trig function. The formulas that you use to do that are known as the *R* formulas:

One set for sine: $a\sin\theta \pm b\cos\theta \equiv R\sin(\theta \pm \alpha)$

And one set for cosine: $a\cos\theta \pm b\sin\theta \equiv R\cos(\theta \mp \alpha)$

where *a* and *b* are positive. Again, you need to be careful with the + and – signs here — see p.18.

Using the R Formulas

1) **You'll start with an identity like $2\sin x + 5\cos x \equiv R\sin(x + \alpha)$, where *R* and α need to be found.**
2) **First, expand the RHS using the addition formulas (see p.18): $2\sin x + 5\cos x \equiv R\sin x\cos\alpha + R\cos x\sin\alpha$.**
3) **Equate the coefficients of $\sin x$ and $\cos x$. You'll get two equations: ① $R\cos\alpha = 2$ and ② $R\sin\alpha = 5$.**
4) **To find α, divide equation ② by equation ①, then take $\tan^{-1}$ of the result.**
5) **To find *R*, square equations ① and ② and add them together, then take the square root of the answer.**

This is because $\frac{R\sin\alpha}{R\cos\alpha} = \tan\alpha$.

$(R\sin\alpha)^2 + (R\cos\alpha)^2 \equiv R^2(\sin^2\alpha + \cos^2\alpha) \equiv R^2$ (using the identity $\sin^2\alpha + \cos^2\alpha \equiv 1$).

This method looks a bit scary, but follow the example below through and it should make more sense.

Solve the equation in Stages

You'll almost always be asked to solve equations like this in different stages — first writing out the equation in the form of one of the *R* formulas, then solving it. You might also have to find the maximum or minimum value.

EXAMPLE (Part 1): Express $2\sin x - 3\cos x$ in the form $R\sin(x - \alpha)$, given that $R > 0$ and $0 \le \alpha \le 90°$.

$2\sin x - 3\cos x \equiv R\sin(x - \alpha)$, so expand the RHS to get $2\sin x - 3\cos x \equiv R(\sin x\cos\alpha - \cos x\sin\alpha)$.

Equating coefficients gives the equations $R\cos\alpha = 2$ and $R\sin\alpha = 3$.

Look at the coefficients of $\sin x$ on each side of the equation — on the LHS it's 2 and on the RHS it's $R\cos\alpha$, so $2 = R\cos\alpha$. You find the coefficient of $\cos x$ in the same way.

Solving for α: $\frac{R\sin\alpha}{R\cos\alpha} = \frac{3}{2} = \tan\alpha$

$\alpha = \tan^{-1} 1.5 = 56.31°$

This value fits into the correct range so you can leave it as it is.

Solving for *R*: $(R\cos\alpha)^2 + (R\sin\alpha)^2 = 2^2 + 3^2 = R^2$

$R = \sqrt{2^2 + 3^2} = \sqrt{13}$

So $2\sin x - 3\cos x = \sqrt{13}\sin(x - 56.31°)$

EXAMPLE (Part 2): Hence solve $2\sin x - 3\cos x = 1$ in the interval $0 \le x \le 360°$.

If $2\sin x - 3\cos x = 1$, that means $\sqrt{13}\sin(x - 56.31°) = 1$,

so $\sin(x - 56.31°) = \frac{1}{\sqrt{13}}$.

$0 \le x \le 360°$, so $-56.31° \le x - 56.31° \le 303.69°$.

Careful — you're looking for solutions between $-56.31°$ and $303.69°$ here.

Solve the equation using $\sin^{-1}$:

$x - 56.31° = \sin^{-1}\left(\frac{1}{\sqrt{13}}\right) = 16.10°$ or $180 - 16.10 = 163.90°$.

So $x = 16.10 + 56.31 = 72.4°$ or $x = 163.90 + 56.31 = 220.2°$

EXAMPLE (Part 3): What are the max and min values of $2\sin x - 3\cos x$?

The maximum and minimum values of sin (and cos) are ± 1, so the maximum and minimum values of $R\sin(x - \alpha)$ are $\pm R$.

As $2\sin x - 3\cos x = \sqrt{13}\sin(x - 56.31°)$, $R = \sqrt{13}$, so the maximum and minimum values are $\pm\sqrt{13}$.

A pirate's favourite trigonometry formula...

The *R* formulas might look a bit scary, but they're OK really — just do lots of examples until you're happy with the method. Careful with the adjusting the interval bit that came up in part 2 above — it's pretty fiddly and easy to get muddled over.

More Trigonometry Stuff

And here we have the final trig page... a collection of random bits that didn't really fit on the other pages. That's one of the scary things about trig questions — you never know what you're going to get.

The **Factor Formulas** come from the **Addition Formulas**

As if there weren't enough trig formulas already, here come a few more. Don't worry though — these ones are given to you on the exam formula sheet so you don't need to learn them off by heart.

$$\sin A + \sin B = 2\sin\left(\frac{A+B}{2}\right)\cos\left(\frac{A-B}{2}\right)$$

$$\sin A - \sin B = 2\cos\left(\frac{A+B}{2}\right)\sin\left(\frac{A-B}{2}\right)$$

$$\cos A + \cos B = 2\cos\left(\frac{A+B}{2}\right)\cos\left(\frac{A-B}{2}\right)$$

$$\cos A - \cos B = -2\sin\left(\frac{A+B}{2}\right)\sin\left(\frac{A-B}{2}\right)$$

These are the factor formulas, and they come from the addition formulas (see below). They come in handy for some integrations — it's a bit tricky to integrate $2\cos 3\theta \cos \theta$, but integrating $\cos 4\theta + \cos 2\theta$ is much easier.

EXAMPLE Use the addition formulas to show that $\cos A + \cos B \equiv 2\cos\left(\frac{A+B}{2}\right)\cos\left(\frac{A-B}{2}\right)$

You can derive the other formulas using the same method.

Use the cos addition formulas: $\cos(x + y) \equiv \cos x \cos y - \sin x \sin y$ and $\cos(x - y) \equiv \cos x \cos y + \sin x \sin y$.

Add them together to get: $\cos(x + y) + \cos(x - y) \equiv \cos x \cos y - \sin x \sin y + \cos x \cos y + \sin x \sin y$
$\equiv 2\cos x \cos y$.

Now substitute in $A = x + y$ and $B = x - y$.

Subtracting these gives $A - B = x + y - (x - y) = 2y$, so $y = \frac{A-B}{2}$.

Adding gives $A + B = x + y + (x - y) = 2x$, so $x = \frac{A+B}{2}$.

So $\cos A + \cos B = 2\cos\left(\frac{A+B}{2}\right)\cos\left(\frac{A-B}{2}\right)$.

You might have to use **Different Bits** of **Trig** in the **Same Question**

Some exam questions might try and catch you out by making you use more than one identity to show that two things are equal...

EXAMPLE Show that $\cos 3\theta \equiv 4\cos^3\theta - 3\cos\theta$.

You have to use both the addition formula and the double angle formulas in this question.

First, write $\cos 3\theta$ as $\cos(2\theta + \theta)$, then you can use the cos addition formula:
$\cos(3\theta) \equiv \cos(2\theta + \theta) \equiv \cos 2\theta \cos\theta - \sin 2\theta \sin\theta$.

Now you can use the cos and sin double angle formulas to get rid of the 2θ:
$\cos 2\theta \cos\theta - \sin 2\theta \sin\theta \equiv (2\cos^2\theta - 1)\cos\theta - (2\sin\theta\cos\theta)\sin\theta$

$\equiv 2\cos^3\theta - \cos\theta - 2\sin^2\theta\cos\theta \equiv 2\cos^3\theta - \cos\theta - 2(1 - \cos^2\theta)\cos\theta$

This uses the identity $\sin^2\theta + \cos^2\theta \equiv 1$ in the form $\sin^2\theta \equiv 1 - \cos^2\theta$.

$\equiv 2\cos^3\theta - \cos\theta - 2\cos\theta + 2\cos^3\theta \equiv 4\cos^3\theta - 3\cos\theta$.

...or even drag up trig knowledge from C2 or even GCSE. This question looks short and sweet, but it's actually pretty nasty — you need to know a sneaky conversion between sin and cos.

EXAMPLE If $y = \sin^{-1}x$ for $-1 \leq x \leq 1$ and $-\frac{\pi}{2} \leq y \leq \frac{\pi}{2}$, show that $\cos^{-1}x = \frac{\pi}{2} - y$.

$y = \sin^{-1}x$, so $x = \sin y$.

Now the next bit isn't obvious — you need to use an identity to switch from sin to cos. This gives... $x = \cos(\frac{\pi}{2} - y)$.

Now, taking inverses gives $\cos^{-1}x = \cos^{-1}(\cos(\frac{\pi}{2} - y))$, so $\cos^{-1}x = \frac{\pi}{2} - y$.

Converting Sin to Cos (and back): $\sin t \equiv \cos(\frac{\pi}{2} - t)$ and $\cos t \equiv \sin(\frac{\pi}{2} - t)$. Remember sin is just cos translated by $\frac{\pi}{2}$ and vice versa.

Trig is like a box of chocolates...

You'll be pleased to know that you've seen all the trig formulas you need for C3. I know there are about 1000 of them (N.B. exaggerations like this may lose you marks in the exam), but any of them could pop up. Examiners particularly like it when you have to use one identity or formula to prove or derive another, so get practising. Then go off and have a nice cup of tea.

C3 Section 3 — Practice Questions

There are a lot of formulas in this section — try writing them all out and sticking them somewhere so you can learn them. The best way to get to grips with them is to practise using them — so here are some questions for you to have a go at.

Warm-up Questions

1) Using your vast knowledge of trig values for common angles, evaluate these (in radians, between 0 and $\frac{\pi}{2}$):
   a) $\sin^{-1}\frac{1}{\sqrt{2}}$ b) $\cos^{-1}0$ c) $\tan^{-1}\sqrt{3}$
2) Sketch the graphs of $\sin^{-1}$, $\cos^{-1}$ and $\tan^{-1}$. Make sure you show their domains and ranges.
3) For $\theta = 30°$, find the exact values of:
   a) $\text{cosec}\,\theta$ b) $\sec\theta$ c) $\cot\theta$
4) Sketch the graphs of cosecant x, secant x and cotangent x for $-2\pi \le x \le 2\pi$.
5) Use the identity $\cos^2\theta + \sin^2\theta \equiv 1$ to produce the identity $\sec^2\theta \equiv 1 + \tan^2\theta$.
6) Use the trig identities to show that $\cot^2\theta + \sin^2\theta \equiv \text{cosec}^2\theta - \cos^2\theta$.
7) State the three different versions of the double angle formula for cos.
8) Use the double angle formula to solve the equation: $\sin 2\theta = -\sqrt{3}\sin\theta,\ 0 \le \theta \le 360°$.
9) Using the addition formula for cos, find the exact value of $\cos\frac{\pi}{12}$.
10) Find the exact value of $\sin(A + B)$, given that $\sin A = \frac{4}{5}$ and $\sin B = \frac{7}{25}$.
    You might find these triangles useful:

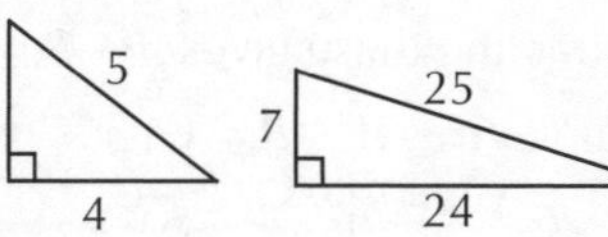

11) Which two R formulas could you use to write $a\cos\theta + b\sin\theta$ $(a, b > 0)$ in terms of just sin or just cos?
12) Write $5\sin\theta - 6\cos\theta$ in the form $R\sin(\theta - \alpha)$, where $R > 0$ and $0 \le \alpha \le 90°$.
13) Use the addition formulas to show that $\sin A - \sin B = 2\cos\left(\frac{A+B}{2}\right)\sin\left(\frac{A-B}{2}\right)$.
14) Show that $\frac{\cos\theta}{\sin\theta} + \frac{\sin\theta}{\cos\theta} \equiv 2\,\text{cosec}\,2\theta$.

Here is a selection of the finest trigonometry exam questions available, matured for 21 days and served with a delicious peppercorn sauce.

Exam Questions

1 a) Sketch the graph of $y = \text{cosec}\,x$ for $-\pi \le x \le \pi$.
(3 marks)

Don't forget to put your calculator in RAD mode when you're using radians (and DEG mode when you're using degrees)...

b) Solve the equation $\text{cosec}\,x = \frac{5}{4}$ for $-\pi \le x \le \pi$.
Give your answers correct to 3 significant figures.
(3 marks)

c) Solve the equation $\text{cosec}\,x = 3\sec x$ for $-\pi \le x \le \pi$.
Give your answers correct to 3 significant figures.
(3 marks)

2 a) Write $9\sin\theta + 12\cos\theta$ in the form $R\sin(\theta + \alpha)$, where $R > 0$ and $0 \le \alpha \le \frac{\pi}{2}$.
(3 marks)

b) Using the result from part (a) solve $9\sin\theta + 12\cos\theta = 3$, giving all solutions for θ in the range $0 \le \theta \le 2\pi$.
(5 marks)

C3 Section 3 — Practice Questions

Take a deep breath and get ready to dive in again — here come some more lovely trig questions...

3 Using the double angle and addition identities for sin and cos, find an expression for $\sin 3x$ in terms of $\sin x$ only. *(4 marks)*

4 **Figure 1** shows the graph of $y = \cos^{-1} x$, where y is in radians. A and B are the end points of the graph.

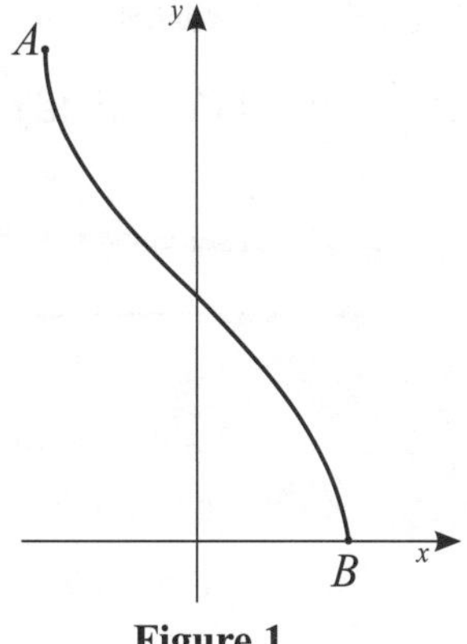

Figure 1

a) Write down the coordinates of A and B. *(2 marks)*

b) Express x in terms of y. *(1 mark)*

c) Solve, to 3 significant figures, the equation $\cos^{-1} x = 2$ for the interval shown on the graph. *(2 marks)*

5 a) Show that $\dfrac{2\sin x}{1 - \cos x} - \dfrac{2\cos x}{\sin x} \equiv 2\operatorname{cosec} x$ *(4 marks)*

b) Use this result to find all the solutions for which

$$\frac{2\sin x}{1 - \cos x} - \frac{2\cos x}{\sin x} = 4 \qquad 0 < x < 2\pi.$$

(3 marks)

6 a) Write $5\cos\theta + 12\sin\theta$ in the form $R\cos(\theta - \alpha)$, where $R > 0$ and $0 \leq \alpha \leq 90°$. *(4 marks)*

b) Hence solve $5\cos\theta + 12\sin\theta = 2$ for $0 \leq \theta \leq 360°$, giving your answers to 2 decimal places. *(5 marks)*

c) Use your results from part a) above to find the minimum value of $(5\cos\theta + 12\sin\theta)^3$. *(2 marks)*

7 a) (i) Using an appropriate identity, show that $3\tan^2\theta - 2\sec\theta = 5$ can be written as $3\sec^2\theta - 2\sec\theta - 8 = 0$. *(2 marks)*

(ii) Hence or otherwise show that $\cos\theta = -\frac{3}{4}$ or $\cos\theta = \frac{1}{2}$. *(3 marks)*

b) Use your results from part a) above to solve the equation $3\tan^2 2x - 2\sec 2x = 5$ for $0 \leq x \leq 180°$. Give your answers to 2 decimal places. *(3 marks)*

Chain Rule

That's right — our old friend differentiation is back again, this time with some new exciting features.
Before you start panicking about how much you've already forgotten, all you need for now is: $\frac{d}{dx}(x^n) = nx^{n-1}$

The Chain Rule is used for Functions of Functions

The chain rule is a nifty little tool that allows you to differentiate complicated functions by splitting them up into easier ones. The trick is spotting how to split them up, and choosing the right bit to substitute.

Chain Rule Method

- **Pick a suitable function of x for 'u' and rewrite y in terms of u.**
- **Differentiate u (with respect to x) to get $\frac{du}{dx}$, and differentiate y (with respect to u) to get $\frac{dy}{du}$.**
- **Stick it all in the formula.**

If $y = f(u)$ and $u = g(x)$ then:
$$\frac{dy}{dx} = \frac{dy}{du} \times \frac{du}{dx}$$

EXAMPLE Find the exact value of $\frac{dy}{dx}$ when $x = 1$ for $y = \frac{1}{\sqrt{x^2 + 4x}}$.

1) First, write y in terms of powers to make it easier to differentiate: $y = (x^2 + 4x)^{-\frac{1}{2}}$.
2) Pick a chunk of the equation to call 'u', and rewrite y in terms of u: e.g. in this case let $u = x^2 + 4x$, so $y = u^{-\frac{1}{2}}$.
3) Now differentiate both bits separately: $u = x^2 + 4x$, so $\frac{du}{dx} = 2x + 4$ and $y = u^{-\frac{1}{2}}$, so $\frac{dy}{du} = -\frac{1}{2}u^{-\frac{3}{2}}$.
4) Use the chain rule to find $\frac{dy}{dx}$: $\frac{dy}{dx} = \frac{dy}{du} \times \frac{du}{dx} = -\frac{1}{2}u^{-\frac{3}{2}} \times (2x + 4)$.
5) Substitute in for u and rearrange: $u = x^2 + 4x$, so $\frac{dy}{dx} = -\frac{1}{2}(x^2 + 4x)^{-\frac{3}{2}}(2x + 4) = -\frac{x + 2}{(\sqrt{x^2 + 4x})^3}$.
6) Finally, put in $x = 1$ to answer the question: $\frac{dy}{dx} = -\frac{1 + 2}{(\sqrt{1^2 + (4 \times 1)})^3} = \frac{-3}{5\sqrt{5}} = \frac{-3\sqrt{5}}{25}$.

Write down all the steps — it'll help you avoid small mistakes that could affect your final answer.

'Exact' means leave in surd form where necessary.

Use dy/dx = 1 ÷ dx/dy for x = f(y)

For $x = f(y)$, use
$$\frac{dy}{dx} = \frac{1}{\left(\frac{dx}{dy}\right)}$$

The principle of the chain rule can also be used where x is given in terms of y (i.e. $x = f(y)$). This comes from a bit of mathematical fiddling, but it's quite useful:

$\frac{dy}{dx} \times \frac{dx}{dy} = \frac{dy}{dy} = 1$, so rearranging gives $\frac{dy}{dx} = \frac{1}{\left(\frac{dx}{dy}\right)}$. Here's how to use it...

EXAMPLE A curve has the equation $x = y^3 + 2y - 7$. Find $\frac{dy}{dx}$ at the point $(-4, 1)$.

1) Forget that the xs and ys are in the 'wrong' places and differentiate as usual: $x = y^3 + 2y - 7$, so $\frac{dx}{dy} = 3y^2 + 2$.
2) Use $\frac{dy}{dx} = \frac{1}{\left(\frac{dx}{dy}\right)}$ to find $\frac{dy}{dx}$: $\frac{dy}{dx} = \frac{1}{3y^2 + 2}$.
3) $y = 1$ at the point $(-4, 1)$, so put this in the equation: $\frac{dy}{dx} = \frac{1}{3(1)^2 + 2} = \frac{1}{5} = 0.2$, so $\frac{dy}{dx} = 0.2$ at the point $(-4, 1)$.

You'll be using this again on the next page so make sure you've learnt it now.

I'm in the middle of a chain rule differentiation...

You know, I'm not sure I've stressed enough just how important differentiation is. It's one of those bits of maths that examiners can tag on to almost any other A-Level topic. It's almost like they have a mantra: 'Give me ANY function and I will ask you to differentiate it, in a multitude of intricate ways'. To which you should respond: 'Bring. It. On.'

Differentiation of e^x and ln x

Remember those special little functions from Section Two? Well you're about to find out just how special they are as we take a look at how to differentiate them. I can tell you're overcome by excitement so I'll not keep you waiting...

The Gradient of $y = e^x$ is e^x by Definition

$$y = e^x \qquad \frac{dy}{dx} = e^x$$

OR

$$f(x) = e^x \qquad f'(x) = e^x$$

Get used to using both types of function notation. You should remember from C2 that $f'(x)$ means the same as dy/dx.

In Section 2 (see p.10) we saw that 'e' was just a number for which the gradient of e^x was e^x. Which makes it pretty simple to differentiate.

EXAMPLE If $f(x) = e^{x^2} + 2e^x$, find $f'(x)$ for $x = 0$.

1) Let's break down the function into its two bits and differentiate them separately:

$y = e^{x^2}$ and $y = 2e^x$

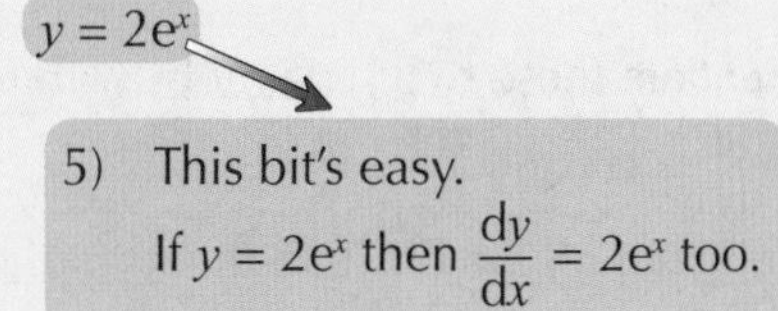

2) This is the tricky bit. Use the chain rule from the last page: $u = x^2$ and $y = e^u$

3) Both u and y are now easy to differentiate: $\frac{du}{dx} = 2x$ and $\frac{dy}{du} = e^u$

4) $\frac{dy}{dx} = \frac{du}{dx} \times \frac{dy}{du} = 2x \cdot e^u = 2x \cdot e^{x^2}$

5) This bit's easy. If $y = 2e^x$ then $\frac{dy}{dx} = 2e^x$ too.

When $y = kf(x)$ where k is a constant, then dy/dx is just $kf'(x)$.

6) Put the bits back together and you end up with $f'(x) = 2xe^{x^2} + 2e^x$.

7) So when $x = 0$, $f'(x) = 0 + 2e^0 = 2$.

Turn $y = \ln x$ into $x = e^y$ to Differentiate

$$y = \ln x \qquad \frac{dy}{dx} = \frac{1}{x}$$

This result you can just learn, but it comes from another bit of mathematical fiddling:

If $y = \ln x$, then $x = e^y$ (see p.10).

Differentiating gives $\frac{dx}{dy} = e^y$, and $\frac{dy}{dx} = \frac{1}{\left(\frac{dx}{dy}\right)} = \frac{1}{e^y} = \frac{1}{x}$ (since $x = e^y$). Nice eh.

EXAMPLE Find $\frac{dy}{dx}$ if $y = \ln(x^2 + 3)$.

1) Use the chain rule again for this one: $y = \ln u$ and $u = x^2 + 3$.

2) $\frac{dy}{du} = \frac{1}{u}$ (from above) and $\frac{du}{dx} = 2x$.

3) So $\frac{dy}{dx} = \frac{dy}{du} \times \frac{du}{dx} = \frac{1}{u} \times 2x = \frac{2x}{x^2 + 3}$.

Look again at your final answer. It comes out to $\frac{f'(x)}{f(x)}$.

This will always be the case for $y = \ln(f(x))$ so you can just learn this result:

$$y = \ln(f(x)) \qquad \frac{dy}{dx} = \frac{f'(x)}{f(x)}$$

These functions pop up everywhere in the e^{x}ams...

There's nothing too tough on this page, so you have no excuse for not getting a good grasp of the basics while you can. The derivatives of e^x and $\ln x$ are just a couple more of those essential little things you've just got to learn. If you don't, you could get stumped by a fairly easy exam question. I know I'd gladly spend every waking hour learning this stuff if I could...

Product Rule

In maths-speak, a 'product' is what you get when you multiply things together. So the 'product rule' is a rule about differentiating things that are multiplied together. And it's yet another rule you have to learn I'm afraid.

Use the *Product Rule* to differentiate *Two Functions Multiplied Together*

This is what it looks like:

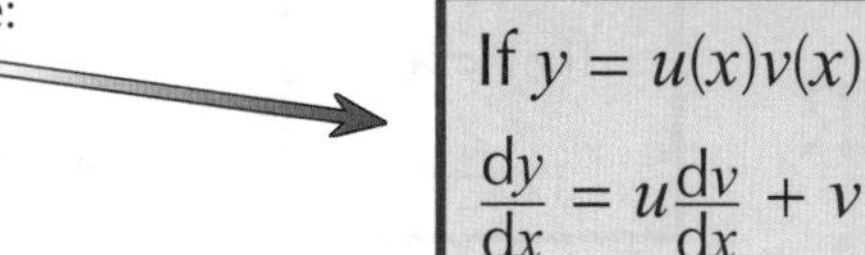

If $y = u(x)v(x)$

$$\frac{dy}{dx} = u\frac{dv}{dx} + v\frac{du}{dx}$$

And here's how to use it: (u and v are functions of x.)

EXAMPLE Differentiate $x^3 \ln x$ with respect to x.

1) The crucial thing is to write down everything in steps. Start with identifying 'u' and 'v':
   $u = x^3$ and $v = \ln x$.
2) Now differentiate these two separately, with respect to x:
   $\frac{du}{dx} = 3x^2$ and $\frac{dv}{dx} = \frac{1}{x}$.
3) Very carefully put all the bits into the formula:
   $\frac{dy}{dx} = u\frac{dv}{dx} + v\frac{du}{dx} = (x^3 \cdot \frac{1}{x}) + (\ln x \cdot 3x^2)$
4) Finally, simplify to make it look nicer:
   $\frac{dy}{dx} = x^2 + 3x^2 \ln x \ (= x^2(1 + 3\ln x))$.

Use the Rules *Together* to differentiate *Complicated Functions*

In the exam they might tell you which rules to use, but chances are they won't.
And you'll probably have to throw a whole load of rules at any one question.

EXAMPLE Solve the equation $\frac{d}{dx}((x^3 + 3x^2)\ln x) = 2x^2 + 5x$, leaving your answer as an exact value of x.

1) The $\frac{d}{dx}$ just tells you to differentiate the bit in brackets first.

   And since $(x^3 + 3x^2)\ln x$ is a product of two functions, use the product rule:
   $u = x^3 + 3x^2 \Rightarrow \frac{du}{dx} = 3x^2 + 6x$ and $v = \ln x \Rightarrow \frac{dv}{dx} = \frac{1}{x}$ (see p.25)

   So $\frac{d}{dx}((x^3 + 3x^2)\ln x) = [(x^3 + 3x^2) \cdot \frac{1}{x}] + [\ln x \cdot (3x^2 + 6x)] = x^2 + 3x + (3x^2 + 6x)\ln x$.
2) Now put this into the equation from the question in place of $\frac{d}{dx}((x^3 + 3x^2)\ln x)$:
   $x^2 + 3x + (3x^2 + 6x)\ln x = 2x^2 + 5x$
3) Rearrange and solve as follows:
   $(3x^2 + 6x)\ln x = 2x^2 + 5x - x^2 - 3x \Rightarrow (3x^2 + 6x)\ln x = x^2 + 2x$
   $\Rightarrow \ln x = \frac{x^2 + 2x}{3(x^2 + 2x)} = \frac{1}{3} \Rightarrow x = e^{\frac{1}{3}}$.

You should be well up on $\ln x$ and e^x after Section 2, but glance back at pages 10-12 if you need to.

You're asked for an exact value so leave in terms of e.

The first rule of maths club is — you do not talk about maths club...

These rules are supposed to make your life easier when differentiating. Learning them means you don't have to do everything from first principles every time. Try not to get the product rule mixed up with the chain rule. Repeat after me: 'The chain rule is for functions of functions but the product rule is for products of functions'. Snappy, I know...

Quotient Rule

The world is a beautiful, harmonious place full of natural symmetry. So of course, if we have a 'product rule' to differentiate products, we must also have a 'quotient rule' to differentiate... er... quotients. Read on and learn.

Use the Quotient Rule for one function Divided By another

A quotient is one function divided by another one.
The rule for differentiating quotients looks like this:

$$\text{If } y = \frac{u(x)}{v(x)}$$

$$\frac{dy}{dx} = \frac{v\frac{du}{dx} - u\frac{dv}{dx}}{v^2}$$

You could, if you wanted to, just use the product rule on $y = uv^{-1}$ (try it — you'll get the same answer).
This way is so much quicker and easier though — and it's on the formula sheet.

EXAMPLE: Find the gradient of the tangent to the curve with equation $y = \frac{(2x^2 - 1)}{(3x^2 + 1)}$, at the point $(1, 0.25)$.

1) 'Gradient of tangent' means differentiate.
2) First identify u and v for the quotient rule, and differentiate separately:
   $u = 2x^2 - 1 \Rightarrow \frac{du}{dx} = 4x$ and $v = 3x^2 + 1 \Rightarrow \frac{dv}{dx} = 6x$.
3) It's very important that you get things in the right order, so concentrate on what's going where:
   $$\frac{dy}{dx} = \frac{v\frac{du}{dx} - u\frac{dv}{dx}}{v^2} = \frac{(3x^2 + 1)(4x) - (2x^2 - 1)(6x)}{(3x^2 + 1)^2}$$
4) Now you can simplify things:
   $$\frac{dy}{dx} = \frac{x[4(3x^2 + 1) - 6(2x^2 - 1)]}{(3x^2 + 1)^2} = \frac{x[12x^2 + 4 - 12x^2 + 6]}{(3x^2 + 1)^2} = \frac{10x}{(3x^2 + 1)^2}.$$
5) Finally, put in $x = 1$ to find the gradient at (1, 0.25): $\frac{dy}{dx} = \frac{10}{(3 + 1)^2} = 0.625.$

This bit's just like the product rule from the last page.

Don't try to simplify straight away or you'll get things mixed up.

If it's a 'normal' rather than a 'tangent' do −1 ÷ gradient.

You can use the quotient rule on Negative Powers

If you have a product where one of the bits has a negative power, you can rewrite it as a quotient then use the quotient rule to differentiate it.

EXAMPLE Differentiate $x^{-3}e^{2x}$.

1) First, write this out as a quotient: $x^{-3}e^{2x} = \frac{e^{2x}}{x^3}$.
2) Now identify $u = e^{2x}$ and $v = x^3$.
3) Differentiating separately gives: $\frac{du}{dx} = 2e^{2x}$ (see p.25), and $\frac{dv}{dx} = 3x^2$.
4) Putting everything in the quotient rule formula gives:
   $$\frac{dy}{dx} = \frac{2x^3e^{2x} - 3x^2e^{2x}}{(x^3)^2} = \frac{x^2e^{2x}(2x - 3)}{x^6} = \frac{e^{2x}(2x - 3)}{x^4}.\ \text{QED*}$$

*Quite Exciting Differentiation

The second rule of maths club is — you do not talk about maths club...

Confused yet? Yes I know, there are three very similar looking rules in this section, all using *u*s and *v*s and *x*s and *y*s all over the shop. You won't remember them by reading them over and over again like some mystical code. You will remember them by using them lots and lots in practice questions. Plain and simple — just how I like my men...

More Differentiation

What?! More differentiation?! Surely not. This page is all about using what you know.

Finding the **Gradient**, **Tangent**, **dy/dx**, **f'(x)**, **d/dx(f(x))** — all mean '**Differentiate**'

Usually in exams, differentiation will be disguised as something else — either through different notation ($f'(x)$, $\frac{dy}{dx}$ etc.) or by asking for the gradient or rate of change of something (see next page).
You could also be asked to find the equation of a tangent or normal to a curve at a given point:

EXAMPLE Find the equation of the tangent to the curve $y = \frac{5x+2}{3x-2}$ at the point (1, 7), in the form $y = mx + c$.

1) The gradient of the tangent is just the gradient of the curve at that point. So differentiate...
2) Use the quotient rule: $u = 5x + 2 \Rightarrow \frac{du}{dx} = 5$ and $v = 3x - 2 \Rightarrow \frac{dv}{dx} = 3$.
   So $\frac{dy}{dx} = \frac{5(3x-2) - 3(5x+2)}{(3x-2)^2} = -\frac{16}{(3x-2)^2}$.
3) Gradient of tangent at (1, 7) is $\frac{dy}{dx}$ at $x = 1$, which is $-\frac{16}{(3-2)^2} = -16$.
4) Use the equation of a straight line $y - y_1 = m(x - x_1)$ with $m = -16$, $y_1 = 7$ and $x_1 = 1$, to give:
   $y - 7 = -16(x - 1) \Rightarrow y = -16x + 23$ is the equation of the tangent.

If you're asked for a 'normal', do $-1 \div$ gradient of tangent here — then the rest is the same.

You might need to use **More Than One** rule

Some questions will really stretch your alphabet with a multitude of *u*s and *v*s:

EXAMPLE Differentiate $y = x^3(\ln x)^2$

1) First off, this is product rule: $u = x^3 \Rightarrow \frac{du}{dx} = 3x^2$ and $v = (\ln x)^2$.
2) To find $\frac{dv}{dx}$ for the product rule, we need the chain rule:
   $v = u_1^2$, where $u_1 = \ln x$.
   $\frac{dv}{du_1} = 2u_1 = 2\ln x$, and $\frac{du_1}{dx} = \frac{1}{x}$. So $\frac{dv}{dx} = \frac{2\ln x}{x}$.
3) Now we can put this result in the product rule formula to get $\frac{dy}{dx}$:
   $\frac{dy}{dx} = (x^3 \cdot \frac{2\ln x}{x}) + ((\ln x)^2 \cdot 3x^2) = 2x^2\ln x + 3x^2(\ln x)^2 = x^2\ln x(2 + 3\ln x)$. Job done.
   (u = x^3, $\frac{dv}{dx}$ = $\frac{2\ln x}{x}$, v = $(\ln x)^2$, $\frac{du}{dx}$ = $3x^2$)

Differentiate **Again** for **d²y/dx²**, **Turning Points**, **Stationary Points** etc.

Refresh your memory on C1, where you learnt all about maximums and minimums...

EXAMPLE Determine the nature of the stationary point of the curve $y = \frac{\ln x}{x^2}$ $(x > 0)$.

1) First use the quotient rule to find $\frac{dy}{dx}$: $u = \ln x \Rightarrow \frac{du}{dx} = \frac{1}{x}$, $v = x^2 \Rightarrow \frac{dv}{dx} = 2x$. So $\frac{dy}{dx} = \frac{1 - 2\ln x}{x^3}$.
2) The stationary points occur where $\frac{dy}{dx} = 0$ (i.e. zero gradient) so this is when:
   $\frac{1 - 2\ln x}{x^3} = 0 \Rightarrow \ln x = \frac{1}{2} \Rightarrow x = e^{\frac{1}{2}}$.
3) To find out whether it's a maximum or minimum, differentiate $\frac{dy}{dx}$ to get $\frac{d^2y}{dx^2}$:
   $u = 1 - 2\ln x \Rightarrow \frac{du}{dx} = -\frac{2}{x}$, $v = x^3 \Rightarrow \frac{dv}{dx} = 3x^2$. So $\frac{d^2y}{dx^2} = \frac{6\ln x - 5}{x^4}$.
4) When $x = e^{\frac{1}{2}}$, $\frac{d^2y}{dx^2} < 0$ (i.e. negative), which means it's a maximum point.

Positive means minimum, negative means maximum — it's all there in C1.

Parlez vous exam?

It's often noted that mathematics has its own language — you need to make sure you're fluent or all your hard work will go to waste. Become an expert in deciphering exam questions so you do exactly what's expected with the minimum of fuss.

Relating Rates of Change

This is one of those topics where the most awkward bit is getting your head round the information in the question. The actual maths is nothing like as bad as the questions usually make it sound. Honest.

The Chain Rule lets you Connect different Rates of Change

1) Some situations have a number of linked variables, like length, surface area and volume, or distance, speed and acceleration.
2) If you know the rate of change of one of these linked variables, and the equations that connect the variables, you can use the chain rule to help you find the rate of change of the other variables.

EXAMPLE A scientist is testing how a new material expands when it is gradually heated. The diagram shows the sample being tested, which is shaped like a triangular prism. After t minutes, the triangle that forms the base of the prism has base length $7x$ cm and height $4x$ cm, and the height of the prism is also $4x$ cm.

If the sample expands at a constant rate, given by $\frac{dx}{dt} = 0.05$ cm min^{-1}, find an expression in terms of x for $\frac{dV}{dt}$, where V is the volume of the prism.

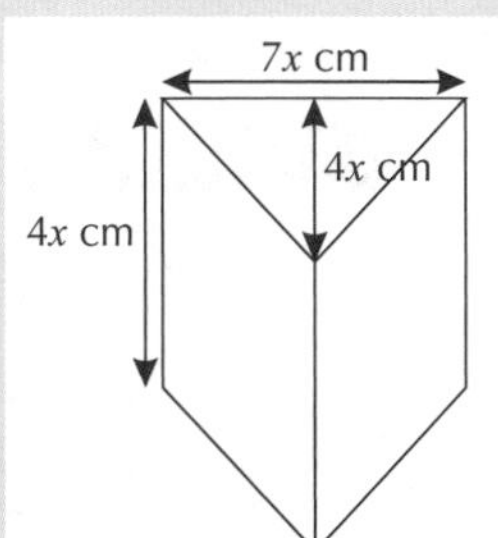

The best way to start this kind of question is to write down what you know. We've got enough information to write an expression for the volume of the prism:

$$V = (\tfrac{1}{2} \times 7x \times 4x) \times 4x = 56x^3 \text{ cm}^3$$

Differentiate this with respect to x:

$$\frac{dV}{dx} = 168x^2$$

We know that $\frac{dx}{dt} = 0.05$. So we can use the chain rule to find $\frac{dV}{dt}$:

$$\frac{dV}{dt} = \frac{dV}{dx} \times \frac{dx}{dt} = 168x^2 \times 0.05 = 8.4x^2$$

Watch out for Slightly Trickier questions

1) There are a couple of sneaky tricks in this type of question that could catch you out if you're not prepared for them.
2) In this next example, you have to spot that there's a hidden derivative described in words.
3) You also need to remember the rule $\frac{dy}{dx} = \frac{1}{\left(\frac{dx}{dy}\right)}$ (see p24).

EXAMPLE A giant metal cube from space is cooling after entering the Earth's atmosphere. As it cools, the surface area of the cube decreases at a constant rate of 0.027 m^2 s^{-1}. If the side length of the cube after t seconds is x m, find $\frac{dx}{dt}$ at the point when $x = 15$ m.

Start with what you know:

We use $\frac{d}{dt}$ because it's a rate of time.

The cube has side length x m, so the surface area of the cube is $A = 6x^2 \quad \Rightarrow \quad \frac{dA}{dx} = 12x$

A decreases at a constant rate of 0.027 m^2 s^{-1} — we can write this as $\frac{dA}{dt} = -0.027$

This value is negative because A is decreasing.

Now use the chain rule to find $\frac{dx}{dt}$:

$$\frac{dx}{dt} = \frac{dx}{dA} \times \frac{dA}{dt} = \frac{1}{\left(\frac{dA}{dx}\right)} \times \frac{dA}{dt} = \frac{1}{12x} \times -0.027 = -\frac{0.00225}{x}$$

So when $x = 15$, $\frac{dx}{dt} = -\frac{0.00225}{x} = -\frac{0.00225}{15} = -0.00015$ m s^{-1}

I'd rate this page 10 out of 10 — if I do say so myself...

If you get stuck on a question like this, don't panic. Somewhere in the question there'll be enough information to write at least one equation linking some of the variables. If in doubt, write down any equations you can make, differentiate them all, and then see which of the resulting expressions you can link using the chain rule to make the thing you're looking for.

Integration of e^x and 1/x

Although it was many moons ago that you last encountered integration, way back at AS level, it's an integral part of A2 Maths. It does the opposite of differentiation, so some of this stuff should look familiar to you.

e^x integrates to give e^x (+ C)

As e^x differentiates to give e^x (see p.25), it makes sense that

$$\int e^x dx = e^x + C$$

Don't forget the constant of integration.

Once you're happy with that, you can use it to solve lots of integrations that have an e^x term in them.
If the coefficient of x isn't 1, you need to divide by that coefficient when you integrate — so $\int e^{kx} dx = \frac{1}{k}e^{kx} + C$

EXAMPLES Integrate the following: a) e^{7x} b) $e^{\frac{x}{2}}$.

a) $\int e^{7x} dx = \frac{1}{7}e^{7x} + C$

If you differentiated e^{7x} using the chain rule, you'd get $7e^{7x}$. So when you integrate, you need to divide by 7 (the coefficient of x). This is so that if you differentiated your answer you'd get back to e^{7x}.

b) $\int e^{\frac{x}{2}} dx = \int e^{\frac{1}{2}x} dx = 2e^{\frac{x}{2}} + C$

If you differentiated this one using the chain rule, you'd get $\frac{1}{2}e^{\frac{x}{2}}$, so you need to multiply by 2 when you integrate.

Whenever you integrate, ALWAYS DIFFERENTIATE YOUR ANSWER TO CHECK IT WORKS

— you should end up with the thing you integrated in the first place. It's the best way to check that you divided or multiplied by the right number.

1/x integrates to ln |x| (+ C)

When you first came across integration in C2, you couldn't integrate $\frac{1}{x}$ $(= x^{-1})$ by increasing the power by 1 and dividing by it, as you ended up dividing by 0 (which is baaaaad).

However, on p.25, you saw that ln x differentiates to give $\frac{1}{x}$, so

$$\int \frac{1}{x} dx = \ln|x| + C$$

Don't worry about where the modulus sign (see p.4) comes from — using $|x|$ just means that there isn't a problem when x is negative.

EXAMPLES Integrate the following: a) $\frac{5}{x}$ b) $\frac{1}{3x}$.

a) $\int \frac{5}{x} dx = 5\int \frac{1}{x} dx = 5\ln|x| + C$

5 is a constant coefficient — you can take it outside the integral if you want.

You could also write $5\ln|x|$ as $\ln|x^5|$.

b) $\int \frac{1}{3x} dx = \frac{1}{3}\int \frac{1}{x} dx = \frac{1}{3}\ln|x| + C$

Be careful with ones like this — 1/3 is just the coefficient, so it goes outside ln $|x|$. Don't make the mistake of putting ln $|3x|$ — this would differentiate to give $1/x$ (as ln $3x$ = ln 3 + ln x, so when you differentiate, ln 3 disappears).

Integrate using a Linear Substitution when there's a Linear Function of x

Integrating using a linear substitution is a simple case of integration by substitution (you do this in C4 — see p.75).

EXAMPLE Integrate $2e^{4-3x}$.

The linear function here is $4 - 3x$, so make the substitution $u = 4 - 3x$. Then $\frac{du}{dx} = -3$, so $dx = \frac{du}{-3}$.
Replace all the x-terms with u-terms and integrate:

$$\int 2e^{4-3x} dx = \int -\frac{2}{3}e^u du = -\frac{2}{3}e^u + C = -\frac{2}{3}e^{4-3x} + C$$

Don't forget to replace u with $4 - 3x$ in your final answer.

$\frac{du}{dx}$ isn't a proper fraction, but you can treat it like one here.

All you actually end up doing in these questions is just dividing by the coefficient of x when you integrate.

Integration feels pretty constant to me...

If x has a coefficient that isn't 1, just work out what you think the answer will look like (e.g. e^x, ln$|x|$, etc.), then differentiate to see what you get. You might have to adjust your answer by dividing or multiplying by the coefficient to get what you started with.

Volumes of Revolution

Sadly, volumes of revolution isn't to do with plotting your own revolution — it calculates the volumes of weird solids.

You have to find the *Volume* of an area *Rotated About the x- or y-axis*

If you're given a definite integral, the solution you come up with is the area under the graph between the two limits (you did this back in AS). If you now rotate that area 2π radians about the x-axis, you'll come up with a solid — and this is what you want to find the volume of. The formula for finding the volume of revolution is:

$$V = \pi \int_{x=x_1}^{x=x_2} y^2\,dx$$

where y is a function of x (i.e. $y = f(x)$) and x_1 and x_2 are the limits of x.

If you wanted to rotate an area about the y-axis, you'd use the formula $V = \pi\int_{y_1}^{y_2} x^2\,dy$ — you'd have to write x^2 as a function of y first.

EXAMPLE Find the volume, V, of the solid formed when the area enclosed by the curve $y = \sqrt{6x^2 - 3x + 2}$, the x-axis and the lines $x = 1$ and $x = 2$ is rotated 2π radians about the x-axis.

If $y = \sqrt{6x^2 - 3x + 2}$, then $y^2 = 6x^2 - 3x + 2$. Putting this into the formula gives:

$$V = \pi\int_1^2 6x^2 - 3x + 2\,dx = \pi\left[2x^3 - \tfrac{3}{2}x^2 + 2x\right]_1^2$$

$$= \pi\left(\left[2(2)^3 - \tfrac{3}{2}(2)^2 + 2(2)\right] - \left[2(1)^3 - \tfrac{3}{2}(1)^2 + 2(1)\right]\right)$$

$$= \pi\left([16 - 6 + 4] - \left[2 - \tfrac{3}{2} + 2\right]\right) = \pi\left(14 - 2\tfrac{1}{2}\right) = 11\tfrac{1}{2}\pi$$

Don't forget to square y — you might think it's obvious, but it's easily done.

EXAMPLE Find the volume, V, of the solid formed when the area enclosed by the curve $y = \sqrt{x^2 + 5}$, the y-axis and the lines $y = 3$ and $y = 6$ is rotated 2π radians about the y-axis.

First, rearrange the equation to get x^2 on its own:

$y = \sqrt{x^2 + 5} \Rightarrow y^2 = x^2 + 5$

so $x^2 = y^2 - 5$.

Now integrate: $V = \pi\int_3^6 y^2 - 5\,dy = \pi\left[\tfrac{1}{3}y^3 - 5y\right]_3^6$

$$= \pi\left(\left[\tfrac{1}{3}(6)^3 - 5(6)\right] - \left[\tfrac{1}{3}(3)^3 - 5(3)\right]\right)$$

$$= \pi(42 - (-6)) = 48\pi$$

It could be the area *Between Curves* that's rotated

Just to try and catch you out, they might ask you to find the volume formed when the area between two curves is rotated. This isn't as nasty as it sounds — all you have to do is work out the volume for each curve separately, then subtract the bit you don't need.

EXAMPLE The region R is enclosed by the lines $y = e^{\frac{x-1}{2}}$, $y = \frac{1}{\sqrt{x}}$ and $x = 3$. Find the volume formed when R is rotated 2π radians about the x-axis.

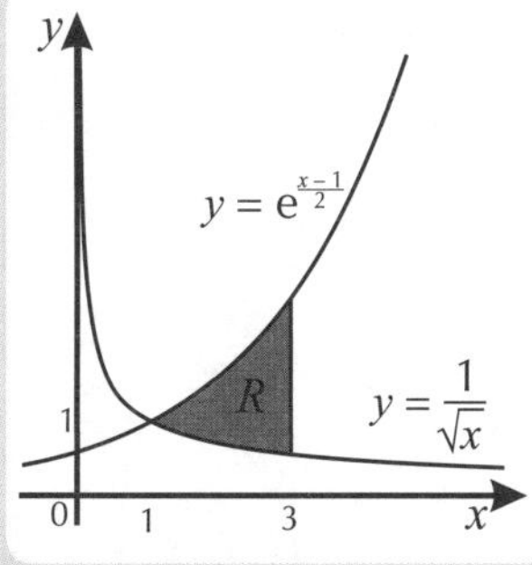

Find the volume for each curve separately:

For the curve $y = e^{\frac{x-1}{2}}$, $y^2 = e^{x-1}$. Putting this into the formula to find the volume of revolution: $V_1 = \pi\int_1^3 e^{x-1}\,dx = \pi[e^{x-1}]_1^3$

$$= \pi(e^{3-1} - e^{1-1}) = \pi(e^2 - e^0)$$

$$= \pi(e^2 - 1).$$

The limit $x = 1$ is the point of intersection of the two curves. It's obvious from the graph, but you can check it by putting $x = 1$ into both equations.

For the curve $y = \frac{1}{\sqrt{x}}$, $y^2 = \frac{1}{x}$. Putting this into the formula to find the volume of revolution:

$V_2 = \pi\int_1^3 \frac{1}{x}\,dx = \pi[\ln x]_1^3$

$$= \pi(\ln 3 - \ln 1) = \pi\ln 3.$$

Look at the graph to work out which bit to subtract.

To find the volume formed when R is rotated, you need to subtract V_2 from V_1:

$\pi(e^2 - 1) - \pi\ln 3 = 16.62$ (4 s.f.).

Come the revolution, I will have to kill you all...

Not to be confused with the French Revolution, the Industrial Revolution or the lesser-known CGP Revolution, volumes of revolution is part of A2 Maths. So don't go getting any ideas about overthrowing your teachers and not letting them eat cake.

C3 Section 4 — Practice Questions

Those who know it, know they know it. Those who think they know it, need to know they know it.
So, you think you know it, no? Try these to make sure.

Warm-up Questions

1) Differentiate with respect to x:
   a) $y = \sqrt{x^3 + 2x^2}$ b) $y = \frac{1}{\sqrt{x^3 + 2x^2}}$ c) $y = e^{5x^2}$ d) $y = \ln(6 - x^2)$
2) Find $\frac{dy}{dx}$ when a) $x = 2e^y$ b) $x = \ln(2y + 3)$
3) Find the value of the gradient for $y = e^{2x}(x^2 - 3)$ when $x = 0$
4) Find the equation of the tangent to the curve $y = \frac{6x^2 + 3}{4x^2 - 1}$ at the point (1, 3).
5) A cuboid has length x cm, width $2x$ cm and height $3x$ cm.
   The cuboid is expanding, for some unexplained reason.
   If A is the surface area of the cuboid and V is its volume, find $\frac{dA}{dx}$ and $\frac{dV}{dx}$, and use them to show that if $\frac{dV}{dt} = 3$, then $\frac{dA}{dt} = \frac{22}{3x}$.
6) Find $\int 4e^{2x}\,dx$.
7) Find $\int e^{3x-5}\,dx$.
8) Find $\int \frac{2}{3x}\,dx$.
9) Find $\int \frac{2}{2x+1}\,dx$.
10) Find the volume of the solid formed when the area bounded by the curve $y = \frac{1}{x}$, the x-axis and the lines $x = 2$ and $x = 4$ is rotated 2π radians about the x-axis.
11) Find the volume of the solid formed when the area bounded by the curve $y = x^2 + 1$, the y-axis and the lines $y = 1$ and $y = 3$ is rotated 2π radians about the y-axis.

Well that's put some colour in your cheeks. Now to really excel yourself on the exam practice, but try not to pull a muscle — you need to be match fit for the real thing.

Exam Questions

1 Find $\int 3e^{(5-6x)}\,dx$. *(2 marks)*

2 The curve shown below has the equation $x = \sqrt{y^2 + 3y}$.

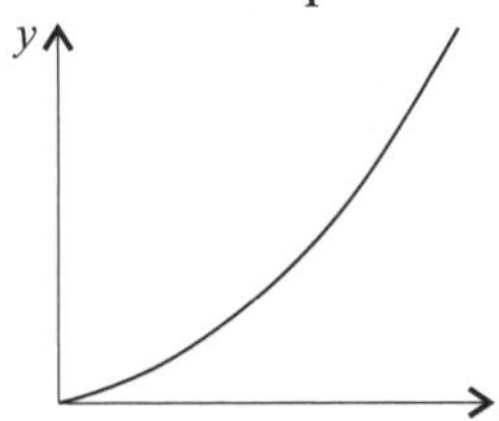

a) Find $\frac{dy}{dx}$ at the point (2, 1). *(5 marks)*

b) Hence find the equation of the tangent to the curve at (2, 1), in the form $y = ax + b$, where a and b are constants. *(2 marks)*

3 Given that $y = \frac{e^x + x}{e^x - x}$, find $\frac{dy}{dx}$ when $x = 0$. *(3 marks)*

C3 Section 4 — Practice Questions

4 Differentiate the following with respect to x.

a) $\sqrt{(e^x + e^{2x})}$. *(3 marks)*

b) $3e^{2x+1} - \ln(1 - x^2) + 2x^3$. *(3 marks)*

5 A sketch of the function $f(x) = 4\ln 3x$ is shown in the diagram on the right.

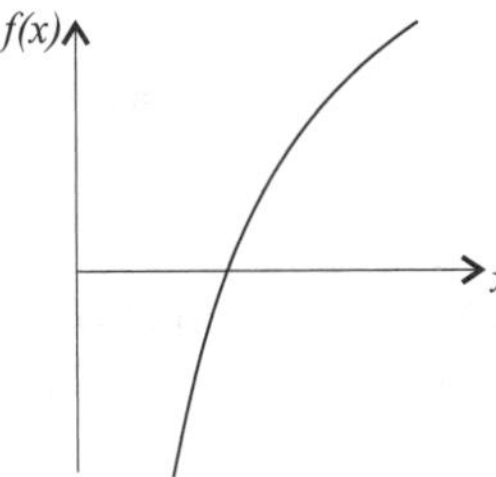

a) Find $f'(x)$ at the point where $x = 1$. *(3 marks)*

b) Find the equation of the tangent to the curve at the point $x = 1$. *(3 marks)*

6

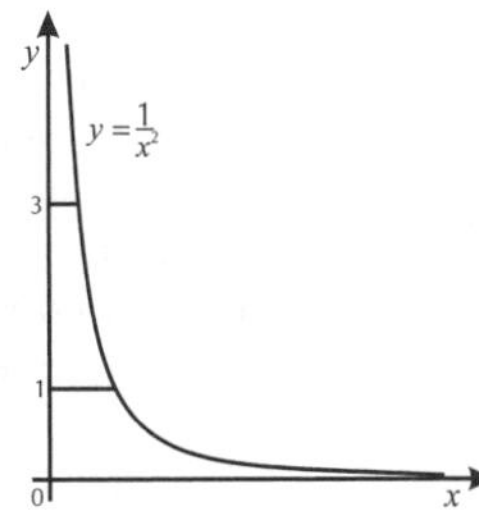

The graph on the left shows the curve of $y = \frac{1}{x^2}$ for $x > 0$.
The region bounded by the curve, the y-axis and the lines $y = 1$ and $y = 3$ is rotated 2π radians about the y-axis. Calculate the exact volume of the solid formed. *(5 marks)*

7 The region R shown right is formed by the curves $y = e^{1.5x}$, $y = \sqrt{x}$, $x = 1$ and $x = 2$. Calculate the volume of the solid formed when R is rotated completely about the x-axis. Give your answer to 4 s.f. *(7 marks)*

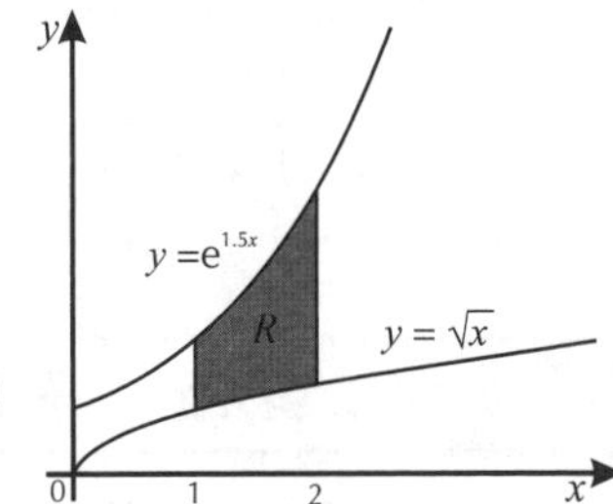

8

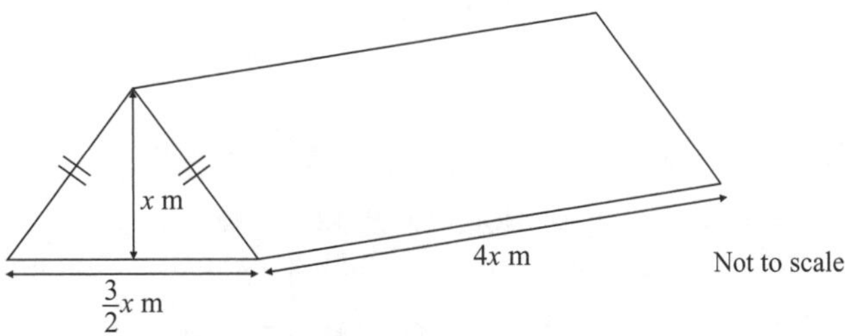

The triangular prism shown in the diagram is expanding.
The dimensions of the prism after t seconds are given in terms of x.
The prism is $4x$ m long, and its cross-section is an isosceles triangle with base $\frac{3}{2}x$ m and height x m.

a) Show that, if the surface area of the prism after t seconds is A m^2, then $A = \frac{35}{2}x^2$. *(3 marks)*

The surface area of the prism is increasing at a constant rate of 0.07 m^2 s^{-1}.

b) Find $\frac{dx}{dt}$ when $x = 0.5$. *(3 marks)*

c) If the volume of the prism is V m^3, find the rate of change of V when $x = 1.2$. *(4 marks)*

Location of Roots

And now to the final leg of the magical mystery tour known as C3. And what a finale. Small but perfectly formed, this section will tell you everything you need to know (for now) about finding approximations of roots. Oh the thrills.

A Change of Sign from f(a) to f(b) means a Root Between a and b

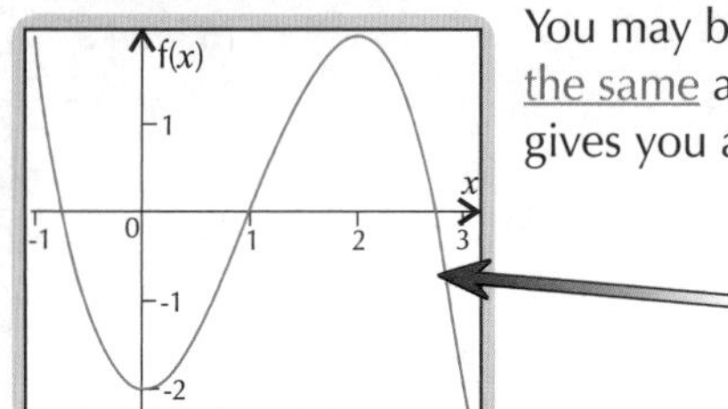

You may be asked to 'solve' or 'find the roots of' an equation (where $f(x) = 0$). This is exactly the same as finding the value of x where the graph crosses the x-axis. The graph of the function gives you a rough idea how many roots there are (if any) and where.

E.g. the function $f(x) = 3x^2 - x^3 - 2$ (shown here) has 3 roots in the interval $-1 \le x \le 3$, since it crosses the x-axis three times (i.e. there are 3 solutions to the equation $3x^2 - x^3 - 2 = 0$). You can also see from the graph that $x = 1$ is a root, and the other roots are close to $x = -1$ and $x = 3$.

Look at the graph above at the root $x = 1$. For x-values just before the root, $f(x)$ is negative, and just after the root, $f(x)$ is positive. It's the other way around for the other two roots, but either way:

> $f(x)$ changes sign as it passes through a root.

This is only true for continuous functions — ones that are joined up all the way along with no 'jumps' or gaps.

> To show that a root lies in the interval between two values 'a' and 'b':
>
> 1) Find f(a) and f(b).
> 2) If the two answers have different signs, and the function is continuous, there's a root somewhere between 'em.

$f(x) = \tan x$ is an example of a non-continuous function — it has gaps where $f(x)$ changes sign even though there's no root.

EXAMPLE Show that $x^4 + 3x - 5 = 0$ has a root in the interval $1.1 \le x \le 1.2$.

1) Put both 1.1 and 1.2 into the expression:
$f(1.1) = (1.1)^4 + (3 \times 1.1) - 5 = -0.2359$. $f(1.2) = (1.2)^4 + (3 \times 1.2) - 5 = 0.6736$.
2) $f(1.1)$ and $f(1.2)$ have different signs, and $f(x)$ is continuous, so there's a root in the interval $1.1 \le x \le 1.2$.

Use an Iteration Formula to find Approximations of Roots

Some equations are just too darn tricky to solve properly. For these, you need to find approximations to the roots, to a certain level of accuracy. You'll usually be told the value of x that a root is close to, and then iteration does the rest.

Iteration is like fancy trial and improvement. You put an approximate value of a root x into an iteration formula, and out pops a slightly more accurate value. Then repeat as necessary until you have an accurate enough answer.

EXAMPLE Use the iteration formula $x_{n+1} = \sqrt[3]{x_n + 4}$ to solve $x^3 - 4 - x = 0$, to 2 d.p. Start with $x_0 = 2$.

1) The notation x_n just means the approximation of x at the nth iteration.
So putting x_0 in the formula for x_n, gives you x_{n+1}, which is x_1, the first iteration.
2) $x_0 = 2$, so $x_1 = \sqrt[3]{x_0 + 4} = \sqrt[3]{2 + 4} = 1.8171...$ ← Leave this in your calculator for accuracy.
3) This value now gets put back into the formula to find x_2:
$x_1 = 1.8171...$, so $x_2 = \sqrt[3]{x_1 + 4} = \sqrt[3]{1.8171... + 4} = 1.7984...$ ← You should now just be able to type '$\sqrt[3]{(ANS + 4)}$' in your calculator and keep pressing enter for each iteration.
4) Carry on until you get answers that are the same when rounded to 2 d.p:
$x_2 = 1.7984...$, so $x_3 = \sqrt[3]{x_2 + 4} = \sqrt[3]{1.7984... + 4} = 1.7965...$
5) x_2, x_3, and all further iterations are the same when rounded to 2 d.p., so the root is $x = 1.80$ to 2 d.p.

The hat — an approximate solution to root problems...

Just to re-iterate (ho ho), the main ways to find those roots are sign changes and iteration formulas. It's a doddle. Don't get confused and go looking for tree roots — that involves a lot of digging, and you'll end up getting all muddy.

Iterative Methods

Now we come to the trickier bits. It's all well and good being able to plug numbers into a formula, but where do those formulas come from? And why don't they always work? Read on to find out...

Rearrange the Equation to get the Iteration Formula

The iteration formula is just a rearrangement of the equation, leaving a single 'x' on one side.

There are often lots of different ways to rearrange the equation, so in the exam you'll usually be asked to 'show that' it can be rearranged in a certain way, rather than starting from scratch.

You can also rearrange $x^3 - x^2 - 9 = 0$ into the iteration formula $x_{n+1} = \sqrt{x_n^3 - 9}$, which behaves differently, as shown below.

EXAMPLE Show that $x^3 - x^2 - 9 = 0$ can be rearranged into $x = \sqrt{\frac{9}{x-1}}$.

1) The '9' is on its own in the fraction so try:
$x^3 - x^2 - 9 = 0 \Rightarrow x^3 - x^2 = 9$
2) The LHS can be factorised now: $x^2(x - 1) = 9$
3) Get the x^2 on its own by dividing by $x - 1$: $x^2 = \frac{9}{x-1}$
4) Finally square root both sides: $x = \sqrt{\frac{9}{x-1}}$

You can now use the iteration formula $x_{n+1} = \sqrt{\frac{9}{x_n - 1}}$ to find approximations of the roots.

Sometimes an iteration formula just will not find a root. In these cases, no matter how close to the root you have x_0, the iteration sequence diverges — the numbers get further and further away from the root. The iteration also might stop working — e.g. if you have to take the square root of a negative number.

EXAMPLE The equation $x^3 - x^2 - 9 = 0$ has a root close to $x = 2.5$.
What is the result of using $x_{n+1} = \sqrt{x_n^3 - 9}$ with $x_0 = 2.5$ to find this root?

1) Start with $x_1 = \sqrt{2.5^3 - 9} = 2.5739...$ (seems okay so far...)
2) Subsequent iterations give: $x_2 = 2.8376...$, $x_3 = 3.7214...$, $x_4 = 6.5221...$ — so the sequence diverges.

Usually though, in an exam question, you'll be given a formula that converges to a certain root — otherwise there's not much point in using it. If your formula diverges when it shouldn't, go back and check you've not made a mistake.

Use Upper and Lower Bounds to 'Show that' a root is correct

Quite often you'll be given an approximation to a root and be asked to show that it's correct to a certain degree of accuracy. This is a lot like showing that the root lies in a certain interval (on the last page) — the trick is to work out the right interval.

EXAMPLE Show that $x = 2.472$ is a root of the equation $x^3 - x^2 - 9 = 0$ to 3 d.p.

1) If $x = 2.472$ is a root rounded to 3 decimal places, the exact root must lie between the upper and lower bounds of this value — 2.4715 and 2.4725. Any value in this interval would be rounded to 2.472 to 3 d.p.

2.471 | 2.4715 | 2.472 | 2.4725 | 2.473

2) The function $f(x) = x^3 - x^2 - 9$ is continuous, so you know the root lies in the interval $2.4715 \le x \le 2.4725$ if f(2.4715) and f(2.4725) have different signs.
3) $f(2.4715) = 2.4715^3 - 2.4715^2 - 9 = -0.0116...$
and $f(2.4725) = 2.4725^3 - 2.4725^2 - 9 = 0.0017...$
4) f(2.4715) and f(2.4725) have different signs, so the root must lie in between them. Since any value between would be rounded to 2.472 to 3 d.p. this answer must be correct.

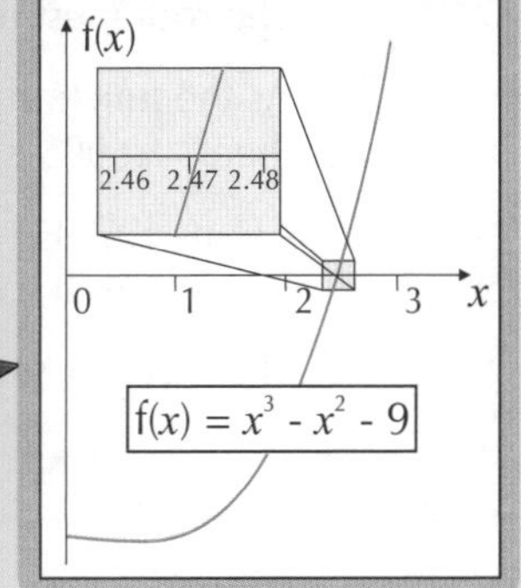

You're bound to be asked questions on this...

There are usually several parts to an exam question on iteration, but it's all pretty standard stuff. I'd put good money on you having to rearrange an equation to get an iteration formula, or show that an approximation to a root is correct.

Iterative Methods

So now that you know all you need to know to be able to tackle the exam questions, let's have a look at how it all fits together in a worked example. Brace yourself...

Questions on Locating Roots combine all the Different Methods

Obviously, the questions you come across in the exam won't be identical to the one below (if only...), but there are, after all, only a limited number of ways you can be asked to find a root using the numerical methods in this section. If you can follow the steps shown below you won't go far wrong.

EXAMPLE The graph below shows both roots of the continuous function $f(x) = 6x - x^2 + 13$.

a) Show that the positive root, α, lies in the interval $7 < x < 8$.

b) Show that $6x - x^2 + 13 = 0$ can be rearranged into the formula: $x = \sqrt{6x + 13}$.

c) Use the iteration formula $x_{n+1} = \sqrt{6x_n + 13}$ and $x_0 = 7$ to find α to 1 d.p.

d) Show that the negative root, β, is -1.690 to 3 d.p.

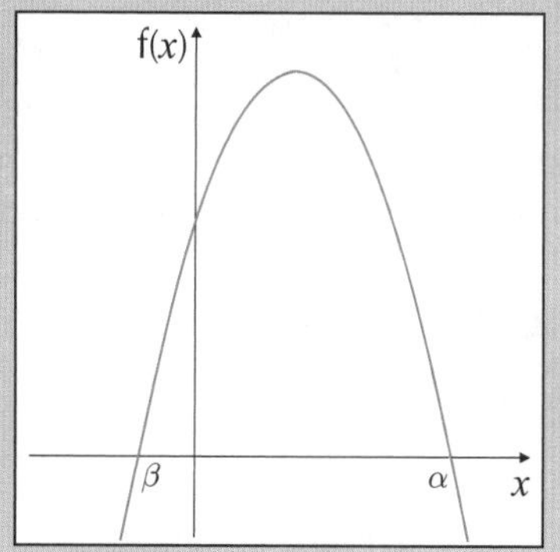

a) $f(x)$ is a continuous function, so if f(7) and f(8) have different signs then there is a root in the interval $7 < x < 8$:

$f(7) = (6 \times 7) - 7^2 + 13 = 6.$
$f(8) = (6 \times 8) - 8^2 + 13 = -3.$

There is a change of sign so $7 < \alpha < 8$.

b) Get the x^2 on its own to make: $6x + 13 = x^2$

Now take the (positive) square root to leave: $x = \sqrt{6x + 13}$.

c) Using $x_{n+1} = \sqrt{6x_n + 13}$ with $x_0 = 7$, gives $x_1 = \sqrt{6 \times 7 + 13} = 7.4161...$

Continuing the iterations:

$x_2 = \sqrt{6 \times 7.4161... + 13} = 7.5826...$ $\quad x_3 = \sqrt{6 \times 7.5826... + 13} = 7.6482...$
$x_4 = \sqrt{6 \times 7.6482... + 13} = 7.6739...$ $\quad x_5 = \sqrt{6 \times 7.6739... + 13} = 7.6839...$
$x_6 = \sqrt{6 \times 7.6839... + 13} = 7.6879...$ $\quad x_7 = \sqrt{6 \times 7.6879... + 13} = 7.6894...$

x_4 to x_7 all round to 7.7 to 1 d.p., so to 1 d.p. $\alpha = 7.7$.

The list of results from each iteration $x_1, x_2, x_3...$ is called the iteration sequence.

d) If $\beta = -1.690$ to 3 d.p. the upper and lower bounds are -1.6895 and -1.6905. The root must lie between these values in order to be rounded to -1.690.

As the function is continuous, if $f(-1.6895)$ and $f(-1.6905)$ have different signs then $-1.6905 \le \beta \le -1.6895$:

$f(-1.6895) = (6 \times -1.6895) - (-1.6895)^2 + 13 = 0.00858...$
$f(-1.6905) = (6 \times -1.6905) - (-1.6905)^2 + 13 = -0.00079...$

There is a change of sign, so $-1.6905 \le \beta \le -1.6895$, and so $\beta = -1.690$ to 3 d.p.

Trouble finding a root? Try sat-nav...

Well, that was a whopper of a question. It's not as bad as it looks though — there are hints in the question to guide you through it. And personally I get quite a bit of satisfaction from putting an iteration formula into my calculator, pressing '=' and watching the numbers (hopefully) converge to a root. I really should get out more.

Numerical Integration

There are a few ways of estimating areas under graphs that don't involve integrating — unfortunately looking at the picture and saying "I reckon that's about 5 cm²" isn't one of them. The one you need is Simpson's Rule.

Simpson's Rule works for an Even Number of Strips

Simpson's Rule is a bit like the Trapezium Rule that you met back in C2 (have a look at your AS notes if you need a reminder) — it lets you estimate the area under a curve by dividing it up into smaller bits. It's given to you on the formula sheet, so you don't have to learn it. You do need to know what it means, and how to use it. It looks like this:

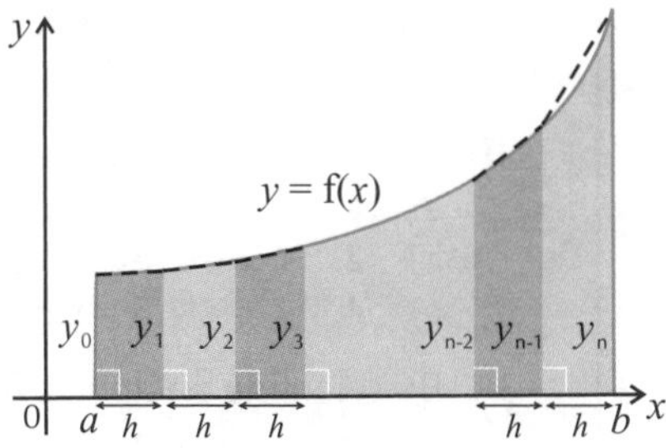

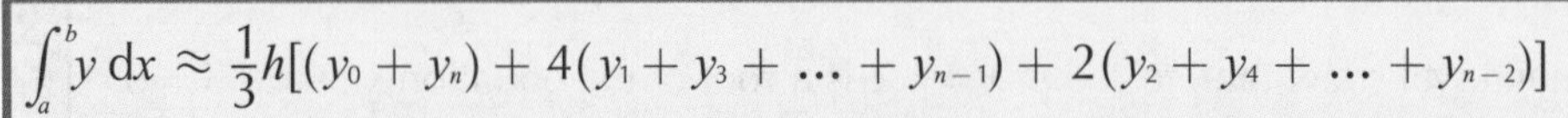

$$\int_a^b y\,dx \approx \frac{1}{3}h[(y_0 + y_n) + 4(y_1 + y_3 + \ldots + y_{n-1}) + 2(y_2 + y_4 + \ldots + y_{n-2})]$$

where $h = \frac{b-a}{n}$ (the width of each strip) and n (the number of strips) is even. $y_0, y_1, y_2, \ldots, y_n$ are the heights of the sides of each strip — you get these by putting the x-values into the equation of the curve (like for the Trapezium Rule).

EXAMPLE Use Simpson's Rule with 4 strips to approximate the area of $\int_0^1 e^{2x^2-1}\,dx$.

The width of each strip is $h = \frac{1-0}{4} = 0.25$, so the x-values are 0, 0.25, 0.5, 0.75 and 1.
Using these, calculate the y-values (to 3 d.p.):

x	$y = e^{2x^2-1}$
$x_0 = 0$	$y_0 = 0.368$
$x_1 = 0.25$	$y_1 = 0.417$
$x_2 = 0.5$	$y_2 = 0.607$
$x_3 = 0.75$	$y_3 = 1.133$
$x_4 = 1$	$y_4 = 2.718$

Now put the y-values into the formula:

$$\int_0^1 e^{2x^2-1}\,dx \approx \tfrac{1}{3}(0.25)[(0.368 + 2.718) + 4(0.417 + 1.133) + 2(0.607)]$$
$$= \tfrac{1}{12}[3.086 + 6.2 + 1.214] = 0.875 \text{ (3 d.p.)}$$

Using more strips will give you a more accurate approximation.

You need the Exact Answer to work out the Percentage Error

To work out the percentage error, calculate or use the exact value of the integral, then use this formula:

$$\% \text{ Error} = \left|\frac{\text{exact value} - \text{approximate value}}{\text{exact value}}\right| \times 100$$

EXAMPLE The exact area of $\int_0^1 e^{2x^2-1}\,dx$ is calculated to be 0.870 (to 3 d.p.). Calculate the percentage error of the estimate you obtained above.

Put the exact value of the integral and your estimate into the formula:

$$\left|\frac{0.870 - 0.875}{0.870}\right| \times 100 = 0.575\% \text{ (3 d.p.)}.$$

An approximation with more strips will have a lower percentage error — so it's a more accurate approximation.

Mmm, Simpson's rule...

And that's your lot — wasn't so bad, was it? All done and dusted for C3, except for those practice questions you've come to know and love so well. Oh, and a couple of practice exams for you to have a go at. Then it's just the tiny wee matter of passing the actual exam... So calculators at the ready, grab your lucky pen and prepare to iterate your heart out...

C3 Section 5 — Practice Questions

Oh happy day, there's light at the end of the C3 tunnel. You're almost there now, but to make up for a very short section I'm giving you lots of lovely practice. Stretch those thinking muscles with this warm-up:

Warm-up Questions

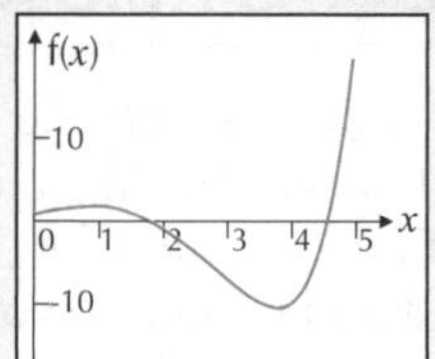

1) The graph shows the function $f(x) = e^x - x^3$ for $0 \leq x \leq 5$.
   How many roots does the equation $e^x - x^3 = 0$ have in the interval $0 \leq x \leq 5$?

2) Show that there is a root in the interval:
   a) $3 < x < 4$ for $\sin(2x) = 0$, Don't forget to use radians when you're given trig functions.
   b) $2.1 < x < 2.2$ for $\ln(x - 2) + 2 = 0$,
   c) $4.3 < x < 4.5$ for $x^3 - 4x^2 = 7$.

3) By selecting an appropriate interval show that, to 1 d.p, $x = 1.2$ is a root of the equation $x^3 + x - 3 = 0$.

4) Use the formula $x_{n+1} = -\frac{1}{2}\cos x_n$, with $x_0 = -1$, to find a root of $\cos x + 2x = 0$ to 2 d.p.

5) Use the formula $x_{n+1} = \sqrt{\ln x_n + 4}$, with $x_0 = 2$, to find a root of $x^2 - \ln x - 4 = 0$ to 3 d.p.

6) a) Show that the equation $2x^2 - x^3 + 1 = 0$ can be written in the form:
   i) $x = \sqrt{\frac{-1}{2-x}}$ ii) $x = \sqrt[3]{2x^2 + 1}$ iii) $x = \sqrt{\frac{x^3 - 1}{2}}$
   b) Use iteration formulas based on each of the above rearrangements with $x_0 = 2.3$ to find a root of $2x^2 - x^3 + 1 = 0$ to 2 d.p. Which of the three formulas converge to a root?

7) a) Use Simpson's Rule with 6 strips to approximate the area of $\int_1^4 \ln(\sqrt{x} + 2)\,dx$.
   b) Why can't you use Simpson's Rule with 5 strips to find an estimate?

And for my final trick... Sadly no magic here, but all the right kinds of questions to prepare you for the exam. Which may not be what you want, but it's definitely what you need.

Exam Questions

1 The sketch below shows part of the graph of the function $f(x) = 2xe^x - 3$.
The curve crosses the x-axis at the point P $(p, 0)$, as shown, so p is a root of the equation $f(x) = 0$.

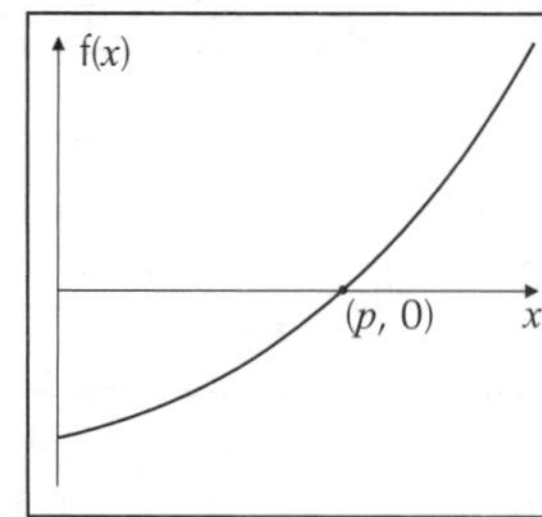

a) Show that $0.7 < p < 0.8$. *(3 marks)*

b) Show that $f(x) = 0$ can be rewritten as:

$$x = \frac{3}{2}e^{-x}.$$

(2 marks)

c) Starting with $x_0 = 0.7$, use the iteration

$$x_{n+1} = \frac{3}{2}e^{-x_n}$$

to find x_1, x_2, x_3 and x_4 to 4 d.p. *(3 marks)*

d) Show that $p = 0.726$, to 3 d.p. *(3 marks)*

C3 Section 5 — Practice Questions

2 The graph of the function:

$$y = \sin 3x + 3x, \quad 0 < x < \pi,$$

meets the line $y = 1$ when $x = a$.

a) Show that $0.1 < a < 0.2$. *(4 marks)*

b) Show that the equation:

$$\sin 3x + 3x = 1$$

can be written as:

$$x = \tfrac{1}{3}(1 - \sin 3x).$$

(2 marks)

c) Starting with $x_0 = 0.2$, use the iteration:

$$x_{n+1} = \tfrac{1}{3}(1 - \sin 3x_n)$$

to find x_4, to 3 d.p. *(2 marks)*

3 The sequence given by:

$$x_{n+1} = \sqrt[3]{x_n^2 - 4}, \quad x_0 = -1$$

converges to a number 'b'.

a) Find the values of x_1, x_2, x_3 and x_4 correct to 4 decimal places. *(3 marks)*

b) Show that $x = b$ is a root of the equation:

$$x^3 - x^2 + 4 = 0$$

(2 marks)

c) Show that $b = -1.315$ to 3 decimal places, by choosing an appropriate interval. *(3 marks)*

4 The function:

$$f(x) = \ln(x + 3) - x + 2, \quad x > -3$$

has a root at $x = m$.

a) Show that m lies between 3 and 4. *(3 marks)*

b) Find, using iteration, the value of m correct to 2 decimal places.
Use the iteration formula: $x_{n+1} = \ln(x_n + 3) + 2$
with $x_0 = 3$. *(3 marks)*

c) Use a suitable interval to verify that your answer to part b) is correct to 2 decimal places. *(3 marks)*

5 Using Simpson's Rule with 4 strips, approximate the area of $\int_1^5 \frac{1}{x^2 + 3x}\,dx$.
Give your answer to 3 s.f. *(4 marks)*

General Certificate of Education
Advanced Subsidiary (AS) and Advanced Level

Core Mathematics C3 — Practice Exam One

Time Allowed: 1 hour 30 min

Graphical calculators may be used for this exam.

Give any non-exact numerical answers to an appropriate degree of accuracy.

There are 72 marks available for this paper.

1 For the function:

$$f(x) = 3 \ln x - \ln 3x, \qquad x > 0$$

find:

a) the exact value of x when $f(x) = 0$. *(2 marks)*

b) $f^{-1}(x)$. *(2 marks)*

c) the exact value of x when $f^{-1}(x) = 1$. *(2 marks)*

d) $f'(x)$ when $x = 1$. *(2 marks)*

2 The graph below shows the function $y = f(x)$, $x \in \mathbb{R}$, with turning points $A(-1, -2)$ and $B(3, 2)$.

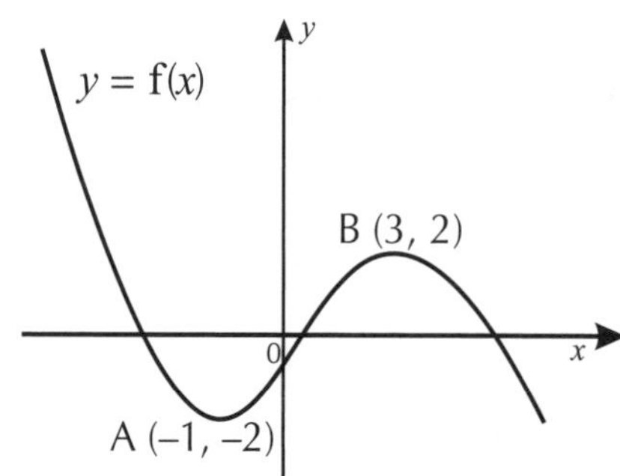

a) On separate axes, sketch the graphs of the following, clearly showing the coordinates of A and B where possible.

(i) $y = f(|x|)$. *(3 marks)*

(ii) $y = 3f(x + 2)$. *(3 marks)*

b) For the functions $g(x) = \sqrt{2x+3}$, $x \geq -1.5$ and $h(x) = \frac{6}{x^2 - 4}$, $x > 2$, find:

(i) gh(4) *(2 marks)*

(ii) hg(3) *(2 marks)*

(iii) hg(x) *(3 marks)*

3 The graph below shows the curve $y = \frac{3\ln x}{x^2}$, $x \geq 0$. The shaded region R is bounded by the curve, the x-axis and the line $x = 3$.

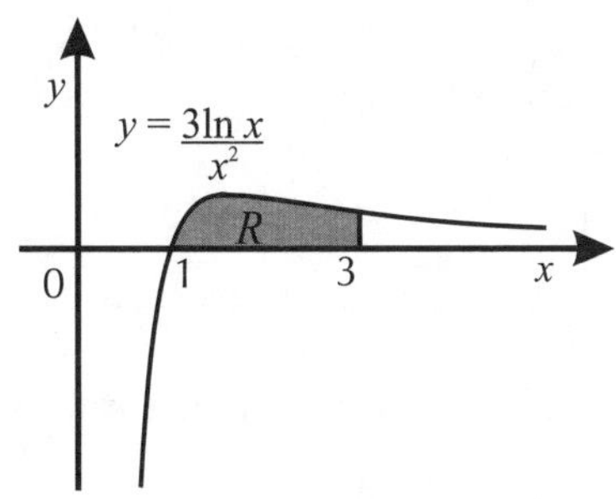

a) Complete the table for the missing y-values. Give your answers to 5 decimal places.

x	1	1.5	2	2.5	3
y	0		0.51986	0.43982	

(2 marks)

b) Find an approximation for the area of R, using Simpson's Rule and all the values in the table. *(4 marks)*

4 a) On the same axes, draw the graphs of $f(x) = |2x + 3|$ and $g(x) = |5x - 4|$, showing clearly where each graph touches the coordinate axes. *(3 marks)*

b) Hence or otherwise solve the equation $|2x + 3| = |5x - 4|$. *(4 marks)*

c) Using your results to parts a) and b), solve the inequality $|2x + 3| \geq |5x - 4|$. *(2 marks)*

5 a) Find the values of θ in the range $0 \leq \theta \leq 2\pi$ for which $\operatorname{cosec} \theta = \frac{5}{3}$.
Give your answers to 3 significant figures. *(2 marks)*

b) (i) Use an appropriate identity to show that $3\operatorname{cosec} \theta = \cot^2\theta - 17$ can be written as $18 + 3\operatorname{cosec} \theta - \operatorname{cosec}^2\theta = 0$. *(2 marks)*

(ii) Hence solve the equation $3\operatorname{cosec} \theta = \cot^2\theta - 17$ for $0 \leq \theta \leq 2\pi$, giving your answers to 3 significant figures. *(4 marks)*

6 The sketch below shows the intersection of the curve $y = 6^x$ with the line $y = x + 2$ at the point P.

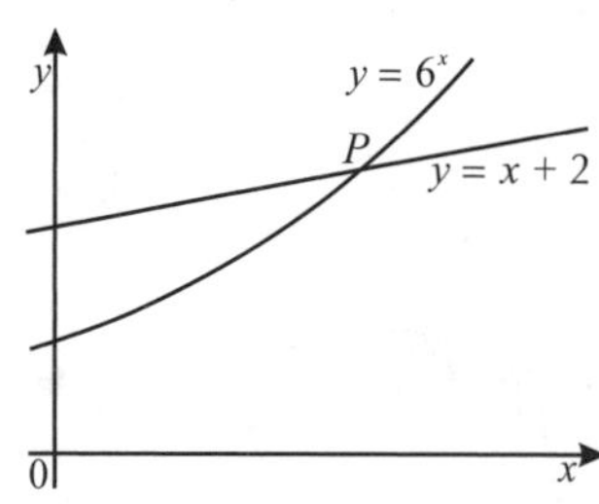

a) Show that the equation $6^x = x + 2$ can be written in the form:

$$x = \frac{\ln(x+2)}{\ln 6}.$$

(2 marks)

b) Starting with $x_0 = 0.5$, use the iteration formula:

$$x_{n+1} = \frac{\ln(x_n + 2)}{\ln 6}$$

to find x_1, x_2 and x_3 correct to 4 decimal places.

(3 marks)

c) By selecting an appropriate interval, show that $x = 0.515$ to 3 decimal places at point P. *(3 marks)*

7 By writing $\sin 2\theta$ in terms of $\sin\theta$ and $\cos\theta$, solve the equation

$$3\sin 2\theta \tan\theta = 5, \qquad \text{for } 0 \le \theta \le 2\pi.$$

Give your answers to 3 significant figures.

(6 marks)

8 A curve has the equation $x = \dfrac{e^y + 2y}{e^y - 2y}$.

a) Find $\dfrac{dy}{dx}$.

(3 marks)

b) Find an equation of the normal to the curve at the point (1, 0) in the form $y = ax + b$. *(3 marks)*

9

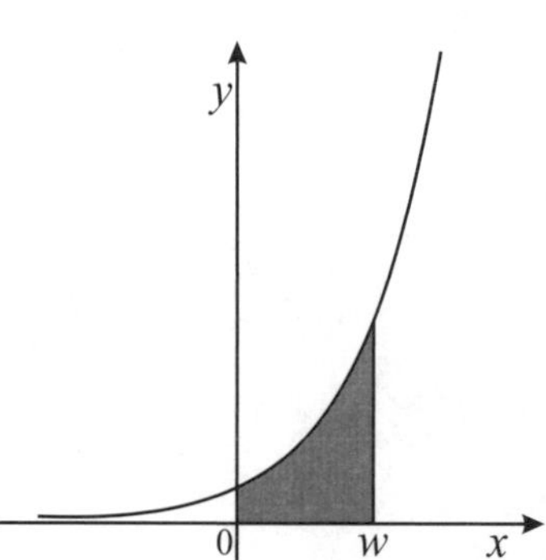

The curve $y = e^{2x+1}$ is shown on the diagram above.

a) Show that V, the volume formed when the shaded region bounded by the curve, the x- and y-axes and the line $x = w$ is rotated 2π radians about the x-axis, is given by the equation:

$$V = \frac{\pi}{4}e^2(e^{4w} - 1).$$

(4 marks)

b) A point $(w, 0)$ is moving along the x-axis with rate of change $\dfrac{dw}{dt} = 2w + 3$ (with respect to time). Find the exact value of $\dfrac{dV}{dt}$ when $w = -0.5$.

(4 marks)

General Certificate of Education
Advanced Subsidiary (AS) and Advanced Level

Core Mathematics C3 — Practice Exam Two

Time Allowed: 1 hour 30 min

Graphical calculators may be used for this exam.

Give any non-exact numerical answers to an appropriate degree of accuracy.

There are 72 marks available for this paper.

1 a) Write $\sqrt{2}\cos\theta - 3\sin\theta$ in the form $R\cos(\theta + \alpha)$, where $R > 0$ and $0 \leq \alpha \leq \frac{\pi}{2}$. *(3 marks)*

b) Hence, or otherwise, solve the equation $\sqrt{2}\cos\theta - 3\sin\theta = 3$ for $0 \leq \theta \leq 2\pi$.
Give your answers to 3 significant figures. *(4 marks)*

c) Hence find the maximum and minimum values of $(\sqrt{2}\cos\theta - 3\sin\theta)^4$, and state where the maximum and minimum points occur in the interval $0 \leq \theta \leq 2\pi$. *(4 marks)*

2 The functions f and g are defined as follows:

$$f(x) = \frac{1}{x^2}, \quad x \in \mathbb{R}, \; x \neq 0$$

$$g(x) = x^2 - 9, \quad x \in \mathbb{R}$$

a) State the range of g. *(1 mark)*

b) Neither f nor g have an inverse. Explain why. *(1 mark)*

c) Find

(i) fg(4) *(2 marks)*

(ii) gf(1) *(2 marks)*

d) (i) Find fg(x), and write down the domain of the composite function fg. *(2 marks)*

(ii) Hence solve fg(x) $= \frac{1}{256}$. *(3 marks)*

3 The curve $y = \ln(x^2 - 1)$, $(x > 1)$ is shown on the graph below.

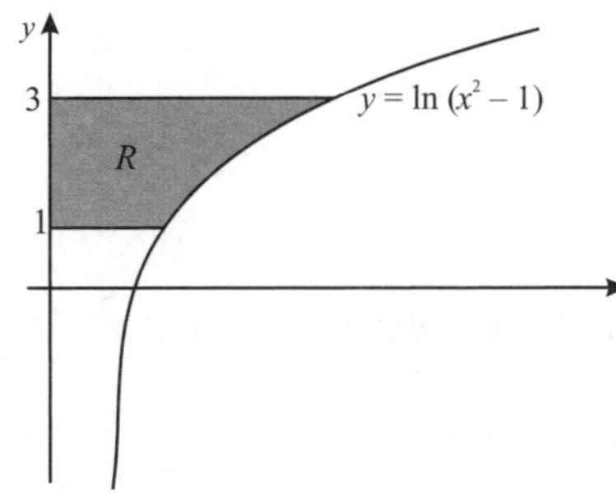

The shaded region R is bounded by the curve, the y-axis and the lines $y = 1$ and $y = 3$.
Find the volume formed when this region is rotated 2π radians about the y-axis.
Give your answer to 4 significant figures. *(5 marks)*

4 For the function:

$$f(x) = (\sqrt{x+2})\ln(x+2) \quad (x > 0)$$

a) Show that $f(x) = 6 \ln 3$ when $x = 7$. *(2 marks)*

b) Show that $f'(x) = \frac{1}{3}(1 + \ln 3)$ when $x = 7$. *(4 marks)*

c) Hence show that the equation of the tangent to the curve:

$$y = (\sqrt{x+2})\ln(x+2).$$

at the point $x = 7$ can be written as:

$$3y = x + x\ln 3 + 11\ln 3 - 7.$$

(2 marks)

5 The graph below shows the curve of $y = \dfrac{1 + \cos x}{2}$:

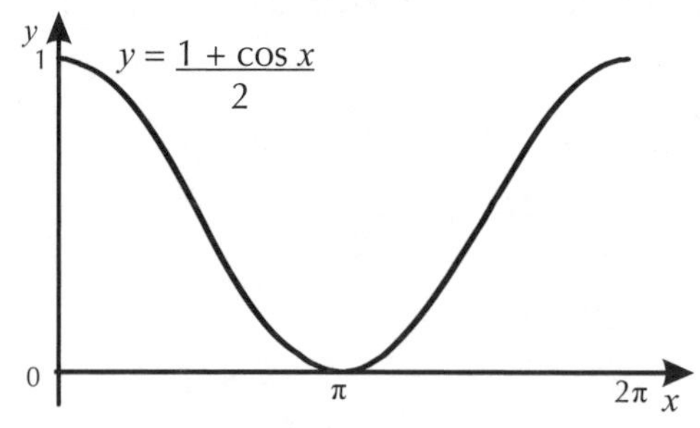

a) Use the double angle formula for cos to show that

$$\frac{1 + \cos x}{2} = \cos^2 \frac{x}{2}.$$

(3 marks)

b) Hence find the exact values of x for which $\cos^2 \frac{x}{2} = 0.75$ in the interval $0 \leq x \leq 2\pi$. *(4 marks)*

6 A curve has the equation:

$$y = e^{2x} - 5e^{x} + 3x.$$

a) Find $\dfrac{dy}{dx}$. *(2 marks)*

b) Find $\dfrac{d^2y}{dx^2}$. *(2 marks)*

c) Show that the stationary points on the curve occur when $x = 0$ and $x = \ln \frac{3}{2}$. *(4 marks)*

d) Determine the nature of each of the stationary points. *(4 marks)*

7 The UK population, P, of an endangered species of bird has been modelled over time, t years, by the function:

$$P = 5700e^{-0.15t} \quad (t \geq 0)$$

The time $t = 0$ is set as the beginning of the year 2010.

a) State the UK population of the species at the start of 2010. *(1 mark)*

b) Predict the UK population of the species at the start of 2020. *(2 marks)*

c) Predict the year in which the population will drop to below 1000. *(2 marks)*

d) Sketch a graph to show the predicted UK population of the species between 2010 and 2025. *(3 marks)*

8 The graph below shows the function:

$$f(x) = 4(x^2 - 1), \qquad x \geq 0,$$

and its inverse function $f^{-1}(x)$.

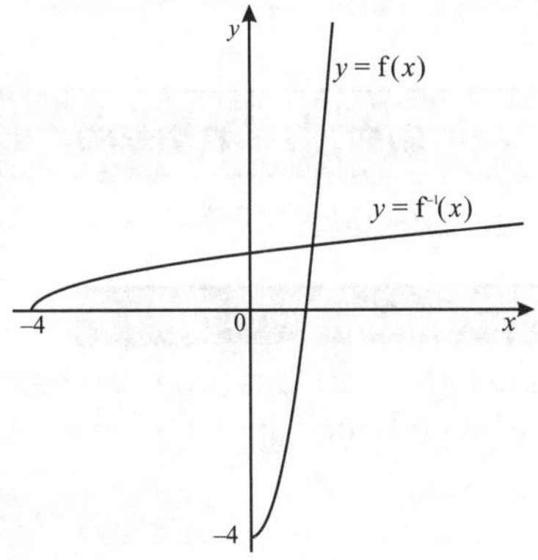

a) By finding an expression for $f^{-1}(x)$, and by considering how the graphs are related, show that $x = \sqrt{\frac{x}{4} + 1}$ at the points where the graphs meet. *(4 marks)*

b) Show that the expression from part a) has a root in the interval $1 < x < 2$. *(3 marks)*

c) Starting with $x_0 = 1$, use the iteration formula:

$$x_{n+1} = \sqrt{\frac{x_n}{4} + 1}$$

to find the x coordinate of the point of intersection, correct to 3 significant figures. *(3 marks)*

Simplifying Expressions

What a lovely way to start C4 — a page on algebraic fractions. Still, at least they're over with early on, so when they pop up later in C4 you'll know what to do. No, not run away and cower in a corner — use the things you learnt on this page.

Simplify algebraic fractions by *Factorising* and *Cancelling Factors*

Algebraic fractions are a lot like normal fractions — and you can treat them in the same way, whether you're multiplying, dividing, adding or subtracting them. All fractions are much easier to deal with when they're in their simplest form, so the first thing to do with algebraic fractions is to simplify them as much as possible.

A function you can write as a fraction where the top and bottom are both polynomials is called a rational function.

1) Look for common factors in the numerator and denominator — factorise top and bottom and see if there's anything you can cancel.
2) If there's a fraction in the numerator or denominator (e.g. $\frac{1}{x}$), multiply the whole thing (i.e. top and bottom) by the same factor to get rid of it (for $\frac{1}{x}$, you'd multiply through by x).

EXAMPLES Simplify the following:

a) $\frac{3x+6}{x^2-4} = \frac{3(x+2)}{(x+2)(x-2)} = \frac{3}{x-2}$

Watch out for the difference of two squares — see C1.

b) $\frac{2+\frac{1}{2x}}{4x^2+x} = \frac{\left(2+\frac{1}{2x}\right)\times 2x}{x(4x+1)\times 2x} = \frac{4x+1}{2x^2(4x+1)} = \frac{1}{2x^2}$

3) You multiply algebraic fractions in exactly the same way as normal fractions — multiply the numerators together, then multiply the denominators. It's a good idea to cancel any common factors before you multiply.
4) To divide by an algebraic fraction, you just multiply by its reciprocal (the reciprocal is 1 ÷ the original thing — for fractions you just turn the fraction upside down).

EXAMPLES Simplify the following:

a) $\frac{x^2-2x-15}{2x+8} \times \frac{x^2-16}{x^2+3x} = \frac{(x+3)(x-5)}{2(x+4)} \times \frac{(x+4)(x-4)}{x(x+3)}$

Factorise both fractions.

$= \frac{(x-5)(x-4)}{2x} \quad \left(= \frac{x^2-9x+20}{2x}\right)$

b) $\frac{3x}{5} \div \frac{3x^2-9x}{20} = \frac{3x}{5} \times \frac{20}{3x(x-3)} = \frac{4}{x-3}$

Turn the second fraction upside down.

Add and *Subtract* fractions by finding a *Common Denominator*

You'll have come across adding and subtracting fractions before in C1, so here's a little reminder of how to do it:

EXAMPLE Simplify:

$$\frac{2y}{x(x+3)} + \frac{1}{y^2(x+3)} - \frac{x}{y}$$

The common denominator is the lowest common multiple (LCM) of all the denominators.

① **Find the Common Denominator**

Take all the individual 'bits' from the bottom lines and multiply them together. Only use each bit once unless something on the bottom line is raised to a power.

The individual 'bits' here are x, $(x + 3)$ and y...

$xy^2(x+3)$

...but you need to use y^2 because there's a y^2 in the second fraction's denominator.

② **Put Each Fraction over the Common Denominator**

Make the denominator of each fraction into the common denominator.

$$\frac{y^2\times 2y}{y^2x(x+3)} + \frac{x\times 1}{xy^2(x+3)} - \frac{xy(x+3)\times x}{xy(x+3)y}$$

Multiply the top and bottom lines of each fraction by whatever makes the bottom line the same as the common denominator.

③ **Combine into One Fraction**

Once everything's over the common denominator you can just add the top lines together.

All the bottom lines are the same — so you can just add the top lines.

$$= \frac{2y^3+x-x^2y(x+3)}{xy^2(x+3)} = \frac{2y^3+x-x^3y-3x^2y}{xy^2(x+3)}$$

Who are you calling common...

Nothing on this page should be a big shock to you — it's all stuff you've done before. You've been using normal fractions for years, and algebraic fractions work in just the same way. They look a bit scary, but they're all warm and fuzzy inside.

Algebraic Division

I'll be honest with you, algebraic division is a bit tricky. But as long as you take it slowly and don't rush, it'll all fall into place. And it's really quick and easy to check your answer if you're not sure. What more could you want?

There are some Terms you need to Know

There are a few words that keep popping up in algebraic division, so make sure you know what they all mean.

1) DEGREE — the highest power of x in the polynomial (e.g. the degree of $4x^5 + 6x^2 - 3x - 1$ is 5).
2) DIVISOR — this is the thing you're dividing by (e.g. if you divide $x^2 + 4x - 3$ by $x + 2$, the divisor is $x + 2$).
3) QUOTIENT — the bit that you get when you divide by the divisor (not including the remainder — see p.48).

Method 1 — Divide by Subtracting Multiples of the Divisor

Back in C2, you learnt how to do algebraic division by subtracting chunks of the divisor.
Here's a quick reminder of how to divide a polynomial by $x - k$:

Algebraic Division

1) **Subtract a multiple of $(x - k)$ to get rid of the highest power of x.**
2) **Repeat step 1 until you've got rid of all the powers of x.**
3) **Work out how many lumps of $(x - k)$, you've subtracted, and read off the remainder.**

Have a look back at your C2 notes if you can't remember how to do this.

EXAMPLE Divide $2x^3 - 3x^2 - 3x + 7$ by $x - 2$.

① Start with $2x^3 - 3x^2 - 3x + 7$, and subtract $2x^2$ lots of $(x - 2)$ to get rid of the x^3 term. → $(2x^3 - 3x^2 - 3x + 7) - 2x^2(x - 2) = x^2 - 3x + 7$

② Now start again with $x^2 - 3x + 7$. The highest power of x is the x^2 term, so subtract x lots of $(x - 2)$ to get rid of that. → $(x^2 - 3x + 7) - x(x - 2) = -x + 7$

③ All that's left now is $-x + 7$. Get rid of $-x$ by subtracting $-1 \times (x - 2)$. → $(-x + 7) - (-1(x - 2)) = 5$

So $(2x^3 - 3x^2 - 3x + 7) \div (x - 2) = 2x^2 + x - 1$ remainder 5.

Method 2 — use Algebraic Long Division

To divide two algebraic expressions, you can use long division (using the same method you'd use for numbers).

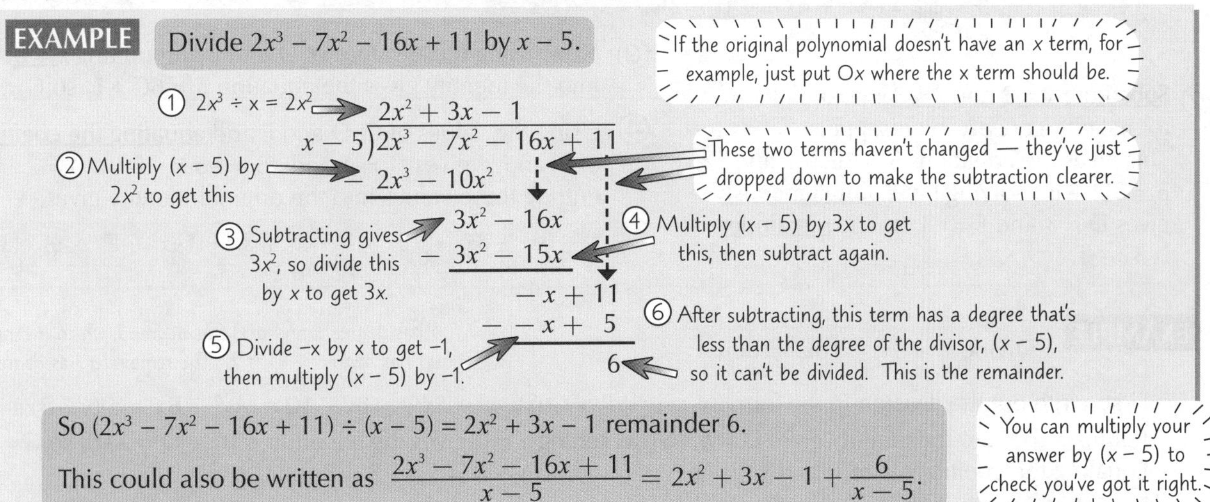

Just keep repeating — divide and conquer, divide and conquer...

For algebraic division to work, the degree of the divisor has to be less than (or equal to) the degree of the original polynomial (for example, you couldn't divide $x^2 + 2x + 3$ by $x^3 + 4$ as $3 > 2$, but you could do it the other way around). If you don't like either of these methods, you'll be pleased to know there's another way to divide coming up on the next page.

Algebraic Division

I really spoil you — as if two different methods for doing algebraic division weren't enough, I'm going to give you a third. If you're not sure about any of the terms, look back at the definitions on p.47.

Method 3 — use the Formula f(x) = q(x)d(x) + r(x)

There's a handy formula you can use to do algebraic division. It looks like this:

> A polynomial $f(x)$ can be written in the form $f(x) \equiv q(x)d(x) + r(x)$, where $q(x)$ is the quotient, $d(x)$ is the divisor and $r(x)$ is the remainder.

This comes from the Remainder Theorem that you met in C2. It's a good method for when you're dividing by a quadratic — long division can get a bit tricky when the divisor has 3 terms.

You'll be given $f(x)$ and $d(x)$ in the question, and it's down to you to work out $q(x)$ and $r(x)$. Here's how you do it:

Using the Formula

1) **First, you have to work out the degrees of the quotient and remainder, which depend on the degrees of the polynomial and the divisor. The degree of the quotient is $\deg f(x) - \deg d(x)$, and the degree of the remainder has to be less than the degree of the divisor.**
2) **Write out the division using the formula above, but replace $q(x)$ and $r(x)$ with general polynomials (i.e. a general polynomial of degree 2 is $Ax^2 + Bx + C$, and a general polynomial of degree 1 is $Ax + B$, where A, B, C, etc. are constants to be found).**
3) **The next step is to work out the values of the constants — you do this by substituting in values for x to make bits disappear, and by equating coefficients.**
4) **It's best to start with the constant term and work backwards from there.**
5) **Finally, write out the division again, replacing A, B, C, etc. with the values you've found.**

Equating coefficients means comparing the coefficients of each power of x on the LHS and the RHS.

The method looks a bit intense, but follow through the examples below to see how it works.

Start with the Remainder and Work Backwards

When you're using this method, you might have to use simultaneous equations to work out some of the coefficients. Have a look back at your C1 notes for a reminder of how to do this if you need to.

EXAMPLE Divide $x^4 - 3x^3 - 3x^2 + 10x + 5$ by $x^2 - 5x + 6$.

① First, write out the division in the form $f(x) \equiv q(x)d(x) + r(x)$:

$$x^4 - 3x^3 - 3x^2 + 10x + 5 \equiv (Ax^2 + Bx + C)(x^2 - 5x + 6) + Dx + E$$
$$\equiv (Ax^2 + Bx + C)(x - 2)(x - 3) + Dx + E.$$

f(x) has degree 4 and d(x) has degree 2, which means that q(x) has degree 4 − 2 = 2. The remainder has degree 1 or 0 — put in Dx + E, as D can always be 0.

d(x) factorises to give (x − 2)(x − 3).

② Substitute $x = 2$ and $x = 3$ into the identity to make the $q(x)d(x)$ bit disappear. This gives the equations $5 = 2D + E$ and $8 = 3D + E$. Solving these simultaneously gives $D = 3$ and $E = -1$, so the remainder is $3x - 1$.

③ Now, using these values of D and E and putting $x = 0$ into the identity gives the equation $5 = 6C + E$, so $C = 1$.

④ Using the values of C, D and E and equating the coefficients of x^4 and x^3 gives: $1 = A$ and $-3 = -5A + B$, so $B = 2$. Putting these values into the original identity gives:

$$x^4 - 3x^3 - 3x^2 + 10x + 5 \equiv (x^2 + 2x + 1)(x^2 - 5x + 6) + 3x - 1.$$

EXAMPLE Divide $x^3 + 5x^2 - 18x - 10$ by $x - 3$.

f(x) has degree 3 and d(x) has degree 1, which means that q(x) has degree 3 − 1 = 2. The remainder has degree 0.

First, write out the division in the form $f(x) \equiv q(x)d(x) + r(x)$: $x^3 + 5x^2 - 18x - 10 \equiv (Ax^2 + Bx + C)(x - 3) + D$.
Putting $x = 3$ into the identity gives $D = 8$. Now, setting $x = 0$ gives the equation $-3C + D = -10$, so $C = 6$.
Equating the coefficients of x^3 and x^2 gives $A = 1$ and $-3A + B = 5$, so $B = 8$.
So $x^3 + 5x^2 - 18x - 10 \equiv (x^2 + 8x + 6)(x - 3) + 8$.

A reminder about remainders...

The degree of the remainder has to be less than the degree of the divisor, otherwise it would be included in the quotient. E.g. if $r(x) = (x + 1)$ and $d(x) = (x - 3)$, then $r(x)$ can be divided by $d(x)$, giving a remainder of 4 (so $x + 1$ wasn't the remainder).

Partial Fractions

Wait, wait — come back. You're not done with fractions yet. Not by a long way (well, 2 pages).

'Expressing in Partial Fractions' is the Opposite of Adding Fractions (sort of)

1) You can split a fraction with more than one linear factor in the denominator into partial fractions.

$\frac{7x-7}{(2x+1)(x-3)}$ can be written as partial fractions of the form $\frac{A}{(2x+1)}+\frac{B}{(x-3)}$.

$\frac{9x^2+x+16}{(x+2)(2x-1)(x-3)}$ can be written as partial fractions of the form $\frac{A}{(x+2)}+\frac{B}{(2x-1)}+\frac{C}{(x-3)}$.

$\frac{x^2+17x+16}{(x+2)^2(3x-1)}$ can be written as partial fractions of the form $\frac{A}{(x+2)^2}+\frac{B}{(x+2)}+\frac{C}{(3x-1)}$.

Watch out here — this one doesn't quite follow the pattern.

2) The tricky bit is figuring out what A, B and C are.
You can use the substitution method or the equating coefficients method:

EXAMPLE Express $\frac{9x^2+x+16}{(x+2)(2x-1)(x-3)}$ in partial fractions.

You know that $\frac{9x^2+x+16}{(x+2)(2x-1)(x-3)} \equiv \frac{A}{(x+2)}+\frac{B}{(2x-1)}+\frac{C}{(x-3)}$. Now to work out A, B and C.

1 Add the partial fractions and cancel the denominators from both sides

$$\frac{A}{(x+2)}+\frac{B}{(2x-1)}+\frac{C}{(x-3)} \equiv \frac{A(2x-1)(x-3)+B(x+2)(x-3)+C(2x-1)(x+2)}{(x+2)(2x-1)(x-3)}$$

So the numerators are equal: $9x^2+x+16 \equiv A(2x-1)(x-3)+B(x+2)(x-3)+C(2x-1)(x+2)$

2 Substitute x for values which get rid of all but one of A, B and C...

Substituting $x = 3$ gets rid of A and B: $(9\times 3^2)+3+16 = 0+0+C((2\times 3)-1)(3+2)$
$100 = 25C \Rightarrow \underline{C=4}$

Substituting $x = -2$ gets rid of B and C: $(9\times(-2)^2)+(-2)+16 = A((2\times -2)-1)(-2-3)+0+0$
$50 = 25A \Rightarrow \underline{A=2}$

Substituting $x = 0.5$ gets rid of A and C: $(9\times(0.5^2))+0.5+16 = 0+B(0.5+2)(0.5-3)+0$
$18.75 = -6.25B \Rightarrow \underline{B=-3}$

...OR compare coefficients in the numerators

$9x^2+x+16 \equiv A(2x-1)(x-3)+B(x+2)(x-3)+C(2x-1)(x+2)$

x^2 coefficients: $9 = 2A + B + 2C$
x coefficients: $1 = -7A - B + 3C$
constant terms: $16 = 3A - 6B - 2C$

Solving these equations simultaneously gives $A = 2$, $B = -3$ and $C = 4$ — the same as the substitution method.

3 Write out the solution $\frac{9x^2+x+16}{(x+2)(2x-1)(x-3)} \equiv \frac{2}{(x+2)}-\frac{3}{(2x-1)}+\frac{4}{(x-3)}$

Watch out for Difference of Two Squares Denominators

Just for added meanness, they might give you an expression like $\frac{4}{x^2-1}$ and tell you to express it as partial fractions.

You have to recognise that the denominator is a difference of two squares, write it as two linear factors, and then carry on as normal. E.g. $\frac{21x-2}{9x^2-4} \equiv \frac{21x-2}{(3x-2)(3x+2)} \equiv \frac{A}{(3x-2)}+\frac{B}{(3x+2)}$

All coefficients are not created equal — but some are...

It's worth getting to grips with both methods for step 2. Sometimes one's easier to use than the other, and sometimes you might want to mix and match. It's just another crucial step on the path to going down in history as a mathematical great.

Partial Fractions

Now things are hotting up in the partial fractions department — here's an example involving a repeated factor.

Sometimes it's best to use Substitution AND Equate Coefficients

EXAMPLE Express $\frac{x^2+17x+16}{(x+2)^2(3x-1)}$ in partial fractions.

You know that $\frac{x^2+17x+16}{(x+2)^2(3x-1)} \equiv \frac{A}{(x+2)^2} + \frac{B}{(x+2)} + \frac{C}{(3x-1)}$. Now to work out A, B and C.

1 Add the partial fractions $\frac{A}{(x+2)^2} + \frac{B}{(x+2)} + \frac{C}{(3x-1)} \equiv \frac{A(3x-1)+B(x+2)(3x-1)+C(x+2)^2}{(x+2)^2(3x-1)}$

Cancel the denominators from both sides $x^2+17x+16 \equiv A(3x-1)+B(x+2)(3x-1)+C(x+2)^2$

2 Substitute x for values which get rid of all but one of A, B and C

Substituting $x = -2$ gets rid of B and C: $(-2)^2+(17\times-2)+16 = A((3\times-2)-1)+0+0$

$-14 = -7A \quad \Rightarrow \underline{A=2}$

Substituting $x = \frac{1}{3}$ gets rid of A and B: $\left(\frac{1}{3}\right)^2 + \left(17\times\frac{1}{3}\right)+16 = 0+0+C\left(\frac{1}{3}+2\right)^2$

$\frac{196}{9} = \frac{49}{9}C \quad \Rightarrow \underline{C=4}$

The trouble is, there's no value of x you can substitute to get rid of A and C to just leave B.

So: **Equate coefficients of x^2**

From $x^2+17x+16 \equiv A(3x-1)+B(x+2)(3x-1)+C(x+2)^2$

Coefficients of x^2 are: $1 = 3B + C$

You know $C = 4$, so: $1 = 3B+4 \quad \Rightarrow \underline{B=-1}$

3 Write out the solution You now know A, B and C, so: $\frac{x^2+17x+16}{(x+2)^2(3x-1)} \equiv \frac{2}{(x+2)^2} - \frac{1}{(x+2)} + \frac{4}{(3x-1)}$

Divide Before Expressing Improper Fractions as Partial Fractions

The numerator of an improper algebraic fraction has a degree equal to or greater than the degree of the denominator.

E.g. $\frac{x^2+4}{(x+3)(x+2)}$ (numerator: degree 2; denominator: degree 2) $\qquad \frac{x^4+2x}{(x-1)^2(x+2)}$ (numerator: degree 4; denominator: degree 3)

The degree of a polynomial is the highest power of x.

There's an extra step involved in expressing an improper fraction as partial fractions:

1) Divide the numerator by the denominator to get the quotient (q(x)) + a proper fraction (r(x) / d(x))
2) Express the proper fraction as partial fractions.

See pages 47-48 for algebraic division methods.

EXAMPLE Express $\frac{x^4-3x^3-3x^2+10x+5}{(x-3)(x-2)}$ as partial fractions.

1) First work out $(x^4-3x^3-3x^2+10x+5) \div (x^2-5x+6)$: (This is $(x-3)(x-2)$ multiplied out.)
   - Write out the result in the form $f(x) \equiv q(x)d(x) + r(x)$: (Exactly as on page 48 — $q(x)$ = quotient, $d(x)$ = divisor and $r(x)$ = remainder.)

     $x^4-3x^3-3x^2+10x+5 \equiv (x^2+2x+1)(x^2-5x+6)+3x-1$.
   - Divide through by $d(x)$: $\frac{x^4-3x^3-3x^2+10x+5}{(x-3)(x-2)} \equiv (x^2+2x+1) + \frac{3x-1}{(x-3)(x-2)}$ ← $q(x) + \frac{r(x)}{d(x)}$
2) Now just express the proper fraction as partial fractions: $\frac{x^4-3x^3-3x^2+10x+5}{(x-3)(x-2)} \equiv (x^2+2x+1) + \frac{A}{(x-3)} + \frac{B}{(x-2)}$

Rid the partial fraction world of improperness — it's only proper...

After you've found the partial fractions, don't forget to go back to the original fraction and write out the full solution...

C4 Section 1 — Practice Questions

It's such a shame that you can no longer use cakes, bars of chocolate or pizzas to help you get your head round fractions — it's not quite as effective on algebraic ones. It's all part of growing up unfortunately.

Warm-up Questions

1) Simplify the following:

a) $\frac{4x^2 - 25}{6x - 15}$ b) $\frac{2x + 3}{x - 2} \times \frac{4x - 8}{2x^2 - 3x - 9}$ c) $\frac{x^2 - 3x}{x + 1} \div \frac{x}{2}$

2) Write the following as a single fraction:

a) $\frac{x}{2x + 1} + \frac{3}{x^2} + \frac{1}{x}$ b) $\frac{2}{x^2 - 1} - \frac{3x}{x - 1} + \frac{x}{x + 1}$

3) Use algebraic long division to divide $x^3 + 2x^2 - x + 19$ by $x + 4$.

4) Write $2x^3 + 8x^2 + 7x + 8$ in the form $(Ax^2 + Bx + C)(x + 3) + D$.
Using your answer, state the result when $2x^3 + 8x^2 + 7x + 8$ is divided by $(x + 3)$.

5) Express the following as partial fractions.

You have to factorise the denominator in Q5 parts d, e and g, and in Q6, part d.

a) $\frac{4x + 5}{(x + 4)(2x - 3)}$ b) $\frac{-7x - 7}{(3x + 1)(x - 2)}$

c) $\frac{x - 18}{(x + 4)(3x - 4)}$ d) $\frac{5x}{x^2 + x - 6}$

e) $\frac{6 + 4y}{9 - y^2}$ f) $\frac{10x^2 + 32x + 16}{(x + 3)(2x + 4)(x - 2)}$

g) $\frac{4x^2 + 12x + 6}{x^3 + 3x^2 + 2x}$ h) $\frac{-11x^2 + 6x + 11}{(2x + 1)(3 - x)(x + 2)}$

6) Express the following as partial fractions — watch out for the repeated factors.

a) $\frac{2x + 2}{(x + 3)^2}$ b) $\frac{6x^2 + 17x + 5}{x(x + 2)^2}$

c) $\frac{-18x + 14}{(2x - 1)^2(x + 2)}$ d) $\frac{8x^2 - x - 5}{x^3 - x^2}$

7) Express the following as partial fractions — they're all improper, so divide them first.

a) $\frac{2x^2 + 18x + 26}{(x + 2)(x + 4)}$ b) $\frac{3x^2 + 9x + 2}{x(x + 1)}$

c) $\frac{24x^2 - 70x + 53}{(2x - 3)^2}$ d) $\frac{3x^3 - 2x^2 - 2x - 3}{(x + 1)(x - 2)}$

That should have got the neurones nicely warmed up. Unless it made you very sleepy instead. Try these exam questions and make sure you can handle them.

Exam Questions

1 Given that, for $x \neq -\frac{1}{3}$, $\frac{5 + 9x}{(1 + 3x)^2} \equiv \frac{A}{(1 + 3x)^2} + \frac{B}{(1 + 3x)}$, where A and B are integers, find the values of A and B.

(3 marks)

C4 Section 1 — Practice Questions

Being able to deal with algebraic fractions is part of the secret to a long and happy life. Or just getting a good mark in your C4 exam. They're the same thing really.

2 Write $\frac{2x^2 - 9x - 35}{x^2 - 49}$ as a fraction in its simplest form.

(3 marks)

3 $\frac{18x^2 - 15x - 62}{(3x + 4)(x - 2)} \equiv A + \frac{B}{(3x + 4)} + \frac{C}{(x - 2)}$

Find the values of the integers A, B and C.

(4 marks)

4 $f(x) = \frac{5x^2 + 3x + 6}{(3 - x)(2x - 1)^2}$

Given that f(x) can be expressed in the form $f(x) = \frac{A}{(3 - x)} + \frac{B}{(2x - 1)^2} + \frac{C}{(2x - 1)}$,

find the values of A and B and C.

(4 marks)

5 Write $x^3 + 15x^2 + 43x - 30$ in the form $(Ax^2 + Bx + C)(x + 6) + D$, where A, B, C and D are constants to be found.

(3 marks)

6 The algebraic fraction $\frac{-80x^2 + 49x - 9}{(5x - 1)(2 - 4x)}$ can be written in the form $4 + \frac{A}{(5x - 1)} + \frac{B}{(2 - 4x)}$, where A and B are constants. Find the values of A and B.

(4 marks)

7 a) Express the algebraic fraction $\frac{3x^2 + 12x - 11}{(x + 3)(x - 1)}$ in the form $A + \frac{B + Cx}{(x + 3)(x - 1)}$, where A, B and C are constants.

(4 marks)

b) Express $\frac{3x^2 + 12x - 11}{(x + 3)(x - 1)}$ as partial fractions.

(3 marks)

Parametric Equations of Curves

Parametric equations seem kinda weirdy to start with, but they're actually pretty clever.
You can use them to replace one horrifically complicated equation with two relatively normal-looking ones.
I bet that's just what you always wanted...

Parametric Equations split up x and y into Separate Equations

1) Normally, graphs in the (x, y) plane are described using a Cartesian equation — a single equation linking x and y.
2) Sometimes, particularly for more complicated graphs, it's easier to have two linked equations, called parametric equations.
3) In parametric equations x and y are each defined separately in terms of a third variable, called a parameter. The parameter is usually either t or θ.

EXAMPLE

This graph is given by the parametric equations $y = t^2 - 1$ and $x = t + 1$:

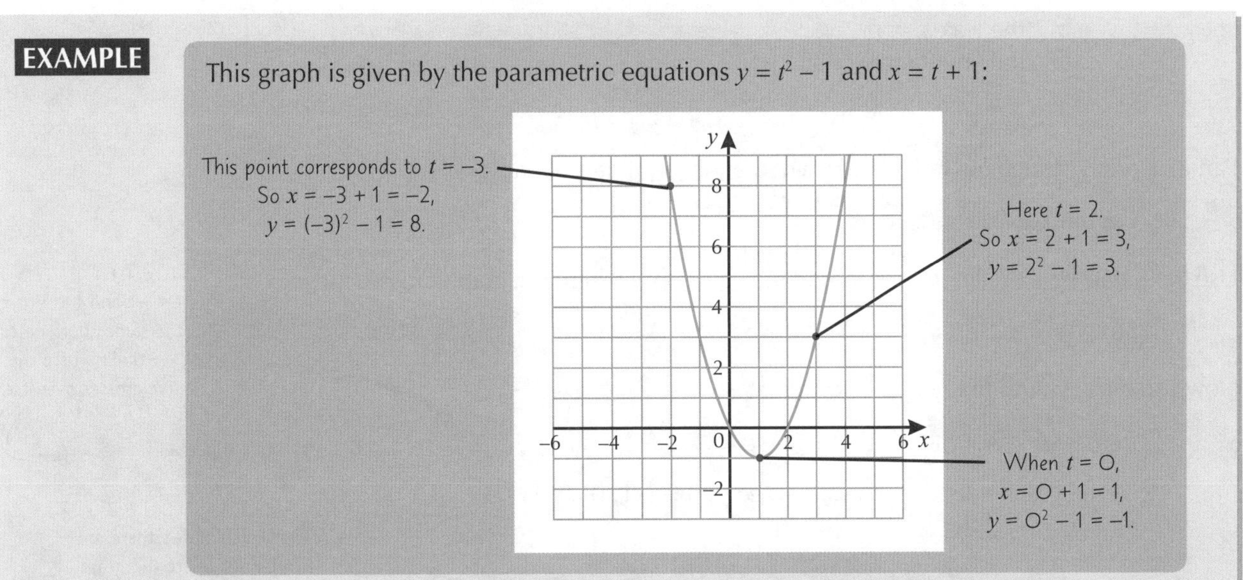

You can use the parametric equations of a graph to find coordinates of points on the graph, and to find the value of the parameter for given x- or y-coordinates.

EXAMPLE

A curve is defined by the parametric equations $y = \frac{1}{3t}$ and $x = 2t - 3$, $t \neq 0$.

a) Find the x- and y- values of the point the curve passes through when $t = 4$.

b) What value of t corresponds to the point where $y = 9$?

c) What is the value of y when $x = -15$?

Nothing to this question — just sub the right values into the right equations and you're away:

a) When $t = 4$, $x = 8 - 3 = 5$, and $y = \frac{1}{12}$

b) $9 = \frac{1}{3t} \Rightarrow t = \frac{1}{27}$

c) $-15 = 2t - 3 \Rightarrow t = -6 \Rightarrow y = -\frac{1}{18}$

Use the equation for x to find t first, then use that value of t in the other equation to find y.

Time to make like x and y in a set of parametric equations, and split...

Well that was a painless introduction to a topic if ever there was one. Yes, I can tell this section's going to be plain sailing... wait a minute... holy flip, would you look at the size of the example on the next page. And I think I see some trig functions looming in the distance. And that's either Godzilla or an integration sign on the horizon. Batten down the hatches...

Using Parametric Equations

There's plenty of tinkering around with equations to be done in this topic, so get your rearranging hat on. My rearranging hat is a jaunty straw boater.

Use *Parametric Equations* to find where graphs *Intersect*

A lot of parametric equations questions involve identifying points on the curve defined by the equations.

EXAMPLE

The curve shown in this sketch has the parametric equations $y = t^3 - t$ and $x = 4t^2 - 1$.

Find the coordinates of the points where the graph crosses:
a) the x-axis,
b) the y-axis,
c) the line $8y = 3x + 3$.

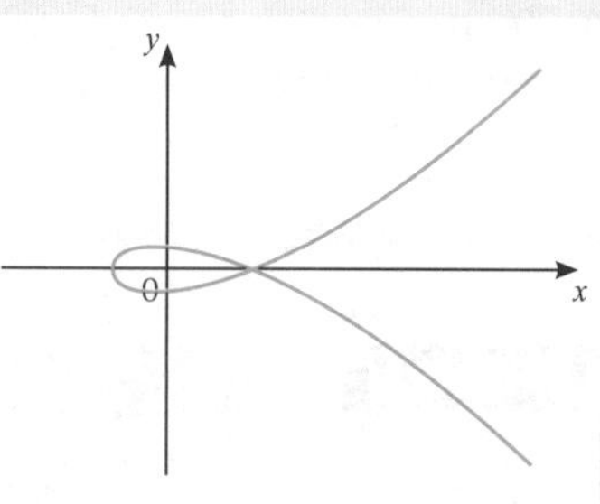

Part a) is pretty straightforward. You've got the y-coordinates already:

a) On the x-axis, $y = 0$.

Use the parametric equation for y to find the values of t where the graph crosses the x-axis:

So $0 = t^3 - t \Rightarrow t(t^2 - 1) = 0 \Rightarrow t(t + 1)(t - 1) = 0 \Rightarrow t = 0, t = -1, t = 1$

$t = -1$ and $t = 1$ give the same coordinates — that's where the curve crosses over itself.

Now use those values to find the x-coordinates:

$t = 0 \Rightarrow x = 4(0)^2 - 1 = -1$ $\quad t = -1 \Rightarrow x = 4(-1)^2 - 1 = 3$ $\quad t = 1 \Rightarrow x = 4(1)^2 - 1 = 3$

So the graph crosses the x-axis at the points $(-1, 0)$ and $(3, 0)$.

The sketch shows there are two points where the graph crosses each axis.

And b) is very similar:

b) On the y-axis, $x = 0$.

So $0 = 4t^2 - 1 \Rightarrow t^2 = \frac{1}{4} \Rightarrow t = \pm\frac{1}{2}$

$t = \frac{1}{2} \Rightarrow y = \left(\frac{1}{2}\right)^3 - \frac{1}{2} = -\frac{3}{8}$ $\qquad t = -\frac{1}{2} \Rightarrow y = \left(-\frac{1}{2}\right)^3 - \left(-\frac{1}{2}\right) = \frac{3}{8}$

So the graph crosses the y-axis at the points $(0, -\frac{3}{8})$ and $(0, \frac{3}{8})$.

Part c) is just a little trickier. First, sub the parametric equations into $8y = 3x + 3$:

c) $8y = 3x + 3 \Rightarrow 8(t^3 - t) = 3(4t^2 - 1) + 3$

Rearrange and factorise to find the values of t you need:

$\Rightarrow 8t^3 - 8t = 12t^2 \Rightarrow 8t^3 - 12t^2 - 8t = 0 \Rightarrow t(2t + 1)(t - 2) = 0 \Rightarrow t = 0, t = -\frac{1}{2}, t = 2$

Go back to the parametric equations to find the x- and y-coordinates:

$t = 0 \Rightarrow x = -1, y = 0$
$t = -\frac{1}{2} \Rightarrow x = 4(\frac{1}{4}) - 1 = 0, y = (-\frac{1}{2})^3 + \frac{1}{2} = \frac{3}{8}$
$t = 2 \Rightarrow x = 4(4) - 1 = 15, y = 2^3 - 2 = 6$

So the graph crosses the line $8y = 3x + 3$ at the points $(-1, 0)$, $(0, \frac{3}{8})$, $(15, 6)$.

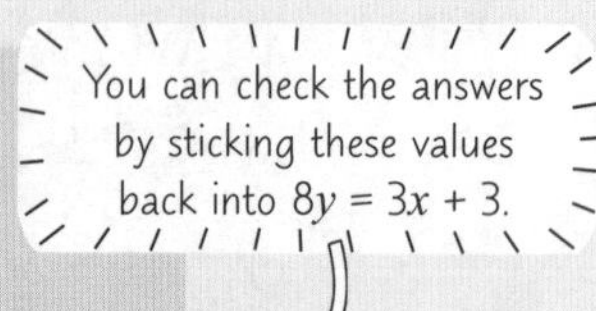

y-coordinates? *y* not...

You quite often get given a sketch of the curve that the parametric equations define. Don't forget that the sketch can be useful for checking your answers — if the curve crosses the x-axis twice, and you've only found one x-coordinate for when $y = 0$, you know something's gone a bit pear-shaped and you should go back and sort it out, sunshine.

Parametric and Cartesian Equations

If you've been dying for θ to put in an appearance since I mentioned it on page 53, then I've got good news. If, on the other hand, you're bored of parametric equations already... I'm sorry.

Rearrange Parametric Equations to get the Cartesian Equation

Some parametric equations can be converted into Cartesian equations. There are two main ways to do this:

To convert Parametric Equations to a Cartesian Equation:

1. **Rearrange one of the equations to make the parameter the subject, then substitute the result into the other equation.**

or

2. **If your equations involve trig functions, use trig identities (see C3 Section 3) to eliminate the parameter.**

You can use the first method to combine the parametrics used in the examples on p53:

EXAMPLE Give the Cartesian equations, in the form $y = f(x)$, of the curves represented by the following pairs of parametric equations:

a) $y = t^2 - 1$ and $x = t + 1$, b) $y = \frac{1}{3t}$ and $x = 2t - 3$, $t \neq 0$.

You want the answer in the form $y = f(x)$, so leave y alone for now, and rearrange the equation for x to make t the subject:

a) $x = t + 1 \Rightarrow t = x - 1$

Now you can eliminate t from the equation for y:

$$y = t^2 - 1 \quad \Rightarrow \quad y = (x-1)^2 - 1 = x^2 - 2x + 1 - 1$$
$$\Rightarrow \quad y = x^2 - 2x$$

b) $x = 2t - 3 \Rightarrow t = \frac{x+3}{2}$

$$\text{So } y = \frac{1}{3t} \Rightarrow y = \frac{1}{3\left(\frac{x+3}{2}\right)} \Rightarrow y = \frac{1}{\frac{3(x+3)}{2}} \Rightarrow y = \frac{2}{3x+9}$$

If there are Trig Functions... use Trig Identities

Things get a little trickier when the likes of sin and cos decide to put in an appearance:

EXAMPLE A curve has parametric equations

$$x = 1 + \sin\theta, \quad y = 1 - \cos 2\theta$$

Give the Cartesian equation of the curve in the form $y = f(x)$.

If you try to make θ the subject of these equations, things will just get messy. The trick is to find a way to get both x and y in terms of the same trig function.

You can get $\sin\theta$ into the equation for y using the identity $\cos 2\theta = 1 - 2\sin^2\theta$:

$$y = 1 - \cos 2\theta = 1 - (1 - 2\sin^2\theta) = 2\sin^2\theta$$

Rearranging the equation for x gives:

$$\sin\theta = x - 1, \quad \text{so} \quad y = 2\sin^2\theta$$
$$\Rightarrow y = 2(x-1)^2 = 2x^2 - 4x + 2$$

If one of the parametric equations includes $\cos 2\theta$ or $\sin 2\theta$, that's probably the one you need to substitute — so make sure you know the double angle formulas.

Cartesy peasy, lemon squeezy...

Sometimes you'll get a nasty question where it's really difficult to get the parameter on its own — in that case you might have to do something clever like think about multiplying x and y or dividing y by x. If something like that comes up in an exam, they'll usually give you a hint — but be aware that you might need to think outside the box.

C4 Section 2 — Practice Questions

Before it became famous in the world of maths, the word 'parametric' had several other jobs. For example, it once starred as the last name of a Bond villain from the former Yugoslavia. Here are some questions. Enjoy.

Warm-up Questions

1) A curve is defined by the parametric equations $y = 2t^2 + t + 4$ and $x = \frac{6-t}{2}$.
   a) Find the values of x and y when $t = 0, 1, 2$ and 3.
   b) What are the values of t when: (i) $x = -7$ (ii) $y = 19$?
   c) Find the Cartesian equation of the curve, in the form $y = f(x)$.
2) The parametric equations of a curve are $x = 2\sin\theta$ and $y = \cos^2\theta + 4$, $-\frac{\pi}{2} \le \theta \le \frac{\pi}{2}$.
   a) What are the coordinates of the points where: (i) $\theta = \frac{\pi}{4}$ (ii) $\theta = \frac{\pi}{6}$
   b) What is the Cartesian equation of the curve?
   c) What restrictions are there on the values of x for this curve?
3) The curve C is defined by the parametric equations $x = \frac{\sin\theta}{3}$ and $y = 3 + 2\cos 2\theta$.
   Find the Cartesian equation of C.
4) A curve has parametric equations $y = 4 + \frac{3}{t}$ and $x = t^2 - 1$.
   What are the coordinates of the points where this curve crosses
   a) the y-axis b) the line $x + 2y = 14$?

Former career of the word 'parametric' #2 — stand-in for the word 'hallelujah' in an early draft of Handel's Messiah. Meanwhile, back at the practice questions...

Exam Questions

1 The curve C is defined by the parametric equations

$$x = 1 - \tan\theta, \quad y = \frac{1}{2}\sin 2\theta, \quad -\frac{\pi}{2} < \theta < \frac{\pi}{2}.$$

a) P is the point on curve C where $\theta = \frac{\pi}{3}$. Find the exact coordinates of P.

(2 marks)

b) Point Q on curve C has coordinates $(2, -\frac{1}{2})$. Find the value of θ at Q.

(2 marks)

c) Using the identity $\sin 2\theta \equiv \frac{2\tan\theta}{1+\tan^2\theta}$, show that the Cartesian equation of C is $y = \frac{1-x}{x^2 - 2x + 2}$.

(3 marks)

2

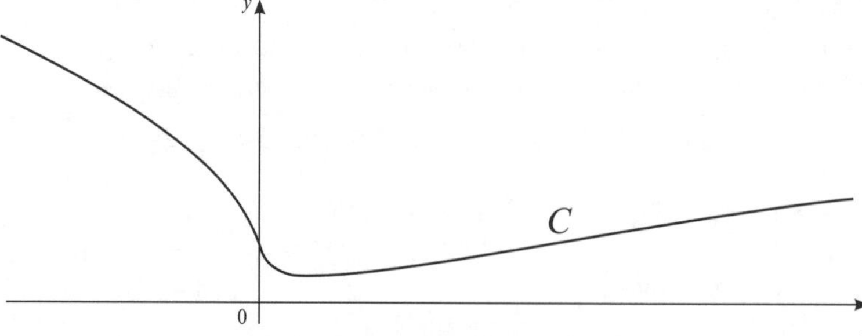

Curve C has parametric equations $x = t^3 + t$, $y = t^2 - 2t + 2$.

a) K is a point on C, and has the coordinates $(a, 1)$. Find the value of a.

(2 marks)

b) The line $8y = x + 6$ passes through C at points K, L and M.
Find the coordinates of L and M, given that the x-coordinate of M is greater than the x-coordinate of L.

(6 marks)

C4 Section 2 — Practice Questions

Former career of the word 'parametric' #3 — proposed name for the next ocean to be discovered. Unfortunately it turned out all the oceans have already been discovered. Ooh look, more questions...

3

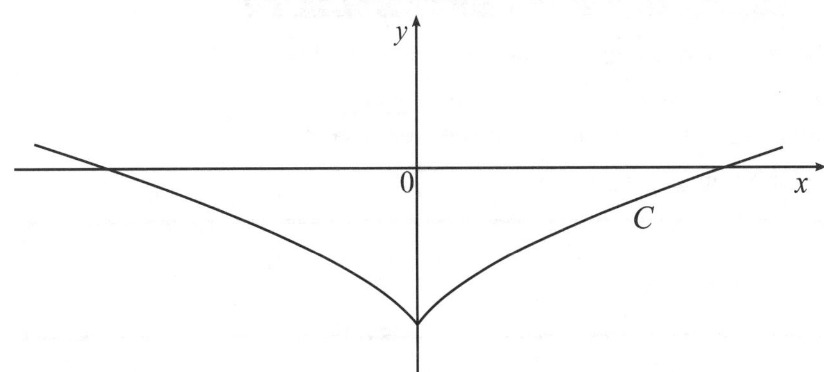

The curve C has parametric equations

$$x = t^3, \qquad y = t^2 - 4.$$

a) The point F lies on C. At F, t has the value 0.5. Find the coordinates of F. *(2 marks)*

b) The line $3y = 2x - 11$ meets C twice. Find the coordinates of the points of intersection. *(6 marks)*

4

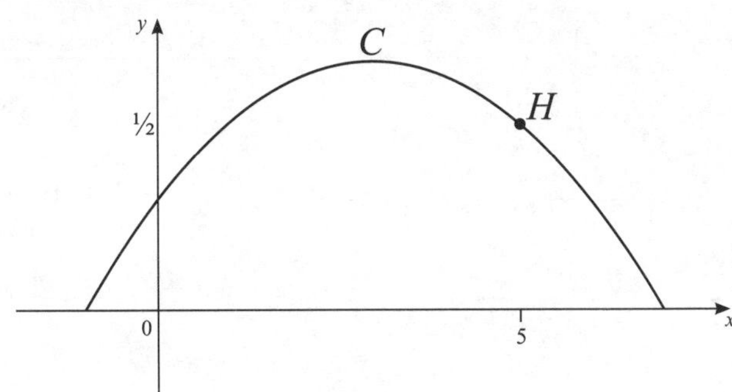

The parametric equations of curve C are

$$x = 3 + 4\sin\theta, \qquad y = \frac{1 + \cos 2\theta}{3}, \qquad -\frac{\pi}{2} \leq \theta \leq \frac{\pi}{2}.$$

Point H on C has coordinates $(5, \frac{1}{2})$.

a) Find the value of θ at point H. *(2 marks)*

b) Show that the Cartesian equation of C can be written $y = \dfrac{-x^2 + 6x + 7}{24}$. *(4 marks)*

c) State the domain of values of x for the curve C. *(1 mark)*

Basic Binomial Expansions

Yeah, I know the binomial expansion. We spent some time together back in C2. Thought I'd never see it again. And then, of all the sections in all the maths books in all the world, the binomial expansion walks into mine...

The Binomial Expansion Formula is pretty useful

The binomial expansion is a way to raise a given expression to any power.

For simpler cases it's basically a fancy way of multiplying out brackets.
You can also use it to approximate more complicated expressions (see p61).

This is the general formula for binomial expansions:

$$(1+x)^n = 1 + nx + \frac{n(n-1)}{1\times 2}x^2 + \ldots + \frac{n(n-1)\ldots(n-r+1)}{1\times 2\times \ldots \times r}x^r + \ldots$$

The Binomial Expansion sometimes gives a Finite Expression

From the general formula, it looks like the expansion always goes on forever.
But if n is a positive integer, the binomial expansion is finite.

EXAMPLE Give the binomial expansion of $(1+x)^5$.

You can use the general formula and plug in $n = 5$:

$$(1+x)^5 = 1 + 5x + \frac{5(5-1)}{1\times 2}x^2 + \frac{5(5-1)(5-2)}{1\times 2\times 3}x^3 + \frac{5(5-1)(5-2)(5-3)}{1\times 2\times 3\times 4}x^4 + \frac{5(5-1)(5-2)(5-3)(5-4)}{1\times 2\times 3\times 4\times 5}x^5 + \frac{5(5-1)(5-2)(5-3)(5-4)(5-5)}{1\times 2\times 3\times 4\times 5\times 6}x^6 + \ldots$$

$$= 1 + 5x + \frac{5\times 4}{1\times 2}x^2 + \frac{5\times 4\times 3}{1\times 2\times 3}x^3 + \frac{5\times 4\times 3\times 2}{1\times 2\times 3\times 4}x^4 + \frac{5\times 4\times 3\times 2\times 1}{1\times 2\times 3\times 4\times 5}x^5 + \frac{5\times 4\times 3\times 2\times 1\times 0}{1\times 2\times 3\times 4\times 5\times 6}x^6 + \ldots$$

$$= 1 + 5x + \frac{20}{2}x^2 + \frac{60}{6}x^3 + \frac{120}{24}x^4 + \frac{120}{120}x^5 + \frac{0}{720}x^6 + \ldots$$

$$= 1 + 5x + 10x^2 + 10x^3 + 5x^4 + x^5$$

$n(n-1)$

$n = 5$

You can stop here — all the terms after this one are zero

The formula still works if the coefficient of x isn't 1.

EXAMPLE Give the binomial expansion of $(1-3x)^4$.

This time $n = 4$, but you also have to replace every x in the formula with $-3x$:

$(1-3x)^4$ ← Think of this as $(1+(-3x))^4$ — you need to put the minus into the formula as well as the $3x$.

$n = 4$ $n(n-1)$ Don't forget to square the -3 as well. Stop here

$$= 1 + 4(-3x) + \frac{4\times 3}{1\times 2}(-3x)^2 + \frac{4\times \not{3}\times \not{2}}{1\times \not{2}\times \not{3}}(-3x)^3 + \frac{\not{4}\times \not{3}\times \not{2}\times \not{1}}{\not{1}\times \not{2}\times \not{3}\times \not{4}}(-3x)^4 + \frac{\not{4}\times \not{3}\times \not{2}\times \not{1}\times 0}{\not{1}\times \not{2}\times \not{3}\times \not{4}\times 5}(-3x)^5 + \ldots$$

$$= 1 + 4(-3x) + \frac{12}{2}(9x^2) + \frac{4}{1}(-27x^3) + (81x^4) + \frac{0}{5}(-243x^5) + \ldots$$

$$= 1 - 12x + 54x^2 - 108x^3 + 81x^4$$

Make life easier for yourself by cancelling down the fractions before you multiply.

Trickier Expansions

Unfortunately, you only get a nice, neat, finite expansion when you've got a positive integer n.
But that pesky n sometimes likes to be a negative number or a fraction. n for nuisance. n for naughty.

If n is Negative the expansion gets more complicated...

EXAMPLE Find the binomial expansion of $\frac{1}{(1+x)^2}$ up to and including the term in x^3.

This is where things start to get a bit more interesting.
First, rewrite the expression: $\frac{1}{(1+x)^2} = (1+x)^{-2}$.

You can still use the general formula. This time $n = -2$:

$n = -2$ $n(n-1)$

$$(1+x)^{-2} = 1 + (-2)x + \frac{(-2)\times(-2-1)}{1\times 2}x^2 + \frac{(-2)\times(-2-1)\times(-2-2)}{1\times 2\times 3}x^3 + \ldots$$
$$= 1 + (-2)x + \frac{(-2)\times(-3)}{1\times 2}x^2 + \frac{(-2)\times(-3)\times(-4)}{1\times 2\times 3}x^3 + \ldots$$
$$= 1 + (-2)x + \frac{3}{1}x^2 + \frac{-4}{1}x^3 + \ldots$$
$$= 1 - 2x + 3x^2 - 4x^3 + \ldots$$

With a negative n, you'll never get zero as a coefficient. If the question hadn't told you to stop, the expansion could go on forever.

Again, you can cancel down before you multiply — but be careful with those minus signs.

We've left out all the terms after $-4x^3$, so the cubic equation you've ended up with is an approximation to the original expression. You could also write the answer like this:

$$\frac{1}{(1+x)^2} \approx 1 - 2x + 3x^2 - 4x^3$$

... and if n is a Fraction things can be tricky too

The binomial expansion formula doesn't just work for integer values of n.

EXAMPLE Find the binomial expansion of $\sqrt[3]{1+2x}$ up to and including the term in x^3.

This time we've got a fractional power: $\sqrt[3]{1+2x} = (1+2x)^{\frac{1}{3}}$

So this time $n = \frac{1}{3}$, and you also need to replace x with $2x$:

$n = \frac{1}{3}$ $n(n-1)$

$$(1+2x)^{\frac{1}{3}} = 1 + \frac{1}{3}(2x) + \frac{\frac{1}{3}\times\left(\frac{1}{3}-1\right)}{1\times 2}(2x)^2 + \frac{\frac{1}{3}\times\left(\frac{1}{3}-1\right)\times\left(\frac{1}{3}-2\right)}{1\times 2\times 3}(2x)^3 + \ldots$$
$$= 1 + \frac{2}{3}x + \frac{\frac{1}{3}\times\left(-\frac{2}{3}\right)}{1\times 2}4x^2 + \frac{\frac{1}{3}\times\left(-\frac{2}{3}\right)\times\left(-\frac{5}{3}\right)}{1\times 2\times 3}8x^3 + \ldots$$
$$= 1 + \frac{2}{3}x + \frac{\left(-\frac{2}{9}\right)}{2}4x^2 + \frac{\left(\frac{10}{27}\right)}{6}8x^3 + \ldots$$
$$= 1 + \frac{2}{3}x + \left(-\frac{2}{9}\times\frac{1}{2}\right)4x^2 + \left(\frac{10}{27}\times\frac{1}{6}\right)8x^3 + \ldots$$
$$= 1 + \frac{2}{3}x - \frac{4}{9}x^2 + \frac{40}{81}x^3 + \ldots$$

Cancelling down is much trickier with this type of expansion — it's usually safer to multiply everything out fully.

Exam questions often ask for the coefficients as simplified fractions.

Trickier Expansions

More binomial goodness... this page is so jam-packed with the stuff, there's only room for a one-line intro...

If the *Constant* in the brackets isn't *1*, you have to *Factorise* first

So the general binomial expansion of $(1 + x)^n$ works fine for any n, and you can replace the x with other x-terms, but that 1 has to be a 1 before you can expand. That means you sometimes need to start with a sneaky bit of factorisation.

EXAMPLE Give the binomial expansion of $(3 - x)^4$.

To use the general formula, you need the constant term in the brackets to be 1.
You can take the 3 outside the brackets by factorising:

The aim here is to get an expression in the form $c(1 + dx)^n$, where c and d are constants.

$$3 - x = 3(1 - \tfrac{1}{3}x)$$
$$\text{so}\quad (3 - x)^4 = [3(1 - \tfrac{1}{3}x)]^4 = 3^4(1 - \tfrac{1}{3}x)^4 = 81(1 - \tfrac{1}{3}x)^4$$

Now we can use the general formula, with $n = 4$, and $-\frac{1}{3}x$ instead of x:

$$\left(1 - \frac{1}{3}x\right)^4 = 1 + 4\left(-\frac{1}{3}x\right) + \frac{4 \times 3}{1 \times 2}\left(-\frac{1}{3}x\right)^2 + \frac{4 \times 3 \times 2}{1 \times 2 \times 3}\left(-\frac{1}{3}x\right)^3 + \frac{4 \times 3 \times 2 \times 1}{1 \times 2 \times 3 \times 4}\left(-\frac{1}{3}x\right)^4$$
$$= 1 - \frac{4}{3}x + 6\left(\frac{1}{9}x^2\right) + 4\left(-\frac{1}{27}x^3\right) + \frac{1}{81}x^4$$
$$= 1 - \frac{4x}{3} + \frac{2x^2}{3} - \frac{4x^3}{27} + \frac{x^4}{81}$$

So now we can expand the original expression:

$$(3 - x)^4 = 81\left(1 - \frac{1}{3}x\right)^4 = 81\left(1 - \frac{4x}{3} + \frac{2x^2}{3} - \frac{4x^3}{27} + \frac{x^4}{81}\right) = 81 - 108x + 54x^2 - 12x^3 + x^4$$

Some *Binomial Expansions* are only *Valid* for *Certain Values* of *x*

When you find a binomial expansion, you usually have to state which values of x the expansion is valid for.

If n is a positive integer, the binomial expansion of $(p + qx)^n$ is valid for all values of x.

If n is not a positive integer, the expansion would be infinite. Because you only write out a few terms, the binomial expansion you get is just an approximation. But the approximation is only valid if the sequence converges — this only happens if x is small enough (for larger values of x, the sequence will diverge)...

If n is a negative integer or a fraction, the binomial expansion of $(p + qx)^n$ is valid when $\left|\frac{qx}{p}\right| < 1$.

You can rewrite this as $|x| < \left|\frac{p}{q}\right|$ — just use the version you find easiest to remember.

This means there's a little bit more to do for the two examples on the previous page:

$(1 + x)^{-2} = 1 - 2x + 3x^2 - 4x^3 + \ldots$ This expansion is valid for $|x| < 1$.

$(1 + 2x)^{\frac{1}{3}} = 1 + \frac{2}{3}x - \frac{4}{9}x^2 + \frac{40}{81}x^3 + \ldots$

This expansion is valid if $|2x| < 1 \Rightarrow 2|x| < 1 \Rightarrow |x| < \frac{1}{2}$.

You might already know the rules $|ab| = |a||b|$ and $\left|\frac{a}{b}\right| = \frac{|a|}{|b|}$. If you don't, then get to know them — they're handy for rearranging these limits.

Lose weight and save money — buy no meals...

Two facts: 1) You can pretty much guarantee that there'll be a binomial expansion question on your C4 exam, and 2) any binomial expansion question they can throw at you will feature some combination of these adaptations of the general formula.

Approximating with Binomial Expansions

Binomial expansions can give you a handy way to estimate various roots.
OK, so it's not that handy... just go with it for now...

*To find **Approximations**, substitute the right value of x*

When you've done an expansion, you can use it to estimate the value of the original expression for given values of x.

EXAMPLE

The binomial expansion of $(1+3x)^{\frac{1}{3}}$ up to the term in x^3 is $(1+3x)^{\frac{1}{3}} \approx 1 + x - x^2 + \frac{5}{3}x^3$.
The expansion is valid for $|x| < \frac{1}{3}$.
Use this expansion to approximate $\sqrt[3]{1.3}$. Give your answer to 4 d.p.

For this type of question, you need to find the right value of x to make the expression you're expanding equal to the thing you're looking for.

In this case it's pretty straightforward: $\sqrt[3]{1.3} = (1+3x)^{\frac{1}{3}}$ when $x = 0.1$.

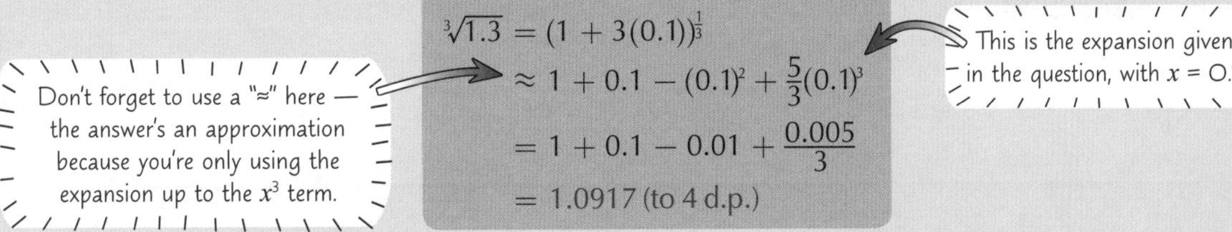

$$\sqrt[3]{1.3} = (1+3(0.1))^{\frac{1}{3}}$$
$$\approx 1 + 0.1 - (0.1)^2 + \frac{5}{3}(0.1)^3$$
$$= 1 + 0.1 - 0.01 + \frac{0.005}{3}$$
$$= 1.0917 \text{ (to 4 d.p.)}$$

In trickier cases you have to do a spot of rearranging to get to the answer.

EXAMPLE

The binomial expansion of $(1-5x)^{\frac{1}{2}}$ up to the term in x^2 is $(1-5x)^{\frac{1}{2}} \approx 1 - \frac{5x}{2} - \frac{25}{8}x^2$.

The expansion is valid for $|x| < \frac{1}{5}$.

Use $x = \frac{1}{50}$ in this expansion to find an approximate value for $\sqrt{10}$.
Find the percentage error in your approximation, to 2 s.f.

First, sub $x = \frac{1}{50}$ into both sides of the expansion:

$$\sqrt{\left(1 - 5\left(\tfrac{1}{50}\right)\right)} \approx 1 - \frac{5}{2}\left(\frac{1}{50}\right) - \frac{25}{8}\left(\frac{1}{50}\right)^2$$
$$\sqrt{\left(1 - \tfrac{1}{10}\right)} \approx 1 - \frac{1}{20} - \frac{1}{800}$$
$$\sqrt{\frac{9}{10}} \approx \frac{759}{800}$$

Now simplify the square root and rearrange to find an estimate for $\sqrt{10}$:

$$\sqrt{\frac{9}{10}} = \frac{\sqrt{9}}{\sqrt{10}} = \frac{3}{\sqrt{10}} \approx \frac{759}{800} \quad \Rightarrow \quad \sqrt{10} \approx 3 \div \frac{759}{800} = \frac{800}{253}$$

The percentage error is $\left|\frac{\text{real value} - \text{estimate}}{\text{real value}}\right| \times 100 = \left|\frac{\sqrt{10} - \frac{800}{253}}{\sqrt{10}}\right| \times 100 = 0.0070\%$ (to 2 s.f.)

You never know when you might need to estimate the cube root of 1.3...

That percentage error bit in the second example is one of those ways they might sneak a seemingly unrelated topic into an exam question. The examiners are allowed to stick a bit from any of the earlier Core modules into C4, so don't freak out if they ask you something slightly unexpected — remember, you will have seen it before and you do know how to do it.

C4 Section 3 — Practice Questions

Ah, here we are on another of these soothing green pages. Relax... this is your happy place... nothing to worry about here... enjoy this tranquil blue pool of shimmering warm-up questions.

Warm-up Questions

1) Give the binomial expansion of:

   a) $(1 + 2x)^3$ b) $(1 - x)^4$ c) $(1 - 4x)^4$

2) For what values of n does the binomial expansion of $(1 + x)^n$ result in a finite expression?

3) Find the binomial expansion of each of the following, up to and including the term in x^3:

   a) $\frac{1}{(1+x)^4}$ b) $\frac{1}{(1-3x)^3}$ c) $\sqrt{1-5x}$

4) a) If the full binomial expansion of $(c + dx)^n$ is an infinite series, what values of x is the expansion valid for?

   b) What values of x are the expansions from question 3 valid for?

5) Give the binomial expansions of the following, up to and including the term in x^2. State which values of x each expansion is valid for.

   a) $\frac{1}{(3+2x)^2}$ b) $\sqrt[3]{8-x}$

By now all your cares should have floated away on the binomial breeze. Time for a bracing dip in an ice-cool bath of exam questions.

Exam Questions

1 $$f(x) = \frac{1}{\sqrt{(9-4x)}}, \text{ for } |x| < \frac{9}{4}.$$

a) Find the binomial expansion of $f(x)$ up to and including the term in x^3. *(5 marks)*

b) Hence find the first three terms in the expansion of $\frac{2-x}{\sqrt{(9-4x)}}$. *(4 marks)*

2 $$f(x) = \frac{2}{(4+3x)} - \frac{2}{(1-3x)} - \frac{1}{(1-3x)^2}$$

a) Find the binomial expansion of $f(x)$, up to and including the term in x^2. *(6 marks)*

b) Find the range of values of x for which the binomial expansion of $f(x)$ is valid. *(2 marks)*

C4 Section 3 — Practice Questions

Congratulations, you've almost achieved C4 Binomial Expansion nirvana.
Just a few more exam question steps and you'll be there...

3 a) Find the binomial expansion of $(16 + 3x)^{\frac{1}{4}}$, for $|x| < \frac{16}{3}$, up to and including the term in x^2. *(5 marks)*

b) (i) Estimate $\sqrt[4]{12.4}$ by substituting a suitable value of x into your expansion from part (a). Give your answer to 6 decimal places. *(2 marks)*

(ii) What is the percentage error in this estimate? Give your answer to 3 s.f. *(2 marks)*

4 a) Find the binomial expansion of $\left(1 - \frac{4}{3}x\right)^{-\frac{1}{2}}$, up to and including the term in x^3. *(4 marks)*

b) Hence find the values of integer constants a, b and c, such that

$$\sqrt{\frac{27}{(3-4x)}} \approx a + bx + cx^2,$$

and state the range of values of x for which this approximation is valid. *(3 marks)*

5 a) (i) Show that $\sqrt{\frac{1+2x}{1-3x}} \approx 1 + \frac{5}{2}x + \frac{35}{8}x^2$. *(5 marks)*

(ii) For what values of x is your expansion valid? *(2 marks)*

b) Using the above expansion with $x = \frac{2}{15}$, show that $\sqrt{19} \approx \frac{127}{30}$. *(2 marks)*

6 It is given that $\frac{13x-17}{(5-3x)(2x-1)} \equiv \frac{2}{(5-3x)} - \frac{3}{(2x-1)}$.

a) (i) Find the binomial expansion of $(2x-1)^{-1}$, up to and including the term in x^2. *(2 marks)*

(ii) Show that $\frac{1}{(5-3x)} \approx \frac{1}{5} + \frac{3}{25}x + \frac{9}{125}x^2$, for $|x| < \frac{5}{3}$. *(5 marks)*

b) Using your answers to parts (i) and (ii) above, find the first three terms of the binomial expansion of $\frac{13x-17}{(5-3x)(2x-1)}$. *(2 marks)*

Differentiation of Sin, Cos and Tan

So you think you know all there is to know about trigonometry. Well think again, 'cos here it comes again. (You see what I did there with the 'cos'? Pun #27 from 'Ye Olde Booke of Maths Punnes'...)

The Rules for dy/dx of Sin, Cos and Tan only work in Radians

For trigonometric functions, where the angle is measured in radians, the following rules apply:

If $y =$		$\frac{dy}{dx} =$
$\sin x$	$\longrightarrow$	$\cos x$
$\cos x$	$\longrightarrow$	$-\sin x$
$\tan x$	$\longrightarrow$	$\sec^2 x$

There's loads more about sec (and cosec and cot) on p.16.

Use the Chain Rule with Sin/Cos/Tan (f(x))

If you can't follow what's happening here, go back to p.24 and brush up on the chain rule.

EXAMPLE: Differentiate $y = \cos 2x + \sin(x + 1)$ with respect to x.

It's the chain rule (again) for both parts of this equation:

1) Differentiate '$y = \cos 2x$': $y = \cos u$, $u = 2x$,
so $\frac{dy}{du} = -\sin u$ (see above) and $\frac{du}{dx} = 2 \Rightarrow \frac{dy}{dx} = -2\sin 2x$.
2) Differentiate '$y = \sin(x + 1)$': $y = \sin u$, $u = x + 1$,
so $\frac{dy}{du} = \cos u$ (see above) and $\frac{du}{dx} = 1 \Rightarrow \frac{dy}{dx} = \cos(x + 1)$.
3) Put it all together to get $\frac{dy}{dx} = -2\sin 2x + \cos(x + 1)$.

EXAMPLE: Find $\frac{dy}{dx}$ when $x = \tan 3y$.

1) First find $\frac{dx}{dy}$ using the chain rule: $x = \tan u$, $u = 3y$, $\frac{dx}{du} = \sec^2 u$, $\frac{du}{dy} = 3$, so $\frac{dx}{dy} = 3\sec^2 3y$.
2) Then use $\frac{dy}{dx} = \frac{1}{\left(\frac{dx}{dy}\right)}$ to get the final answer: $\frac{dy}{dx} = \frac{1}{3\sec^2 3y} = \frac{1}{3}\cos^2 3y$.

See p.24 if you can't remember this.

Remember to use Trig Identities where Necessary

EXAMPLE For $y = 2\cos^2 x + \sin 2x$, show that $\frac{dy}{dx} = 2(\cos 2x - \sin 2x)$.

1) Writing out the equation in a slightly different way helps with the chain rule: $y = 2(\cos x)^2 + \sin 2x$.
2) For the first bit, $y = 2u^2$, $u = \cos x$, so $\frac{dy}{du} = 4u$ and $\frac{du}{dx} = -\sin x$.
For the second bit, $y = \sin u$, $u = 2x$, so $\frac{dy}{du} = \cos u$ and $\frac{du}{dx} = 2$.
3) Putting it all in the chain rule formula gives $\frac{dy}{dx} = -4\sin x \cos x + 2\cos 2x$.
4) From the target answer in the question it looks like we need a $\sin 2x$ from somewhere, so use the 'double angle' formula (see p.19) $\sin 2x \equiv 2\sin x \cos x$:
$\frac{dy}{dx} = -2\sin 2x + 2\cos 2x$, which rearranges nicely to give $\frac{dy}{dx} = 2(\cos 2x - \sin 2x)$. Et voilà.

You could also use the identity $\cos 2x \equiv 2\cos^2 x - 1$ before differentiating. You'll get the same answer.

I'm having an identity crisis — I can't differentiate between sin and cos...

Differentiating sin and cos are pretty easy really — just watch out for that sneaky negative when you differentiate cos. Tan is a bit harder, but it's actually given to you on the formula sheet if you forget it.

More Trig Differentiation

After whetting your appetite with the little taste on the last page, let's have a gander at some more trig differentiation. Namely, the rules for differentiating cosec x, sec x and cot x, and the vast array of things you can do with them.

d/dx of Cosec, Sec and Cot come from the Quotient Rule

Since cosec, sec and cot are just the reciprocals of sin, cos and tan, the quotient rule can be used to differentiate them.

$$y = \text{cosec } x = \frac{1}{\sin x}$$

1) For the quotient rule:
$u = 1 \Rightarrow \frac{du}{dx} = 0$ and $v = \sin x \Rightarrow \frac{dv}{dx} = \cos x$

2) $\frac{dy}{dx} = \frac{v\frac{du}{dx} - u\frac{dv}{dx}}{v^2} = \frac{(\sin x \cdot 0) - (1 \cdot \cos x)}{\sin^2 x} = -\frac{\cos x}{\sin^2 x}$

3) Since $\cot x = \frac{\cos x}{\sin x}$, and $\text{cosec } x = \frac{1}{\sin x}$,
$\frac{dy}{dx} = -\frac{\cos x}{\sin x} \times \frac{1}{\sin x} = -\text{cosec } x \cot x$.

$$y = \sec x = \frac{1}{\cos x}$$

1) For the quotient rule:
$u = 1 \Rightarrow \frac{du}{dx} = 0$ and $v = \cos x \Rightarrow \frac{dv}{dx} = -\sin x$

2) $\frac{dy}{dx} = \frac{v\frac{du}{dx} - u\frac{dv}{dx}}{v^2} = \frac{(\cos x \cdot 0) - (1 \cdot -\sin x)}{\cos^2 x} = \frac{\sin x}{\cos^2 x}$

3) Since $\tan x = \frac{\sin x}{\cos x}$, and $\sec x = \frac{1}{\cos x}$,
$\frac{dy}{dx} = \frac{\sin x}{\cos x} \times \frac{1}{\cos x} = \sec x \tan x$.

If $y =$		$\frac{dy}{dx} =$
cosec x	$\longrightarrow$	$-\text{cosec } x \cot x$
sec x	$\longrightarrow$	$\sec x \tan x$
cot x	$\longrightarrow$	$-\text{cosec}^2 x$

Go back a page for this one. Have a go at writing it out like the ones above, starting with $y = \cos x / \sin x$.

If you can't remember which trig functions give a negative result when you differentiate them, just remember it's all the ones that begin with c — cos, cosec and cot.

Use the Chain, Product and Quotient Rules with Cosec, Sec and Cot

So once you're familiar with the three rules in the box above you can use them with the chain, product and quotient rules and in combination with all the other functions we've seen so far.

EXAMPLES Find $\frac{dy}{dx}$ for the following functions: a) $y = \sec(2x^2)$ and b) $y = e^x \cot x$.

a) $y = \sec(2x^2)$

1) This is a function of a function, so think 'chain rule':
$y = \sec u$ and $u = 2x^2$

2) $\frac{dy}{du} = \sec u \tan u$ (see above) $= \sec(2x^2)\tan(2x^2)$

3) $\frac{du}{dx} = 4x$

4) So $\frac{dy}{dx} = \frac{dy}{du} \times \frac{du}{dx} = 4x\sec(2x^2)\tan(2x^2)$.

b) $y = e^x \cot x$

Have a look back at p.26 if you've forgotten the product rule.

1) This is a product of two functions, so think 'product rule':
$u = e^x$ and $v = \cot x$

2) $\frac{du}{dx} = e^x$

3) $\frac{dv}{dx} = -\text{cosec}^2 x$ (see above)

4) So $\frac{dy}{dx} = u\frac{dv}{dx} + v\frac{du}{dx} = (e^x \cdot -\text{cosec}^2 x) + (\cot x \cdot e^x)$
$= e^x(\cot x - \text{cosec}^2 x)$.

Get it? Got it? Good.

I'm co-sec-sy for my shirt — co-sec-sy it hurts...

I have some good news and some good news. The good news is — that's all the trig differentiation you need for C4. The other good news is — the ones on this page will be on the formula sheet in the exam so you only need to know how to use them. Watch out for rules from C3 popping up here though — they might try throwing in the product rule or quotient rule.

Differentiation with Parametric Equations

This page sees the return of an old friend. If you've forgotten what parametric equations are already, go back to Section 2. Go on, I'll wait for you... ... ...OK, are you back now? Ready? Right, on we go...

Differentiating Parametric Equations is a lot Simpler than you might expect

Just suppose you've got a curve defined by two parametric equations, with the parameter t: $y = \text{f}(t)$ and $x = \text{g}(t)$.

If you can't find the Cartesian equation, it seems like it would be a bit tricky to find the gradient, $\frac{dy}{dx}$.

Luckily the chain rule (see p24) is on hand to help out:

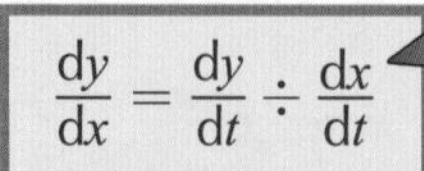

This is exactly the same as on p24, except we've replaced '$\times \frac{dt}{dx}$' with '$\div \frac{dx}{dt}$'

EXAMPLE The curve C is defined by the parametric equations $y = t^3 - 2t + 4$ and $x = t^2 - 1$.
Find: a) $\frac{dy}{dx}$ in terms of t, b) the gradient of C when $t = -1$.

Start by differentiating the two parametric equations with respect to t:

a) $\frac{dy}{dt} = 3t^2 - 2$, $\frac{dx}{dt} = 2t$

Now use the chain rule to combine them:

$$\frac{dy}{dx} = \frac{dy}{dt} \div \frac{dx}{dt} = \frac{3t^2 - 2}{2t}$$

Use the answer to a) to find the gradient for a specific value of t:

b) When $t = -1$, $\frac{dy}{dx} = \frac{3(-1)^2 - 2}{2(-1)} = \frac{3-2}{-2} = -\frac{1}{2}$

Use the Gradient to find Tangents and Normals

Of course, it's rarely as straightforward as just finding the gradient. A lot of the time, you'll then have to use it in the equation of a tangent or normal to the parametric curve.

EXAMPLE For the curve C in the example above, find:
a) the equation of the tangent to the curve when $t = 2$,
b) the equation of the normal to the curve when $t = 2$.

First you need the coordinates of the point where $t = 2$:

a) When $t = 2$, $x = (2)^2 - 1 = 3$ and $y = (2)^3 - 2(2) + 4 = 8 - 4 + 4 = 8$.

You also need the gradient at that point:

When $t = 2$, $\frac{dy}{dx} = \frac{3(2)^2 - 2}{2(2)} = \frac{10}{4} = \frac{5}{2}$

Now use that information to find the equation of the tangent:

The tangent to C at (3, 8) has an equation of the form $y = mx + c$.

So $8 = \frac{5}{2}(3) + c \Rightarrow c = \frac{1}{2}$.

The tangent to curve C when $t = 2$ is $y = \frac{5}{2}x + \frac{1}{2}$.

You could also use $y - y_1 = m(x - x_1)$ to get the equation.

You can find the normal in a similar way:

b) The normal to C at (3, 8) has gradient $-\frac{1}{\left(\frac{5}{2}\right)} = -\frac{2}{5}$.

So $8 = -\frac{2}{5}(3) + c \Rightarrow c = \frac{46}{5}$.

The normal to curve C when $t = 2$ is $y = -\frac{2}{5}x + \frac{46}{5}$.

If you're not quite following all this tangents and normals business, take a look back at C1 to refresh your memory.

And now, yet another chocolate biscuit reference...

To an examiner, adding a 'find the tangent' or 'find the normal' part to a parametric equations question is like adding chocolate to a digestive biscuit — it makes it at least 4 times better. In other words: this is very likely to show up in your C4 exam, so be ready for it. And in case you were wondering, tangent = milk chocolate, normal = dark chocolate.

Implicit Differentiation

This really isn't as complicated as it looks... in fact, I think you'll find that if something's implicit between x and y, it can be ximplicity itself. No, that's not a typo, it's a hilarious joke... 'implicit' between 'x' and 'y'... do you see?...

You need **Implicit Differentiation** if you can't write the **Equation** as $y = f(x)$

1) An 'implicit relation' is the maths name for any equation in x and y that's written in the form $f(x, y) = g(x, y)$ instead of $y = f(x)$.

f(x, y) and g(x, y) don't actually both have to include x and y — one of them could even be a constant.

2) Some implicit relations are either awkward or impossible to rewrite in the form $y = f(x)$. This can happen, for example, if the equation contains a number of different powers of y, or terms where x is multiplied by y.
3) This can make implicit relations tricky to differentiate — the solution is implicit differentiation:

Implicit Differentiation

To find $\frac{dy}{dx}$ for an implicit relation between x and y:

1) **Differentiate terms in x^n only (and constant terms) with respect to x, as normal.**
2) **Use the chain rule to differentiate terms in y^m only:**

$$\frac{d}{dx}f(y) = \frac{d}{dy}f(y)\frac{dy}{dx}$$

In other words, 'differentiate with respect to y, and stick a $\frac{dy}{dx}$ on the end'.

3) **Use the product rule to differentiate terms in both x and y:**

$$\frac{d}{dx}u(x)v(y) = u(x)\frac{d}{dx}v(y) + v(y)\frac{d}{dx}u(x)$$

This version of the product rule is slightly different from the one on p26 — it's got v(y) instead of v(x).

4) **Rearrange the resulting equation in x, y and $\frac{dy}{dx}$ to make $\frac{dy}{dx}$ the subject.**

EXAMPLE Use implicit differentiation to find $\frac{dy}{dx}$ if $2x^2y + y^3 = 6x^2 + 5$.

We need to differentiate each term of the equation with respect to x.

Start by sticking '$\frac{d}{dx}$' in front of each term:

$$\frac{d}{dx}2x^2y + \frac{d}{dx}y^3 = \frac{d}{dx}6x^2 + \frac{d}{dx}5$$

First, deal with the terms in x and constant terms — in this case that's the two terms on the RHS:

$$\Rightarrow \frac{d}{dx}2x^2y + \frac{d}{dx}y^3 = 12x + 0$$

Now use the chain rule on the term in y:

$$\Rightarrow \frac{d}{dx}2x^2y + 3y^2\frac{dy}{dx} = 12x + 0$$

Using the chain rule from the box above, $f(y) = y^3$.

Leave this $\frac{dy}{dx}$ where it is for now.

And use the product rule on the term in x and y:

$$\Rightarrow 2x^2\frac{d}{dx}(y) + y\frac{d}{dx}(2x^2) + 3y^2\frac{dy}{dx} = 12x + 0$$

$$\Rightarrow 2x^2\frac{dy}{dx} + y4x + 3y^2\frac{dy}{dx} = 12x + 0$$

So in terms of the box above, $u(x) = 2x^2$ and $v(y) = y$.

You get a $\frac{dy}{dx}$ term here too (from the '$\frac{d}{dx}v(y)$' bit).

Finally, rearrange to make $\frac{dy}{dx}$ the subject:

$$\Rightarrow \frac{dy}{dx}(2x^2 + 3y^2) = 12x - 4xy$$

$$\Rightarrow \frac{dy}{dx} = \frac{12x - 4xy}{2x^2 + 3y^2}$$

If an imp asks to try your ice lolly, don't let the imp lick it...

Learn the versions of the chain rule and product rule from the box above. All the different bits of the method for implicit differentiation can make it confusing — read the example carefully and make sure you understand every little bit of it.

Implicit Differentiation

If you've gone to all the hard work of differentiating an implicit relation, it would be a shame not to use it. It'd be like a shiny toy that's been kept in its box and never played with. Don't make the maths sad — play with it.

Implicit Differentiation still gives you an expression for the *Gradient*

Most implicit differentiation questions aren't really that different at heart to any other differentiation question. Once you've got an expression for the gradient, you'll have to use it to do the sort of stuff you'd normally expect.

EXAMPLE Curve A has the equation $x^2 + 2xy - y^2 = 10x + 4y - 21$

a) Show that when $\frac{dy}{dx} = 0$, $y = 5 - x$.

b) Find the coordinates of the stationary points of A.

For starters, we're going to need to find $\frac{dy}{dx}$ by implicit differentiation:

a) $$\frac{d}{dx}x^2 + \frac{d}{dx}2xy - \frac{d}{dx}y^2 = \frac{d}{dx}10x + \frac{d}{dx}4y - \frac{d}{dx}21$$

$$\Rightarrow 2x + \frac{d}{dx}2xy - \frac{d}{dx}y^2 = 10 + \frac{d}{dx}4y - 0$$

Differentiate x^2, 10x and 21 with respect to x.

$$\Rightarrow 2x + \frac{d}{dx}2xy - 2y\frac{dy}{dx} = 10 + 4\frac{dy}{dx}$$

Use the chain rule to differentiate y^2 and 4y.

$$\Rightarrow 2x + 2x\frac{dy}{dx} + y\frac{d}{dx}2x - 2y\frac{dy}{dx} = 10 + 4\frac{dy}{dx}$$

Use the product rule to differentiate 2xy.

$$\Rightarrow 2x + 2x\frac{dy}{dx} + 2y - 2y\frac{dy}{dx} = 10 + 4\frac{dy}{dx}$$

$$\Rightarrow 2x\frac{dy}{dx} - 2y\frac{dy}{dx} - 4\frac{dy}{dx} = 10 - 2x - 2y$$

Collect '$\frac{dy}{dx}$' terms on one side, and everything else on the other side.

$$\Rightarrow \frac{dy}{dx} = \frac{10 - 2x - 2y}{2x - 2y - 4}$$

So when $\frac{dy}{dx} = 0$, $\quad \frac{10 - 2x - 2y}{2x - 2y - 4} = 0 \quad \Rightarrow \quad 10 - 2x - 2y = 0 \quad \Rightarrow \quad y = 5 - x$

Now we can use the answer to part a) in the equation of the curve to find the points where $\frac{dy}{dx} = 0$.

b) When $\frac{dy}{dx} = 0$, $y = 5 - x$. So at the stationary points,

$$x^2 + 2xy - y^2 = 10x + 4y - 21$$

$$\Rightarrow x^2 + 2x(5 - x) - (5 - x)^2 = 10x + 4(5 - x) - 21$$

Substitute y = 5 – x into the original equation to find the values of x at the stationary points.

$$\Rightarrow x^2 + 10x - 2x^2 - 25 + 10x - x^2 = 10x + 20 - 4x - 21$$

$$\Rightarrow -2x^2 + 20x - 25 = 6x - 1$$

$$\Rightarrow -2x^2 + 14x - 24 = 0$$

$$\Rightarrow x^2 - 7x + 12 = 0$$

$$\Rightarrow (x - 3)(x - 4) = 0$$

$$\Rightarrow x = 3 \text{ or } x = 4$$

$x = 3 \Rightarrow y = 5 - 3 = 2 \qquad x = 4 \Rightarrow y = 5 - 4 = 1$

So the stationary points of A are (3, 2) and (4, 1).

Pah, differentiation? They should have called it same-iation...

...you know, cos all the questions basically end up asking for the same thing. Other familiar faces that are likely to show up in implicit differentiation questions include finding tangents and normals to implicitly defined curves. All these differentiation questions set off in different ways to end up asking you the same thing, so make sure you know the basics.

C4 Section 4 — Practice Questions

If you think that was a lot of differentiation, be thankful you didn't live in Ancient Molgarahenia, where differentiation was the only maths permitted. Try these tasty warm-up questions for an authentic taste of Molgarahenian life.

Warm-up Questions

1) Find $f'(x)$ for the following functions:
   a) $f(x) = \sin^2(x + 2)$
   b) $f(x) = 2\cos 3x$
   c) $f(x) = \sqrt{\tan x}$
2) Find $\frac{dy}{dx}$ when $x = 0$ for $y = \operatorname{cosec}(3x - 2)$.
3) A curve is defined by the parametric equations $x = t^2$, $y = 3t^3 - 4t$.
   a) Find $\frac{dy}{dx}$ for this curve.
   b) Find the coordinates of the stationary points of the curve.
4) Use implicit differentiation to find $\frac{dy}{dx}$ for each of the following equations:
   a) $4x^2 - 2y^2 = 7x^2y$
   b) $3x^4 - 2xy^2 = y$
   c) $\cos x \sin y = xy$
5) Using your answers to question 4, find:
   a) the gradient of the tangent to the graph of $4x^2 - 2y^2 = 7x^2y$ at $(1, -4)$,
   b) the gradient of the normal to the graph of $3x^4 - 2xy^2 = y$ at $(1, 1)$.

It is said that the Great Molgarahenian Plain was carpeted with differentiation as far as the eye could see. The C4 exam won't be quite that bad, but there will be some differentiation in there, so get practising...

Exam Questions

1 The curve C is defined by the parametric equations

$$x = 3\theta - \cos 3\theta, \quad y = 2\sin\theta, \quad -\pi \leq \theta \leq \pi.$$

a) Find an expression for $\frac{dy}{dx}$. *(3 marks)*

b) (i) Show that the gradient of C at the point $(\pi + 1, \sqrt{3})$ is $\frac{1}{3}$. *(3 marks)*

(ii) Find the equation of the normal to C when $\theta = \frac{\pi}{6}$. *(4 marks)*

2 The equation of curve C is $6x^2y - 7 = 5x - 4y^2 - x^2$.

a) The line T has the equation $y = c$ and passes through a point on C where $x = 2$. Find c, given that $c > 0$. *(2 marks)*

b) T also crosses C at point Q.

(i) Find the coordinates of Q. *(2 marks)*

(ii) Find the gradient of C at Q. *(6 marks)*

C4 Section 4 — Practice Questions

In 272 BC, the famous Molgarahenian philosopher, Bobby the Wise, was put to death for straying from the path of differentiation and doing some simultaneous equations. Don't be like Bobby, stick with these questions (for now)...

3 The curve C has the equation $3e^x + 6y = 2x^2y$.

a) (i) Use implicit differentiation to find an expression for $\frac{dy}{dx}$. *(3 marks)*

(ii) Show that at the stationary points of C, $y = \frac{3e^x}{4x}$. *(2 marks)*

b) Hence find the exact coordinates of the two stationary points of C. *(4 marks)*

4 A curve, C, has parametric equations

$x = t^2 + 2t - 3, \qquad y = 2 - t^3.$

a) The line L is the tangent to C at $y = -6$. Show that the equation of L is $y = -2x + 4$. *(4 marks)*

b) L also meets C at point P.

(i) Find the coordinates of P. *(4 marks)*

(ii) Find the equation of the normal to the curve at P. *(3 marks)*

5 Use the quotient rule to show that, for the function $f(x) = \sec x$:

$$f'(x) = \sec x \tan x.$$

(4 marks)

6 Find the gradient of the tangent to the curve:

$$y = \sin^2 x - 2\cos 2x$$

at the point where $x = \frac{\pi}{12}$ radians. *(4 marks)*

7 Find the equation of the normal to the curve $x = \sin 4y$ that passes through the point $\left(0, \frac{\pi}{4}\right)$.

Give your answer in the form $y = mx + c$, where m and c are constants to be found. *(6 marks)*

Integration of Sin and Cos

If you thought you'd killed off the dragon that is trigonometry, you're sadly mistaken. It rears its ugly head again, and now you need to know how to integrate trig functions. Find your most trusty dragon-slaying sword and read on...

Sin and Cos are Easy to integrate

From Section 4, you know that $\sin x$ differentiates to give $\cos x$, $\cos x$ differentiates to give $-\sin x$ and $\tan x$ differentiates to give $\sec^2 x$ (where the angle x is in radians). So it's pretty obvious that:

$$\int \sin x \, dx = -\cos x + C$$
$$\int \cos x \, dx = \sin x + C$$
$$\int \sec^2 x \, dx = \tan x + C$$

Integrating tan x is a bit different — see p.72.

If x has a coefficient that isn't 1 (e.g. sin $3x$), you just divide by the coefficient when you integrate..

EXAMPLE Find $\int \cos 4x - 2\sin 2x + \sec^2 \frac{1}{2}x \, dx$.

Integrate each term separately using the results from above:

$\int \cos 4x \, dx = \frac{1}{4}\sin 4x$ $\quad \int -2\sin 2x \, dx = -2\left(-\frac{1}{2}\cos 2x\right) = \cos 2x$ $\quad \int \sec^2 \frac{1}{2}x \, dx = \frac{1}{\frac{1}{2}}\tan \frac{1}{2}x = 2\tan \frac{1}{2}x$

Putting these terms together and adding the constant gives:

$$\int \cos 4x - 2\sin 2x + \sec^2 \tfrac{1}{2}x \, dx = \frac{1}{4}\sin 4x + \cos 2x + 2\tan \tfrac{1}{2}x + C$$

There are some Results you can just Learn

There are a list of trig integrals that you can just learn — you don't need to know where they came from, you can just use them. You've met these ones before — they're the results of differentiating cosec x, sec x and cot x (see p.65).

$$\int \operatorname{cosec} x \cot x \, dx = -\operatorname{cosec} x + C$$
$$\int \sec x \tan x \, dx = \sec x + C$$
$$\int \operatorname{cosec}^2 x \, dx = -\cot x + C$$

The coefficients of x have to be the same in each term — e.g. you couldn't integrate sec x tan $3x$.

As usual, you need to divide by the coefficient of x when you integrate.

EXAMPLE Find $\int 10\sec 5x \tan 5x + \frac{1}{2}\operatorname{cosec} 3x \cot 3x - \operatorname{cosec}^2(6x+1) \, dx$.

You can integrate the last bit using a linear substitution (see p.30).

This one looks a bit scary, but take it one step at a time. Integrate each bit in turn to get:

1. $\int 10\sec 5x \tan 5x \, dx = \frac{1}{5} \cdot 10\sec 5x = 2\sec 5x$

2. $\int \frac{1}{2}\operatorname{cosec} 3x \cot 3x \, dx = -\frac{1}{3} \cdot \frac{1}{2}\operatorname{cosec} 3x = -\frac{1}{6}\operatorname{cosec} 3x$

3. $\int -\operatorname{cosec}^2(6x+1) \, dx = -\frac{1}{6}(-\cot(6x+1)) = \frac{1}{6}\cot(6x+1)$

The + 1 inside the brackets has no effect on the integration — differentiate to see why.

Putting these terms together and adding the constant gives:

$$\int 10\sec 5x \tan 5x + \frac{1}{2}\operatorname{cosec} 3x \cot 3x - \operatorname{cosec}^2(6x+1) \, dx = 2\sec 5x - \frac{1}{6}\operatorname{cosec} 3x + \frac{1}{6}\cot(6x+1) + C$$

This is starting to grate on me now...

Although you're not given all of these integrals on the formula sheet, some of the trickier ones (e.g. sec x tan x and cosec$^2 x$) are on the list of differentiation formulas. As long as you work backwards (i.e. from f′(x) to f(x)) you can just use these results without having to remember them all. Be careful with the coefficients — don't forget to divide by them when you integrate.

Integration of f′(x)/f(x)

Sometimes you get integrals that look really nasty — like fractions. However, there are a couple of clever tricks that can make them easy to integrate.

Some Fractions integrate to ln

If you have a fraction that has a function of x on the numerator and a different function of x on the denominator (e.g. $\frac{x-2}{x^3+1}$), you'll probably struggle to integrate it. However, if you have a fraction where the numerator is the derivative of the denominator (e.g. $\frac{3x^2}{x^3+1}$), it integrates to give ln of whatever the denominator is (in this case, $x^3 + 1$).

In general terms, this is written as:

$$\int \frac{f'(x)}{f(x)}\,dx = \ln|f(x)| + C$$

This is another one that comes from the chain rule (p.24) — if you differentiated ln |f(x)|, you'd end up with the fraction on the left.

The hardest bit about questions like this is recognising that the denominator differentiates to give the numerator. Once you've spotted that, it's dead easy. They might make the numerator a multiple of the denominator just to confuse things, so watch out for that.

EXAMPLES

Find a) $\int \frac{8x^3-4}{x^4-2x}\,dx$ and b) $\int \frac{3\sin 3x}{\cos 3x+2}\,dx$.

Trig identities can even sneak into questions like this, but you probably won't get anything too nasty.

a) $\frac{d}{dx}(x^4-2x) = 4x^3 - 2$

and $8x^3 - 4 = 2(4x^3-2)$

The numerator is 2 × the derivative of the denominator, so

$\int \frac{8x^3-4}{x^4-2x}\,dx = 2\ln|x^4-2x| + C$

b) $\frac{d}{dx}(\cos 3x+2) = -3\sin 3x$

The numerator is minus the derivative of the denominator, so

$\int \frac{3\sin 3x}{\cos 3x+2}\,dx = -\ln|\cos 3x + 2| + C$

$= -\ln|\cos 3x+2| + \ln k = -\ln|k(\cos 3x+2)|$

Using $C = \ln k$, you can combine all the terms into one using the laws of logs. $\ln k$ is just a constant.

You can get ln of Trig Functions too

You might have noticed from part (b) above that you can work out the integral of $\tan x$ using this method:

$\tan x = \frac{\sin x}{\cos x}$, and $\frac{d}{dx}(\cos x) = -\sin x$

The numerator is minus the derivative of the denominator, so

$\int \tan x\,dx = \int \frac{\sin x}{\cos x}\,dx = -\ln|\cos x| + C$

$-\ln|\cos x|$ is the same as $\ln|\sec x|$ — this comes from the laws of logs on p.10.

There are some other trig functions that you can integrate in the same way:

$$\int \cot x\,dx = \ln|\sin x| + C$$
$$\int \operatorname{cosec} x\,dx = -\ln|\operatorname{cosec} x + \cot x| + C$$
$$\int \sec x\,dx = \ln|\sec x + \tan x| + C$$

This list is given in the formula booklet — so you don't need to learn them (just be able to use them).

EXAMPLE

Find $\int \frac{1}{2}\operatorname{cosec} 2x\,dx$.

You can just use the result above — so all you have to do is work out what happens to the coefficient. The coefficient is 2, so you need to divide by 2 when you integrate:

$\int \frac{1}{2}\operatorname{cosec} 2x\,dx = -\frac{1}{4}\ln|\operatorname{cosec} 2x + \cot 2x| + C$

Check this by differentiating (using the chain rule with $u = \operatorname{cosec} 2x + \cot 2x$).

2 pages in and I've run out of jokes on integration. Please help...

If you come across an integration question with a fraction that doesn't seem to integrate easily, have a quick look and see if one bit is the derivative of the other. If it is, use the rule above and you'll be as happy as Larry (and Larry's always happy).

Integration Using the Chain Rule Backwards

Most integrations aren't as bad as they look — on the previous page, you saw how to integrate special fractions, and now it's time for certain products. There are some things you can look out for when you're integrating...

You can use the Chain Rule in Reverse

You came across the chain rule in C3 (back on p.24) — it's where you write the thing you're differentiating in terms of u (and u is a function of x). You end up with the product of two derivatives ($\frac{dy}{du}$ and $\frac{du}{dx}$).

When it comes to integrating, if you spot that your integral is a product where one bit is the derivative of part of the other bit, you can use this rule:

$$\int \frac{du}{dx} f'(u)\,dx = f(u) + C$$

where u is a function of x.

EXAMPLE

Find a) $\int 6x^5 e^{x^6}\,dx$ and b) $\int e^{\sin x}\cos x\,dx$.

a) $\int 6x^5 e^{x^6}\,dx = e^{x^6} + C$

If you differentiated $y = e^{x^6}$ using the chain rule, you'd get $6x^5e^{x^6}$. This is the function you had to integrate.

b) $\int e^{\sin x}\cos x\,dx = e^{\sin x} + C$

If you differentiated $y = e^{\sin x}$ using the chain rule, you'd get $e^{\sin x}\cos x$. This is the function you had to integrate.

Some Products are made up of a Function and its Derivative

Similarly, if you spot that part of a product is the derivative of the other part of it (which is raised to a power), you can integrate it using this rule:

$$\int (n+1)f'(x)[f(x)]^n\,dx = [f(x)]^{n+1} + C$$

Remember that the derivative will be a multiple of $n + 1$ (not n) — watch out for any other multiples too. This will probably make more sense if you have a look at an example:

EXAMPLE

Find a) $\int 12x^3(2x^4 - 5)^2\,dx$ and b) $\int 8\,\mathrm{cosec}^2 x\cot^3 x\,dx$.

This one looks pretty horrific, but it isn't too bad once you spot that $-\mathrm{cosec}^2 x$ is the derivative of $\cot x$.

a) Here, $f(x) = 2x^4 - 5$, so differentiating gives $f'(x) = 8x^3$. $n = 2$, so $n + 1 = 3$.
Putting all this into the rule above gives:
$\int 3(8x^3)(2x^4 - 5)^2\,dx = \int 24x^3(2x^4 - 5)^2\,dx = (2x^4 - 5)^3 + C$
Divide everything by 2 to match the original integral:
$\int 12x^3(2x^4 - 5)^2\,dx = \frac{1}{2}(2x^4 - 5)^3 + C.$

b) For this one, $f(x) = \cot x$, so differentiating gives $f'(x) = -\mathrm{cosec}^2 x$. $n = 3$, so $n + 1 = 4$.
Putting all this into the rule gives:
$\int -4\,\mathrm{cosec}^2 x\cot^3 x\,dx = \cot^4 x + C$
Multiply everything by –2 to match the original integral:
$\int 8\,\mathrm{cosec}^2 x\cot^3 x\,dx = -2\cot^4 x + C$

To get rid of hiccups, drink a glass of water backwards...

It seems to me that most of this section is about reversing the things you learnt earlier. I don't know why they ask you to differentiate stuff if you're just going to have to integrate it again and end up where you started. At least it keeps you busy.

Integrating Trig Things Using Trig Identities

Examiners have a nasty habit of expecting you to remember things from previous modules — they just can't let go of the past. In this case, it's the trig identities that popped up in C3 Section 3 (see p.17-21 if you need a reminder).

The *Double Angle Formulas* are useful for *Integration*

If you're given a tricky trig function to integrate, see if you can simplify it using one of the double angle formulas. They're especially useful for things like $\cos^2 x$, $\sin^2 x$ and $\sin x \cos x$. Here are the double angle formulas (see p.19):

$$\sin 2x \equiv 2\sin x \cos x$$

$$\tan 2x \equiv \frac{2\tan x}{1-\tan^2 x}$$

$$\cos 2x \equiv \cos^2 x - \sin^2 x$$

$$\cos 2x \equiv 2\cos^2 x - 1$$

$$\cos 2x \equiv 1 - 2\sin^2 x$$

You can rearrange the second two cos $2x$ formulas to get expressions for $\cos^2 x$ and $\sin^2 x$: $\cos^2 x = \frac{1}{2}(\cos 2x + 1)$
$\sin^2 x = \frac{1}{2}(1 - \cos 2x)$

Once you've replaced the original function with one of the double angle formulas, you can just integrate as normal.

Don't forget to double the coefficient of x here. You'll also need to divide by 10 when you integrate.

EXAMPLE Find a) $\int \sin^2 x\,dx$ b) $\int \cos^2 5x\,dx$ c) $\int \sin x \cos x\,dx$.

a) Using the double angle formula above, write $\sin^2 x$ as $\frac{1}{2}(1 - \cos 2x)$, then integrate.

$$\int \sin^2 x\,dx = \int \frac{1}{2}(1-\cos 2x)dx$$

$$= \frac{1}{2}\left(x - \frac{1}{2}\sin 2x\right) + C = \frac{1}{2}x - \frac{1}{4}\sin 2x + C$$

b) Using the double angle formula above, write $\cos^2 5x$ as $\frac{1}{2}(\cos 10x + 1)$, then integrate.

$$\int \cos^2 5x\,dx = \int \frac{1}{2}(\cos 10x + 1)dx$$

$$= \frac{1}{2}\left(\frac{1}{10}\sin 10x + x\right) + C = \frac{1}{20}\sin 10x + \frac{1}{2}x + C$$

c) Using the double angle formula above, write $\sin x \cos x$ as $\frac{1}{2}\sin 2x$, then integrate.

$$\int \sin x \cos x\,dx = \int \frac{1}{2}\sin 2x\,dx = \frac{1}{2}\left(-\frac{1}{2}\cos 2x\right) + C = -\frac{1}{4}\cos 2x + C$$

Use the *Identities* to get a function you *Know* how to *Integrate*

There are a couple of other identities you can use to simplify trig functions (see p.17):

$$\sec^2\theta \equiv 1 + \tan^2\theta \qquad \operatorname{cosec}^2\theta \equiv 1 + \cot^2\theta$$

These two identities are really useful if you have to integrate $\tan^2 x$ or $\cot^2 x$, as you already know how to integrate $\sec^2 x$ and $\operatorname{cosec}^2 x$ (see p.71). Don't forget the stray 1s flying around — they'll just integrate to x.

EXAMPLE Find a) $\int \tan^2 x - 1\,dx$ b) $\int \cot^2 3x\,dx$.

a) Rewrite the function in terms of $\sec^2 x$:
$\tan^2 x - 1 \equiv \sec^2 x - 1 - 1 \equiv \sec^2 x - 2$.
Now integrate:

$$\int \sec^2 x - 2\,dx = \tan x - 2x + C$$

b) Get the function in terms of $\operatorname{cosec}^2 x$:
$\cot^2 3x \equiv \operatorname{cosec}^2 3x - 1$.
Now integrate:

$$\int \operatorname{cosec}^2 3x - 1\,dx = -\frac{1}{3}\cot 3x - x + C$$

Remember to divide by 3, the coefficient of x, when you integrate.

EXAMPLE Evaluate $\int_0^{\frac{\pi}{3}} 6\sin 3x \cos 3x + \tan^2 \frac{1}{2}x + 1\,dx$.

Using the identities, $6\sin 3x \cos 3x \equiv 3\sin 6x$ and $\tan^2\frac{1}{2}x + 1 \equiv \sec^2\frac{1}{2}x$ gives:

$$\int_0^{\frac{\pi}{3}} 3\sin 6x + \sec^2\frac{1}{2}x\,dx = \left[-\frac{3}{6}\cos 6x + 2\tan\frac{1}{2}x\right]_0^{\frac{\pi}{3}}$$

$$= \left[-\frac{1}{2}\cos 6\left(\frac{\pi}{3}\right) + 2\tan\frac{1}{2}\left(\frac{\pi}{3}\right)\right] - \left[-\frac{1}{2}\cos 6(0) + 2\tan\frac{1}{2}(0)\right]$$

$$= \left[-\frac{1}{2}\cos(2\pi) + 2\tan\left(\frac{\pi}{6}\right)\right] - \left[-\frac{1}{2}\cos(0) + 2\tan(0)\right]$$

$$= \left[-\frac{1}{2}(1) + 2\left(\frac{1}{\sqrt{3}}\right)\right] - \left[-\frac{1}{2}(1) + 2(0)\right] = -\frac{1}{2} + \frac{2}{\sqrt{3}} + \frac{1}{2} = \frac{2}{\sqrt{3}}$$

Use the table of common trig angles on p.18 to help you here.

I can't help feeling I've seen these somewhere before...

If you're given a trig function that you don't know how to integrate, play around with these identities and see if you can turn it into something you can integrate. Watch out for coefficients though — they can trip you up if you're not careful.

Integration by Substitution

I know, I know — you've already done 4 pages on integration, surely there can't be more? Well, I'm afraid there is. And this time, there's nowhere to run...

Use Integration by Substitution on Products of Two Functions

On p.24, you saw how to differentiate functions of functions using the chain rule. Integration by substitution lets you integrate functions of functions by simplifying the integral. Like the chain rule, you have to write part of the function in terms of u, where u is some function of x. You had a sneak preview of this in C3 using a linear substitution (see p.30).

Integration by Substitution

1) **You'll be given an integral that's made up of several functions of x — e.g. $\cos x(1 + \sin^2 x)$.**
2) **Substitute u for one of the functions of x — e.g. $u = \sin x$.**
3) **Next, find $\frac{du}{dx}$, and rewrite it so that dx is on its own — e.g. $\frac{du}{dx} = \cos x$, so $dx = \frac{1}{\cos x}du$.**
4) **Rewrite the original integral in terms of u and du — e.g. $\int \cos x(1 + \sin^2 x)\,dx$ becomes $\int \cos x(1 + u^2)\frac{1}{\cos x}du = \int 1 + u^2\,du$.**
5) **You should now be left with something that's easier to integrate — just integrate as normal, then at the last step replace u with the original substitution (so for this one, replace u with $\sin x$).**

$\frac{du}{dx}$ isn't really a fraction, but you can treat it as one for this bit.

You'll be told what substitution to use (unless it's a really easy one).

Check to make sure all the original function has been accounted for.

EXAMPLE

Use the substitution $u = x^2 - 2$ to find $\int 4x(x^2 - 2)^4\,dx$.

As $u = x^2 - 2$, $\frac{du}{dx} = 2x$, so $dx = \frac{1}{2x}du$.

Substituting gives $\int 4x(x^2 - 2)^4\,dx = \int 4xu^4\frac{1}{2x}du = \int 2u^4\,du$.

The x's cancel, making it a lot easier to integrate — this often happens.

Integrate... $\int 2u^4\,du = \frac{2}{5}u^5 + C$.

...and substitute x back in:

$= \frac{2}{5}(x^2 - 2)^5 + C$.

For Definite Integrals, you have to Change the Limits

If you're given a definite integral, it's really important that you remember to change the limits to u. Doing it this way means you don't have to put x back in at the last step — just put the numbers into the integration for u.

EXAMPLE

Use the substitution $u = \cos x$ to find $\int_{\frac{\pi}{2}}^{2\pi} -12\sin x\cos^3 x\,dx$.

As $u = \cos x$, $\frac{du}{dx} = -\sin x$, so $dx = -\frac{1}{\sin x}du$.

Find the limits of u:

when $x = \frac{\pi}{2}$, $u = \cos\frac{\pi}{2} = 0$,

when $x = 2\pi$, $u = \cos 2\pi = 1$.

So the limits of u are 0 and 1.

Substituting all this gives:

$$\int_{\frac{\pi}{2}}^{2\pi} -12\sin x\cos^3 x\,dx = \int_0^1 -12\sin x\,u^3\frac{-1}{\sin x}du = \int_0^1 12u^3\,du$$

Integrating and putting in the values of the limits gives:

$[3u^4]_0^1 = [3(1)^4] - [3(0)^4] = 3$

You could also have solved this one using the method on p.73.

Never substitute salt for sugar...

Life is full of limits — age limits, time limits, height limits, limits of how many times I can gaze at my Hugh Jackman poster while still getting my work done... But at least limits of integration will get you exam marks, so it's worth practising them.

Integration by Parts

Just like you can differentiate products using the product rule (see p.26), you can integrate products using the... er... integration by parts. Not quite as catchy I know, but just as thrilling.

Integration by Parts is the Reverse of the Product Rule

If you have to integrate a product but can't use integration by substitution (see previous page), you might be able to use integration by parts. The formula for integrating by parts is:

$$\int u\frac{dv}{dx}\,dx = uv - \int v\frac{du}{dx}\,dx$$

where u and v are both functions of x.

The hardest thing about integration by parts is deciding which bit of your product should be u and which bit should be $\frac{dv}{dx}$. There's no set rule for this — you just have to look at both parts and see which one differentiates to give something nice, then set that one as u. For example, if you have a product that has a single x as one part of it, choose this to be u. It differentiates to 1, which makes integrating $v\frac{du}{dx}$ dead easy.

EXAMPLE Find $\int 2xe^x\,dx$.

Let $u = 2x$ and let $\frac{dv}{dx} = e^x$. Then u differentiates to give $\frac{du}{dx} = 2$ and $\frac{dv}{dx}$ integrates to give $v = e^x$.

Putting these into the formula gives: $\int 2xe^x\,dx = 2xe^x - \int 2e^x\,dx$

$$= 2xe^x - 2e^x + C$$

If you have a product that has $\ln x$ as one of its factors, let $u = \ln x$, as $\ln x$ is easy to differentiate but quite tricky to integrate (see below).

You can integrate ln x using Integration by Parts

Up till now, you haven't been able to integrate $\ln x$, but all that is about to change. There's a little trick you can use — write $\ln x$ as $1\cdot\ln x$ then integrate by parts.

To find $\int \ln x\,dx$, write $\ln x = 1\cdot\ln x$.

Let $u = \ln x$ and let $\frac{dv}{dx} = 1$. Then u differentiates to give $\frac{du}{dx} = \frac{1}{x}$ and $\frac{dv}{dx}$ integrates to give $v = x$.

$$\int \ln x\,dx = x\ln x - \int x\frac{1}{x}\,dx = x\ln x - \int 1\,dx = x\ln x - x + C$$

You might have to integrate by parts More Than Once

If you have an integral that doesn't produce a nice, easy-to-integrate function for $v\frac{du}{dx}$, you might have to carry out integration by parts more than once.

EXAMPLE Find $\int x^2\sin x\,dx$.

Let $u = x^2$ and let $\frac{dv}{dx} = \sin x$.
Then u differentiates to give $\frac{du}{dx} = 2x$ and $\frac{dv}{dx}$ integrates to give $v = -\cos x$.

Putting these into the formula gives:

$$\int x^2\sin x\,dx = -x^2\cos x - \int -2x\cos x\,dx$$
$$= -x^2\cos x + \int 2x\cos x\,dx$$

$2x\cos x$ isn't very easy to integrate, so integrate by parts again (the $-x^2\cos x$ at the front just stays as it is):

Let $u = 2x$ and let $\frac{dv}{dx} = \cos x$. Then u differentiates to give $\frac{du}{dx} = 2$ and $\frac{dv}{dx}$ integrates to give $v = \sin x$.

Putting these into the formula gives:

$$\int 2x\cos x\,dx = 2x\sin x - \int 2\sin x\,dx = 2x\sin x + 2\cos x$$

So $\int x^2\sin x\,dx = -x^2\cos x + 2x\sin x + 2\cos x + C$.

Every now and then I fall apart...

After you've had a go at some examples, you'll probably realise that integrals with e^x, $\sin x$ or $\cos x$ in them are actually quite easy, as all three are really easy to integrate and differentiate. Fingers crossed you get one of them in the exam.

Tough Integrals

With a name like 'Tough Integrals', it doesn't sound like it's going to be a very nice page. However, names can be deceiving. Maybe not in this case, but they can be.

You can integrate *Partial Fractions*

In Section 1 (pages 49-50), you saw how to break down a scary-looking algebraic fraction into partial fractions. This comes in pretty handy when you're integrating — you could try integration by parts on the original fraction, but it would get messy and probably end in tears. Fortunately, once you've split it up into partial fractions, it's much easier to integrate, using the methods on p.30 and p.72.

EXAMPLE Find $\int \frac{9x^2 + x + 16}{(x+2)(2x-1)(x-3)} \, dx$.

This is the example from p.49, and it can be written as partial fractions like this: $\frac{2}{(x+2)} - \frac{3}{(2x-1)} + \frac{4}{(x-3)}$

Integrating the partial fractions is much easier: $\int \frac{2}{(x+2)} - \frac{3}{(2x-1)} + \frac{4}{(x-3)} \, dx = 2\ln|x+2| - \frac{3}{2}\ln|2x-1| + 4\ln|x-3| + C$

$$= \ln\left|\frac{(x+2)^2(x-3)^4}{(2x-1)^{\frac{3}{2}}}\right| + C$$

Don't forget the coefficients here. Have a look back at p.30 if you can't remember how to do this.

EXAMPLE Find $\int \frac{x^2 + 17x + 16}{(x+2)^2(3x-1)} \, dx$.

This is the example from p.50. It's a bit trickier because it has a repeated factor. Written in partial fractions, it looks like this: $\frac{2}{(x+2)^2} - \frac{1}{(x+2)} + \frac{4}{(3x-1)}$

You might find it easiest to use integration by substitution (p.75) on the first fraction: Let $u = x + 2$, then $\frac{du}{dx} = 1$, so $du = dx$. Substituting gives:

$$\int \frac{2}{(x+2)^2} \, dx = \int \frac{2}{u^2} \, du = -\frac{2}{u} = -\frac{2}{(x+2)}$$

Putting it all together: $\int \frac{2}{(x+2)^2} - \frac{1}{(x+2)} + \frac{4}{(3x-1)} \, dx = -\frac{2}{x+2} - \ln|x+2| + \frac{4}{3}\ln|3x-1| + C$

$$= -\frac{2}{x+2} + \ln\left|\frac{(3x-1)^{\frac{4}{3}}}{x+2}\right| + C$$

Some *Trig Integrals* can be really *Nasty*

Unfortunately, the vast range of trig identities and formulas you've seen, as well as lots of different rules for integration, mean that there's no end of evil integration questions they can ask you. Here's a particularly nasty example:

EXAMPLE Use the substitution $u = \tan x$ to find $\int \frac{\sec^4 x}{\sqrt{\tan x}} \, dx$.

1) First, work out what all the substitutions will be: If $u = \tan x$, then $\frac{du}{dx} = \sec^2 x$, so $dx = \frac{du}{\sec^2 x}$.
2) This will leave $\sec^2 x$ on the numerator — you need to find this in terms of u: From the identity $\sec^2 x \equiv 1 + \tan^2 x$, you get $\sec^2 x \equiv 1 + u^2$.
3) Then substitute all these bits into the integral:

$$\int \frac{\sec^4 x}{\sqrt{\tan x}} \, dx = \int \frac{1+u^2}{\sqrt{u}} \, du$$

$$= \int \frac{1}{\sqrt{u}} + \frac{u^2}{\sqrt{u}} \, du = \int u^{-\frac{1}{2}} + u^{\frac{3}{2}} \, du$$

$$= 2u^{\frac{1}{2}} + \frac{2}{5}u^{\frac{5}{2}} + C$$

Remember to stick $u = \tan x$ back into the equation.

$$= 2\sqrt{\tan x} + \frac{2}{5}\sqrt{\tan^5 x} + C$$

I'm partial to a cup of tea...

Partial fractions quite often pop up in a two-part question — for the first part, you'll have to write a tricky fraction in partial fractions, and in the second part you'll have to integrate it. It's a good job you're such a whizz at integrating.

Differential Equations

Differential equations are tricky little devils that have a lot to do with differentiation as well as integration. They're often about rates of change, so the variable t pops up quite a lot.

Differential Equations have a dy/dx Term

(or $\frac{dP}{dt}$, $\frac{ds}{dt}$, $\frac{dV}{dr}$, etc. — depending on the variables)

1) A differential equation is an equation that includes a derivative term (such as $\frac{dy}{dx}$), as well as other variables (like x and y).
2) Before you even think (or worry) about solving them, you have to be able to set up ('formulate') differential equations.
3) Differential equations tend to involve a rate of change (giving a derivative term) and a proportion relation. Remember — if $a \propto b$, then $a = kb$ for some constant k.

EXAMPLE The number of bacteria in a petri dish is increasing over time, t, at a rate directly proportional to the number of bacteria at a given time, b. Formulate a differential equation that shows this information.

The rate of change, $\frac{db}{dt}$, is proportional to b, so $\frac{db}{dt} \propto b$. This means that $\frac{db}{dt} = kb$ for some constant k, $k > 0$.

EXAMPLE The volume of interdimensional space jelly, V, in a container is decreasing over time, t, at a rate directly proportional to the square of its volume. Show this as a differential equation.

The rate of change, $\frac{dV}{dt}$, is proportional to V^2, so $\frac{dV}{dt} \propto V^2$. $\frac{dV}{dt} = -kV^2$ for some constant k, $k > 0$.

V is decreasing, so don't forget the –.

Solve differential equations by Integrating

Now comes the really juicy bit — solving differential equations. It's not as bad as it looks (honest).

Solving Differential Equations

1) **You can only solve differential equations if they have separable variables — where x and y can be separated into functions f(x) and g(y).**
2) **Write the differential equation in the form $\frac{dy}{dx} = f(x)g(y)$.**
3) **Then rearrange the equation to get all the terms with y on the LHS and all the terms with x on the RHS. It'll look something like this: $\frac{1}{g(y)}dy = f(x)dx$.**
4) **Now integrate both sides: $\int \frac{1}{g(y)}dy = \int f(x)dx$.**
5) **Rearrange your answer to get it in a nice form — you might be asked to find it in the form $y = h(x)$. Don't forget the constant of integration (you only need one — not one on each side). It might be useful to write the constant as $\ln k$ rather than C (see p.72).**
6) **If you're asked for a general solution, leave C (or k) in your answer. If they want a particular solution, they'll give you x and y values for a certain point. All you do is put these values into your equation and use them to find C (or k).**

Remember — it might not be in terms of x and y.

Like in integration by substitution, you can treat dy/dx as a fraction here.

EXAMPLE Find the particular solution of $\frac{dy}{dx} = 2y(1 + x)^2$ when $x = -1$ and $y = 4$.

This equation has separable variables: $f(x) = 2(1 + x)^2$ and $g(y) = y$.

Rearranging this equation gives: $\frac{1}{y}dy = 2(1 + x)^2dx$

And integrating: $\int \frac{1}{y}dy = \int 2(1 + x)^2dx$

$\Rightarrow \ln|y| = \frac{2}{3}(1 + x)^3 + C$

If you were asked for a general solution, you could just leave it in this form.

Now put in the values of x and y to find the value of C:

$\ln 4 = \frac{2}{3}(1 + (-1))^3 + C \Rightarrow \ln 4 = C$

so $\ln|y| = \frac{2}{3}(1 + x)^3 + \ln 4$

I will formulate a plan to take over the world...

...starting with Cumbria. I've always liked Cumbria. You're welcome to join my army of minions, but first you'll have to become an expert on solving differential equations. Do that, and I'll give you Grasmere — or name a mountain after you.

Differential Equations

One of the most exciting things about differential equations is that you can apply them to real-life situations. Well, I say exciting, but perhaps I should say 'mildly interesting', or maybe just 'more stuff for you to learn'.

You might be given *Extra Information*

1) In the exam, you might be given a question that takes a real-life problem and uses differential equations to model it.
2) Population questions come up quite often — the population might be increasing or decreasing, and you have to set up and solve differential equations to show it. In cases like this, one of your variables will usually be t, time.
3) You might be given a starting condition — e.g. the initial population. The important thing to remember is that:

   the starting condition occurs when $t = 0$.

   This is pretty obvious, but it's really important.

4) You might also be given extra information — e.g. the population after a certain number of years (where you have to figure out what t is), or the number of years it takes to reach a certain population (where you have to work out what the population will be). Make sure you always link the numbers you get back to the situation.

Exam Questions are often *Broken Down* into lots of *Parts*

Questions like the one below can be a bit overwhelming, but follow it through step by step and it shouldn't be too bad.

EXAMPLE

The population of rabbits in a park is decreasing as winter approaches.
The rate of decrease is directly proportional to the current number of rabbits (P).

a) Formulate a differential equation to model the rate of decrease in terms of the variables P, t (time in days) and k, a positive constant.

b) If the initial population is P_0, solve your differential equation to find P in terms of P_0, k and t.

c) Given that $k = 0.1$, find the time at which the population of rabbits will have halved, to the nearest day.

a) If the rate of decrease is proportional to the number of rabbits, then $\frac{dP}{dt} = -kP$ (it's negative because the population is decreasing).

b) First, solve the differential equation to find the general solution: $\frac{dP}{dt} = -kP \Rightarrow \frac{1}{P}\,dP = -k\,dt$

Integrating this gives: $\int \frac{1}{P}\,dP = \int -k\,dt$

$\Rightarrow \ln P = -kt + C$ ← You don't need modulus signs for ln P as $P \geq 0$ — you can't have a negative population.

At $t = 0$, $P = P_0$. Putting these values into the equation gives: $\ln P_0 = -k(0) + C$

$\Rightarrow \ln P_0 = C$

So the differential equation becomes: $\ln P = -kt + \ln P_0$

$\Rightarrow P = e^{(-kt + \ln P_0)} = e^{-kt}e^{\ln P_0}$ ← Remember that $e^{\ln x} = x = \ln e^x$.

$\Rightarrow P = P_0 e^{-kt}$

c) When the population of rabbits has halved, $P = ½P_0$. You've been told that $k = 0.1$, so substitute these values into the equation above and solve for t:

$\frac{1}{2}P_0 = P_0 e^{-0.1t}$

$\frac{1}{2} = e^{-0.1t}$

$\ln\frac{1}{2} = -0.1t$

$-0.6931 = -0.1t \Rightarrow t = 6.931$

So, to the nearest day, $t = 7$. This means that it will take 7 days for the population of rabbits to halve.

At t = 10, we kill all the bunnies...

These questions can get a bit morbid — just how I like them. They might look a bit scary, as they throw a lot of information at you in one go, but once you know how to solve them, they're a walk in the park. Rabbit traps optional.

C4 Section 5 — Practice Questions

Phew, that was a whopper of a section. I bet you could do with a break. Well, hold on just a minute — here are some practice questions to do first to check you know your stuff. Let's start with a gentle warm-up.

Warm-up Questions

1) Find
   a) $\int \cos 4x - \sec^2 7x \, dx$,
   b) $\int 6 \sec 3x \tan 3x - \operatorname{cosec}^2 \frac{x}{5} \, dx$.

2) Integrate $\int \frac{\cos x}{\sin x} \, dx$.

3) Integrate $\int 3x^2 e^{x^3} \, dx$.

4) Integrate $\int \frac{20x^4 + 12x^2 - 12}{x^5 + x^3 - 3x} \, dx$.

5) Use the appropriate trig identity to find $\int \frac{2 \tan 3x}{1 - \tan^2 3x} \, dx$.

6) Use the trig identity $\sec^2 x \equiv 1 + \tan^2 x$ to find $\int 2 \tan^2 3x + 2 \, dx$.

7) Use the substitution $u = e^x - 1$ to find $\int e^x (e^x + 1)(e^x - 1)^2 \, dx$.

8) Find the exact value of $\int_{\frac{\pi}{4}}^{\frac{\pi}{3}} \sec^4 x \tan x \, dx$, using the substitution $u = \sec x$.

9) Use integration by parts to solve $\int 3x^2 \ln x \, dx$.

10) Use integration by parts to solve $\int 4x \cos 4x \, dx$.

11) Use $\frac{3x + 10}{(2x + 3)(x - 4)} \equiv \frac{A}{2x + 3} + \frac{B}{x - 4}$ to find $\int \frac{3x + 10}{(2x + 3)(x - 4)} \, dx$.

12) Find the general solution to the differential equation $\frac{dy}{dx} = \frac{1}{y} \cos x$. Give your answer in the form $y^2 = f(x)$.

13) The population of squirrels is increasing suspiciously quickly. The rate of increase is directly proportional to the current number of squirrels, S.
   a) Formulate a differential equation to model the rate of increase in terms of S, t (time in weeks) and k, a positive constant.
   b) The squirrels need a population of 150 to successfully take over the forest. If the initial population is 30 and the value of k is 0.2, how long (to the nearest week) will it take before they can overthrow the evil hedgehogs?

Unfortunately the exam questions are less likely to be about rebel squirrels, as the examiners tend to be on the hedgehogs' side. If you ever meet an examiner, look closely to make sure he's not a hedgehog in disguise.

Exam Questions

1 Use an appropriate identity to find $\int 2 \cot^2 x \, dx$.

(3 marks)

2 Find $\int \frac{\operatorname{cosec}^2 x - 2}{\cot x + 2x} \, dx$.

(3 marks)

C4 Section 5 — Practice Questions

One more page of questions, then you're onto the final section of C4. That's right, the last one.

3 **Figure 1** shows the graph of $y = x \sin x$. The region R is bounded by the curve and the x-axis ($0 \leq x \leq \pi$).

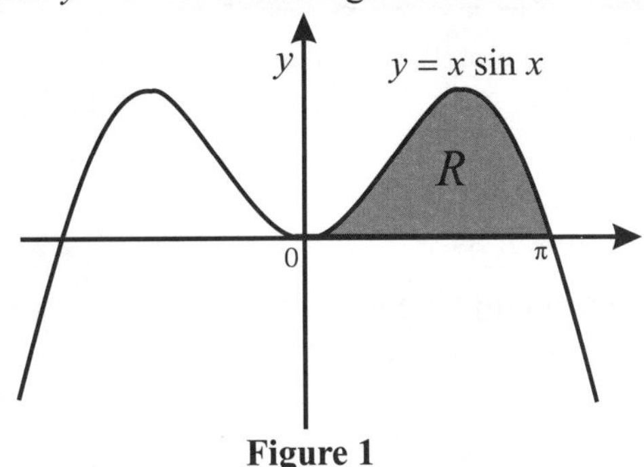

Figure 1

Find the exact area of R using integration by parts. *(4 marks)*

4 a) Find the general solution to the differential equation

$$\frac{dy}{dx} = \frac{\cos x \cos^2 y}{\sin x}.$$

(4 marks)

b) Given that $y = \pi$ when $x = \frac{\pi}{6}$, solve the differential equation above. *(2 marks)*

5 Find the value of $\int_1^2 \frac{8}{x}(\ln x + 2)^3 \, dx$ using the substitution $u = \ln x$. Give your answer to 4 s.f. *(6 marks)*

6 A company sets up an advertising campaign to increase sales of margarine. After the campaign, the number of tubs of margarine sold each week, m, increases over time, t weeks, at a rate that is directly proportional to the square root of the number of tubs sold.

a) Formulate a differential equation in terms of t, m and a constant k. *(2 marks)*

b) At the start of the campaign, the company was selling 900 tubs of margarine a week. Use this information to solve the differential equation, giving m in terms of k and t. *(4 marks)*

c) Hence calculate the number of tubs sold in the fifth week after the campaign, given that $k = 2$. *(3 marks)*

Vectors

If you did M1, then you've probably seen some of this vector stuff before. If not, you've got lots to look forward to. In any case, we're going to start with the basics — like what vectors are.

Vectors have Magnitude and Direction — Scalars Don't

1) Vectors have both size and direction — e.g. a velocity of 2 m/s on a bearing of 050°, or a displacement of 3 m north. Scalars are just quantities without a direction, e.g. a speed of 2 m/s, a distance of 3 m.
2) Vectors are drawn as lines with arrowheads on them.
   - The length of the line represents the magnitude (size) of the vector (e.g. the speed component of velocity). Sometimes vectors are drawn to scale.
   - The direction of the arrowhead shows the direction of the vector.

There are two ways of writing vectors:

1) Using a lower case, bold letter. **a**

   When you're handwriting a vector like this, you should underline the letter, i.e. a.

2) Putting an arrow over the endpoints. A B $\overrightarrow{AB}$

Find the Resultant by Drawing Vectors Nose to Tail

You can add vectors together by drawing the arrows nose to tail.
The single vector that goes from the start to the end of the vectors is called the resultant vector.

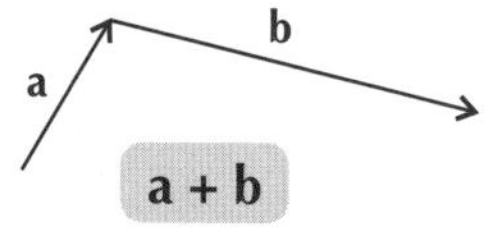

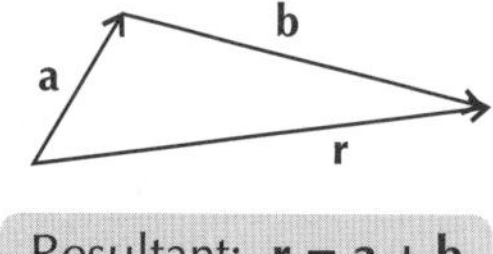

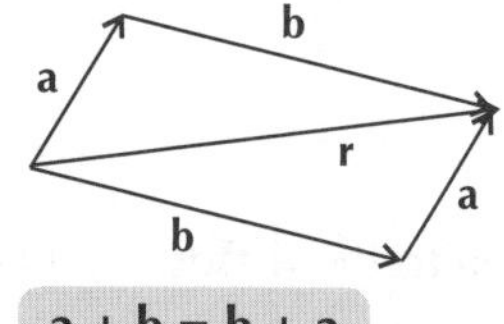

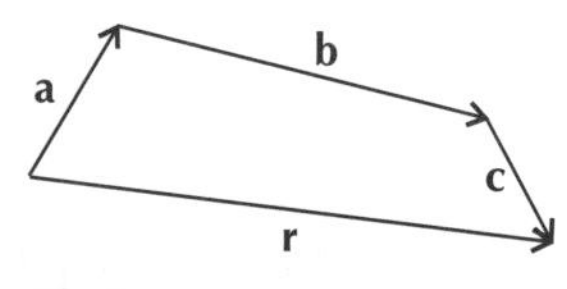

Subtracting a Vector is the Same as Adding a Negative Vector

1) The vector **–a** is in the opposite direction to the vector **a**. They're both exactly the same size.

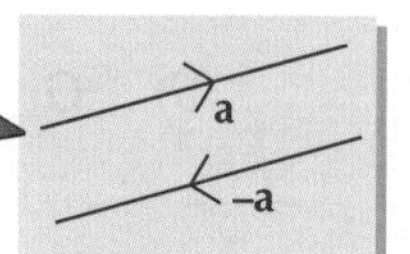

2) So subtracting a vector is the same as adding the negative vector:

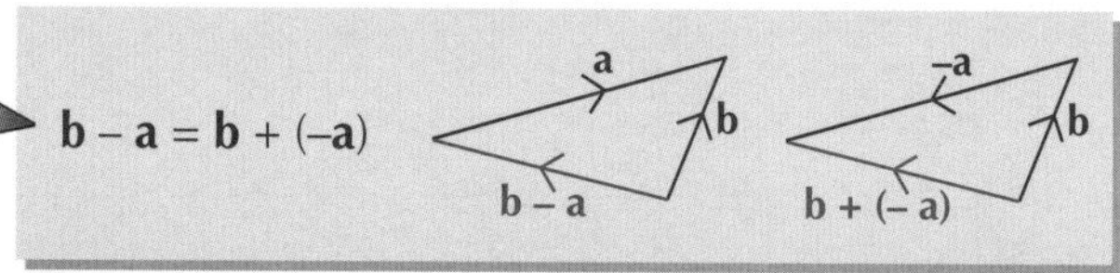

3) You can use the adding and subtracting rules to find a vector in terms of other vectors.

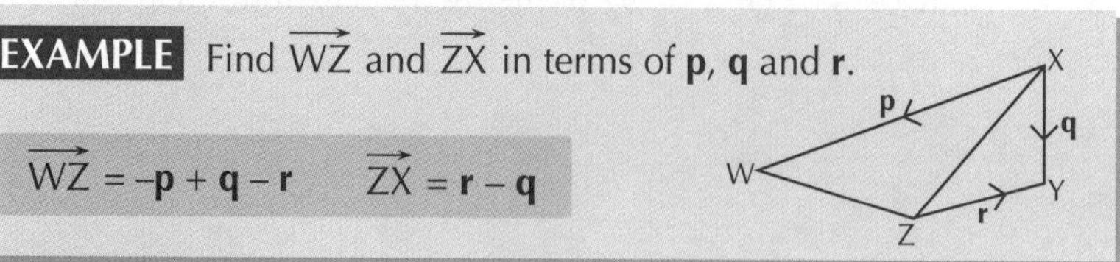

EXAMPLE Find $\overrightarrow{WZ}$ and $\overrightarrow{ZX}$ in terms of **p**, **q** and **r**.

$\overrightarrow{WZ} = -\mathbf{p} + \mathbf{q} - \mathbf{r}$ $\quad$ $\overrightarrow{ZX} = \mathbf{r} - \mathbf{q}$

Vectors a, 2a and 3a are all Parallel

You can multiply a vector by a scalar (just a number, remember) — the length changes but the direction stays the same.

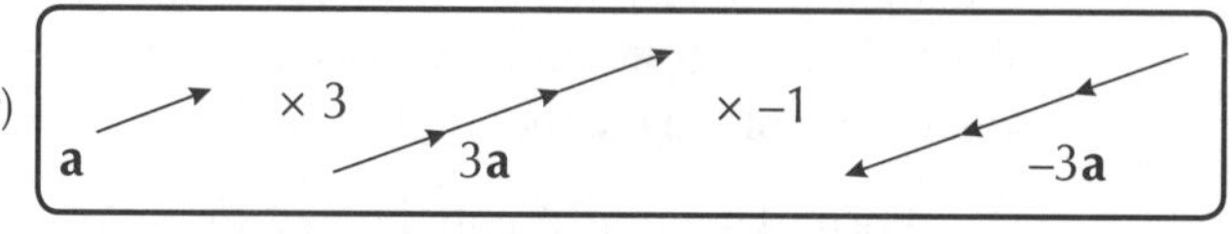

Multiplying a vector by a non-zero scalar always produces a parallel vector.

All these vectors are parallel: $9\mathbf{a} + 15\mathbf{b}$ $\quad 18\mathbf{a} + 30\mathbf{b}$ $\quad 6\mathbf{a} + 10\mathbf{b}$ $\quad 3\mathbf{a} + 5\mathbf{b}$

This is $2(9\mathbf{a} + 15\mathbf{b})$.

This is $\frac{2}{3}(9\mathbf{a} + 15\mathbf{b})$.

This is $\frac{1}{3}(9\mathbf{a} + 15\mathbf{b})$.

Eating pasta = buying anti-pasta?...

If an exam question asks you to show that two lines are parallel, you just have to show that one vector's a multiple of the other. By the way — exam papers often use λ and μ as scalars in vector questions (so you don't confuse them with vectors).

Vectors

There are a few more ways of representing vectors that you need to know about. Then it's off to the third dimension...

Position Vectors Describe Where a Point Lies

You can use a vector to describe the position of a point, in relation to the origin, O.

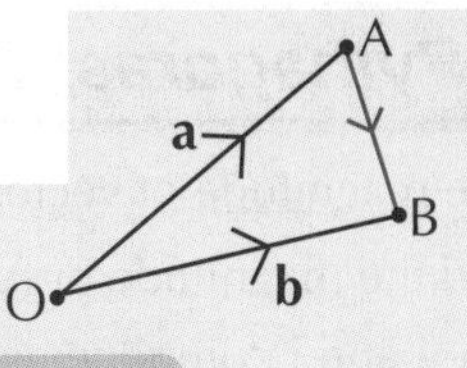

The position vector of point A is $\overrightarrow{OA}$. It's usually called vector **a**.
The position vector of point B is $\overrightarrow{OB}$. It's usually called vector **b**.

You can write other vectors in terms of position vectors: (these are known as displacement vectors).

$$\overrightarrow{AB} = -\overrightarrow{OA} + \overrightarrow{OB} = \overrightarrow{OB} - \overrightarrow{OA} = -\mathbf{a} + \mathbf{b} = \mathbf{b} - \mathbf{a}$$

Vectors can be described using i + j Units

1) A unit vector is any vector with a magnitude of 1 unit. (There's more on unit vectors on the next page.)
2) The vectors **i** + **j** are standard unit vectors. **i** is in the direction of the x-axis, and **j** is in the direction of the y-axis. They each have a magnitude of 1 unit, of course.
3) They're a dead handy way of describing any vector. You use them to say how far horizontally and vertically you have to go to get from the start of the vector to the end.

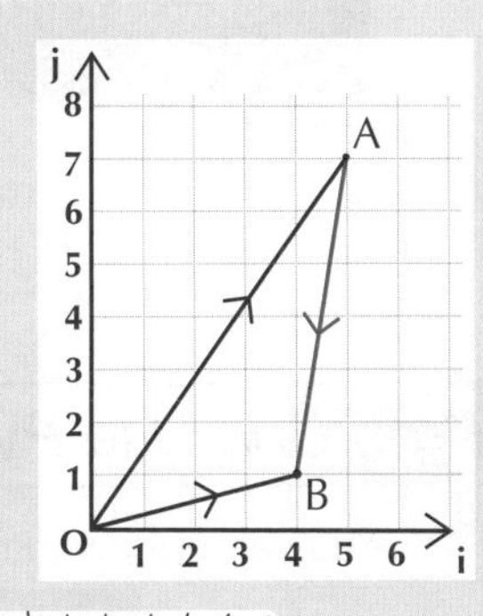

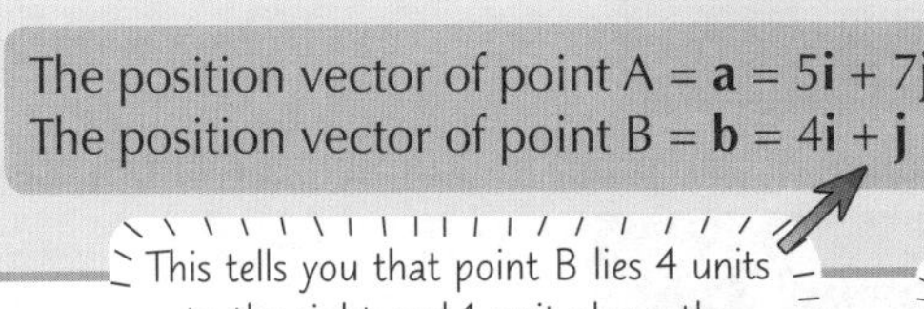
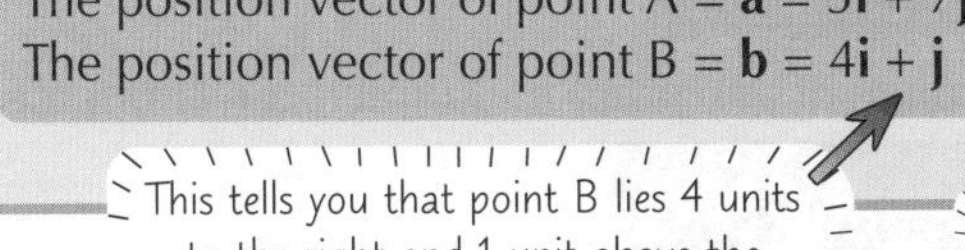

The position vector of point A = **a** = 5**i** + 7**j**
The position vector of point B = **b** = 4**i** + **j**

This tells you that point B lies 4 units to the right and 1 unit above the origin — it's just like coordinates.

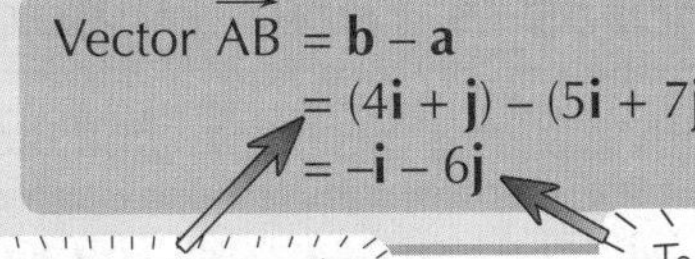

Vector $\overrightarrow{AB}$ = **b** – **a**
= (4**i** + **j**) – (5**i** + 7**j**)
= –**i** – 6**j**

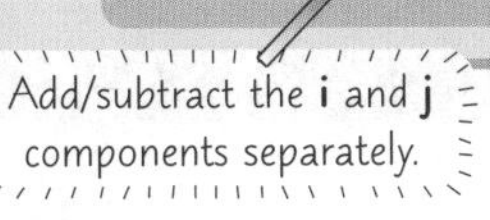

Add/subtract the **i** and **j** components separately.

To go from A to B, you go 1 unit left and 6 units down. It's just like a translation.

And then there are Column Vectors

1) If writing i's and j's gets a bit much for your wrists, you can use column vectors instead. $x\mathbf{i} + y\mathbf{j} = \begin{pmatrix} x \\ y \end{pmatrix}$
2) Calculating with them is a breeze. Just add or subtract the top row, then add or subtract the bottom row separately.
3) When you're multiplying a column vector by a scalar, you multiply each number in the column vector by the scalar.

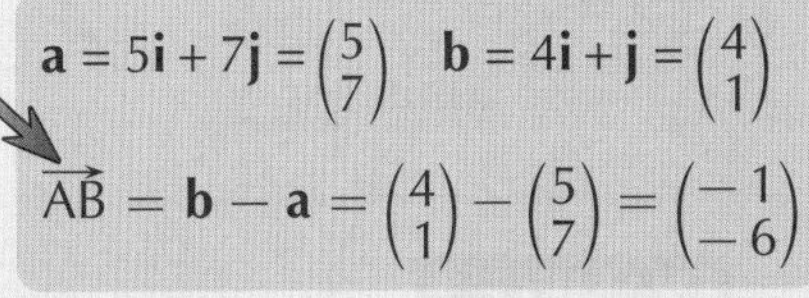

$$\mathbf{a} = 5\mathbf{i} + 7\mathbf{j} = \begin{pmatrix} 5 \\ 7 \end{pmatrix} \quad \mathbf{b} = 4\mathbf{i} + \mathbf{j} = \begin{pmatrix} 4 \\ 1 \end{pmatrix}$$

$$\overrightarrow{AB} = \mathbf{b} - \mathbf{a} = \begin{pmatrix} 4 \\ 1 \end{pmatrix} - \begin{pmatrix} 5 \\ 7 \end{pmatrix} = \begin{pmatrix} -1 \\ -6 \end{pmatrix}$$

$$2\mathbf{b} - 3\mathbf{a} = 2\begin{pmatrix} 4 \\ 1 \end{pmatrix} - 3\begin{pmatrix} 5 \\ 7 \end{pmatrix} = \begin{pmatrix} 8 \\ 2 \end{pmatrix} - \begin{pmatrix} 15 \\ 21 \end{pmatrix} = \begin{pmatrix} -7 \\ -19 \end{pmatrix}$$

You Can Have Vectors in Three Dimensions Too

1) Imagine that the x- and y-axes lie flat on the page. Then imagine a third axis sticking straight through the page at right angles to it — this is the z-axis.
2) The points in three dimensions are given (x, y, z) coordinates.
3) When you're talking vectors, **k** is the unit vector in the direction of the z-axis.
4) You can write three-dimensional vectors as column vectors like this:

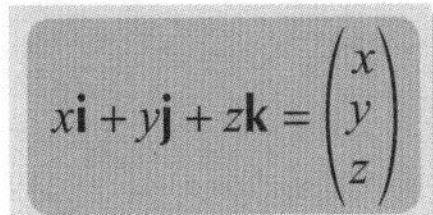

$$x\mathbf{i} + y\mathbf{j} + z\mathbf{k} = \begin{pmatrix} x \\ y \\ z \end{pmatrix}$$

5) So the position vector of point Q is:

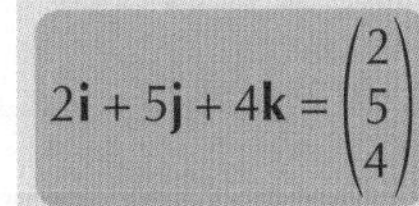

$$2\mathbf{i} + 5\mathbf{j} + 4\mathbf{k} = \begin{pmatrix} 2 \\ 5 \\ 4 \end{pmatrix}$$

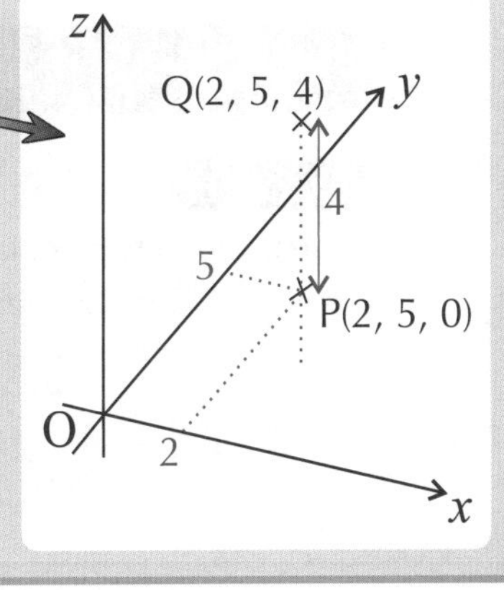

I've got B + Q units in my kitchen...

Three dimensions doesn't really make things much more difficult — it just gives you an extra number to calculate with. You add, subtract and multiply 3D column vectors in the same way as 2D ones — you just have three rows to deal with.

Vectors

Pythagoras pops up all over the place, and here he is again. Fascinating fact — Pythagoras refused to say words containing the Greek equivalent of the letter c. I read it on the internet, so it has to be true.

Use Pythagoras' Theorem to Find Vector Magnitudes

1) The magnitude of vector **a** is written as $|\mathbf{a}|$, and the magnitude of $\overrightarrow{AB}$ is written as $|\overrightarrow{AB}|$.
2) The **i** and **j** components of a vector form a convenient right-angled triangle, so just bung them into the Pythagoras formula to find the vector's magnitude.
3) You might be asked to find a unit vector in the direction of a particular vector. Remember — a unit vector has a magnitude of 1 (see the previous page).

A vector's magnitude is sometimes called its modulus.

EXAMPLE

$\mathbf{a} = 5\mathbf{i} + 3\mathbf{j}$

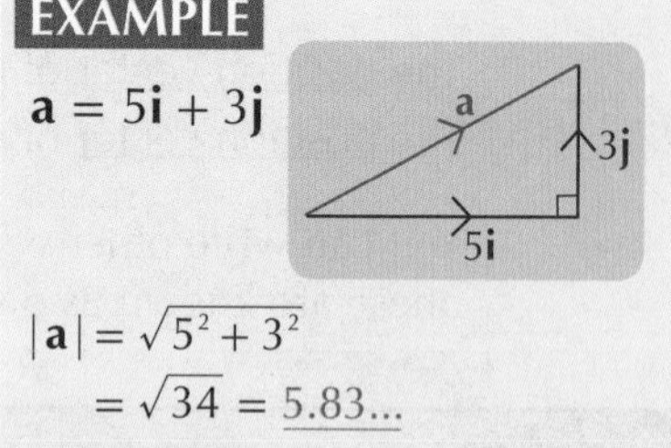

$|\mathbf{a}| = \sqrt{5^2 + 3^2}$
$= \sqrt{34} = 5.83...$

A unit vector in the direction of vector $\mathbf{a} = \frac{\mathbf{a}}{|\mathbf{a}|}$

EXAMPLE If vector **p** has a magnitude of 12 units, find a unit vector parallel to **p**.

$$\frac{\mathbf{p}}{|\mathbf{p}|} = \frac{\mathbf{p}}{12} = \frac{1}{12}\mathbf{p}$$

You Can Use Pythagoras in Three Dimensions Too

1) You can use a variation of Pythagoras' theorem to find the distance of any point in 3 dimensions from the origin, O.

The distance of point (x, y, z) from the origin is $\sqrt{x^2 + y^2 + z^2}$

EXAMPLE 1

Find $|\overrightarrow{OQ}|$.

$|\overrightarrow{OQ}| = \sqrt{x^2 + y^2 + z^2}$
$= \sqrt{2^2 + 5^2 + 4^2}$
$= \sqrt{45}$
$= 6.7$ units

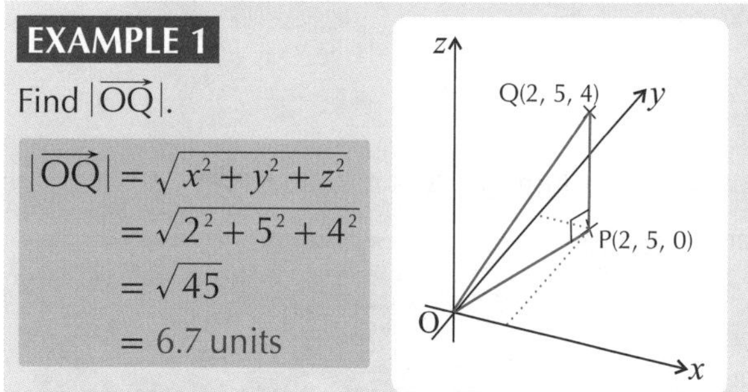

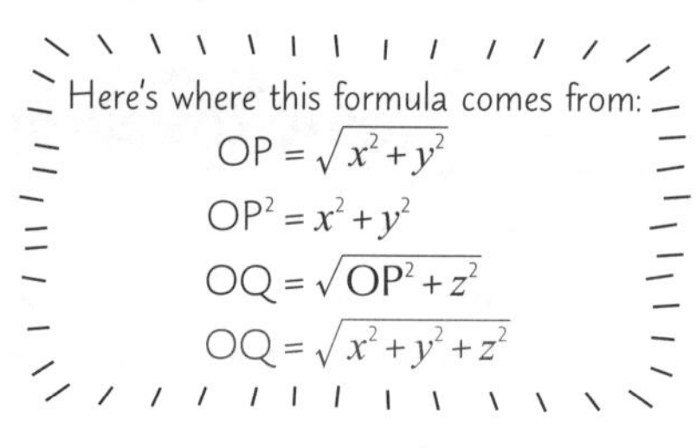

EXAMPLE 2 Find the magnitude of the vector $\mathbf{r} = 5\mathbf{i} + 7\mathbf{j} + 3\mathbf{k}$.

$|\mathbf{r}| = \sqrt{5^2 + 7^2 + 3^2}$
$= \sqrt{83} = 9.1$ units

2) There's also a Pythagoras-based formula for finding the distance between any two points.

The distance between points (x_1, y_1, z_1) and (x_2, y_2, z_2) is $\sqrt{(x_1 - x_2)^2 + (y_1 - y_2)^2 + (z_1 - z_2)^2}$

EXAMPLE

The position vector of point A is $3\mathbf{i} + 2\mathbf{j} + 4\mathbf{k}$, and the position vector of point B is $2\mathbf{i} + 6\mathbf{j} - 5\mathbf{k}$. Find $|\overrightarrow{AB}|$.

A has the coordinates (3, 2, 4),
B has the coordinates (2, 6, –5).

$|\overrightarrow{AB}| = \sqrt{(x_1 - x_2)^2 + (y_1 - y_2)^2 + (z_1 - z_2)^2}$
$= \sqrt{(3-2)^2 + (2-6)^2 + (4-(-5))^2}$
$= \sqrt{1 + 16 + 81} = 9.9$ units

You can play Battleships with 3D coordinates too — but you don't have to...

The magnitude is just a scalar, so it doesn't have a direction — the magnitude of $\overrightarrow{AB}$ is the same as the magnitude of $\overrightarrow{BA}$. Squaring the numbers in the formulas gets rid of any minus signs, so you don't have to worry about which way round you subtract the coordinates (phew). There's not a lot new on this page, in fact, it's mostly just good old Pythagoras.

Vector Equations of Lines

At first glance, vector equations of straight lines don't look much like normal straight-line equations. But they're pretty similar if you look closely. In any case, just learn the formulas really well and you'll be fine.

Learn the Equation of the Line *Through a Point* and *Parallel to Another Vector*

A straight line which goes through point A, and is parallel to vector **b**, has the vector equation: $\mathbf{r} = \mathbf{a} + t\mathbf{b}$

a = position vector of point A
r = position vector of a point on the line, and t = a scalar.

A is a fixed point.

This is pretty much a 3D version of the old $y = mx + c$ equation. **b** is similar to the gradient, m, and **a** gives a point that the line passes through, just like c gives the y-axis intercept.

Each different value you stick in for t in the vector equation gives you the position vector, **r**, of a different point on the line.

EXAMPLE A straight line is parallel to the vector $\mathbf{i} + 3\mathbf{j} - 2\mathbf{k}$. It passes through a point with the position vector $3\mathbf{i} + 2\mathbf{j} + 6\mathbf{k}$. Find its vector equation.

$$\mathbf{r} = \mathbf{a} + t\mathbf{b} = (3\mathbf{i} + 2\mathbf{j} + 6\mathbf{k}) + t(\mathbf{i} + 3\mathbf{j} - 2\mathbf{k})$$

Alternative ways of writing this are: $\mathbf{r} = (3 + t)\mathbf{i} + (2 + 3t)\mathbf{j} + (6 - 2t)\mathbf{k}$,

$$\mathbf{r} = \begin{pmatrix}3\\2\\6\end{pmatrix} + t\begin{pmatrix}1\\3\\-2\end{pmatrix} \text{ and } \mathbf{r} = \begin{pmatrix}3+t\\2+3t\\6-2t\end{pmatrix}$$

And the Equation of the Line Passing *Through Two Known Points*

A straight line through points C and D, with position vectors **c** and **d**, has the vector equation:

$$\mathbf{r} = \mathbf{c} + t(\mathbf{d} - \mathbf{c})$$

r = position vector of a point on the line, t = a scalar.

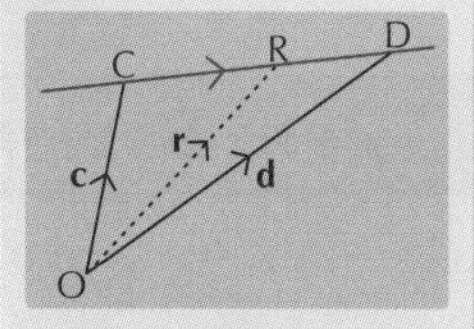

This is basically the same as the vector equation above. You just have to find a vector in the direction of CD first (i.e. $\mathbf{d} - \mathbf{c}$).

EXAMPLE

A line passes through points with the coordinates (3, 2, 4) and (–1, 3, 0). Find the vector equation for this line.

$$\text{If } \mathbf{c} = \begin{pmatrix}3\\2\\4\end{pmatrix}, \text{ and } \mathbf{d} = \begin{pmatrix}-1\\3\\0\end{pmatrix}, \text{ then } \mathbf{r} = \begin{pmatrix}3\\2\\4\end{pmatrix} + t\left(\begin{pmatrix}-1\\3\\0\end{pmatrix} - \begin{pmatrix}3\\2\\4\end{pmatrix}\right) \Rightarrow \mathbf{r} = \begin{pmatrix}3\\2\\4\end{pmatrix} + t\begin{pmatrix}-4\\1\\-4\end{pmatrix}$$

Find the *Point of Intersection* of two Lines with *Simultaneous Equations*

If Line 1, $\mathbf{r} = \begin{pmatrix}5\\2\\-1\end{pmatrix} + \mu\begin{pmatrix}1\\-2\\-3\end{pmatrix}$, and Line 2, $\mathbf{r} = \begin{pmatrix}2\\0\\4\end{pmatrix} + \lambda\begin{pmatrix}1\\2\\-1\end{pmatrix}$, intersect, there'll be a value for μ and a value for λ that result in the same point for both lines. This is the point of intersection.

Pairs of lines in three dimensions don't always intersect — in fact, only a tiny proportion do. Lines that don't intersect and aren't parallel are called **skew lines**.

EXAMPLE Determine whether Line 1 and Line 2 (above) intersect. If they do, find the point of intersection.

At the point of intersection, $\begin{pmatrix}5\\2\\-1\end{pmatrix} + \mu\begin{pmatrix}1\\-2\\-3\end{pmatrix} = \begin{pmatrix}2\\0\\4\end{pmatrix} + \lambda\begin{pmatrix}1\\2\\-1\end{pmatrix}$. You can get 3 equations from this:

① $5 + \mu = 2 + \lambda$
② $2 - 2\mu = 0 + 2\lambda$
③ $-1 - 3\mu = 4 - \lambda$

Solve the first two simultaneously: $2 \times$①: $10 + 2\mu = 4 + 2\lambda$ ④
④ – ②: $8 + 4\mu = 4 \Rightarrow \mu = -1$
sub. in ②: $2 - 2(-1) = 0 + 2\lambda \Rightarrow \lambda = 2$

Substitute the values for μ and λ into equation ③. If they make the equation true, then the lines do intersect:
$-1 - (3 \times -1) = 4 - 2 \Rightarrow 2 = 2$ —True, so they do intersect.

Now find the intersection point: $\mathbf{r} = \begin{pmatrix}5\\2\\-1\end{pmatrix} + \mu\begin{pmatrix}1\\-2\\-3\end{pmatrix} = \begin{pmatrix}5\\2\\-1\end{pmatrix} - 1\begin{pmatrix}1\\-2\\-3\end{pmatrix} \Rightarrow \mathbf{r} = \begin{pmatrix}4\\4\\2\end{pmatrix} = 4\mathbf{i} + 4\mathbf{j} + 2\mathbf{k}$

This is the position vector of the intersection point. The coordinates are (4, 4, 2).

Stardate 45283.5, position vector 20076i + 23485j + 48267k...

You might be given vector equations in **i**, **j**, **k** form or in column form, so practise these examples using each vector form.

Scalar Product

The scalar product of two vectors is kind of what it says on the tin — two vectors multiplied together to give a scalar result. But this is A2, so it's going to be trickier than simple multiplying. It even involves a bit of cos-ing.

Learn the Definition of the **Scalar Product of Two Vectors**

Scalar Product of Two Vectors

$$\mathbf{a}.\mathbf{b} = |\mathbf{a}||\mathbf{b}|\cos\theta$$

θ is the angle between position vectors **a** and **b**.

Both vectors have to be directed away from the intersection point.

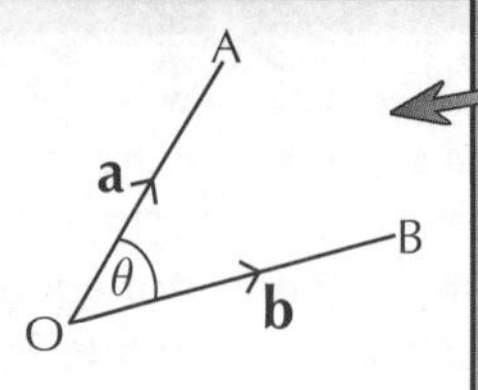

Watch out — the correct angle might not always be obvious.

θ is the angle in the definition.

Here you have to continue **b** on so that it's also directed away from the intersection point.

1) The scalar product of two vectors is always a scalar quantity — it's never a vector.
2) The scalar product can be used to calculate the angle between two lines (see the next page):

   $\mathbf{a}.\mathbf{b} = |\mathbf{a}||\mathbf{b}|\cos\theta$ rearranges to $\cos\theta = \frac{\mathbf{a}.\mathbf{b}}{|\mathbf{a}||\mathbf{b}|}$.
3) The scalar product $\mathbf{a}\,.\,\mathbf{b}$ is read '**a** dot **b**'. It's really, really important to put the dot in, as it shows you mean the scalar product (rather than a different sort of vector product that you don't have to worry about in C4).

A **Zero Scalar Product** Means the Vectors are **Perpendicular**

1) If the two vectors are perpendicular, they're at 90° to each other.
2) Cos 90° = 0, so the scalar product of the two vectors is 0.

Scalar Product of Two Perpendicular Vectors

$$\mathbf{a}.\mathbf{b} = |\mathbf{a}||\mathbf{b}|\cos 90^\circ = 0$$

3) The unit vectors **i**, **j** and **k** are all perpendicular to each other.

   So, $\mathbf{i}\,.\,\mathbf{j} = 1 \times 1 \times 0 = 0$ and $3\mathbf{j}\,.\,4\mathbf{k} = 3 \times 4 \times 0 = 0$
4) This all assumes that the vectors are non-zero. Because if either vector was 0, you'd always get a scalar product of 0, regardless of the angle between them.

The Scalar Product of **Parallel Vectors** is just the **Product of the Magnitudes**

1) If two vectors are parallel, the angle between them is 0°. And cos 0° = 1, so...

Scalar Product of Two Parallel Vectors

$$\mathbf{a}.\mathbf{b} = |\mathbf{a}||\mathbf{b}|\cos 0^\circ = |\mathbf{a}||\mathbf{b}|$$

2) Two **i** unit vectors are parallel to each other (as are two **j**s or two **k**s).

   So, $\mathbf{j}\,.\,\mathbf{j} = 1 \times 1 \times 1 = 1$ and $3\mathbf{k}\,.\,4\mathbf{k} = 3 \times 4 \times 1 = 12$
3) Again, this all assumes that the vectors are non-zero.

Scaly product — a lizard-skin handbag...

The fact that two perpendicular vectors have a zero scalar product is the key to loads of vector exam questions. E.g. you might be asked to show two vectors are perpendicular, or told that two vectors are perpendicular and asked to find a missing vector. Whatever they ask, you'll definitely have to multiply the two vectors — and you're about to learn how.

Scalar Product

Finding the scalar product of two vectors is super quick and easy once you know how to do it.

Learn This Result for the **Scalar Product**

1) You can use this result to find the scalar product of two known vectors:

   If $\mathbf{a} = a_1\mathbf{i} + a_2\mathbf{j} + a_3\mathbf{k}$, and $\mathbf{b} = b_1\mathbf{i} + b_2\mathbf{j} + b_3\mathbf{k}$, then $\mathbf{a.b} = a_1b_1 + a_2b_2 + a_3b_3$

2) The normal laws of multiplication apply to scalar products too — e.g. the commutative law ($\mathbf{a.b} = \mathbf{b.a}$) and the distributive law ($\mathbf{a.(b + c)} = \mathbf{a.b} + \mathbf{a.c}$).

3) By applying these laws, you can derive the result above...

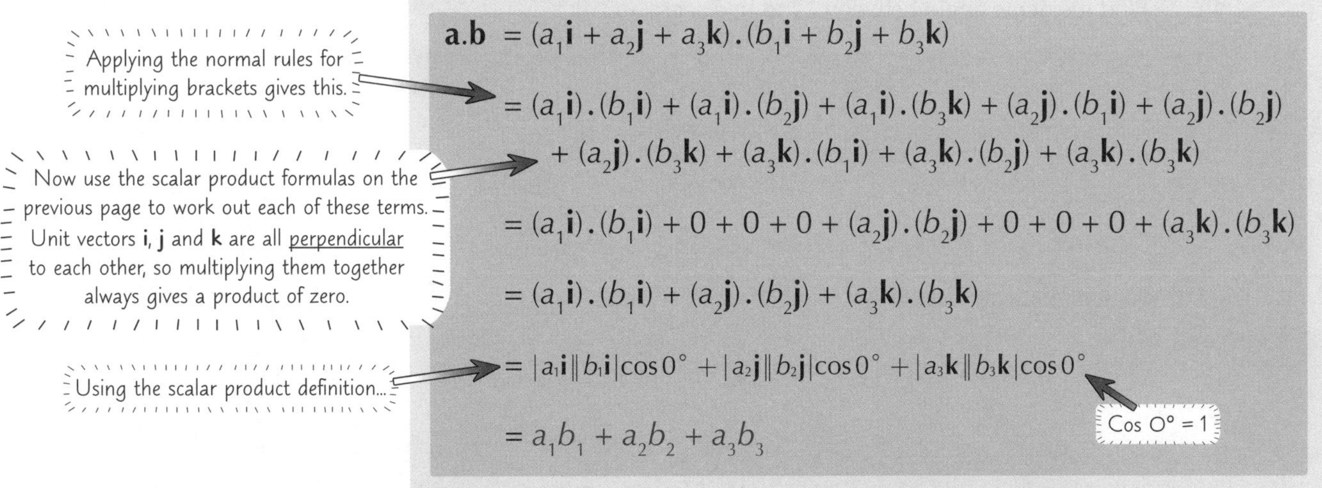

Use the **Scalar Product** to Find the **Angle** Between Two Vectors

Finding the angle between two vectors often crops up in vector exam questions. It's just a matter of using the above result to find the scalar product of the two vectors, then popping it into the scalar product definition, $\cos\theta = \frac{\mathbf{a.b}}{|\mathbf{a}||\mathbf{b}|}$, to find the angle.

EXAMPLE Find the angle between the vectors $-\mathbf{i} - 6\mathbf{j}$ and $4\mathbf{i} + 2\mathbf{j} + 8\mathbf{k}$.

$\cos\theta = \frac{\mathbf{a.b}}{|\mathbf{a}||\mathbf{b}|}$. Let $\mathbf{a} = -\mathbf{i} - 6\mathbf{j}$ and $\mathbf{b} = 4\mathbf{i} + 2\mathbf{j} + 8\mathbf{k}$.

1) Find the scalar product of the vectors.

   $\mathbf{a.b} = (-1 \times 4) + (-6 \times 2) + (0 \times 8) = -4 - 12 + 0 = -16$

   This uses the result above.

2) Find the magnitude of each vector (see page 84).

   $|\mathbf{a}| = \sqrt{(-1)^2 + (-6)^2 + (0)^2} = \sqrt{37}$ $\quad |\mathbf{b}| = \sqrt{(4)^2 + (2)^2 + (8)^2} = \sqrt{84}$

3) Now plug these values into the equation and find the angle.

   $\cos\theta = \frac{\mathbf{a.b}}{|\mathbf{a}||\mathbf{b}|} = \frac{-16}{\sqrt{37}\sqrt{84}} \Rightarrow \theta = 106.7°$

Scalar product — Ooops. I best stop eating chips every day...

So when you scalar multiply two vectors, you basically multiply the **i** components together, multiply the **j** components together, multiply the **k** components together, then add up all the products. You end up with just a number, with no **i**s, **j**s or **k**s attached to it. You'll see this more in the examples on the next page, so don't worry if it seems a bit strange at the mo.

Scalar Product

Right, you've learnt the definitions and the facts. Now it's time to put them to good use.

You Might have to Find the Angle from **Vector Equations** *or from* **Two Points**

1) If you're given the vector equations for lines that you're finding the angle between, it's important to use the correct bits of the vector equations.
2) You use the **b** bit in **r** = **a** + *t***b** (the 'parallel to' or the 'direction' bit).

EXAMPLE Line l has the equation $\mathbf{r} = \begin{pmatrix}2\\0\\4\end{pmatrix} + \lambda\begin{pmatrix}1\\2\\-1\end{pmatrix}$.

Point A and point B have the coordinates (4, 4, 2) and (1, 0, 3) respectively. Point A lies on l. Find the acute angle between l and line segment AB.

1) First draw a diagram — it'll make everything clearer.

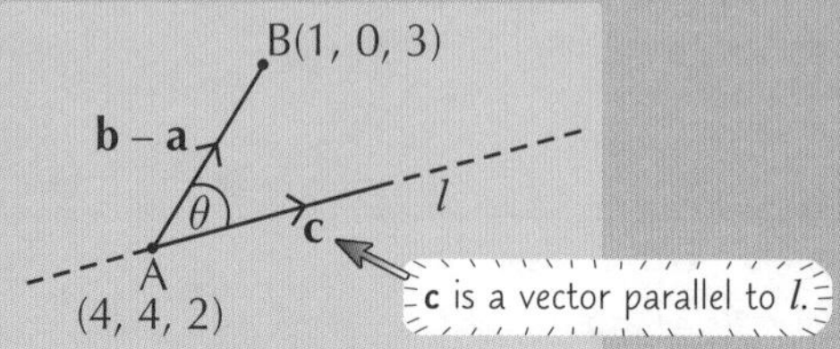

2) Find the vectors that you want to know the angle between.

$$\overrightarrow{AB} = \mathbf{b} - \mathbf{a} = \begin{pmatrix}1\\0\\3\end{pmatrix} - \begin{pmatrix}4\\4\\2\end{pmatrix} = \begin{pmatrix}-3\\-4\\1\end{pmatrix}$$ and the 'parallel to' bit of l (which we've called **c**): $\mathbf{c} = \begin{pmatrix}1\\2\\-1\end{pmatrix}$

3) Find the scalar product of these vectors. $\overrightarrow{AB} \cdot \mathbf{c} = (-3 \times 1) + (-4 \times 2) + (1 \times -1) = -3 - 8 - 1 = -12$

4) Find the magnitude of each vector.

$$|\overrightarrow{AB}| = \sqrt{(-3)^2 + (-4)^2 + (1)^2} = \sqrt{26} \quad |\mathbf{c}| = \sqrt{(1)^2 + (2)^2 + (-1)^2} = \sqrt{6}$$

5) Now plug these values into the equation and find the angle.

$$\cos\theta = \frac{\overrightarrow{AB}.\mathbf{c}}{|\overrightarrow{AB}||\mathbf{c}|} = \frac{-12}{\sqrt{26}\sqrt{6}} \Rightarrow \theta = 164^\circ \text{ (3 s.f.)}$$

6) Whoops. The formula gives the non-acute angle — the situation must have been more like this:

B b − a θ x A c l

Remember — the vectors diverge on each side of the angle given by the formula.

Don't panic — just subtract this angle from 180° to get the acute angle, x, between the lines.

$180° - 164° = 16°$

Prove Lines are **Perpendicular** *by Showing that the* **Scalar Product = 0**

EXAMPLE Show that the lines $\mathbf{r}_1 = (\mathbf{i} + 6\mathbf{j} + 2\mathbf{k}) + \lambda(\mathbf{i} + 2\mathbf{j} + 2\mathbf{k})$ and $\mathbf{r}_2 = (3\mathbf{i} - \mathbf{j} + \mathbf{k}) + \mu(4\mathbf{i} - 3\mathbf{j} + \mathbf{k})$ are perpendicular.

1) Make sure you've got the right bit of each vector equation — it's the direction you're interested in, so it's **b** in **r** = **a** + *t***b**. $\mathbf{i} + 2\mathbf{j} + 2\mathbf{k}$ and $4\mathbf{i} - 3\mathbf{j} + \mathbf{k}$
2) Find the scalar product of the vectors. $(\mathbf{i} + 2\mathbf{j} + 2\mathbf{k}).(4\mathbf{i} - 3\mathbf{j} + \mathbf{k}) = 4 - 6 + 2 = 0$
3) Draw the correct conclusion. The scalar product is 0, so the vectors are perpendicular.

P...P...P... — prove perpendicularity using products...

They'll word these questions in a zillion different ways. Drawing a diagram can often help you figure out what's what.

C4 Section 6 — Practice Questions

Vectors might cause some mild vexation. It's not the simplest of topics, but practising does help. Try these warm-up questions and see if you can remember what you've just read.

Warm-up Questions

1) Give two vectors that are parallel to each of the following: a) $2\mathbf{a}$ b) $3\mathbf{i} + 4\mathbf{j} - 2\mathbf{k}$ c) $\begin{pmatrix} 1 \\ 2 \\ -1 \end{pmatrix}$

2) Using the diagram, find these vectors in terms of vectors **a**, **b** and **c**:

   a) $\overrightarrow{AB}$ b) $\overrightarrow{BA}$ c) $\overrightarrow{CB}$ d) $\overrightarrow{AC}$

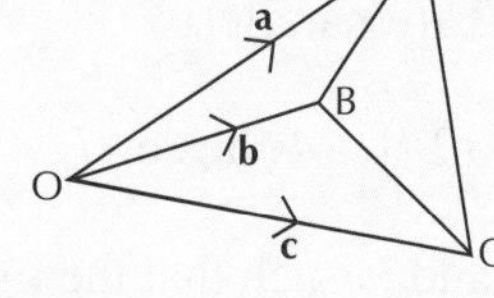

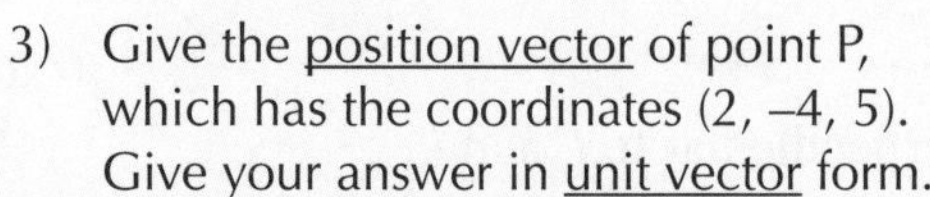

3) Give the position vector of point P, which has the coordinates (2, –4, 5). Give your answer in unit vector form.

4) Find the magnitudes of these vectors:

   a) $3\mathbf{i} + 4\mathbf{j} - 2\mathbf{k}$ b) $\begin{pmatrix} 1 \\ 2 \\ -1 \end{pmatrix}$

5) If A(1, 2, 3) and B(3, –1, –2), find: a) $|\overrightarrow{AB}|$ b) $|\overrightarrow{OA}|$ c) $|\overrightarrow{OB}|$

6) Find the vector equations of the following lines. Give your answer in **i**, **j**, **k** form and in column vector form.

   a) a straight line through (4, 1, 2), parallel to vector $3\mathbf{i} + \mathbf{j} - \mathbf{k}$.

   b) a straight line through (2, –1, 1) and (0, 2, 3).

7) Find three points that lie on the line with vector equation $\mathbf{r} = \begin{pmatrix} 3 \\ 2 \\ 4 \end{pmatrix} + t\begin{pmatrix} -1 \\ 3 \\ 0 \end{pmatrix}$.

8) Find **a.b** if: a) $\mathbf{a} = 3\mathbf{i} + 4\mathbf{j}$ and $\mathbf{b} = \mathbf{i} - 2\mathbf{j} + 3\mathbf{k}$ b) $\mathbf{a} = \begin{pmatrix} 4 \\ 2 \\ 1 \end{pmatrix}$ and $\mathbf{b} = \begin{pmatrix} 3 \\ -4 \\ -3 \end{pmatrix}$

9) $\mathbf{r}_1 = \begin{pmatrix} 2 \\ -1 \\ 2 \end{pmatrix} + t\begin{pmatrix} -4 \\ 6 \\ -2 \end{pmatrix}$ and $\mathbf{r}_2 = \begin{pmatrix} 3 \\ 2 \\ 4 \end{pmatrix} + u\begin{pmatrix} -1 \\ 3 \\ 0 \end{pmatrix}$

   a) Show that these lines intersect and find the position vector of their intersection point.

   b) Find the angle between these lines.

10) Find a vector that is perpendicular to $3\mathbf{i} + 4\mathbf{j} - 2\mathbf{k}$.

You might look at an exam question and think that it's complete gobbledegook. But chances are, when you look at it carefully, you can use what you know to solve it. If you don't know what you need to, you can peek back while doing these questions. You won't be able to in the proper exam, so all the more reason to practise on these.

Exam Questions

1 The quadrilateral ABCD has vertices A(1, 5, 9), B(3, 2, 1), C(–2, 4, 3) and D(5, –1, –7).

   a) Find the vector $\overrightarrow{AB}$. *(2 marks)*

   b) C and D lie on line l_1. Using the parameter μ, find the vector equation of l_1. *(2 marks)*

   c) Find the coordinates of the intersection point of l_1 and the line that passes through AB. *(5 marks)*

   d) (i) Find the acute angle between l_1 and AB. Give your answer to 1 decimal place. *(4 marks)*

   (ii) Find the shortest distance from point A to l_1. *(4 marks)*

C4 Section 6 — Practice Questions

And there's more, as Jimmy Cricket (not to be confused with Jiminy Cricket) used to say.

2 The lines l_1 and l_2 are given by the vector equations:

$l_1: \quad \mathbf{r} = (3\mathbf{i} - 3\mathbf{j} - 2\mathbf{k}) + \mu(\mathbf{i} - 4\mathbf{j} + 2\mathbf{k})$

$l_2: \quad \mathbf{r} = (10\mathbf{i} - 21\mathbf{j} + 11\mathbf{k}) + \lambda(-3\mathbf{i} + 12\mathbf{j} - 6\mathbf{k})$

a) Show that l_1 and l_2 are parallel. *(1 mark)*

b) Show that point A(2, 1, –4) lies on l_1. *(2 marks)*

c) Point B lies on l_2 and is such that the line segment AB is perpendicular to l_1 and l_2.
Find the position vector of point B. *(6 marks)*

d) Find $|\overrightarrow{AB}|$. *(2 marks)*

3 The lines l_1 and l_2 are given by the equations: $l_1: \mathbf{r} = \begin{pmatrix} 3 \\ 0 \\ -2 \end{pmatrix} + \lambda\begin{pmatrix} 1 \\ 3 \\ -2 \end{pmatrix}$ $\quad l_2: \mathbf{r} = \begin{pmatrix} 0 \\ 2 \\ 1 \end{pmatrix} + \mu\begin{pmatrix} 2 \\ -5 \\ -3 \end{pmatrix}$

a) Show that l_1 and l_2 are skew. *(4 marks)*

b) Point P has position vector $\begin{pmatrix} 5 \\ 8 \\ -3 \end{pmatrix}$. Point Q is the image of point P after reflection in line l_1.

Point P and Q both lie on the line with equation $\mathbf{r} = \begin{pmatrix} 5 \\ 4 \\ -9 \end{pmatrix} + t\begin{pmatrix} 0 \\ 2 \\ 3 \end{pmatrix}$.

(i) Find the intersection point of line segment PQ and line l_1. *(4 marks)*

(ii) Show that the line segment PQ and line l_1 are perpendicular. *(2 marks)*

(iii) Find the position vector of point Q. *(3 marks)*

4 Point A has the position vector $3\mathbf{i} + 2\mathbf{j} + \mathbf{k}$ and point B has position vector $3\mathbf{i} - 4\mathbf{j} - \mathbf{k}$.

a) Show that AOB is a right-angled triangle. *(3 marks)*

b) Find angle ABO in the triangle using the scalar product definition. *(5 marks)*

c) (i) Point C has the position vector $3\mathbf{i} - \mathbf{j}$. Show that triangle OAC is isosceles. *(3 marks)*

(ii) Calculate the area of triangle OAC. *(4 marks)*

d) (i) Find the vector equation for line l, which passes through points A and B. *(2 marks)*

(ii) The point D lies on line l and has the position vector $a\mathbf{i} + b\mathbf{j} + \mathbf{k}$. Find a and b. *(3 marks)*

General Certificate of Education
Advanced Subsidiary (AS) and Advanced Level

Core Mathematics C4 — Practice Exam One

Time Allowed: 1 hour 30 min

Graphical calculators may be used for this exam.

Give any non-exact numerical answers to an appropriate degree of accuracy.

There are 72 marks available for this paper.

1 a) Express $\dfrac{(x^2 - 9)(3x^2 - 10x - 8)}{(6x + 4)(x^2 - 7x + 12)}$ as a fraction in its simplest form. *(2 marks)*

b) Divide $2x^3 - x^2 - 16x + 3$ by $x^2 - 3x - 1$, stating the quotient and remainder. *(4 marks)*

2 The graph below shows the curve $y = \dfrac{3\ln x}{x^2}$, $x \geq 0$. The shaded region R is bounded by the curve, the x-axis and the line $x = 3$.

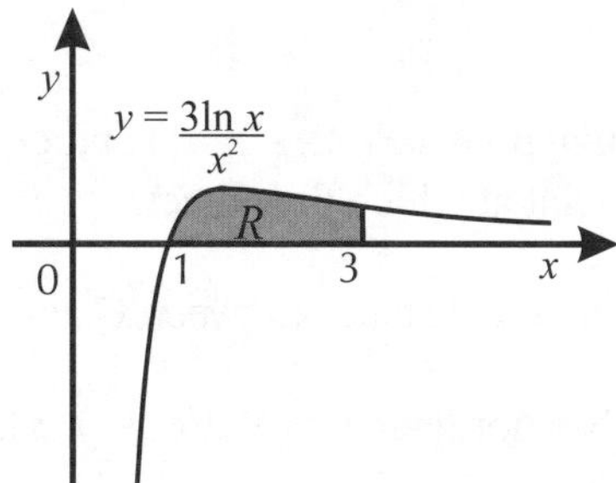

Find the area of R by evaluating the integral $\displaystyle\int_1^3 \frac{3\ln x}{x^2}\,dx$ using integration by parts.
Give your answer to 5 decimal places. *(5 marks)*

3 Find the exact value of

$$\int_0^{\frac{1}{2}} \frac{x}{1 - x^2}\,dx$$

using the substitution $x = \sin\theta$. *(6 marks)*

4 The curve C is defined by the parametric equations $x = \dfrac{\sin\theta}{2} - 3$, $y = 5 - \cos 2\theta$.

a) (i) Show that $\dfrac{dy}{dx}$ can be written as $8\sin\theta$. *(4 marks)*

(ii) Hence find the equation of the tangent to C at the point where $\theta = \dfrac{\pi}{6}$. *(3 marks)*

(iii) Find the coordinates of the stationary point when $0 < \theta < 2\pi$. *(2 marks)*

b) Find a Cartesian equation for C in the form $y = f(x)$. *(3 marks)*

5 a) (i) Find the binomial expansion of $(p + x)^{-3}$, up to and including the term in x^3.
(4 marks)

(ii) If the coefficient of the x^2 term is $\frac{3}{16}$, find the value of p.
(1 mark)

b) Using your value of p, find the binomial expansion of $\frac{2 + x^2}{(p + x)^3}$, up to and including the term in x^3.
(5 marks)

6 A curve has the equation $x^3 + x^2y = y^2 - 1$.

a) Use implicit differentiation to find an expression for $\frac{\mathrm{d}y}{\mathrm{d}x}$.
(4 marks)

The points P and Q lie on the curve. P has coordinates $(1, a)$ and Q has coordinates $(1, b)$.

b) (i) Find the values of a and b, given that $a > b$.
(2 marks)

(ii) Find the equation of the normal to the curve at Q.
(3 marks)

7 Line L_1 has vector equation: $\mathbf{r} = \begin{pmatrix} -1 \\ 0 \\ 3 \end{pmatrix} + \lambda \begin{pmatrix} 2 \\ 2 \\ 1 \end{pmatrix}$.

a) Show that the line passing through points $P(-2, -2, -1)$ and $Q(-5, -4, 1)$ intersects with L_1 and find the point at which they meet.
(5 marks)

b) Given that $\overrightarrow{OT} = 3\overrightarrow{OP}$, show that the distance between Q and T is $\sqrt{21}$.
(3 marks)

c) $\overrightarrow{PV}$ is perpendicular to L_1. If the coordinates of V are $(0, f, g)$, show that $2f + g = -9$.
(3 marks)

d) The line L_2 is parallel to the vector $\begin{pmatrix} 1 \\ 1 \\ 1 \end{pmatrix}$. Find the acute angle between L_1 and L_2.
(3 marks)

8 a) An ecologist is monitoring the population of newts in a colony. The rate of increase of the population is directly proportional to the square root of the current number of newts in the colony. When there were 36 newts in the colony, the rate of change was calculated to be 0.36.

Formulate a differential equation to model the rate of change, in terms of the variables N (number of newts), t (time in weeks).
(4 marks)

b) After more research, the ecologist decides that the differential equation

$$\frac{\mathrm{d}N}{\mathrm{d}t} = \frac{kN}{\sqrt{t}},$$

for a positive constant k, is a better model for the population.
When the ecologist began the survey, the initial population of newts in the colony was 25.

(i) Solve the differential equation, leaving your answer in terms of k and t.
(3 marks)

(ii) Given that the value of k is 0.05, calculate how long (to the nearest week) it will take for the population to double.
(3 marks)

General Certificate of Education
Advanced Subsidiary (AS) and Advanced Level

Core Mathematics C4 — Practice Exam Two

Time Allowed: 1 hour 30 min

Graphical calculators may be used for this exam.

Give any non-exact numerical answers to an appropriate degree of accuracy.

There are 72 marks available for this paper.

1 a) Express $\frac{5x^2 + 10x - 13}{(2-x)^2(1+4x)}$ in partial fractions of the form $\frac{A}{(2-x)} + \frac{B}{(2-x)^2} + \frac{C}{(1+4x)}$, where A, B and C are constants to be found. *(5 marks)*

b) Hence find $\int \frac{5x^2 + 10x - 13}{(2-x)^2(1+4x)} \, dx$. *(4 marks)*

2 a) Find the binomial expansion of $(1-x)^{-\frac{1}{2}}$, up to and including the term in x^3. *(3 marks)*

b) (i) Hence show that $(25 - 4x)^{-\frac{1}{2}} \approx \frac{1}{5} + \frac{2}{125}x + \frac{6}{3125}x^2 + \frac{4}{15625}x^3$ for small values of x. *(4 marks)*

(ii) State the range of values of x for which the expansion from part (i) is valid. *(1 mark)*

c) Use your expansion from b) with a suitable value of x to show that $\frac{1}{\sqrt{20}} \approx \frac{447}{2000}$. *(3 marks)*

3 a) Use integration by parts to find $\int 4xe^{-2x} \, dx$. *(5 marks)*

b) Find $\int_1^2 \left(\frac{\ln x}{\sqrt{x}}\right)^2 dx$, using the substitution $u = \ln x$. Give your answer to 3 significant figures. *(5 marks)*

4 The curve C, shown on the diagram below, is given by the parametric equations:

$$x = \tan\theta, \qquad y = \sin\theta, \qquad 0 < \theta < \frac{\pi}{2}.$$

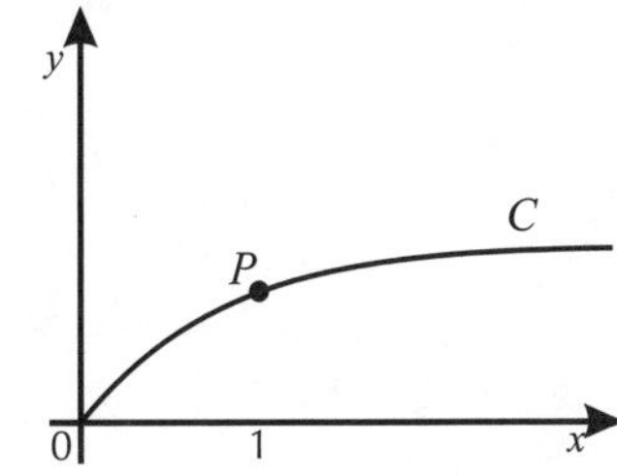

The point P has coordinates $(1, \frac{1}{\sqrt{2}})$.

a) Find an expression for $\frac{dy}{dx}$, giving your answer in terms of θ, and hence find the exact value of the gradient at the point P. *(5 marks)*

b) Find the equation of the normal to the curve at P. *(3 marks)*

5 a) Express $\frac{x^2 + 5x - 14}{2x^2 - 4x}$ as a fraction in its simplest form.

(3 marks)

b) Using your answer to part (a) or otherwise, write $\frac{x^2 + 5x - 14}{2x^2 - 4x} + \frac{14}{x(x-4)}$ as a single fraction, simplifying your answer as much as possible.

(3 marks)

6 a) Find the general solution to the differential equation

$$\frac{e^{2x} + x^2}{e^{2x} + x}\frac{dy}{dx} = 2y, \quad x,y \geq 0.$$

(7 marks)

b) (i) Given that $y = 3$ when $x = 0$, find the particular solution to the differential equation above.

(2 marks)

(ii) Hence find the exact value of y for this particular solution when $x = 3$.

(2 marks)

7 A set of curves is defined by the implicit equation $\sin \pi x - \cos\left(\frac{\pi y}{2}\right) = 0.5$, for $0 \leq x \leq 2$, $0 \leq y \leq 2$.

a) Show that $\frac{dy}{dx} = -\frac{2\cos \pi x}{\sin \frac{\pi y}{2}}$.

(2 marks)

b) Hence find:

(i) the coordinates of the stationary point of the curve,

(4 marks)

(ii) the gradient of the tangent to the curve when $x = \frac{1}{6}$.

(3 marks)

8 Vector **x** is perpendicular to both vector **y** and vector **z**.

$\mathbf{x} = p\mathbf{i} + \frac{3}{5}\mathbf{j} + q\mathbf{k}$

$\mathbf{y} = 15\mathbf{i} - 20\mathbf{j} + 3\mathbf{k}$

$\mathbf{z} = \frac{3}{2}\mathbf{i} - 2\mathbf{j} + 4\mathbf{k}$

a) (i) Find the values of p and q.

(3 marks)

(ii) Find a unit vector in the direction of **y**.

(2 marks)

b) Given that the scalar product of **y** and **z** is 74.5, show that the angle between these vectors is 51° to the nearest degree.

(3 marks)

The Poisson Distribution

Welcome to S2 and the Poisson distribution. If you speak French, you'll know that poisson means fish. I think.

A Poisson Distribution has Only One Parameter

A Poisson Distribution has just one parameter: λ.
If the random variable X follows a Poisson distribution, then you can write $X \sim \text{Po}(\lambda)$.

The Greek letter lambda is often used for the Poisson parameter. You might also see the Greek letter mu (μ) used.

Poisson Probability Distribution Po(λ)

If $X \sim \text{Po}(\lambda)$, then X can take values 0, 1, 2, 3... with probability:

$$P(X = x) = \frac{e^{-\lambda}\lambda^x}{x!}$$

Random variables following a Poisson distribution are discrete — there are 'gaps' between the possible values.

EXAMPLE If $X \sim \text{Po}(2.8)$, find:
a) $P(X = 0)$, b) $P(X = 1)$, c) $P(X = 2)$, d) $P(X < 3)$, e) $P(X \geq 3)$

Use the formula:

a) $P(X = 0) = \frac{e^{-2.8} \times 2.8^0}{0!} = e^{-2.8} = 0.061$ (to 3 d.p.). ← Remember... $0! = 1$.

b) $P(X = 1) = \frac{e^{-2.8} \times 2.8^1}{1!} = e^{-2.8} \times 2.8 = 0.170$ (to 3 d.p.).

c) $P(X = 2) = \frac{e^{-2.8} \times 2.8^2}{2!} = \frac{e^{-2.8} \times 2.8^2}{2 \times 1} = 0.238$ (to 3 d.p.).

If $X \sim \text{Po}(\lambda)$, then it can only take whole number values, so $P(X < 3)$ is the same as $P(X \leq 2)$.

d) $P(X < 3) = P(X \leq 2) = P(X = 0) + P(X = 1) + P(X = 2) = 0.061 + 0.170 + 0.238 = 0.469$.

e) $P(X \geq 3) = 1 - P(X < 3) = 1 - 0.469 = 0.531$. ← All the normal probability rules apply.

For a Poisson Distribution: Mean = Variance

For a Poisson distribution, the mean and the variance are the same — and they both equal λ, the Poisson parameter. Remember that and you've probably learnt the most important Poisson fact. Ever.

Poisson Mean and Variance

If $X \sim \text{Po}(\lambda)$: **Mean ($\mu$) of X = E(X) = λ**

Variance (σ^2) of X = Var(X) = λ

So the standard deviation is: $\sigma = \sqrt{\lambda}$

EXAMPLE If $X \sim \text{Po}(7)$, find: a) E(X), b) Var(X).
It's Poisson, so $E(X) = \text{Var}(X) = \lambda = 7$.

This is the easiest question ever. So enjoy it while it lasts.

EXAMPLE If $X \sim \text{Po}(1)$, find: a) $P(X \leq \mu)$, b) $P(X \leq \mu - \sigma)$
$E(X) = \mu = 1$, and $\text{Var}(X) = \sigma^2 = 1$, and so $\sigma = 1$.

a) $P(X \leq \mu) = P(X \leq 1) = P(0) + P(1) = \frac{e^{-1} \times 1^0}{0!} + \frac{e^{-1} \times 1^1}{1!} = 0.736$ (to 3 d.p.).

b) $P(X \leq \mu - \sigma) = P(X \leq 0) = P(0) = \frac{e^{-1} \times 1^0}{0!} = 0.368$ (to 3 d.p.).

The Poisson distribution is named after its inventor...

...the great French mathematician Monsieur Siméon-Denis Distribution. Boom boom. I always tell that joke at parties (which probably explains why I don't get to go to many parties these days). Most important thing here is that bit about the mean and variance being equal... so if you ever come across a distribution where $\mu = \sigma^2$, think 'Poisson' immediately.

The Poisson Parameter

I know what you're thinking... if only everything could be as accommodating as the Poisson distribution, with only one parameter and most things of interest being equal to it, then life would be so much easier. (Sigh.)

The Poisson Parameter is a **Rate**

The number of events/things that occur/are present in a particular period often follows a Poisson distribution. It could be a period of: time (e.g. minute/hour etc.), or space (e.g. litre/kilometre etc.).

Poisson Probability Distribution: Po(λ)

If X represents the number of events that occur in a particular space or time, then X will follow a Poisson distribution as long as:

1) The events occur randomly, and are all independent of each other.
2) The events happen singly (i.e. "one at a time").
3) The events happen (on average) at a constant rate (either in space or time).

The Poisson parameter λ is then the average rate at which these events occur (i.e. the average number of events in a given interval of space or time).

So the expected number of events that occur is proportional to the length of the period.

The random variable X represents the number of a certain type of cell in a particular volume of a blood sample. Assuming that the blood sample has been stirred, and that a given volume of blood always contains the same number of cells, show that X follows a Poisson distribution.

The sample has been stirred, so that should mean the cells of interest aren't all clustered together. This should ensure the 'events' (i.e. the cells you're interested in) occur randomly and singly. And since the total number of cells in a given volume is constant, the cells of interest should occur (on average) at a constant rate. Since X is the total number of 'events' in a given volume, X must follow a Poisson distribution.

The Poisson Parameter is **Additive**

Additive Property of the Poisson Distribution

- If X represents the number of events in 1 unit of time/space (e.g. 1 minute / hour / m^2 / m^3), and $X \sim \text{Po}(\lambda)$, then the number of events in x units of time/space follows the distribution $\text{Po}(x\lambda)$.
- If X and Y are independent variables with $X \sim \text{Po}(\lambda)$ and $Y \sim \text{Po}(\mu)$, then $X + Y \sim \text{Po}(\lambda + \mu)$.

EXAMPLE Sunflowers grow singly and randomly in a field with an average of 10 sunflowers per square metre. What is the probability that a randomly chosen area of 0.25 m^2 contains no sunflowers?

The number of sunflowers in 1 m^2 follows the distribution Po(10).

So the number of sunflowers in 0.25 m^2 must follow the distribution Po(2.5).

This means $\text{P(no sunflowers)} = \frac{e^{-2.5} \times 2.5^0}{0!} = e^{-2.5} = 0.082$ (to 3 d.p.).

EXAMPLE The number of radioactive atoms that decay per second follows the Poisson distribution Po(5). If the probability of no atoms decaying in t seconds is 0.5, verify that $t = 0.1386$.

If the random variable X represents the number of radioactive atoms that decay in t seconds, then $X \sim \text{Po}(5t)$.

This means $P(X = 0) = \frac{e^{-5t}(5t)^0}{0!} = e^{-5t} = 0.5$.

This equation is satisfied by $t = 0.1386$, since $e^{-5 \times 0.1386} = e^{-0.693} = 0.500$ (to 3 d.p.).

If events happen randomly, singly and at a constant rate, it's Poisson...

Lots of things follow a Poisson distribution — e.g. the number of radioactive atoms that decay in a given time, the number of sixes in 5 minutes of dice-throwing, the number of raindrops per minute that hit a bit of your tongue as you stare open-mouthed at the sky on a rainy day. Think of a few others... make sure events happen randomly, singly and at a constant rate.

Using Poisson Tables

You've seen statistical tables before — for example, in S1 you saw how great they are for working out probabilities for the binomial distribution. So this should all seem eerily familiar.

Look up Probabilities in Poisson Tables

EXAMPLE In a field, sunflowers grow singly and randomly with an average of 9 sunflowers per square metre. Find the probability that a randomly chosen square metre contains no more than 7 sunflowers.

If the random variable X represents the number of sunflowers in 1 m², then $X \sim \text{Po}(9)$.
You need to find $P(X \leq 7)$.

① You could do this 'manually': $P(X = 0) + P(X = 1) + ... + P(X = 7) = \frac{e^{-9} \times 9^0}{0!} + \frac{e^{-9} \times 9^1}{1!} + ... + \frac{e^{-9} \times 9^7}{7!}$

② But it's much quicker and easier to use tables of the Poisson cumulative distribution function (c.d.f.). The c.d.f. is a function that gives the probability that X will be less than or equal to a particular value. So the tables show $P(X \leq x)$, for $X \sim \text{Po}(\lambda)$.

Here's a bit of a Poisson table:

- Find your value of λ (here, 9), and the value of x (here, 7).
- You can quickly see that $P(X \leq 7) = 0.3239$.

Cumulative Poisson Probabilities

λ	5.00	5.50	6.00	6.50	7.00	7.50	8.00	8.50	9.00	9.50
$x = 0$	0.0067	0.0041	0.0025	0.0015	0.0009	0.0006	0.0003	0.0002	0.0001	0.0001
1	0.0404	0.0266	0.0174	0.0113	0.0073	0.0047	0.0030	0.0019	0.0012	0.0008
2	0.1247	0.0884	0.0620	0.0430	0.0296	0.0203	0.0138	0.0093	0.0062	0.0042
3	0.2650	0.2017	0.1512	0.1118	0.0818	0.0591	0.0424	0.0301	0.0212	0.0149
4	0.4405	0.3575	0.2851	0.2237	0.1730	0.1321	0.0996	0.0744	0.0550	0.0403
5	0.6160	0.5289	0.4457	0.3690	0.3007	0.2414	0.1912	0.1496	0.1157	0.0885
6	0.7622	0.6860	0.6063	0.5265	0.4497	0.3782	0.3134	0.2562	0.2068	0.1649
7	0.8666	0.8095	0.7440	0.6728	0.5987	0.5246	0.4530	0.3856	0.3239	0.2687
8	0.9319	0.8944	0.8472	0.7916	0.7291	0.6620	0.5925	0.5231	0.4557	0.3918
9	0.9682	0.9462	0.9161	0.8774	0.8305	0.7764	0.7166	0.6530	0.5874	0.5218

You Need to Use Poisson Tables with a Bit of Cunning

See p136 for the full set of Poisson tables.

These cumulative probabilities can help you out more than you might think...

EXAMPLE When cloth is manufactured, faults occur randomly in the cloth at a rate of 8 faults per square metre. Use the above Poisson table to find:
a) The probability of 7 or fewer faults in a square metre of cloth.
b) The probability of more than 4 faults in a square metre of cloth.
c) The probability of exactly 6 faults in a square metre of cloth.
d) The probability of at least 9 faults in a square metre of cloth.
e) The probability of exactly 4 faults in 0.75 m² of cloth.

The faults occur randomly, singly and at a constant rate (= 8 faults per square metre).
So if X represents the number of faults in a square metre, then $X \sim \text{Po}(8)$.

So use the column showing $\lambda = 8$.

a) $P(X \leq 7) = 0.4530$

b) $P(X > 4) = 1 - P(X \leq 4) = 1 - 0.0996 = 0.9004$

c) $P(X = 6) = P(X \leq 6) - P(X \leq 5) = 0.3134 - 0.1912 = 0.1222$

d) $P(X \geq 9) = 1 - P(X < 9) = 1 - P(X \leq 8) = 1 - 0.5925 = 0.4075$

e) Let the random variable Y represent the number of faults in 0.75 m² of cloth.
If the number of faults in 1 m² of cloth ~ Po(8), then $Y \sim \text{Po}(0.75 \times 8) = \text{Po}(6)$.

Now use the column showing $\lambda = 6$.

So P(exactly 4 faults in 0.75 m² of cloth) $= P(Y \leq 4) - P(Y \leq 3) = 0.2851 - 0.1512 = 0.1339$

Poisson tables — the best thing since binomial tables...

Learn the ways of the Poisson tables, and you shall prove your wisdom. In the exam, you'll be given a big booklet of fun containing all the statistical tables you could ever want. You need to think carefully about how to use them though — e.g. you might have to subtract one figure from another, or subtract one of the figures from 1. Or something else similar.

Po(λ) as an Approximation to B(n, p)

This page is a bit like a buy-one-get-one-free offer. Hopefully you remember binomial distributions from S1. Well, this page is about using Poisson distributions to solve binomial problems. This really is your lucky day...

For Big n and Small p — Po(np) Approximates a Binomial Distribution

Sometimes, a Poisson distribution can be used as an approximation to a binomial distribution.

If you're struggling to remember much about the binomial distribution, this would be a good time to brush up on your knowledge.

Po(np) as an Approximation to B(n, p)

If $X \sim B(n, p)$, and: 1) **n is large**, 2) **p is small**,

then X can be approximated by **Po(np)**.

The mean of the binomial distribution is np, so use that as the mean of your Poisson approximation.

EXAMPLE In a school of 1460 students, what is the probability that at least 6 of them were born on June 21st? Use a suitable approximation to find your answer.
(You may assume that all birthdays are independent, and are distributed evenly throughout the year.)

If X represents the number of children in the school born on June 21st, then $X \sim B(1460, \frac{1}{365})$.

You need to find $P(X \geq 6)$.

So far so good. However, your binomial tables don't go past n = 30. And working this out 'by hand' isn't easy. But look at those values of n and p...

Since n is large and p is small, $B(1460, \frac{1}{365})$ can be approximated by $Po(1460 \times \frac{1}{365}) = Po(4)$.

So $P(X \geq 6) = 1 - P(X < 6) = 1 - P(X \leq 5) = 1 - 0.7851 = 0.2149$.

From Poisson tables — see p136.

If you work it out using $B(1460, \frac{1}{365})$, you get 0.2147 — so this is a pretty good approximation.

You need to Check that n and p Satisfy Certain Conditions

1) To use the Poisson approximation to $B(n, p)$, you ideally want n to be large and p "as small as possible". The smaller p is, the better the approximation will be.

2) It's important p is small because then the mean and the variance of $B(n, p)$ are approximately equal — something you need if Po(np) is going to be a good approximation.

   If $X \sim B(n, p)$, then $E(X) = np$.
   And if p is small, $(1 - p) \approx 1$ — this means $Var(X) = np(1 - p) \approx np \times 1 = np$.

3) Before using Po(np) to approximate $B(n, p)$, you need to check that your values of n and p satisfy the conditions $n > 50$ and $np < 5$. If they do, you know that n is large enough, p is small enough, and a Poisson approximation is likely to be the most suitable approximation to use (you can also approximate some binomial distributions with a normal distribution — see p.112).

EXAMPLES:

① Factory A forgets to add icing to its chocolate cakes with a uniform probability of 0.02. Use a suitable approximation to find the probability that fewer than 6 of the next 100 cakes made will not be iced.

If X represents the number of "un-iced" cakes, then $X \sim B(100, 0.02)$.

Since n is quite large (> 50) and p is quite small, a Poisson approximation should be suitable. Checking the value of np you get $100 \times 0.02 = 2$, which is less than 5, so $X \sim Po(100 \times 0.02) = Po(2)$ can be used.

So $P(X < 6) = P(X \leq 5) = 0.9834$

If you work it out using B(100, 0.02), you get 0.9845.

Sometimes you can still use the approximation if p is very close to 1.

② Factory B adds icing to its chocolate cakes with a uniform probability of 0.99. Use a suitable approximation to find the probability that more than 95 of the next 100 cakes made will be iced.

- If Y represents the number of iced cakes produced by Factory B, then $Y \sim B(100, 0.99)$.
  Here, n is quite large, but p is not small, meaning that np is far too big.
- However, if you let W represent the number of "un-iced" cakes made, then $W \sim B(100, 0.01)$.
  Now you can use a Poisson approximation, since $np = 100 \times 0.01 = 1$: $W \sim Po(100 \times 0.01) = Po(1)$.
  So $P(Y > 95) = P(W < 5) = P(W \leq 4) = 0.9963$

  Using B(100, 0.01), you get 0.9966.

Worked Problems

Make sure you understand what's going on in these examples.

EXAMPLE 1: A breaking-down car

A car randomly breaks down twice a week on average.
The random variable X represents the number of times the car will break down next week.

a) What probability distribution could be used to model X? Explain your answer.
b) Find the probability that the car breaks down fewer than 3 times next week.
c) Find the probability that the car breaks down more than 4 times next week.
d) Find the probability that the car breaks down exactly 6 times in the next fortnight.

a) Since the breakdowns occur randomly, singly and (on average) at a constant rate, and X is the total number of breakdowns in one week, X follows a Poisson distribution: $X \sim \text{Po}(2)$

b) Using tables for $\lambda = 2$: $P(X < 3) = P(X \leq 2) = 0.6767$

c) Again, using tables for $\lambda = 2$: $P(X > 4) = 1 - P(X \leq 4) = 1 - 0.9473 = 0.0527$

d) If the random variable Y represents the number of breakdowns in the next fortnight, then $Y \sim \text{Po}(2 \times 2) = \text{Po}(4)$.
So using tables for $\lambda = 4$: $P(Y = 6) = P(Y \leq 6) - P(Y \leq 5) = 0.8893 - 0.7851 = 0.1042$

EXAMPLE 2: Bad apples

A restaurant owner needs to buy several crates of apples, so she visits a farm that sells apples by the crate. Each crate contains 150 apples. On average 1.5% of the apples are bad, and these bad apples are randomly distributed between the crates. The restaurant owner opens a random crate and inspects each apple.

- If there are no bad apples in this crate, then the restaurant owner will buy the apples she needs from this farm.
- If more than 2 apples in this first crate are bad, then the restaurant owner will not buy from this farm.
- If only 1 or 2 apples in the first crate are bad, then a second crate is opened.
  The restaurant owner will then only buy from this farm if the second crate contains at most 1 bad apple.

a) Find the probability that none of the apples in the first crate are bad.
b) Find the probability that more than 2 apples in the first crate are bad.
c) Find the probability that a second crate is opened.
d) What is the probability of the restaurant owner buying the apples she needs from this farm?

a) The average number of bad apples in each crate is $150 \times 0.015 = 2.25$.
So if X represents the number of bad apples in each crate, then $X \sim \text{Po}(2.25)$.

$$P(X = 0) = \frac{e^{-2.25} \times 2.25^0}{0!} = e^{-2.25} = 0.1054 \text{ (to 4 d.p.)}.$$

Definitely Poisson.

b) 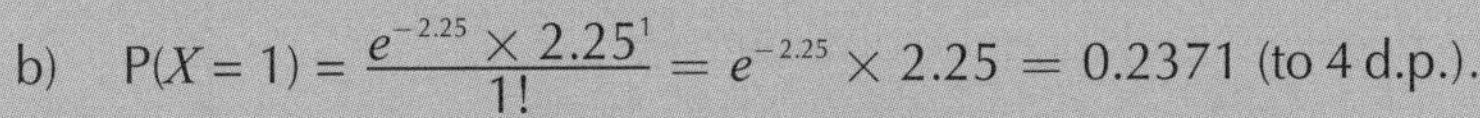

$$P(X = 1) = \frac{e^{-2.25} \times 2.25^1}{1!} = e^{-2.25} \times 2.25 = 0.2371 \text{ (to 4 d.p.)}.$$

$$P(X = 2) = \frac{e^{-2.25} \times 2.25^2}{2!} = \frac{e^{-2.25} \times 2.25^2}{2} = 0.2668 \text{ (to 4 d.p.)}.$$

So $P(X > 2) = 1 - P(X = 0) - P(X = 1) - P(X = 2) = 1 - 0.1054 - 0.2371 - 0.2668 = 0.3907$

c) A second crate is opened if $X = 1$ or $X = 2$. $P(X = 1 \text{ OR } X = 2) = 0.2371 + 0.2668 = 0.5039$

d) There are two ways the owner will buy apples from this farm:
- Either the first crate will contain no bad apples (probability = 0.1054),
- Or the first crate will contain 1 or 2 bad apples AND the second crate will contain 0 or 1 bad apples.

P(1st crate has 1 or 2 bad AND 2nd crate has 0 or 1 bad) = $0.5039 \times (0.1054 + 0.2371) = 0.1726$
So P(restaurant owner buys from this farm) = $0.1054 + 0.1726 = 0.278$

All it takes is one bad apple question and everything starts to go wrong...

I admit that apple question looks a nightmare at first... but just hold your nerve and take things nice and slowly. For example, in that last part, ask yourself: "What individual things need to happen before the restaurant owner will buy from this farm?" Work out the individual probabilities, add or multiply them as necessary, and Bob's your uncle.

S2 Section 1 — Practice Questions

Well, that's the first section completed, which is as good a reason as most to celebrate. But wait... put that celebratory cup of tea on ice for a few minutes more, because you've still got some questions to answer to prove that you really do know everything. So try the questions... and if you get any wrong, do some more revision and try them again.

Warm-up Questions

1) If $X \sim \text{Po}(3.1)$, find (correct to 4 decimal places):
   a) $P(X = 2)$, b) $P(X = 1)$, c) $P(X = 0)$, d) $P(X < 3)$, e) $P(X \geq 3)$

2) If $X \sim \text{Po}(8.7)$, find (correct to 4 decimal places):
   a) $P(X = 2)$, b) $P(X = 1)$, c) $P(X = 0)$, d) $P(X < 3)$, e) $P(X \geq 3)$

3) For the following distributions, find: (i) $E(X)$, (ii) $\text{Var}(X)$, and (iii) the standard deviation of X.
   a) Po(8), b) Po(12.11) c) Po(84.2227)

4) For the following distributions, find: (i) $P(X \leq \mu)$, (ii) $P(X \leq \mu - \sigma)$
   a) Po(9), b) Po(4)

5) Which of the following would follow a Poisson distribution? Explain your answers.
   a) The number of defective products coming off a factory's production line in one day if defective products occur at random at an average of 25 per week.
   b) The number of heads thrown using a coin in 25 tosses if the probability of getting a head is always 0.5.
   c) The number of people joining a post-office queue each minute during lunchtime if people arrive at an average rate of 3 every five minutes.
   d) The total number of spelling mistakes in a document if mistakes are randomly made at an average rate of 3 per page.

6) In a radioactive sample, atoms decay at an average rate of 2000 per hour.
   State how the following quantities are distributed, giving as much detail as possible.
   a) The number of atoms decaying per minute.
   b) The number of atoms decaying per day.

7) Atoms in one radioactive sample decay at an average rate of 60 per minute, while in another they decay at an average rate of 90 per minute.
   a) How would the total number of atoms decaying each minute be distributed?
   b) How would the total number of atoms decaying each hour be distributed?

8) If $X \sim \text{Po}(8)$, use Poisson tables to find:
   a) $P(X \leq 2)$, b) $P(X \leq 7)$, c) $P(X \leq 5)$, d) $P(X < 9)$, e) $P(X \geq 8)$
   f) $P(X > 1)$, g) $P(X > 7)$, h) $P(X = 6)$, i) $P(X = 4)$, j) $P(X = 3)$

9) A gaggle of 100 geese is randomly scattered throughout a field measuring 10 m × 10 m. What is the probability that in a randomly selected square metre of field, I find:
   a) no geese? b) 1 goose? c) 2 geese? d) more than 2 geese?

10) Which of the following random variables could be approximated by a Poisson distribution? Where it is possible, state the Poisson distribution that could be used.
   a) $X \sim B(4, 0.4)$, b) $Y \sim B(700, 0.001)$, c) $W \sim B(850, 0.34)$
   d) $X \sim B(8, 0.1)$, e) $W \sim B(1000, 0.0025)$, f) $Y \sim B(80, 0.95)$ *(harder)*

S2 Section 1 — Practice Questions

Nearly there — just... one... more... page...

Exam Questions

1 a) State two conditions needed for a Poisson distribution to be a suitable model for a quantity.

(2 marks)

b) A birdwatcher knows that the number of chaffinches visiting a particular observation spot per hour follows a Poisson distribution with mean 7.

Find the probability that in a randomly chosen hour during the day:

(i) fewer than 4 chaffinches visit the observation spot,

(2 marks)

(ii) at least 7 chaffinches visit the observation spot,

(2 marks)

(iii) exactly 9 chaffinches visit the observation spot.

(2 marks)

c) Find the length of time (to the nearest minute) for which the probability that no chaffinches visit the observation spot is 0.24.

(4 marks)

2 The number of calls received at a call centre each hour can be modelled by a Poisson distribution with mean 20.

a) Find the probability that in a random 30-minute period:

(i) exactly 8 calls are received,

(3 marks)

(ii) more than 8 calls are received.

(2 marks)

b) For a Poisson distribution to be a suitable model, events have to occur independently. What is meant by "independently" in this context?

(1 mark)

3 When a particular engineer is called out to fix a fault, the probability of him being unable to fix the fault is always 0.02.

a) The engineer's work is assessed after every 200 call-outs. The random variable X represents the number of faults the engineer is unable to fix over those 200 call-outs. Specify the statistical distribution that X will follow, stating the values of any parameters.

(2 marks)

b) (i) Under what conditions can a binomial distribution be approximated by a Poisson distribution?

(2 marks)

(ii) Write down a Poisson distribution that could be used to approximate X.

(1 mark)

(iii) Write down the mean and variance of your Poisson distribution.

(1 mark)

(iv) Using your Poisson approximation, calculate the probability that the engineer will be unable to fix fewer than 5 faults over a period of 200 call-outs.

(2 marks)

Probability Density Functions

A lot of this section should look kinda familiar, but at the same time slightly different. That's because this section covers the same sorts of things as you've seen before with discrete random variables, only now the variables are continuous.

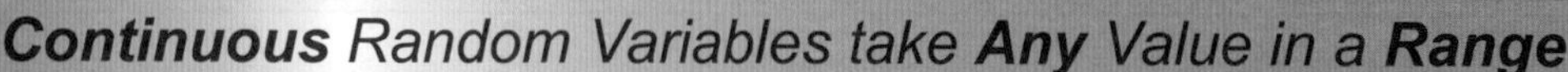

Continuous Random Variables take Any Value in a Range

1) With discrete random variables (like the Poisson ones in Section 1), there are 'gaps' between the possible values the random variable can take. The random variable's probability function tells you the probability of each of these values occurring.

   For example, if $X \sim \text{Po}(1)$, then you know that X can only take the values 0, 1, 2, etc., and you can work out the probability of each of these values using the Poisson probability function on p.95. You could even draw a graph of what this probability function looks like.

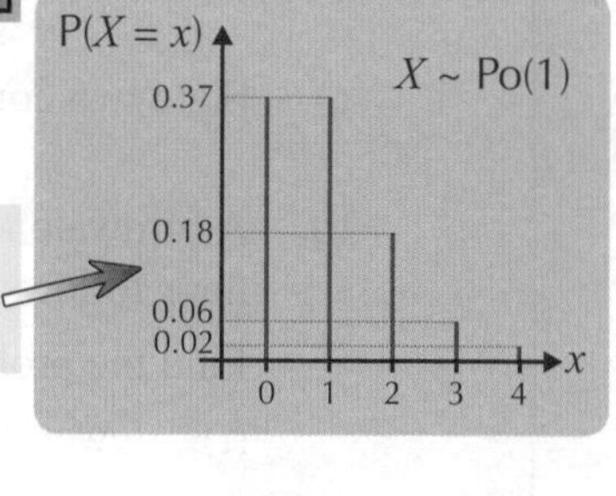

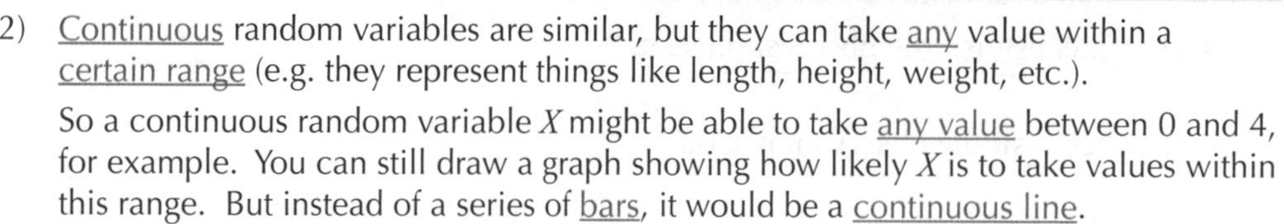

2) Continuous random variables are similar, but they can take any value within a certain range (e.g. they represent things like length, height, weight, etc.).

   So a continuous random variable X might be able to take any value between 0 and 4, for example. You can still draw a graph showing how likely X is to take values within this range. But instead of a series of bars, it would be a continuous line.

3) These graphs that show how likely continuous random variables are to take various values are called probability density functions (or p.d.f.s). Here, f(x) is a p.d.f.

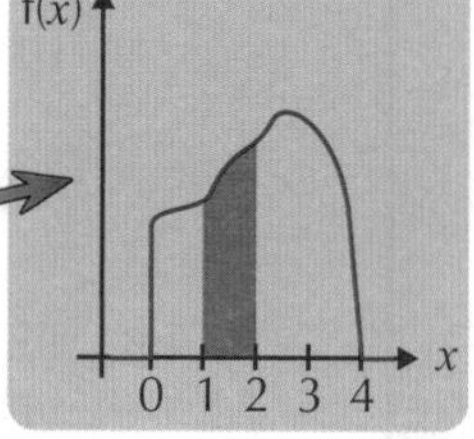

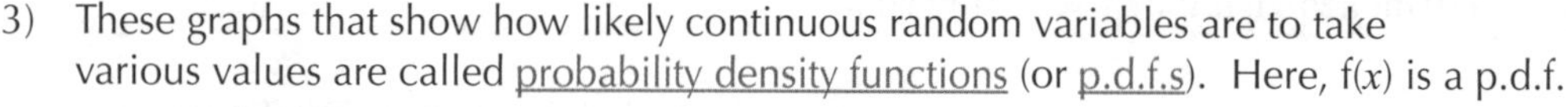

4) It's actually the area under a p.d.f. that shows probability. For example, the shaded area shows the probability that this continuous random variable will take a value between 1 and 2.

The Total Area under a p.d.f. is 1

Remember... it's the area under a p.d.f. that shows probability, and you find the area under a curve by integrating.

EXAMPLE a) Explain why a p.d.f. can never take negative values.
b) Explain why the total area under any p.d.f. must equal 1.

a) A p.d.f. can never be negative, since probabilities can never be negative.

b) The total area under a p.d.f. must always equal 1 since that's just the total probability of the random variable taking one of its possible values.

In maths-speak, this means $f(x) \geq 0$ for all x, and $\int_{-\infty}^{\infty} f(x)dx = 1$.

Where a formula to do with a discrete random variable involves a summation (Σ), the equivalent formula relating to a continuous random variable involves an integral.

This is the 'continuous equivalent' of $\sum p_i = 1$.

Find Probabilities by Calculating Areas

Some of the p.d.f.s you'll come across are defined "piecewise" (bit by bit). Don't let that faze you.

EXAMPLE The continuous random variable X has the probability density function below.

$$f(x) = \begin{cases} kx & \text{for } 0 < x < 4 \\ 0 & \text{otherwise} \end{cases}$$

This is a piecewise definition — it's in 2 bits.

a) Find the value of k. b) Find $P(2 < X \leq 3)$. c) Find $P(X = 2.5)$.

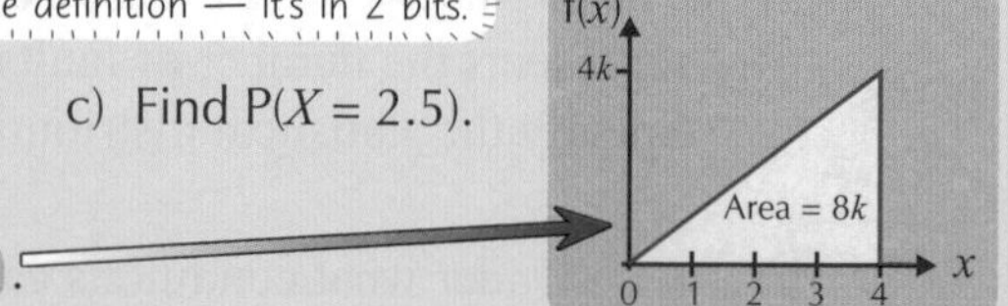

a) The total area under the p.d.f. must equal 1.
Using a sketch of f(x), you can tell that $8k = 1$, or $k = 0.125$.

b) You need to find the area under the graph between $x = 2$ and $x = 3$.
Using the formula for the area of a trapezium, $P(2 < X \leq 3) = 0.3125$

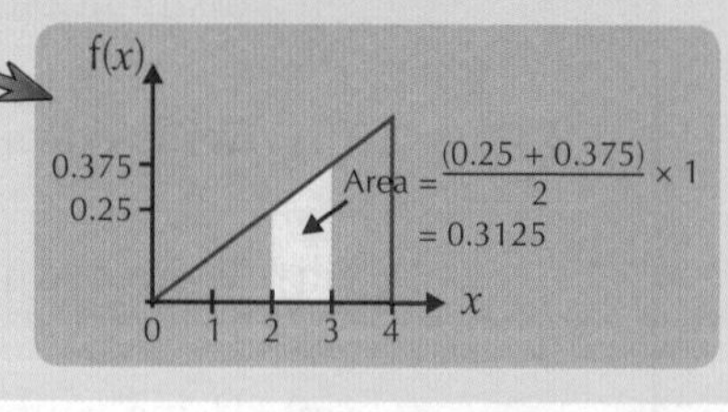

c) The area under a graph at a single point is zero (since it would be the area of a trapezium with zero width). So $P(X = 2.5) = 0$.

The probability of a continuous random variable equalling any single value is always zero — it only makes sense to find the probability of it taking a value within a particular range. It also means that for a continuous random variable, $P(X < k) = P(X \leq k)$, for any k.

Sometimes, statistics all seems a little bit odd...

That thing about $P(X = x) = 0$ always seems weird to me. I mean... X has to take some value, so it seems peculiar that the probability of it taking any particular value equals zero. But that's the way it is. It makes a bit more sense if you remember that probabilities are represented by areas under a graph. Not many calculations here, but learn the ideas carefully.

Probability Density Functions

It's time to put on your best <u>integrating trousers</u>, because you'll be finding more "areas under curves" on this page.

*Some Probabilities Need to be Found by **Integrating***

Remember — <u>probabilities</u> are represented by <u>areas</u>, so if X has p.d.f. f(x):

$$P(a < X \leq b) = \int_a^b f(x)dx$$

EXAMPLE The continuous random variable X has the probability density function below.

$$f(x) = \begin{cases} x^2 + a & \text{for } 0 \leq x \leq 1 \\ 0 & \text{otherwise} \end{cases}$$

a) Sketch f(x), and find the value of a.

b) Find $P(X > \frac{1}{2})$.

a) The non-zero bit of the p.d.f. is a <u>quadratic</u> function, and so f(x) looks like this:
The area under the graph must equal 1, so <u>integrate</u>.

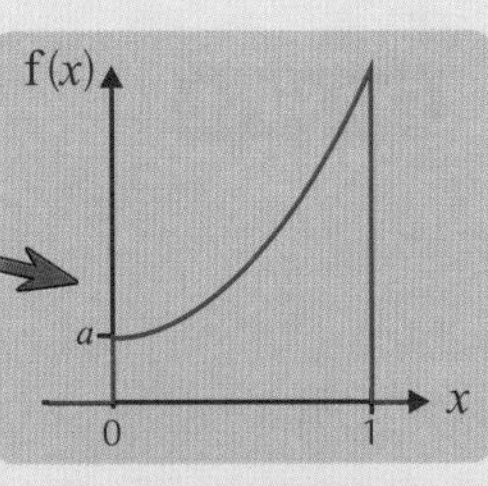

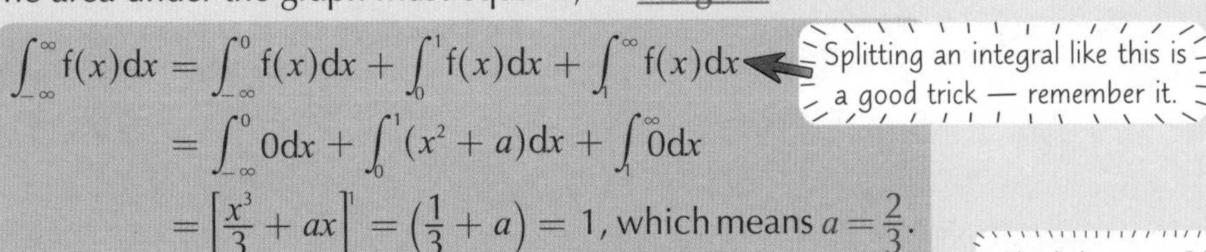

$$\int_{-\infty}^{\infty} f(x)dx = \int_{-\infty}^{0} f(x)dx + \int_0^1 f(x)dx + \int_1^{\infty} f(x)dx$$

$$= \int_{-\infty}^{0} 0dx + \int_0^1 (x^2 + a)dx + \int_1^{\infty} 0dx$$

$$= \left[\frac{x^3}{3} + ax\right]_0^1 = \left(\frac{1}{3} + a\right) = 1, \text{ which means } a = \frac{2}{3}.$$

Splitting an integral like this is a good trick — remember it.

b) Integrate again — this time between $x = \frac{1}{2}$ and $x = 1$.

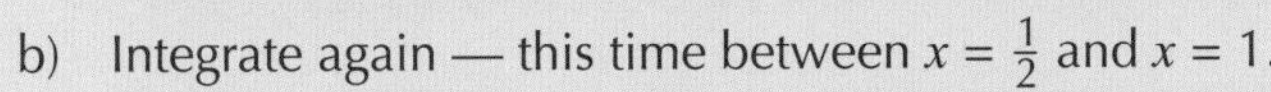

$$P\left(X > \frac{1}{2}\right) = \int_{\frac{1}{2}}^{1} \left(x^2 + \frac{2}{3}\right)dx = \left[\frac{x^3}{3} + \frac{2}{3}x\right]_{\frac{1}{2}}^{1} = \left(\frac{1}{3} + \frac{2}{3}\right) - \left(\frac{1}{24} + \frac{1}{3}\right) = \frac{15}{24} = \frac{5}{8}$$

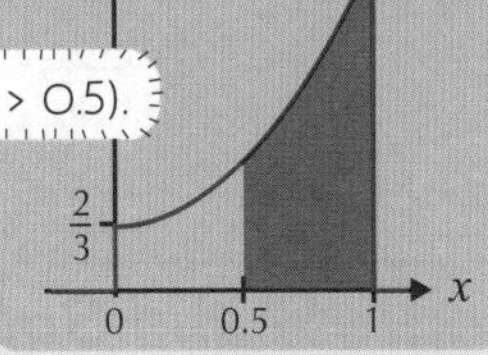

Shaded area = P(X > 0.5).

*You Might Need to Spot a Function that's **NOT** a p.d.f.*

EXAMPLE Which of the following could be probability density functions?

a) $f(x) = \begin{cases} 3x & \text{for } -1 \leq x \leq 1 \\ 0 & \text{otherwise} \end{cases}$ b) $g(x) = \begin{cases} kx & \text{for } 2 \leq x \leq 4 \\ 0 & \text{otherwise} \end{cases}$ c) $h(x) = \begin{cases} kx & \text{for } -2 \leq x \leq 2 \\ 0 & \text{otherwise} \end{cases}$

a) The graph of f(x) looks like this:
But a p.d.f. can <u>never</u> take negative values, so this cannot be a probability density function.

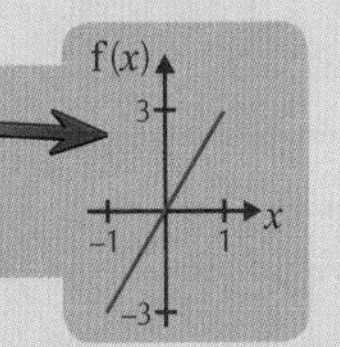

The yellow area must equal 1 for g(x) to be a p.d.f.

b) Since a p.d.f. can never take a negative value, k <u>cannot</u> be <u>negative</u>.

If k is <u>positive</u>, then the graph of g(x) looks like this,

and the <u>total area</u> under the graph is $\frac{2k + 4k}{2} \times 2 = 6k$.

So g(x) could be a p.d.f. as long as $k = \frac{1}{6}$.

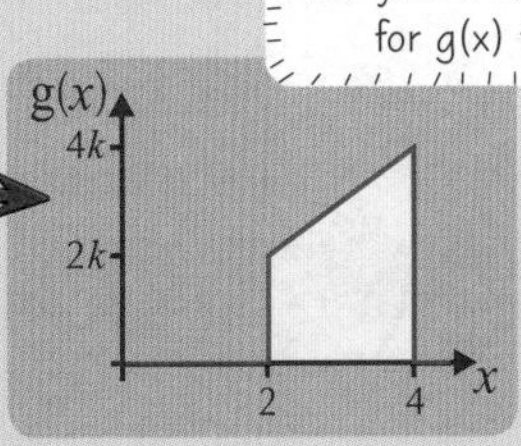

c) If k is <u>positive</u>, then h(x) is negative for $-2 \leq x < 0$, so k <u>cannot be positive</u>.
If k is <u>negative</u>, then h(x) is negative for $0 < x \leq 2$, so k <u>cannot be negative</u>.

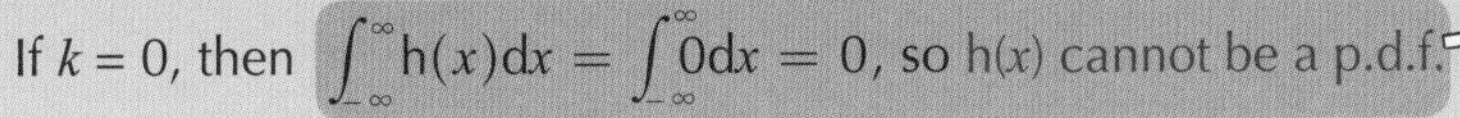

If $k = 0$, then $\int_{-\infty}^{\infty} h(x)dx = \int_{-\infty}^{\infty} 0dx = 0$, so h($x$) cannot be a p.d.f.

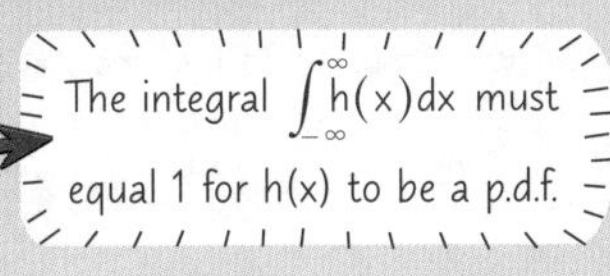

Three things you should definitely know about a p.d.f...

There's not really heaps to say about probability density functions. They <u>can't be negative</u>, the <u>total area under a p.d.f. must equal 1</u>, and you can find probabilities by finding areas under the p.d.f. <u>between different limits</u>. If you remember just those facts and can do a bit of integration, then you'll be well on the way to earning a few easy marks come exam time.

Mean and Variance

You'll have seen something a bit like this in S1 — except there, the random variables were discrete and the formulas involved a summation (Σ). Here, the random variables are continuous, and you're going to need to integrate.

Integrate to Find the Mean of a Continuous Random Variable

Mean of a Continuous Random Variable

If X is a continuous random variable with p.d.f. $f(x)$, then its mean (μ) or expected value ($E(X)$) is given by:

$$\mu = E(X) = \int_{-\infty}^{\infty} x f(x)dx$$

This is a bit like the formula for the mean (expected value) of a discrete random variable — except the sigma (Σ) has been replaced with an integral sign, and p_i with $f(x)dx$.

EXAMPLE Find the expected value of the continuous random variable X with p.d.f. $f(x)$ given below.

$$f(x) = \begin{cases} \frac{3}{32}(4 - x^2) & \text{for } -2 \leq x \leq 2 \\ 0 & \text{otherwise} \end{cases}$$

$$E(X) = \int_{-\infty}^{\infty} xf(x)dx = \int_{-2}^{2} x \cdot \frac{3}{32}(4 - x^2)dx$$

$$= \int_{-2}^{2}\left(\frac{3}{8}x - \frac{3x^3}{32}\right)dx = \left[\frac{3x^2}{16} - \frac{3x^4}{128}\right]_{-2}^{2}$$

$$= \left(\frac{3 \times 2^2}{16} - \frac{3 \times 2^4}{128}\right) - \left(\frac{3 \times (-2)^2}{16} - \frac{3 \times (-2)^4}{128}\right) = 0$$

You'd expect a mean of 0 here, since $f(x)$ is symmetrical about the y-axis. So you didn't actually need to integrate.

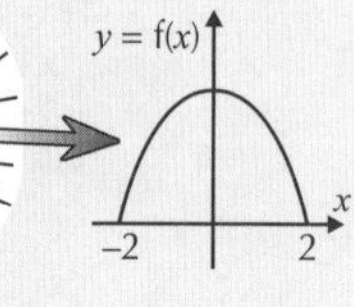

Integrate and Subtract the Square of the Mean to Find the Variance

More integrating, I'm afraid. But stick with it — it'll soon be over.

Variance of a Continuous Random Variable

If X is a continuous random variable with p.d.f. $f(x)$, then its variance is given by:

$$Var(X) = E(X^2) - [E(X)]^2 = E(X^2) - \mu^2$$

$$= \int_{-\infty}^{\infty} x^2 f(x)dx - \mu^2$$

This is exactly the same formula that you've used before for discrete random variables.

EXAMPLE The continuous random variable X has p.d.f. $f(x)$ given below, and a mean of 0. Find the variance of X.

$$f(x) = \begin{cases} \frac{3}{32}(4 - x^2) & \text{for } -2 \leq x \leq 2 \\ 0 & \text{otherwise} \end{cases}$$

You saw above that the mean of this p.d.f. is 0.

$$Var(X) = E(X^2) - \mu^2 = \int_{-\infty}^{\infty} x^2 f(x)dx - \mu^2 = \int_{-2}^{2} x^2 \cdot \frac{3}{32}(4 - x^2)dx - 0^2$$

$$= \int_{-2}^{2}\left(\frac{3x^2}{8} - \frac{3x^4}{32}\right)dx = \left[\frac{x^3}{8} - \frac{3x^5}{160}\right]_{-2}^{2}$$

$$= \left(\frac{2^3}{8} - \frac{3 \times 2^5}{160}\right) - \left(\frac{(-2)^3}{8} - \frac{3 \times (-2)^5}{160}\right) = 0.8.$$

As usual, to find the standard deviation of X, you take the square root of the variance.

Don't be fooled by the easy-looking formulas above...

...there are a couple of traps lurking here for the unwary:

1) Remember what goes inside the integral when you're calculating the variance... it's $x^2 f(x)$.
2) Don't obsess so much about getting that integral right that you forget to subtract the square of the mean.

More on Continuous Random Variables

Find the Median using the Area Under the p.d.f.

The median, M, is the value which splits the area under the p.d.f. in half — i.e. the area to the left of M is 0.5 and the area to the right of M is 0.5.

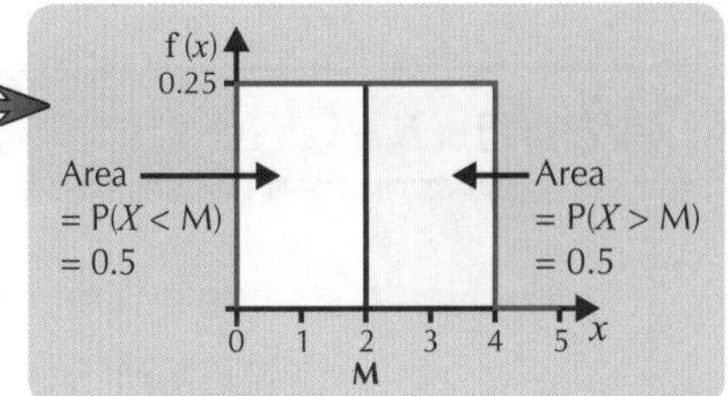

Median of a Continuous Random Variable

If X is a continuous random variable with probability density function f(x), then:

The median (M) of X is given by $\int_{-\infty}^{M} f(x)dx = 0.5$. ⟸ P(X ≤ M) = 0.5

EXAMPLE The continuous random variable X has the p.d.f. $f(x) = \begin{cases} \frac{x}{6} & \text{for } 2 \le x \le 4 \\ 0 & \text{otherwise} \end{cases}$

Find the value of the median (M) of X.

$$\int_{-\infty}^{M} f(x)dx = 0.5 \Rightarrow \int_{2}^{M} \frac{x}{6}dx = 0.5 \Rightarrow \frac{1}{6}\int_{2}^{M} xdx = 0.5 \Rightarrow \frac{1}{6}\left[\frac{x^2}{2}\right]_2^M = 0.5$$

$$\Rightarrow \frac{1}{6}\left[\frac{M^2}{2} - \frac{4}{2}\right] = 0.5 \Rightarrow \frac{M^2 - 4}{12} = 0.5 \Rightarrow M^2 - 4 = 6 \Rightarrow M = \sqrt{10}$$

Always check that your answer seems sensible. Here, it has to be between 2 and 4, so $\sqrt{10}$ = 3.16... looks fine.

The Shape of f(x) can tell you something about the Distribution of X

By sketching the graph of a probability density function f(x), you can see the shape of the distribution of the random variable X. And the shape can tell you, for example, about the probability of different values, or the spread of the distribution.

EXAMPLE The continuous random variables X and Y have the probability density functions shown below.

$$X:\ f(x) = \begin{cases} \frac{3x^2}{2} & \text{for } -1 \le x \le 1 \\ 0 & \text{otherwise} \end{cases}$$

$$Y:\ g(x) = \begin{cases} \frac{1}{2} & \text{for } -1 \le x \le 1 \\ 0 & \text{otherwise} \end{cases}$$

a) Sketch the graphs of f(x) and g(x).

b) Describe the difference between the distributions of the random variables X and Y.

a)

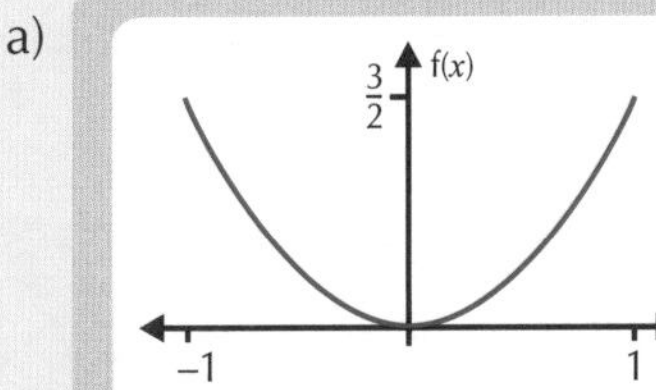

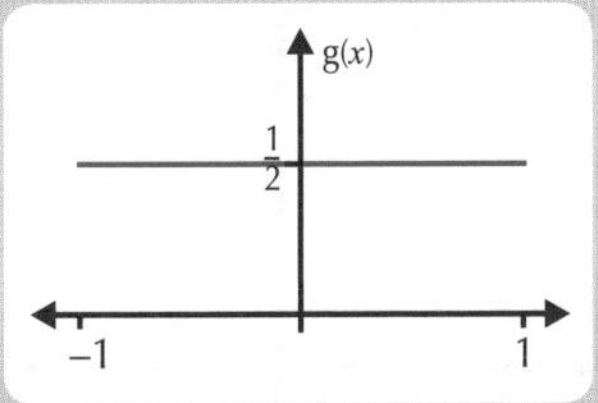

A sketch means you just need to outline the basic shape of the graph — you don't need to plot individual points.

b) X is more likely to take a value close to the ends of the interval — i.e. close to –1 or 1.
Y is equally likely to take any value in the interval (–1, 1).

Make sure you talk about the random variables and not just the shapes of the graphs.

Median — hmmm, that rings a vague bell from S1...

You should know the term, but the difference here is that you're finding a theoretical value for the median of a distribution, not the actual median value for a set of data. And the shape of f(x) shows how likely X is to take different values.

S2 Section 2 — Practice Questions

It's the end of Section 2, and I'm going to assume that you know what you're supposed to do.
And if you get any wrong, well... I'll say no more.

Warm-up Questions

1) Find the value of k for each of the probability density functions below.

a) $f(x) = \begin{cases} kx & \text{for } 1 \le x \le 10 \\ 0 & \text{otherwise} \end{cases}$ b) $g(x) = \begin{cases} 0.2x + k & \text{for } 0 \le x \le 1 \\ 0 & \text{otherwise} \end{cases}$

2) For each of the probability density functions below, find: (i) $P(X < 1)$, (ii) $P(2 \le X \le 5)$, (iii) $P(X = 4)$.

a) $f(x) = \begin{cases} 0.08x & \text{for } 0 \le x \le 5 \\ 0 & \text{otherwise} \end{cases}$ b) $g(x) = \begin{cases} 0.02(10 - x) & \text{for } 0 \le x \le 10 \\ 0 & \text{otherwise} \end{cases}$

3) Find the exact value of k for each of the probability density functions below.
Then for each p.d.f., find $P(X < 1)$.

a) $f(x) = \begin{cases} kx^2 & \text{for } 0 \le x \le 5 \\ 0 & \text{otherwise} \end{cases}$ b) $g(x) = \begin{cases} 0.1x^2 + kx & \text{for } 0 \le x \le 2 \\ 0 & \text{otherwise} \end{cases}$

4) Say whether the following are probability density functions. Explain your answers.

a) $f(x) = \begin{cases} 0.1x^2 + 0.2 & \text{for } 0 \le x \le 2 \\ 0 & \text{otherwise} \end{cases}$ b) $g(x) = \begin{cases} x & \text{for } -1 \le x \le 1 \\ 0 & \text{otherwise} \end{cases}$

5) The random variables X and Y have p.d.f.s. $f(x)$ and $g(y)$ respectively, where

$f(x) = \begin{cases} 0.08x & \text{for } 0 \le x \le 5 \\ 0 & \text{otherwise} \end{cases}$ and $g(y) = \begin{cases} 0.02(10 - y) & \text{for } 0 \le y \le 10 \\ 0 & \text{otherwise} \end{cases}$

a) Find the mean of X and Y.

b) Find the variance of X and Y.

c) Find the median of X.

6) The random variables X and Y have probability density functions $f(x)$ and $g(x)$ respectively.
The graphs of $f(x)$ and $g(x)$ are shown below.

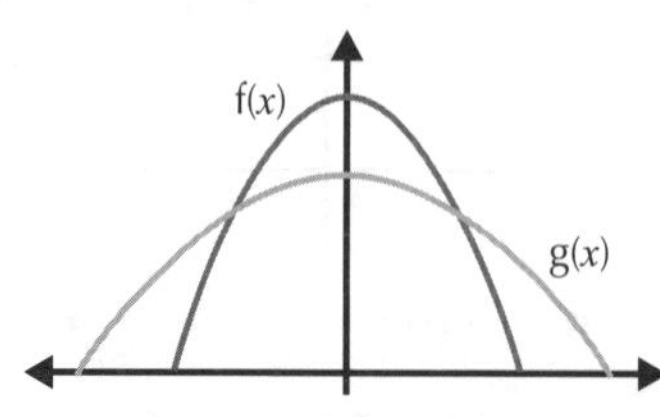

Use the graphs to compare the variance of the random variables X and Y.

S2 Section 2 — Practice Questions

Think of this page as a game. To win the game, you have to get all the answers to the questions right. I know what you're thinking... it's a terrible game. In fact, it's not a game at all, but a shameless fib.

Exam Questions

1 The continuous random variable X has probability density function f(x), as defined below.

$$f(x) = \begin{cases} \frac{1}{k}(x+4) & \text{for } 0 \leq x \leq 2 \\ 0 & \text{otherwise} \end{cases}$$

a) Find the value of k. *(3 marks)*

b) Calculate:

(i) E(X) *(3 marks)*

(ii) Var(X) *(3 marks)*

c) Find P($0 < X < 1.5$). *(2 marks)*

d) Find the median of X. *(5 marks)*

2 The continuous random variable X has probability density function f(x), as defined below.

$$f(x) = \begin{cases} 1.5(1-x^2) & \text{for } 0 \leq x \leq 1 \\ 0 & \text{otherwise} \end{cases}$$

a) Sketch the graph of f(x). *(1 mark)*

b) Find the mean of X. *(3 marks)*

c) Find the variance of X. *(3 marks)*

d) Find P($X < 0.2$). *(2 marks)*

20 observations of X are recorded.

e) Find the probability that exactly 5 of these observations are less than 0.2. *(4 marks)*

Normal Distributions

The normal distribution is everywhere in statistics. Everywhere, I tell you. So learn this well...

The Normal Distribution is 'Bell-Shaped'

1) Loads of things in real life are most likely to fall 'somewhere in the middle', and are much less likely to take extremely high or extremely low values. In this kind of situation, you often get a normal distribution.
2) If you were to draw the p.d.f. of a normally distributed random variable, it would look a bit like a bell. There's a peak in the middle at the mean (or expected value). And the graph is symmetrical — so values the same distance above and below the mean are equally likely.

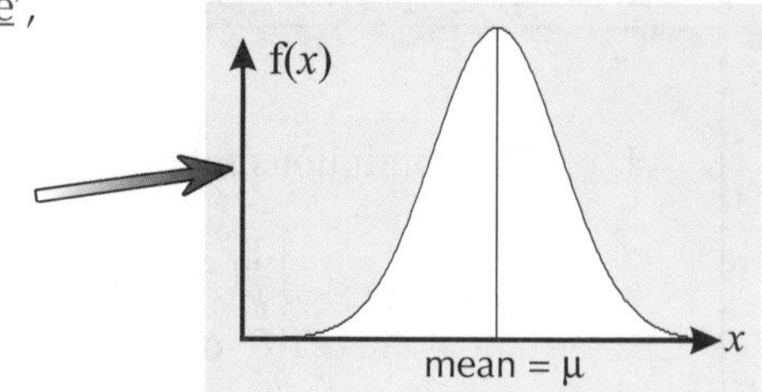

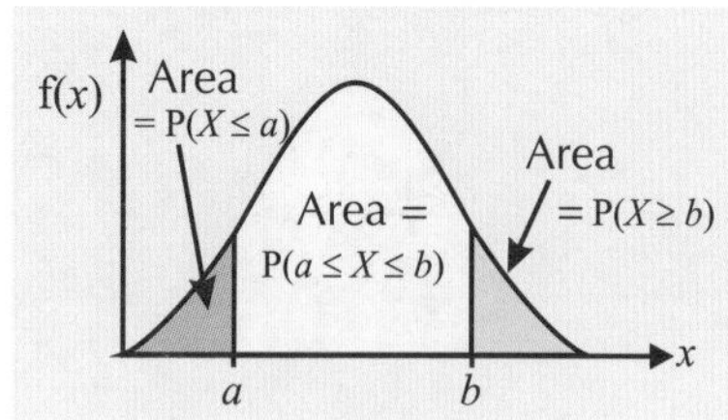

3) Normal distributions are continuous distributions, so the probability of a normally distributed random variable taking a value between two limits is the area under the p.d.f. between those limits. And the total area under the p.d.f. equals the total probability, which is 1.

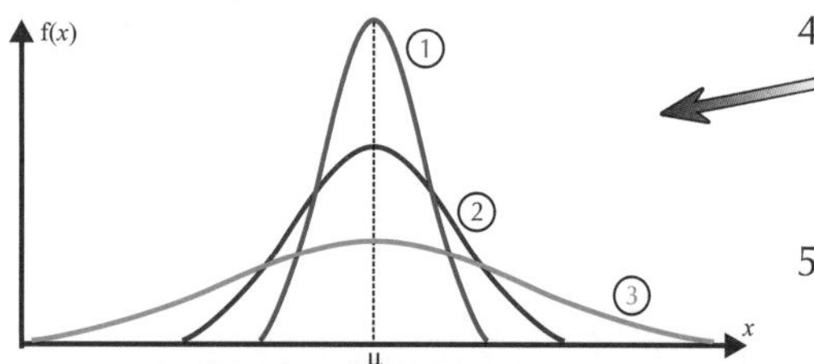

4) These three p.d.f.s all show normal distributions with the same mean (μ), but different variances (σ^2). Graph 1 has a small variance, and graph 3 has a larger variance — but the total area under all three curves is the same (= 1).
5) The most important normal distribution is the standard normal distribution, or Z — this has a mean of zero and a variance of 1.

Normal Distribution $N(\mu, \sigma^2)$

- If X is normally distributed with **mean** μ and **variance** σ^2, it's written $X \sim N(\mu, \sigma^2)$.
- The standard normal distribution Z has **mean** 0 and **variance** 1, i.e. $Z \sim N(0, 1)$.

Use Tables to Work Out Probabilities of Z

Working out the area under a normal distribution curve is usually hard. But for Z, there are tables you can use (see p139). You look up a value of z and these tables (labelled $\Phi(z)$) tell you the probability that $Z \leq z$.

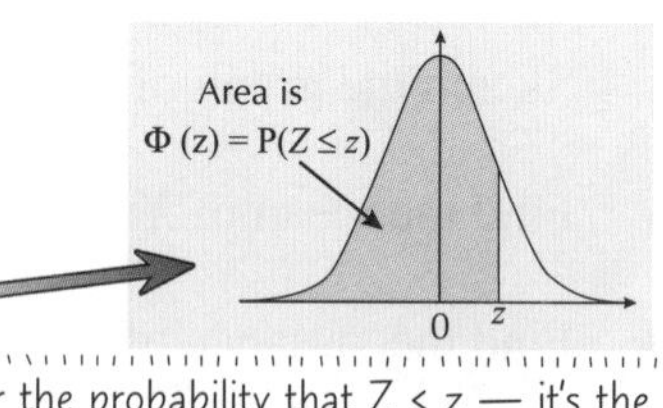

Or the probability that Z < z — it's the same thing.

EXAMPLE Find the probability that:

a) $Z \leq 0.1$, b) $Z < 0.64$, c) $Z > 0.23$, d) $Z \geq -0.42$, e) $Z \leq -1.942$, f) $0.123 < Z \leq 0.824$

Tables only tell you the probability of Z being less than a particular value — use a sketch to work out anything else.

a) $P(Z \leq 0.1) = 0.5398$ ← Just look up z = 0.1 in the tables.

b) $P(Z < 0.64) = 0.7389$ ← For continuous distributions like Z (i.e. with 'no gaps' between its possible values): P(Z < 0.64) = P(Z ≤ 0.64).

c) $P(Z > 0.23) = 1 - P(Z \leq 0.23) = 1 - 0.5910 = 0.4090$

d) $P(Z \geq -0.42) = P(Z \leq 0.42) = 0.6628$ ← Use the symmetry of the graph:

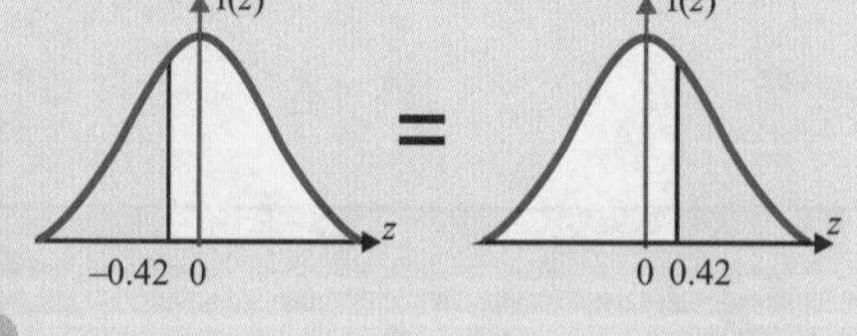

e) $P(Z \leq -1.942) = P(Z \geq 1.942) = 1 - P(Z < 1.942) = 1 - 0.9739 = 0.0261$

f) $P(0.123 < Z \leq 0.824) = P(Z \leq 0.824) - P(Z \leq 0.123)$
$= 0.7950 - 0.5490 = 0.2460$

Again, draw a graph and use the symmetry:

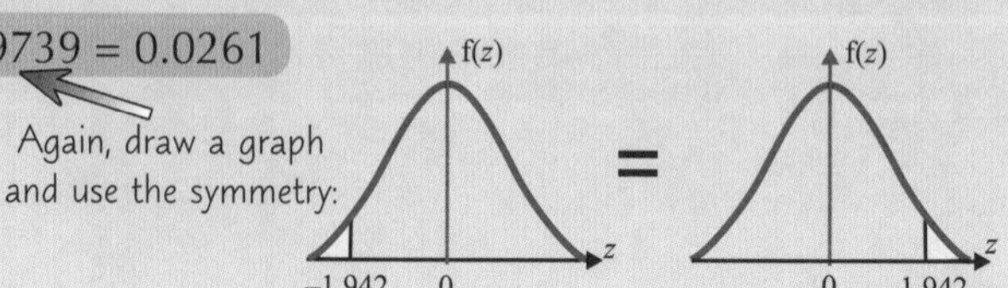

The Standard Normal Distribution, Z

You can use that big table of the normal distribution function ($\Phi(z)$) 'the other way round' as well — by starting with a probability and finding a value for z.

Use **Tables** to Find a **Value** of z if You're Given a **Probability**

EXAMPLE If $P(Z < z) = 0.9554$, then what is the value of z?

Using the table for $\Phi(z)$ (the normal cumulative distribution function), $z = 1.700$.

All the probabilities in the table of $\Phi(z)$ are greater than 0.5, but you can still use the tables with values less than this. You'll most likely need to subtract the probability from 1, and then use a sketch.

EXAMPLE If $P(Z < z) = 0.2611$, then what is the value of z?

① Subtract from 1 to get a probability greater than 0.5: $1 - 0.2611 = 0.7389$

② If $P(Z < z) = 0.7389$, then from the table, $z = 0.640$.

③ So if $P(Z < z) = 0.2611$, then, $z = -0.640$.

If P(Z < z) = 0.2611, then z must be negative.

f(z)
Area = 0.2611
z
–0.640 0

f(z)
Area = 1 – 0.2611 = 0.7389
z
0 0.640

The **Critical Values Table** also Tells You z if You're Given a **Probability**

You use the critical values table in a similar way — you start with a probability, and look up a value for z. Again, the probability you look up is the probability that z is less than a certain number.

EXAMPLE If $P(Z \le z) = 0.9$, then what is the value of z?

Using the critical values table, $z = 1.282$.

You might need to use a bit of imagination and a sketch to get the most out of the critical values table.

EXAMPLE Find z if: a) $P(Z < z) = 0.99$, b) $P(Z > z) = 0.1$, c) $P(Z < z) = 0.05$

a) If $P(Z < z) = 0.99$, then $z = 2.326$.

b) If $P(Z > z) = 0.1$, then $P(Z \le z) = 0.9$. Using the critical values table, $z = 1.282$.

c) $p = 0.05$ isn't in the critical values table, so you have to look up $p = 1 - 0.05 = 0.95$ instead.

If $P(Z \le z) = 0.95$, then $z = 1.645$, which means $P(Z > 1.645) = 0.05$.

Then $P(Z < -1.645) = 0.05$, so z must equal -1.645.

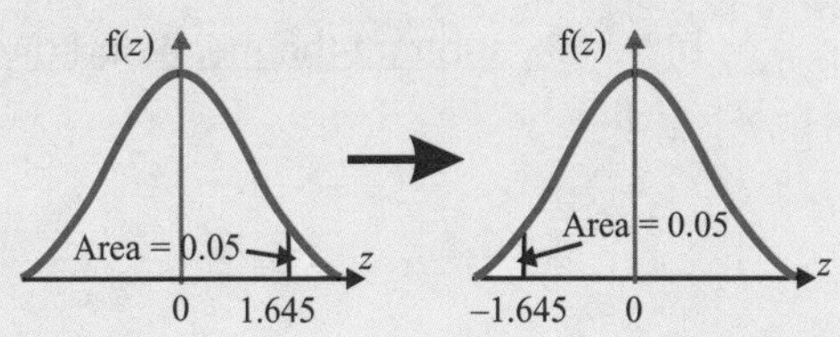

The medium of a random variable follows a paranormal distribution...

It's definitely worth sketching the graph when you're finding probabilities using a normal distribution — you're much less likely to make a daft mistake. So even if the question looks a simple one, draw a quick sketch — it's probably worth it.

Normal Distributions and Z-Tables

All normally-distributed variables can be transformed to Z — which is a marvellous thing.

Transform to Z by Subtracting μ, then dividing by σ

1) You can convert any normally-distributed variable to Z by:
   i) subtracting the mean, and then
   ii) dividing by the standard deviation.

This means that if you subtract μ from any numbers in the question and then divide by σ — you can use your tables for Z.

If $X \sim N(\mu, \sigma^2)$, then $\frac{X-\mu}{\sigma} = Z$, where $Z \sim N(0, 1)$

2) Once you've transformed a variable like this, you can use the Z-tables.

EXAMPLE If $X \sim N(5, 16)$ find: a) $P(X < 7)$, b) $P(X > 9)$, c) $P(5 < X < 11)$

Subtract μ (= 5) from any numbers and divide by σ (= $\sqrt{16}$ = 4) — then you'll have a value for $Z \sim N(0, 1)$.

N(5, 16) means the variance is 16 — take the square root to find the standard deviation.

a) $P(X < 7) = P\left(Z < \frac{7-5}{4}\right) = P(Z < 0.5) = 0.6915$

Look up $P(Z < 0.5)$ in the big table on p.139.

b) $P(X > 9) = P\left(Z > \frac{9-5}{4}\right) = P(Z > 1) = 1 - P(Z \leq 1) = 1 - 0.8413 = 0.1587$

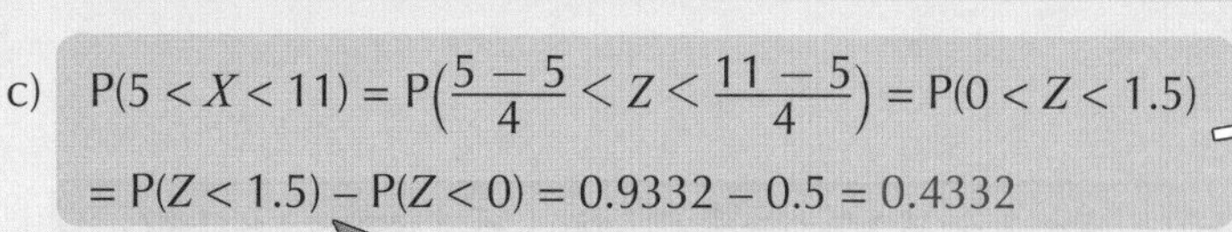

c) $P(5 < X < 11) = P\left(\frac{5-5}{4} < Z < \frac{11-5}{4}\right) = P(0 < Z < 1.5)$

$= P(Z < 1.5) - P(Z < 0) = 0.9332 - 0.5 = 0.4332$

Find the area to the left of 1.5 and subtract the area to the left of 0.

The Z-Distribution Can be Used in Real-Life Situations

EXAMPLE The times taken by a group of people to complete an assault course are normally distributed with a mean of 600 seconds and a variance of 105 seconds. Find the probability that a randomly selected person took: a) less than 575 seconds, b) more than 620 seconds.

If X represents the time taken in seconds, then $X \sim N(600, 105)$.
It's a normal distribution — so your first thought should be to try and 'standardise' it by converting it to Z.

a) Subtract the mean and divide by the standard deviation: $P(X < 575) = P\left(\frac{X-600}{\sqrt{105}} < \frac{575-600}{\sqrt{105}}\right)$
$= P(Z < -2.440)$

So $P(Z < -2.440) = 1 - P(Z \leq 2.440) = 1 - 0.9927 = 0.0073$.

b) Again, subtract the mean and divide by the standard deviation: $P(X > 620) = P\left(\frac{X-600}{\sqrt{105}} > \frac{620-600}{\sqrt{105}}\right)$
$= P(Z > 1.952)$
$= 1 - P(Z \leq 1.952)$
$= 1 - 0.9745 = 0.0255$

Transform to Z and use Z-tables — I repeat: transform to Z and use Z-tables...

The basic idea is always the same — transform your normally-distributed variable to Z, and then use the Z-tables. Statisticians call this the "normal two-step". Well... some of them probably do, anyway. I admit, this stuff is all a bit weird and confusing at first. But as always, work through a few examples and it'll start to click. So get some practice.

Normal Distributions and Z-Tables

You might be given some probabilities and asked to find μ and σ. Just use the same old ideas...

Find μ and σ by First Transforming to Z

EXAMPLE $X \sim N(\mu, 2^2)$ and $P(X < 23) = 0.9015$. Find μ.

This is a normal distribution — so your first thought should be to convert it to Z.

① $P(X < 23) = P[\frac{X-\mu}{2} < \frac{23-\mu}{2}] = P[Z < \frac{23-\mu}{2}] = 0.9015$

Substitute Z for $\frac{X-\mu}{\sigma}$.

$p = 0.9015$ is one of the values in the table for $\Phi(z)$.

② If $P(Z < z) = 0.9015$, then $z = 1.290$

③ So $\frac{23-\mu}{2} = 1.290$ — now solve this to find $\mu = 23 - (2 \times 1.290) = 20.42$

EXAMPLE $X \sim N(53, \sigma^2)$ and $P(X < 50) = 0.1$. Find σ.

Again, this is a normal distribution — so you need to use that lovely standardising equation again.

① $P(X < 50) = P[Z < \frac{50-53}{\sigma}] = P[Z < -\frac{3}{\sigma}] = 0.1$.

Ideally, you'd look up 0.1 in the critical values table to find $-\frac{3}{\sigma}$. Unfortunately, it isn't there, so you have to think a bit...

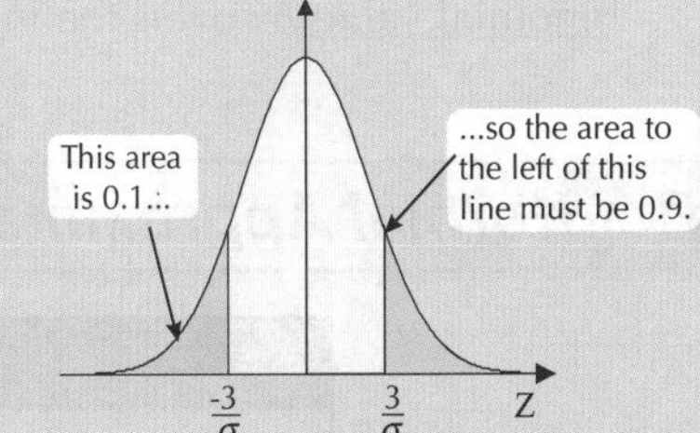

② $P[Z < -\frac{3}{\sigma}]$ is 0.1, so from the symmetry of the graph, $P[Z < \frac{3}{\sigma}]$ must be 0.9.

So look up 0.9 in the critical values table to find that:

$\frac{3}{\sigma} = 1.282$, or $\sigma = 2.34$ (to 3 sig. fig.)

If You Have to Find μ and σ, You'll Need to Solve Simultaneous Equations

EXAMPLE The random variable $X \sim N(\mu, \sigma^2)$. If $P(X < 9) = 0.5596$ and $P(X > 14) = 0.0322$, then find μ and σ.

① $P(X < 9) = P[Z < \frac{9-\mu}{\sigma}] = 0.5596$.

Using the table for $\Phi(z)$, this tells you that $\frac{9-\mu}{\sigma} = 0.150$, or $9 - \mu = 0.15\sigma$.

② $P(X > 14) = P[Z > \frac{14-\mu}{\sigma}] = 0.0322$, which means that $P[Z < \frac{14-\mu}{\sigma}] = 1 - 0.0322 = 0.9678$.

Using the table for $\Phi(z)$, this tells you that $\frac{14-\mu}{\sigma} = 1.850$, or $14 - \mu = 1.85\sigma$.

③ Subtract the equations: $(14 - \mu) - (9 - \mu) = 1.85\sigma - 0.15\sigma$, or $5 = 1.7\sigma$. This gives $\sigma = 5 \div 1.7 = 2.94$ (to 3 sig. fig.).

Now use one of the other equations to find μ: $\mu = 9 - (0.15 \times 2.94) = 8.56$ (to 3 sig. fig.).

The Norman distribution — came to England in 1066...

It's always the same — you always need to do the normal two-step of subtracting the mean and dividing by the standard deviation. Just make sure you don't use the variance by mistake — remember, in $N(\mu, \sigma^2)$, the second number always shows the variance. I'm sure you wouldn't make a mistake... it's just that I'm such a worrier and I do so want you to do well.

Normal Approximation to B(n, p)

If n is big, a binomial distribution (B(n, p)) can be tricky to work with. You saw the Poisson approximation on p.98, but sometimes a normal distribution is a better approximation. But there's a snag.

Use a Continuity Correction to Approximate a Binomial with a Normal

The binomial distribution is discrete but the normal distribution is continuous. To allow for this you need to use a continuity correction. Like a lot of this stuff, it sounds more complicated than it is.

- A binomially-distributed variable X is discrete, so you can work out P(X = 0), P(X = 1), etc.
- A normally-distributed variable is continuous, and so P(X = 0) = P(X = 1) = 0, etc.

So what you do is assume that the 'binomial 1' is spread out over the interval 0.5 - 1.5.

0 ⟸1⟹⟸2⟹⟸3⟹⟸4⟹
0.5 1.5 2.5 3.5 4.5

Then to approximate the binomial P(X = 1), you find the normal P(0.5 < X < 1.5).

Similarly, the 'binomial 2' is spread out over the interval 1.5 - 2.5, and so on.

Learn these Continuity Corrections

The interval you need to use with your normal distribution depends on the binomial probability you're trying to find out.

The general principle is the same, though — each binomial value b covers the interval from $b - \frac{1}{2}$ up to $b + \frac{1}{2}$.

Binomial	Normal	
$P(X = b)$	$P(b - \frac{1}{2} < X < b + \frac{1}{2})$	
$P(X \leq b)$	$P(X < b + \frac{1}{2})$	...to include b
$P(X < b)$	$P(X < b - \frac{1}{2})$	...to exclude b
$P(X \geq b)$	$P(X > b - \frac{1}{2})$	...to include b
$P(X > b)$	$P(X > b + \frac{1}{2})$	...to exclude b

The Normal Approximation Only Works Well under Certain Conditions

Normal Approximation to the Binomial

Suppose the random variable X follows a binomial distribution, i.e. $X \sim \mathbf{B}(n, p)$.

If (i) $np > 5$ and (ii) $nq > 5$, where $q = 1 - p$,

then $X \sim \mathbf{N}(np, npq)$ (approximately).

The approximation works best when n is large and $p \approx \frac{1}{2}$.

Since for a binomial distribution, $\mu = np$ and $\sigma^2 = npq$.

EXAMPLE If $X \sim$ B(80, 0.4), use a suitable approximation to find: (i) P(X < 45) and (ii) P($X \geq$ 40).

You need to make sure first that the normal approximation is suitable...

$np = 32 > 5$, and $nq = 48 > 5$, so the normal approximation is valid.

$q = 1 - p$

You already know $np = 80 \times 0.4 = 32$. You also need to work out npq: $npq = 80 \times 0.4 \times (1 - 0.4) = 19.2$.

So the approximation you need is: $X \sim N(32, 19.2)$

So the standard deviation is $\sqrt{19.2}$.

Now apply a continuity correction, transform the variable to the standard normal distribution (Z), and use tables.

(i) You need P(X < 45) — so with the continuity correction this is P(X < 44.5).

$$P(X < 44.5) = P\left(\frac{X - 32}{\sqrt{19.2}} < \frac{44.5 - 32}{\sqrt{19.2}}\right) = P(Z < 2.853) = 0.9978$$

See page 139 for the normal distribution tables.

(ii) Now you need P($X \geq$ 40) — with the continuity correction this is P(X > 39.5).

$$P(X > 39.5) = P\left(\frac{X - 32}{\sqrt{19.2}} > \frac{39.5 - 32}{\sqrt{19.2}}\right) = P(Z > 1.712) = 1 - P(Z \leq 1.712) = 1 - 0.9566 = 0.0434$$

Normal Approximation to B(n, p)

I know what you're thinking — you want to know just how good a normal approximation actually is. Well, let's see...

EXAMPLE: Newborn babies

The average number of births per year in a hospital is 228. If each baby is equally likely to be a boy or a girl, then use a suitable approximation to find the probability that next year:

(i) there will be more boys born than girls,

(ii) exactly 100 boys will be born.

Mean = np = 228 × 0.5 = 114
Variance = npq = 228 × 0.5 × 0.5 = 57

If X represents the number of boys born next year, then you can assume that $X \sim B(228, 0.5)$.
Since $np > 5$ and $nq > 5$, you can use a normal approximation: $X \sim N(114, 57)$.

(i) You need to find $P(X > 114)$. With a continuity correction, this is $P(X > 114.5)$.
It's a normal distribution, so transform this to Z, the standard normal distribution.

$$P(X > 114.5) = P\left(\frac{X - 114}{\sqrt{57}} > \frac{114.5 - 114}{\sqrt{57}}\right) = P(Z > 0.066)$$
$$= 1 - P(Z \leq 0.066) = 1 - 0.5263 = 0.4737$$

Using B(228, 0.5) instead of the normal approximation, you get 0.4736 — so this is a really good approximation.

(ii) With a continuity correction, you need to find $P(99.5 < X < 100.5)$.

$$P(99.5 < X < 100.5) = P(X < 100.5) - P(X < 99.5)$$
$$= P\left(\frac{X - 114}{\sqrt{57}} < \frac{100.5 - 114}{\sqrt{57}}\right) - P\left(\frac{X - 114}{\sqrt{57}} < \frac{99.5 - 114}{\sqrt{57}}\right)$$
$$= P(Z < -1.788) - P(Z < -1.921)$$
$$= (1 - P(Z \leq 1.788)) - (1 - P(Z \leq 1.921))$$
$$= 1 - 0.9632 - 1 + 0.9727 = 0.0095$$

Using B(228, 0.5) instead of the normal approximation, you also get 0.0095.

EXAMPLE: Survival rates

a) On average, only 23% of the young of a particular species of bird survive to adulthood. If 80 chicks of this species are randomly selected, use a suitable approximation to find the probability that at least 30% of them survive.

b) If the survival rate were instead 18%, find the probability that more than three-quarters of the 80 chicks would die.

If X represents the number of survivors, then $X \sim B(80, 0.23)$.
Here, p isn't particularly close to 0.5, but n is quite large.
Check the values of np and nq: $np = 80 \times 0.23 = 18.4$ and $nq = 80 \times (1 - 0.23) = 61.6$.

Both np and nq are much greater than 5, so a normal approximation is suitable — N(18.4, 14.168).

Mean = np = 80 × 0.23 = 18.4
Variance = npq = 80 × 0.23 × 0.77 = 14.168

30% of 80 = 24, so with a continuity correction, you need to find $P(X > 23.5)$.

$$P(X > 23.5) = P\left(Z > \frac{23.5 - 18.4}{\sqrt{14.168}}\right) = P(Z > 1.355) = 1 - P(Z \leq 1.355)$$
$$= 1 - 0.9123 = 0.0877$$

Using the original binomial distribution gives an answer of 0.0904, so this is a fairly good approximation.

b) This time, $X \sim B(80, 0.18)$, which means $np = 80 \times 0.18 = 14.4$ and $nq = 80 \times (1 - 0.18) = 65.6$.
So even though p is now quite far from 0.5, use the normal approximation — N(14.4, 11.808).
If more than three-quarters do not survive, that means $X < 20$, so you need to find $P(X < 19.5)$.

$$P(X < 19.5) = P\left(Z < \frac{19.5 - 14.4}{\sqrt{11.808}}\right) = P(Z < 1.484) = 0.9312$$

Using the original binomial distribution gives an answer of 0.9270, so this is another pretty good approximation.

Admit it — the normal distribution is the most amazing thing ever...

So the normal approximation works pretty well, even when p isn't really all that close to 0.5. But even so, you should always show that your approximation is 'suitable'. In fact, the question will usually tell you to use a 'suitable approximation', so part of your answer should be to show that you've made sure that it is actually okay. Remember that.

Normal Approximation to Po(λ)

More approximations, I'm afraid. But on the bright side, Mr Poisson is back. Good old Mr Poisson.

The Normal Approximation to Po(λ) Works Best if λ is Big

Normal Approximation to the Poisson Distribution

Suppose the random variable X follows a Poisson distribution, i.e. $X \sim \mathbf{Po}(\lambda)$.
If λ is large, then (approximately) $X \sim N(\lambda, \lambda)$.

Since for a Poisson distribution, mean = variance = λ (see page 95).

Ideally, you want λ 'as large as possible' — but in practice as long as $\lambda > 15$, then you're fine.

Use a Continuity Correction to Approximate a Poisson with a Normal

Since a Poisson distribution is discrete (it can only take values 0, 1, 2...) but a normal distribution is continuous, you need to use a continuity correction. (See p.112 for more about continuity corrections.)

EXAMPLE If $X \sim \text{Po}(49)$, find: a) $P(X < 50)$, b) $P(X \geq 45)$, c) $P(X = 60)$.

Since λ is large (it's greater than 15), you can use a normal approximation — $X \sim N(49, 49)$.

a) The continuity correction means you need to find $P(X < 49.5)$.

Transform to Z and use tables: $P(X < 49.5) = P\left(\frac{X-49}{7} < \frac{49.5-49}{7}\right) = P(Z < 0.071) = 0.5283$

b) This time you need to find $P(X > 44.5)$: $P(X > 44.5) = P\left(Z > \frac{44.5-49}{7}\right) = P(Z > -0.643)$
$= 1 - P(Z \leq -0.643) = P(Z \leq 0.643) = 0.7399$

c) $P(X = 60) = P(59.5 < X < 60.5) = P(X < 60.5) - P(X < 59.5)$
$= P\left(Z < \frac{60.5-49}{7}\right) - P\left(Z < \frac{59.5-49}{7}\right) = P(Z < 1.643) - P(Z < 1.5)$
$= 0.9498 - 0.9332 = 0.0166$

EXAMPLE A sloppy publishing company produces books containing an average of 25 random errors per page. Use a suitable approximation to find the probability of: a) fewer than 20 errors on a particular page, b) exactly 25 errors on a particular page.

The errors happen randomly, singly and (on average) at a constant rate, and so the number of errors that occur on a single page (X) will follow a Poisson distribution. Since there's an average of 25 errors per page, $X \sim \text{Po}(25)$.

a) Since λ is large (greater than 15), you can use a normal approximation — i.e. $X \sim N(25, 25)$.
You need to use a continuity correction here, so P(fewer than 20 errors) $\approx P(X < 19.5)$.

Transform to Z and use tables: $P(X < 19.5) = P\left(\frac{X-25}{5} < \frac{19.5-25}{5}\right) = P(Z < -1.1)$
$= 1 - P(Z \leq 1.1)$
$= 1 - 0.8643 = 0.1357$

b) P(exactly 25 errors on a page) $\approx P(24.5 < X < 25.5) = P(X < 25.5) - P(X < 24.5)$.

Transform to Z and use tables: $P(X < 25.5) - P(X < 24.5) = P\left(Z < \frac{25.5-25}{5}\right) - P\left(Z < \frac{24.5-25}{5}\right)$
$= P(Z < 0.1) - P(Z < -0.1)$
$= P(Z < 0.1) - (1 - P(Z \leq 0.1)) = 0.5398 - (1 - 0.5398) = 0.0796$

The abnormal approximation — guess wildly then say 'Close enough'...

Lordy, lordy... the number of times you've had to read 'transform something to Z and use tables'. But that's the thing... if you can find probabilities from a normal distribution, then it's bound to be worth marks in the exam. On a different note, continuity corrections are fairly easy to use — it's remembering to use one in the first place that can be a bit tricky.

More About Approximations

You need to know a few different approximations for S2 — and to be honest, it can all get a bit confusing. But although the picture below looks like a complex wiring diagram, it's actually an easy-to-use flowchart to sum up your options.

Approximate if You're **Told to**, or if Your **Tables** 'Don't Go High Enough'

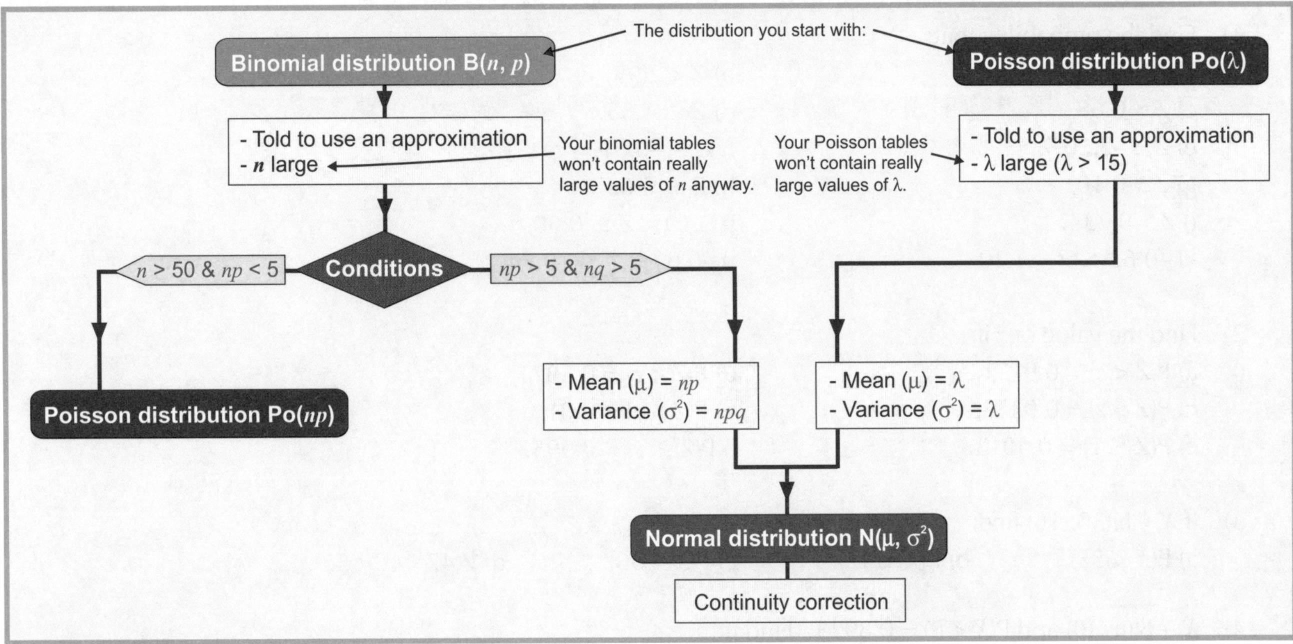

EXAMPLE:

A supermarket gives a customer a free bag when that customer can fit no more items into their existing bags. The number of bags given away was counted. It was found that 62% of customers needed at least one free bag, 1% of customers needed more than 5 free bags, and an average of 8 bags were given away each minute.

If the supermarket has 400 customers one particular morning, use suitable approximations to find:

a) the probability that more than 250 customers take at least one bag,
b) the probability that fewer than 10 customers take more than 5 bags,
c) the probability that more than 500 bags are given away in the first hour after the store opens.

a) Let X represent how many of the 400 customers take at least one bag.
Then $X \sim B(400, 0.62)$, and you need to find $P(X > 250)$.
Here, $np = 248 > 5$ and $nq = 152 > 5$ — so approximate X with $N(248, 94.24)$.

$$P(X > 250) \approx P(X > 250.5) = P\left(\frac{X - 248}{\sqrt{94.24}} > \frac{250.5 - 248}{\sqrt{94.24}}\right) = P(Z > 0.258) = 1 - P(Z \leq 0.258) = 0.3982$$

b) Let M represent the total number of customers taking more than 5 bags.
Then $M \sim B(400, 0.01)$, and you need to find $P(M < 10)$.
Here, $n = 400 > 50$ and $np = 4 < 5$ — so use a Poisson approximation: $Po(4)$

$$P(M < 10) = P(M \leq 9) = 0.9919$$

Bags given away per minute ~ Po(8). So bags per hour ~ Po(8 × 60).

c) Let R represent the number of bags given away in the first hour. This is not a fixed number of trials, so it's not a binomial distribution. But the period is fixed (1 hour), so it's Poisson — in fact, $R \sim Po(480)$.
You need to find $P(R > 500)$. Approximate R with $N(480, 480)$.

$$P(R > 500) \approx P(R > 500.5) = P\left(\frac{R - 480}{\sqrt{480}} > \frac{500.5 - 480}{\sqrt{480}}\right) = P(Z > 0.936) = 1 - 0.8253 = 0.1747$$

Check your values of n, np and nq — then decide what to do...

The trickiest decision you face when approximating is whether to approximate $B(n, p)$ with a Poisson or a normal distribution — and it all depends on np really. So once you've made that decision, you should be off and running. But don't forget that continuity correction if you're using the normal approximation. You have been warned.

S2 Section 3 — Practice Questions

You've come this far... don't give up now... only two more pages to go. And they're only questions — so it's not like there's loads more you're going to need to cram into your already crowded head. Loins girded? Good, here we go...

Warm-up Questions

1) Find the probability that:
   a) $Z < 0.84$, b) $Z < 2.95$,
   c) $Z > 0.68$, d) $Z \geq 1.55$,
   e) $Z < -2.10$, f) $Z \leq -0.01$,
   g) $Z > 0.10$, h) $Z \leq 0.647$,
   i) $Z > 0.234$, j) $0.10 < Z \leq 0.50$,
   k) $-0.62 \leq Z < 1.10$, l) $-0.99 < Z \leq -0.74$.

2) Find the value of z if:
   a) $P(Z < z) = 0.9131$, b) $P(Z < z) = 0.5871$,
   c) $P(Z > z) = 0.0359$, d) $P(Z > z) = 0.01$,
   e) $P(Z \leq z) = 0.4013$, f) $P(Z \geq z) = 0.995$.

3) If $X \sim N(50, 16)$ find:
   a) $P(X < 55)$, b) $P(X < 42)$, c) $P(X > 56)$ d) $P(47 < X < 57)$.

4) $X \sim N(\mu, 10)$ and $P(X < 8) = 0.8925$. Find μ.

5) $X \sim N(11, \sigma^2)$ and $P(X > 26) = 0.05$. Find σ.

6) The mass of items produced by a factory is normally distributed with a mean of 55 grams and a standard deviation of 4.4 grams. Find the probability of a randomly chosen item having a mass of:
   a) less than 55 grams, b) less than 50 grams, c) more than 60 grams.

7) The mass of eggs laid by an ostrich is normally distributed with a mean of 1.4 kg and a standard deviation of 300 g. Find the probability of a randomly chosen egg from this bird having a mass of:
   a) less than 1 kg, b) more than 1.5 kg, c) between 1300 and 1600 g.

8) The random variable X follows a binomial distribution: $X \sim B(100, 0.45)$.
   Using a normal approximation and continuity corrections, find:
   a) $P(X > 50)$, b) $P(X \leq 45)$, c) $P(40 < X \leq 47)$.

9) The random variable X follows a Poisson distribution: $X \sim Po(25)$.
   Using a normal approximation and continuity corrections, find:
   a) $P(X \leq 20)$, b) $P(X > 15)$, c) $P(20 \leq X < 30)$.

10) Seven people on average join the queue in the local post office every 15 minutes during the 7 hours it is open. The number of people working in the post office is constantly adjusted depending on how busy it is, with the result that there is a constant probability of 0.7 of any person being served within 1 minute.
    a) Find the probability of more than 200 people joining the queue in the post office on a particular day.
    b) If exactly 200 people come to the post office on a particular day, what is the probability that less than 70% of them are seen within a minute?

S2 Section 3 — Practice Questions

One last hurdle before you can consider yourself fully up to speed with the normal distribution...

Exam Questions

1 The lifetimes of a particular type of battery are normally distributed with mean μ and standard deviation σ. A student using these batteries finds that 25% last less than 20 hours and 90% last less than 30 hours. Find μ and σ.
(7 marks)

2 The random variable X is binomially distributed with $X \sim B(100, 0.6)$.

a) (i) State the conditions needed for X to be well approximated by a normal distribution. *(2 marks)*

(ii) Explain why a continuity correction is necessary in these circumstances. *(2 marks)*

b) Using a suitable approximation, find:

(i) $P(X \geq 65)$ *(4 marks)*

(ii) $P(50 < X < 62)$ *(3 marks)*

3 The random variable X follows a binomial distribution: $X \sim B(n, p)$.
X is approximated by the normally distributed random variable Y.
Using this normal approximation, $P(X \leq 151) = 0.8944$ and $P(X > 127) = 0.9970$.

a) Find the mean and standard deviation of the normal approximation. *(8 marks)*

b) Use your results from a) to find n and p. *(4 marks)*

4 A factory has the capacity to increase its output by 50 items per week. A potential new customer has said it could sign a contract to order an average of 40 items per week, although the exact number of items needed each week will vary according to a Poisson distribution.

a) Specify a distribution that could be used to model the number of extra items that will be ordered per week if the new contract is signed. *(1 mark)*

b) Using a suitable approximation, find the probability that the number of items the potential new customer will order in a given week will exceed the factory's spare capacity. *(3 marks)*

c) The contract says that if the factory does not meet the new customer's order in two consecutive weeks, the factory must pay compensation. The factory's manager decides that he will only sign the contract if the probability of having to pay compensation in a given week is less than 0.01. Should the factory's manager sign the contract? Explain your answer. *(1 mark)*

Sampling

No time for any small talk, I'm afraid. It's straight on with the business of populations and how to find out about them.

A Population is a Group of People or Items

In any statistical investigation, there'll be a group of people or items you want to find out about. This group is called the population, and could be:

- All the students in a maths class
- All the penguins in Antarctica
- All the chocolate puddings produced by a company in a year

You could find out about a population by collecting information from every single member. But that's usually difficult, expensive and time-consuming — so it's more common to use a sample instead.

A Sample needs to be Representative of its Population

1) If collecting information from every member of a population is impossible or impractical, you can find out about a population by questioning or examining just a selection of people or items. This selected group is called a sample.
2) Data collected from a sample is used to draw conclusions about the whole population. So it's vital that the sample is as much like the population as possible. A biased sample is one which doesn't fairly represent the population.

To Avoid Sampling Bias:

① Select from the correct population and make sure none of the population is excluded. This usually involves making an accurate list of everyone/everything in the population. E.g. if you want to find out the views of residents from a particular street, your sample should only include residents from that street and should be chosen from a full list of the residents.

② Select your sample at random — see below. Non-random sampling methods include things like the sampler just asking their friends (who might all give similar answers), or asking for volunteers (meaning they only get people with strong views on a subject).

③ Make sure all your sample members respond — otherwise the results could be biased. E.g. if some of your sampled residents are out when you go to interview them, it's important that you go back and get their views another time.

3) Using a random sample means there will be no systematic bias in your sample. A 'simple random sample of size n' is one where n members of the population are chosen at random from a full list of the population.

In a Simple Random Sample...

- Every person or item in the population has an equal chance of being in the sample.
- Each selection is independent of every other selection.

This means every single possible sample is equally likely.

To choose a simple random sample, give every member of the population a unique number, then generate a list of random numbers and match them to the population to select your sample.

Use a computer, calculator, dice or random number tables to generate random numbers.

You can also generate a random sample by choosing the first sample member randomly, then selecting every nth member after that. However, using this method the selections aren't independent, so all possible samples are not equally likely.

Statistics are Calculated Using Only the Values from your Sample

You're nearly at the end of the A2 Statistics sections now. So it must be time to say what a statistic actually is.

Statistics

A statistic is a quantity calculated only from the known observations in a sample.
A statistic is a random variable — it takes different values for different samples.

EXAMPLE If $X_1, \ldots, X_{10}$ form a random sample from a population with unknown mean, μ, then:

- $X_{10} - X_1$ and $\frac{\sum X_i}{n}$ are both statistics.
- $\sum X_i^2 - \mu$ isn't a statistic (since it depends on the unknown value of μ).

$\frac{\sum X}{n}$ is the sample mean, usually written $\overline{X}$.

1) If you took a sample of observations and calculated a particular statistic, then took another sample and calculated the same statistic, then took another sample, etc., you'd end up with lots of values of the same statistic.
2) The probability distribution of a statistic is called a sampling distribution.

Sampling Distribution of $\overline{X}$

Knowing the sampling distribution of a statistic is essential when it comes to hypothesis testing (see p.121).
For now, here are two important results for the sampling distribution of the sample mean, $\overline{X}$.

If X follows a Normal Distribution, the Sampling Distribution of $\overline{X}$ is Normal too

1) Suppose you've got a random variable X, with mean μ and variance σ^2.
2) When you take a sample of n readings from the distribution of X, you can work out the sample mean $\overline{X} = \frac{\sum X}{n}$.
   If you now keep taking samples of size n from that distribution and working out the sample means, then you get a collection of sample means, drawn from the sampling distribution of $\overline{X}$.
3) This sampling distribution also has mean μ, but the variance is $\frac{\sigma^2}{n}$.
4) And if X follows a normal distribution, then the sampling distribution of $\overline{X}$ will also be normal.

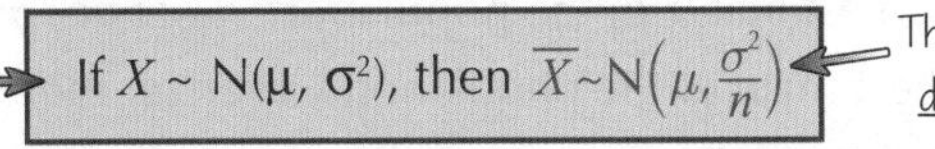

If $X \sim N(\mu, \sigma^2)$, then $\overline{X} \sim N\left(\mu, \frac{\sigma^2}{n}\right)$

This is the sampling distribution of $\overline{X}$.

EXAMPLE A continuous random variable X has the distribution $X \sim N(20, 16)$. The mean of a sample of 10 observations of X is defined as $\overline{X}$. Write down the sampling distribution of $\overline{X}$.

$X \sim N(20, 16)$, so $\overline{X} \sim N\left(20, \frac{16}{10}\right) \Rightarrow \overline{X} \sim N(20, 1.6)$

EXAMPLE A continuous random variable X has the distribution N(45, 25).
If $\overline{X}$ is the mean of n observations of X and $P(\overline{X} < 45.5) = 0.8413$, find the value of n.

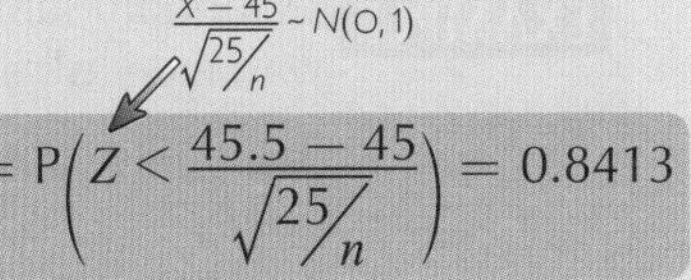

(1) $X \sim N(45, 25)$, so $\overline{X} \sim N\left(45, \frac{25}{n}\right)$. Since $\overline{X}$ has a normal distribution, you can standardise it and use tables for Z (see p.139).
Subtract the mean and divide by the standard deviation to get: $P(\overline{X} < 45.5) = P\left(Z < \frac{45.5 - 45}{\sqrt{25/n}}\right) = 0.8413$

(Here you're transforming $\overline{X}$ rather than an individual observation.)

(2) Looking up $P(Z < z) = 0.8413$ in the tables, you find that $z = 1$ — and so: $\frac{0.5}{5/\sqrt{n}} = 1 \Rightarrow 0.5 = \frac{5}{\sqrt{n}} \Rightarrow \sqrt{n} = 10 \Rightarrow n = 100$

Even when X Isn't Normally Distributed, $\overline{X} \sim N(\mu, \sigma^2/n)$ (approx.) for Large n

The Central Limit Theorem tells you something about $\overline{X}$ — even if you know nothing at all about the distribution of X.

The Central Limit Theorem

Suppose you take a sample of n readings from any distribution with mean μ and variance σ^2.

- For large n, the distribution of the sample mean, $\overline{X}$, is approximately normal: $\overline{X} \sim N\left(\mu, \frac{\sigma^2}{n}\right)$.
- The bigger n is, the better the approximation will be. (For $n > 30$ it's pretty good.)

EXAMPLE A sample of size 50 is taken from a population with mean 20 and variance 10.
Find the probability that the sample mean is less than 19.

(1) Since n (= 50) is quite large, you can use the Central Limit Theorem. Here $\overline{X} \sim N\left(20, \frac{10}{50}\right) = N(20, 0.2)$ (approx).

(2) You need $P(\overline{X} < 19)$. Standardising gives: $P(\overline{X} < 19) = P\left(Z < \frac{19 - 20}{\sqrt{0.2}}\right) = P(Z < -2.236)$

(3) Now you can use your normal-distribution tables (see p.139).

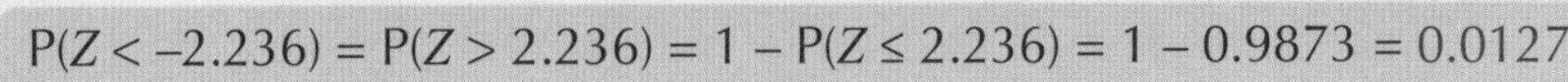

$P(Z < -2.236) = P(Z > 2.236) = 1 - P(Z \leq 2.236) = 1 - 0.9873 = 0.0127$

As always... if you need to, draw a sketch.

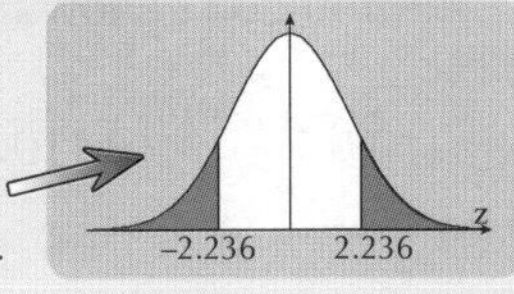

So if in doubt, it's probably normal then...

Now, you can't say the results on this page aren't useful. Especially that Central Limit Theorem. But remember, you can only apply the theorem for big n. Another vital thing to remember is that the variance of the sample mean is σ^2/n not σ^2.

Estimation

The real reason people are interested in statistics is to find out about the population they came from.

Statistics are used to Estimate Population Parameters

1) Parameters are quantities that describe the characteristics of a population, such as the mean or variance. Statistics are used to estimate these parameters. For example, you can use the sample mean, $\overline{X}$, to estimate the population mean, μ (and the sample mean is called an estimator of the population mean).
2) The sample mean is actually an unbiased estimator of the population mean — this means the expected value of the sample mean is the same as the population mean (a good thing).
3) However, if you have a sample $X_1, ..., X_n$ taken from a population, then $\frac{\sum(X_i - \overline{X})^2}{n} = \frac{\sum X_i^2}{n} - \left(\frac{\sum X_i}{n}\right)^2$ is not an unbiased estimator of the population variance, σ^2.
For an unbiased estimate of the population variance, there's a slightly different statistic...

This is the formula for variance you've seen previously.

Unbiased Estimators of Population Variance and Standard Deviation

These are unbiased estimators of the population variance (σ^2) and population standard deviation (σ):

Variance: $S^2 = \frac{n}{n-1}\left[\frac{\sum X_i^2}{n} - \left(\frac{\sum X_i}{n}\right)^2\right] = \frac{\sum(X_i - \overline{X})^2}{n-1}$

Standard deviation: $S = \sqrt{S^2}$

This one's in your formula booklet, but the one in red is more useful: "the mean of the squares minus the square of the mean, multiplied by $\frac{n}{n-1}$".

Greek letters, like σ, are often used for parameters, and Latin letters (e.g. S) are used for statistics.

EXAMPLE A random sample of 5 observations of X was taken from a population whose mean (μ) and variance (σ^2) are unknown. The data is summarised by $\sum x = 28.4$ and $\sum x^2 = 161.38$.

Find unbiased estimates of μ and σ^2.

$\bar{x} = \frac{\sum x}{n} = \frac{28.4}{5} = 5.68$, and $s^2 = \frac{5}{4}\left[\frac{161.38}{5} - \left(\frac{28.4}{5}\right)^2\right] = 0.017$

You should remember from S1 that if you've got lots of raw data it'll be in a table...

EXAMPLE The table shows how many sisters a random sample of 95 students from a school have.

a) Calculate unbiased estimates of the mean and variance for the whole school.

Number of sisters, x	0	1	2	3	4
Frequency, f	30	45	11	8	1

By adding extra rows to the table you can calculate:
$\sum f = 95, \sum fx = 95$ and $\sum fx^2 = 177$

Number of sisters, x	0	1	2	3	4
Frequency, f	30	45	11	8	1
fx	0	45	22	24	4
x^2	0	1	4	9	16
fx^2	0	45	44	72	16

Then, $\bar{x} = \frac{\sum fx}{\sum f} = \frac{95}{95} = 1$

And $s^2 = \frac{\sum(x_i - \bar{x})^2 f_i}{n-1}$, where f_i is the frequency of the data value x_i.

Rearranging to $s^2 = \frac{n}{n-1}\left[\frac{\sum fx^2}{\sum f} - \left(\frac{\sum fx}{\sum f}\right)^2\right]$ gives you: $s^2 = \frac{95}{94}\left[\frac{177}{95} - 1^2\right] = \frac{95}{94} \times \frac{82}{95} = \frac{41}{47} = 0.87$ (2 d.p.)

b) Another random sample of 30 is selected and the number of sisters the students have is recorded. If $\overline{X}$ is the mean of these 30 observations, calculate an estimate of $P(\overline{X} < 1.5)$.

Since n (= 30) is quite large, you can use the Central Limit Theorem to say that $\overline{X} \sim N\left(\mu, \frac{\sigma^2}{n}\right)$ (approx.).

You don't know the true values of μ and σ^2, but you can estimate them using the values you calculated in part a).

So $\overline{X} \sim N\left(1, \frac{41}{1410}\right)$ (approx.) and $P(\overline{X} < 1.5) = P\left(Z < \frac{1.5 - 1}{\sqrt{41/1410}}\right) = P(Z < 2.932) = 0.9983$

I rather like this page — but then I am biased...

... unlike $\overline{X}$ and S^2. You don't need to worry about understanding why these estimators are unbiased — just know that they are and that it's a good thing. So now you know two formulas for variance, which could be confusing, but at least they give you this one on the formula sheet. Remember, you only use this one when you're estimating population variance.

Null and Alternative Hypotheses

As well as estimating population parameters, you can also test theories about them. Hypothesis testing means checking if your theories about a population are consistent with the observations from your sample.

A Hypothesis is a Statement you want to Test

Hypothesis testing is about using statistics to test statements about population parameters.
Unfortunately, it comes with a fleet of terms you need to know.

- **Null Hypothesis (H_0)** — a statement about the value of a population parameter. Your data may allow you to reject this hypothesis.
- **Alternative Hypothesis (H_1)** — a statement that describes the value of the population parameter if H_0 is rejected.
- **Hypothesis test** — a statistical test that tests the claim made about a parameter by H_0 against that made by H_1. It tests whether H_0 should be rejected or not, using evidence from sample data.
- **Test Statistic** — a statistic calculated from sample data which is used to decide whether or not to reject H_0.

1) For any hypothesis test, you need to write two hypotheses — a null hypothesis and an alternative hypothesis.
2) You often choose the null hypothesis to be something you actually think is false. This is because hypothesis tests can only show that statements are false — they can't prove that things are true. So, you're aiming to find evidence for what you think is true, by disproving what you think is false.
3) H_0 needs to give a specific value to the parameter, since all your calculations will be based on this value. You assume this value holds true for the test, then see if your data allows you to reject it. H_1 is then a statement that describes how you think the value of the parameter differs from the value given by H_0.
4) The test statistic you choose depends on the parameter you're interested in. It should be a 'summary' of the sample data, and should have a sampling distribution that can be calculated using the parameter value specified by H_0.

EXAMPLE Jemma thinks that the average length of the worms in her worm farm is greater than 8 cm. She measures the lengths of a random sample of 50 of the worms and calculates the sample mean.

a) Write down a suitable null hypothesis to test Jemma's theory.
b) Write down a suitable alternative hypothesis.
c) Describe the test statistic Jemma should use.

a) The parameter Jemma is interested in is the mean length of all the worms, μ.
She thinks that μ is greater than 8, so she's looking to find evidence that μ does not equal 8.
So, $H_0: \mu = 8$ ← H_0 gives μ the specific value of 8. Jemma is then interested in disproving this hypothesis.

b) H_1 says what Jemma actually thinks. So: $H_1: \mu > 8$

c) The test statistic is the sample mean $\overline{X}$. ← Assuming H_0 is true, by the Central Limit Theorem (p.119), $\overline{X} \sim N\left(8, \frac{\sigma^2}{50}\right)$, where σ^2 = variance.

You actually use the standardised sample mean — you'll see what I mean when you get to page 123.

Hypothesis Tests can be One-Tailed or Two-Tailed

The 'tailed' business is to do with the critical region used by the test — see next page.

For H_0: $\theta = a$, where θ is a parameter and a is a number:

1) The test is one-tailed if H_1 is specific about the value of θ compared to a, i.e. H_1: $\theta > a$, or H_1: $\theta < a$.
2) The test is two-tailed if H_1 specifies only that θ doesn't equal a, i.e. H_1: $\theta \neq a$.

Whether you use a one-tailed or a two-tailed test depends on how you define H_1. And that depends on what you want to find out about the parameter and any suspicions you might have about it.

E.g. in the example above, Jemma suspects that the average worm length is greater than 8 cm. This is what she wants to test, so it is sensible to define H_1: $\mu > 8$.

If she was unsure whether the length was greater than or less than 8 cm, she could define H_1: $\mu \neq 8$.

A statistician's party game — pin two tails on the donkey...

Or should it be one? Anyway, a very important thing to remember is that the results of a hypothesis test are either 'reject H_0', or 'do not reject H_0' — which means you haven't found enough evidence to disprove H_0, and not that you've proved it.

Significance Levels and Critical Regions

You use the value of your test statistic to decide whether or not to reject your null hypothesis. Poor little unloved H_0.

If your Data is **Significant, Reject H_0**

1) You would reject H_0 if the observed value of the test statistic is unlikely under the null hypothesis.
2) The significance level (α) of a test determines how unlikely the value needs to be before H_0 is rejected. It also determines the strength of the evidence that the test has provided — the lower the value of α, the stronger the evidence you have for saying H_0 is false. You'll usually be told what level to use — e.g. 1% (α = 0.01), 5% (α = 0.05) or 10% (α = 0.1). α is also the probability of incorrectly rejecting H_0 — i.e. of getting extreme data by chance.
3) To decide whether your result is significant:
   - Define the sampling distribution of the test statistic under the null hypothesis.
   - Calculate the probability of getting a value that's at least as extreme as the observed value from this distribution.
   - If the probability is less than or equal to the significance level, reject H_0 in favour of H_1.

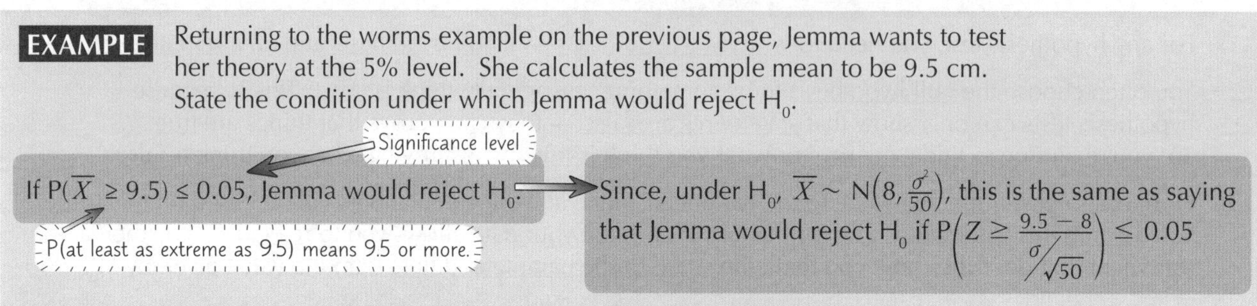

The **Critical Region** *is the* **Set of Significant Values**

The critical region is also known as the rejection region.

1) The critical region (CR) is the set of all values of the test statistic that would cause you to reject H_0. And the acceptance region is the set of values that would mean you do not reject H_0. The critical region is chosen so that P(test statistic is in CR, assuming H_0 is true) = α, and the value on the boundary of the critical region is called the critical value.

   Or, for discrete distributions, as close to α (but not greater than this value) as you can get.
2) One-tailed tests have a single critical region (and critical value), containing the highest or lowest values. For two-tailed tests, the region is split into two — half at the lower end and half at the upper end, so there are two critical values. Each half of the region has a probability of $\frac{1}{2}\alpha$ (or as close as possible, but not greater than).
3) To test whether your result is significant, find the relevant critical value and compare it to the value of your test statistic. If the observed value of the test statistic is 'more extreme' than the critical value and so falls in the critical region, reject H_0.
4) Hypothesis tests for the mean of a normal distribution are usually done using this critical region method. You'll see how on the next page.

In Hypothesis Testing, you can **Work Out How Likely Things are to go Wrong**

1) The significance level (α) of a test is the probability of rejecting H_0 (assuming H_0 is true). So it's the probability of incorrectly rejecting H_0 — i.e. rejecting H_0 when it's true. Another incorrect decision you can make is to not reject H_0 when it's not true.

   For discrete distributions, the actual significance level of a test can be lower than the level of significance specified in the test. There's more on this on page 125.

   TYPE I ERROR — reject H_0 when H_0 is true, TYPE II ERROR — do not reject H_0 when H_0 is not true

2) You can calculate the probability of making each of these errors when doing a hypothesis test:

   P(Type I error) = P(value of test statistic is significant, assuming H_0 is true) — the significance level (α)

   Or the actual significance level — see p.125.

   P(Type II error) = P(value of test statistic isn't significant, assuming H_1 is true) — where a value for H_1 is given

I repeat, X has entered the critical region — we have a significant situation...

Hope you've been following the last two pages closely. Basically, you need two hypotheses and the value of a test statistic calculated from sample data. By assuming H_0 is true, you can find the probabilities of the different values this statistic can take — if the observed value is unlikely enough, reject H_0. But bear in mind there's a chance you might have got it wrong...

Hypothesis Tests and Normal Distributions

OK, it's time to pick your best 'hypothesis testing' foot and put it firmly forward.
If you like normal distributions and you like hypothesis testing, you're going to *love* this page.

For a Normal Population with Known Variance — use a z-Test

1) Suppose $X \sim N(\mu, \sigma^2)$, where you know the value of σ^2 but μ is unknown. If you take a random sample of n observations from the distribution of X, and calculate the sample mean $\overline{X}$, you can use your observed value $\bar{x}$ to test theories about the population mean μ.

2) You want to test whether your value of $\overline{X}$ is likely enough, under the hypothesised value of μ (remember that $\overline{X} \sim N\left(\mu, \frac{\sigma^2}{n}\right)$). So that means finding the critical region for an $N\left(\mu, \frac{\sigma^2}{n}\right)$ distribution.
If your sample mean lies in this critical region, you should reject H_0.

3) However, the only normal distribution that you can look up the probabilities of different values for is the standard normal distribution Z. So, to get your final test statistic, you need to use the classic 'normal trick' — standardise your sample mean by subtracting the mean (use the value you're assuming for the mean — the one in H_0) and dividing by the standard deviation. Then you can compare this test statistic to a critical value from N(0, 1).

Hypothesis Test for the Mean of a Normal Distribution — Known Variance

The test statistic is: $$Z = \frac{\overline{X} - \mu}{\sigma / \sqrt{n}} \sim N(0,1)$$

4) The critical value(s) depends on the significance level α, and whether it's a one-tailed or a two-tailed test.

For example, for a two-tailed test at the 5% level of significance, the critical values are $z = -1.96$ and $z = 1.96$, since $P(Z < -1.96) = 0.025$ and $P(Z > 1.96) = 0.025$. So the critical region is: $Z < -1.96$ or $Z > 1.96$.

Example

The times, in minutes, taken by the athletes in a running club to complete a certain run have been found to follow an N(12, 4) distribution. The coach increases the number of training sessions per week, and a random sample of 20 times run since the increase gives a mean time of 11.2 minutes. Assuming that the variance has remained unchanged, test at the 5% significance level whether there is evidence that the average time has decreased.

Let μ = mean time since increase in training sessions. Then $H_0: \mu = 12$, $H_1: \mu < 12$, $\alpha = 0.05$.

You assume that there's been no change in the value of the parameter (μ), so you can give it a value of 12.

This is what you're looking to find evidence for.

Under H_0, $\overline{X} \sim N(12, 4/20) \Rightarrow \overline{X} \sim N(12, 0.2)$ and $Z = \frac{\overline{X} - 12}{\sqrt{0.2}} \sim N(0,1)$.

Since $\bar{x} = 11.2$, $z = \frac{11.2 - 12}{\sqrt{0.2}} = -1.789$.

This is a one-tailed test and you're interested in the lower end of the distribution. So the critical value is z such that $P(Z < z) = 0.05$. Using the 'normal' tables you find that $P(Z < 1.645) = 0.95$, which means $P(Z > 1.645) = 0.05$, and so by symmetry, $P(Z < -1.645) = 0.05$. So the critical value is -1.645 and the critical region is $Z < -1.645$.

If you want, you can instead do the test by working out P(value at least as extreme as observed sample mean) and comparing it to α. So here you'd do: $P(\overline{X} \le 11.2) = P\left(Z \le \frac{11.2 - 12}{\sqrt{0.2}}\right) = P(Z \le -1.789) = 1 - P(Z \le 1.789) = 1 - 0.9633 = 0.0367 < 0.05$, so reject H_0.

Since $z = -1.789 < -1.645$, the result is significant and there is evidence at the 5% level of significance to reject H_0 and to suggest that the average time has decreased.

Always say "there is evidence to reject H_0", or "there is insufficient evidence to reject H_0". Never talk about "accepting H_0" or "rejecting H_1".

Hypothesis Tests and Normal Distributions

If n is large, you can always use a z-Test

The z-test can also be used in the following situations:

1) The population variance is unknown, but the sample size is large ($n > 30$).

   Use the same test statistic but replace σ with its estimate s, where $s = \sqrt{\frac{n}{n-1}\left[\frac{\sum x^2}{n} - \left(\frac{\sum x}{n}\right)^2\right]}$.

2) The distribution of the population is unknown, but the sample size is large ($n > 30$).

   As long as n is large, you can use the z-test for any population (since you can use the Central Limit Theorem (see p.119) to approximate the sampling distribution of the mean of any distribution by a normal distribution).

The z-test works fine here because for large n, s should be pretty close to σ.

EXAMPLE The average volume of the drinks dispensed by a drinks machine is claimed to be 250 ml. Greg thinks that the machine has developed a fault and wants to test whether the average volume has changed. He measures the volumes, x, of a random sample of 40 drinks from the machine and calculates the following:

$$\sum x = 9800 \quad \text{and} \quad \sum(x - \bar{x})^2 = 3900$$

Carry out Greg's test at the 5% level of significance.

Since n is fairly large, you can apply the Central Limit Theorem and use a z-test with σ estimated by s.

$$\bar{x} = \frac{\sum x}{n} = \frac{9800}{40} = 245\,\text{ml} \quad \text{and} \quad s^2 = \frac{\sum(x-\bar{x})^2}{n-1} = \frac{3900}{39} = 100$$

You can use s^2 in this form, or in the other form shown on p.120. Use whichever is easier with the summary statistics they give you.

The average volume is assumed to be 250 ml, so H_0: $\mu = 250$ and H_1: $\mu \neq 250$. The significance level $\alpha = 0.05$.

Under H_0, $\bar{X} \sim N(250, {}^{100}\!/\!_{40}) \Rightarrow \bar{X} \sim N(250, 2.5)$ and $Z = \frac{\bar{X} - 250}{\sqrt{2.5}} \sim N(0,1)$. $\bar{x} = 245$, so $z = \frac{245 - 250}{\sqrt{2.5}} = -3.16$

This is a two-tailed test at the 5% level. So the critical values are $z = \pm 1.960$, and the CR is $Z < -1.96$ or $Z > 1.96$.

Since $z = -3.16 < -1.96$, the result is significant and there is evidence at the 5% level of significance to reject H_0 and to suggest that the average volume has changed.

EXAMPLE Packets of a particular type of sweets are claimed to have a mean weight of 300 g and a standard deviation of 4 g. The manufacturer checks that the mean weight hasn't fallen below 300 g by selecting a random sample of 100 packets, calculating their mean weight, and carrying out a hypothesis test of the mean (using the assumption that the standard deviation is unchanged from 4 g).

a) For a test at the 5% level of significance, find the critical region in terms of the sample mean $\bar{X}$.
b) Calculate the probability of a Type II error, given that the mean weight has actually fallen to 299 g.

a) First define your hypotheses: H_0: $\mu = 300$ and H_1: $\mu < 300$ ← Since you're only interested in whether the mean weight has decreased.

   Since n is large, the Central Limit Theorem says that $\bar{X} \sim N\left(\mu, \frac{\sigma^2}{n}\right)$.

   Under H_0, $\bar{X} \sim N\left(300, \frac{16}{100}\right) \Rightarrow \bar{X} \sim N(300, 0.16)$ and $Z = \frac{\bar{X} - 300}{0.4} \sim N(0,1)$

   This is a one-tailed test at the 5% level. So the critical value is $z = -1.645$, and the critical region is $Z < -1.645$.

   $Z < -1.645 \Rightarrow \frac{\bar{X} - 300}{0.4} < -1.645$. And rearranging for $\bar{X}$ gives: $\bar{X} < 299.342$

   Remember to give the answer in terms of the sample mean.

b) P(Type II error) = P(test statistic is not significant, assuming H_1 true)

   $$= P(\bar{X} > 299.342 \mid \mu = 299) = P\left(Z > \frac{299.342 - 299}{0.4}\right) = P(Z > 0.855)$$
   $$= 1 - P(Z < 0.855) = 1 - 0.8037 = 0.1963$$

   This is the acceptance region.

Hypothesis Tests and Binomial Distributions

You're only about 57.1% of the way through hypothesis testing, so now might be a good time for a cup of tea. It's also a good time to reacquaint yourself with binomial distributions before you go any further.

Use a *Hypothesis Test* to *Find Out* about the *Population Parameter p*

You can also carry out hypothesis tests using discrete distributions. A population proportion, p, can be tested using the test statistic X = the number of 'successes' in a sample of size n. X will follow a binomial distribution, $B(n, p)$.

EXAMPLE: In a past survey of all of a firm's employees, 20% were in favour of a change to working hours. A later survey is carried out on a random sample of 30 employees, and 2 vote for a change to hours. The manager claims that there has been a decrease in the proportion of employees in favour of a change to working hours.

Stating your hypotheses clearly, test the manager's claim at the 5% level of significance.

1) Start by identifying the population parameter that you're going to test:

   Let p = proportion of employees in favour of change to hours.

2) Write null and alternative hypotheses for p.
   If you assume there's been no change in the proportion: $H_0: p = 0.2$

   The manager's interested in whether the proportion has decreased, so: $H_1: p < 0.2$

   You assume there's been no change in the value of the parameter, so you can give it a value of 0.2. The alternative hypothesis states what the manager actually thinks.

3) State the test statistic X — the number of 'successes', and its sampling distribution under H_0.
   $X \sim B(n, p)$ where n is the number in the sample and p is the probability of 'success' under H_0.

   Let X = number of employees in sample who are in favour of change. Under H_0, $X \sim B(30, 0.2)$.

   The sampling distribution of the test statistic uses the value $p = 0.2$.

4) State the significance level of the test. Here it's 5%, so $\alpha = 0.05$.

5) Test for significance by finding the probability of a value for your test statistic at least as extreme as the observed value. This is a one-tailed test and you're interested in the lower end of the distribution.
   So you want to find the probability of X taking a value less than or equal to 2.

   Using the binomial tables (see p.140): $P(X \leq 2) = 0.0442$, and since $0.0442 < 0.05$, the result is significant.

6) Now write your conclusion. And don't forget to answer the original question:

   There is evidence at the 5% level of significance to reject H_0 and to support the manager's claim that the proportion in favour of change has decreased.

Critical Regions for *Discrete* Distributions are *slightly Different*

You can also do the hypothesis test for p by finding the critical region for the test statistic. However, it's unlikely that you'll be able to find a critical region such that P(test statistic is in CR, assuming H_0 is true) is exactly α.

Instead, the critical region is defined as: P(test statistic is in CR, assuming H_0 is true) $\leq \alpha$.

And P(test statistic is in CR, assuming H_0 is true) is called the actual significance level of the test.

Going back to the example above, step 5) would look like this...

5) Test for significance by finding the critical region for a test at this level of significance.
   This is a one-tailed test and you're interested in the lower end of the distribution.
   The critical region is the biggest possible set of 'low' values of X with a total probability of ≤ 0.05.

   Using the binomial tables: Try $X \leq 2$: $P(X \leq 2) = 0.0442 < 0.05$. Now try $X \leq 3$: $P(X \leq 3) = 0.1227 > 0.05$.
   So, CR is $X \leq 2$. These results fall in the CR, so the result is significant.

   The actual significance level is 0.0442.

The probability of a Type I error is the probability of rejecting H_0 when H_0 is true — the actual significance level.

EXAMPLE Find: a) P(Type I error) and b) P(Type II error), given that the proportion in favour of change is actually 0.15.

a) P(test stat is significant, assuming H_0 true) = $P(X \leq 2 \mid X \sim B(30, 0.2)) = 0.0442$
b) P(test stat not significant, assuming H_1 true) = $P(X > 2 \mid X \sim B(30, 0.15)) = 1 - P(X \leq 2 \mid p = 0.15) = 1 - 0.1514 = 0.8486$

Hypothesis Tests and Binomial Distributions

A couple more examples here of the sorts of questions that might come up in the exam. Aren't I kind.

EXAMPLES:

If you can't use the tables for your value of p, you have to use the binomial formula to work things out.

EXAMPLE 1 — WITHOUT USING TABLES

The proportion of pupils at a school who support the local football team is found to be $\frac{1}{8}$. Nigel attends a school nearby and claims that there is less support for the same local team at his school. In a random sample of 20 pupils from Nigel's school, 1 supports the local team. Use a 5% level of significance to test Nigel's claim.

Let p = proportion of pupils who support the local team.

$H_0: p = \frac{1}{8}$ $H_1: p < \frac{1}{8}$

Let X = number of sampled pupils supporting the team. Under H_0, $X \sim B(20, \frac{1}{8})$. $\alpha = 0.05$.

Now you need to find the probability of getting a value less than or equal to 1. The tables don't have values for $p = \frac{1}{8}$, so you need to work out the probabilities individually and add them up:

Remember the binomial formula: $P(X = x) = \binom{n}{x} \times p^x \times q^{n-x}$ $= \binom{20}{x}(\frac{1}{8})^x(\frac{7}{8})^{20-x}$

$P(X \leq 1) = P(X = 0) + P(X = 1)$

$= (\frac{7}{8})^{20} + 20(\frac{1}{8})(\frac{7}{8})^{19} = 0.267$

$0.267 > 0.05$, so the result is not significant. There is insufficient evidence at the 5% level of significance to reject H_0 and to support Nigel's claim that there is less support for the team.

And if n is large, you'll need to use an approximation.

See p.112 for a reminder of the normal approximation to the binomial.

EXAMPLE 2 — USING THE NORMAL APPROXIMATION

Records show that the proportion of trees in a wood that suffer from a particular leaf disease is 15%. Chloe thinks that recent weather conditions might have increased this proportion. She examines a random sample of 50 of the trees and finds that 15 of them have the leaf disease.

Using a suitable approximation, test Chloe's theory at the 5% level of significance.

Let p = proportion of trees with the leaf disease.

$H_0: p = 0.15$ $H_1: p > 0.15$

Let X = number of sampled trees with the disease. Under H_0, $X \sim B(50, 0.15)$.

$n = 50$ is too big to look up in the binomial tables, so an approximation is needed.
First, check that a normal approximation is suitable:

$np = 7.5 > 5$ and $nq = 42.5 > 5$, so $X \sim B(50, 0.15)$ can be approximated by $N(7.5, 6.375)$.

You want to find the probability of getting a value greater than or equal to 15 — $P(X \geq 15)$, but applying the continuity correction makes this $P(X > 14.5)$.

So $P(X > 14.5) = P\left(Z > \frac{14.5 - 7.5}{\sqrt{6.375}}\right) = P(Z > 2.772)$

$= 1 - P(Z \leq 2.772) = 1 - 0.9972 = 0.0028$

If you want, you can instead do the test by finding the critical value ($z = 1.645$), and therefore the critical region $Z > 1.645$. $Z = 2.772$ lies in the critical region, so reject H_0.

Since $0.0028 < 0.05$, the result is significant. So there is evidence at the 5% level of significance to reject H_0 and to support Chloe's theory that there has been an increase in the proportion of affected trees.

If your value of p isn't in the binomial tables, don't panic...

You won't find $p = 0.2438$ in the tables, or even $p = 0.24$, for that matter. But this isn't a problem as long as you know how to use the binomial probability function. And remember to apply the continuity correction when you're approximating.

Hypothesis Tests and Poisson Distributions

If you were hoping to catch one last glimpse of Mr Poisson before the end of the book, you're in luck. Before you get going here, have a look back at Section 1 for a reminder of all things Poisson.

*Use a **Hypothesis Test** to **Find Out** about the **Population Parameter** λ*

If λ is the average rate at which an event occurs in a population and X is the number of those events that occur in a random interval, then X can be used as the test statistic for testing theories on λ. The hypothesis test works in the same way as the binomial test you've just seen.

EXAMPLE A bookshop sells copies of the book *'All you've never wanted to know about the Poisson distribution'* at a (surprisingly high) rate of 10 a week. The shop's manager decides to reduce the price of the book. In one randomly selected week after the price change, 16 copies are sold. Use a 10% level of significance to test whether there is evidence to suggest that sales of the book have increased.

Let λ = the average number of copies of the book sold per week.
$H_0: \lambda = 10 \quad H_1: \lambda > 10$
Let X = number of copies sold in a random week. Under H_0, $X \sim \text{Po}(10)$. $\alpha = 0.1$.

The mention of 'rate' tells you that the situation can be modelled by a Poisson distribution.

To find the probability of X taking a value greater than or equal to 16, use the Poisson tables (see p.136):
$P(X \geq 16) = 1 - P(X \leq 15) = 1 - 0.9513 = 0.0487$, and since $0.0487 < 0.1$, the result is significant.

Don't forget the conclusion:
There is evidence at the 10% level of significance to reject H_0 and to suggest that sales have increased.

Remember that the Poisson parameter is additive. So, if X represents the number of events in an interval of 1 unit, and $X \sim \text{Po}(\lambda)$, then the number of events in an interval of x units follows the distribution $\text{Po}(x\lambda)$.

EXAMPLE An automated sewing machine produces faults randomly, at an average of 1 every two days. The machine is serviced, and in the following ten-day period, each fault is recorded. Sonia wishes to test whether the machine now produces fewer faults.

a) Find the critical region for the test at the 5% significance level.
b) What is the probability that the test results in a Type I error?
c) Given that 4 faults occurred in the ten-day period, carry out the test.

a) $H_0: \lambda = \frac{1}{2}$ and $H_1: \lambda < \frac{1}{2}$.

1 fault every two days means that λ = average number of faults per day = ½.

Let X = number of faults in ten days. Under H_0, $X \sim \text{Po}(10 \times \frac{1}{2}) = \text{Po}(5)$.

This is a one-tailed test and you're interested in the lower end of the distribution.
The critical region is the biggest possible set of 'low' values of X with a total probability of ≤ 0.05.

Using the Poisson tables: Try $X \leq 1$: $P(X \leq 1) = 0.0404 < 0.05$. Now try $X \leq 2$: $P(X \leq 2) = 0.1247 > 0.05$.
So the critical region is $X \leq 1$.

b) P(Type I error) = P(test statistic is significant, assuming H_0 true) = $P(X \leq 1 \mid X \sim \text{Po}(5)) = 0.0404$.

The actual significance level.

c) Since 4 doesn't lie in the critical region, there is insufficient evidence at the 5% level to reject H_0.
There is insufficient evidence to support the view that the number of faults has decreased.

My hypothesis is — this is very likely to come up in the exam...

So that was hypothesis testing. Now I'll be frank — exam questions on this topic can be pretty tricky. However, as long as you know the general methods covered here inside out, you should be able to adapt that knowledge to cope with any type of exam question that comes up. And now, I think you've earned a snack... and some practice questions to go with it...

S2 Section 4 — Practice Questions

Phew, that section really did have a bit of everything — you could say it was a smorgasbord of tasty S2 treats. To make sure you've fully digested everything on offer, finish off with these delicious practice questions.

Warm-up Questions

1) Why is it a good idea to use simple random sampling to select a sample?

2) The weights of a population of jars of pickled onions have unknown mean μ and standard deviation σ. A random sample of 50 weights (X_1, ..., X_{50}) are recorded. Say whether each of these is a statistic or not:

   a) $\frac{X_{25}+X_{26}}{2}$ b) $\sum X_i - \sigma$ c) $\sum X_i^2 + \mu$ d) $\frac{\sum X_i}{50}$

3) If $X \sim N(8, 2)$, find $P(\overline{X} < 7)$ where $\overline{X}$ is the mean of a random sample of 10 observations of X.

4) A random sample was taken from a population whose mean (μ) and variance (σ^2) are unknown. Find unbiased estimates of μ and σ^2 if the sample values were: 8.4, 8.6, 7.2, 6.5, 9.1, 7.7, 8.1, 8.4, 8.5, 8.0.

5) a) For each of the following, state whether a one-tailed or a two-tailed hypothesis test should be used:
      i) Salma wants to test whether the average height of the students at her college is greater than 160 cm.
      ii) An investigation into the diameter of the metal discs produced by a machine found that the mean diameter was 2.2 cm. Joy wants to test the claim that the mean diameter has changed since the investigation was done.
      iii) Henry thinks a coin might be biased. He wants to find out about p, the proportion of coin tosses that result in 'heads'.
      iv) The number of errors made by a typist every hour follows a Poisson distribution with mean $\lambda = 20$. After receiving some training, the typist wants to test whether he now makes fewer errors.

   b) Define suitable null and alternative hypotheses for each test above.

6) Andrew carries out a hypothesis test concerning the mean of a normal distribution. His conclusion is to reject the null hypothesis that $\mu = 10$. If it turned out that the mean was actually 10, what type of error would Andrew have made?

7) Carry out the following test of the mean, μ, of a normal distribution with variance $\sigma^2 = 9$. A random sample of 16 observations from the distribution was taken and the sample mean ($\overline{x}$) calculated. Test H_0: $\mu = 45$ against H_1: $\mu < 45$, at the 5% significance level, using $\overline{x} = 42$.

8) Carry out the following test of the proportion (p) of people in a population who own a pet. Let X represent the number of people who own a pet in a random sample of size 20. Test H_0: $p = 0.2$ against H_1: $p < 0.2$, at the 5% significance level, using $x = 2$.

9) Carry out the following test of the population parameter λ. Let X represent the number of events in a given interval and λ be the average rate at which they are assumed to occur in intervals of identical size. Test H_0: $\lambda = 2.5$ against H_1: $\lambda > 2.5$, at the 10% significance level, using $x = 4$.

10) a) Find the critical region for the following test, where the test statistic $X \sim B(10, p)$: Test H_0: $p = 0.3$ against H_1: $p < 0.3$, at the 5% significance level.

    b) Find the critical region for the following test, where the test statistic $X \sim Po(\lambda)$: Test H_0: $\lambda = 6$ against H_1: $\lambda < 6$, at the 10% significance level.

S2 Section 4 — Practice Questions

Aha, some exam-style practice questions to test whether you've got this section sussed. Wasn't expecting that.

Exam Questions

1 The heights of trees in an area of woodland are known to be normally distributed with a mean of 5.0 m. A random sample of 100 trees from a second area of woodland is selected and the heights, X, of the trees are measured giving the following results:

$$\sum x = 490 \text{ and } \sum x^2 = 2421$$

a) Calculate unbiased estimates of the population mean, μ, and variance, σ^2, for this area. *(3 marks)*

b) Test at the 1% level of significance whether the trees in the second area of woodland have a different mean height from the trees in the first area. *(6 marks)*

The researchers wish to carry out a second test with the following condition: The probability that the test results in a Type I error should be less than 0.01 when the sample mean is 4.95 m.

c) Calculate an estimate of the smallest sample size required for this test. *(3 marks)*

2 A tennis player serves a fault on her first serve at an average rate of 3 per service game. The player receives some extra coaching. In a randomly selected set of tennis, she serves 6 first-serve faults in 4 service games. She wants to test whether her average rate of first-serve faults has decreased.

a) Write down the conditions needed for the number of first-serve faults per service game to be modelled by a Poisson distribution. *(2 marks)*

Assume the conditions you stated in part a) hold.

b) Carry out the test at the 5% level of significance. *(5 marks)*

3 The residents of a town are being asked their views on a plan to build a wind farm in the area. Environmental campaigners claim that 20% of the residents are against the plan. A random sample of 30 residents is surveyed.

a) State two reasons why surveying a random sample of 30 residents will allow reliable conclusions to be drawn. *(2 marks)*

b) Using a 10% significance level, find the critical region for a two-tailed test of this claim. *(5 marks)*

c) What is the probability that the above test will result in a Type I error? *(2 marks)*

It's found that 5 of the sampled residents say they are against the plan.

d) Comment on this finding in relation to the environmental campaigners' claim. *(2 marks)*

General Certificate of Education
Advanced Subsidiary (AS) and Advanced Level

Statistics S2 — Practice Exam One

Time Allowed: 1 hour 30 min

Graphical calculators may be used for this exam.

Give any non-exact numerical answers to 3 significant figures.

Statistical tables can be found on page 136.

There are 72 marks available for this paper.

1 The probability that any chocolate bar made by a particular manufacturer contains a 'golden ticket' is always 0.05, independently of whether other bars contain a ticket. Two students each buy 40 chocolate bars.

Using a suitable approximation, which should be justified, find the probability that they find a total of at least 3 golden tickets between them.

(4 marks)

2 The random variable X follows a normal distribution with mean μ and variance σ^2.
Given that $P(X < 60) = 0.1587$ and $P(X < 97.5) = 0.9332$, find the values of μ and σ.

(6 marks)

3 The number of houses, X, sold each week by an estate agent in a small town can be modelled by a Poisson distribution. The estate agent sells houses at an average rate of 2 per week.

a) Find the probability that in a randomly selected week, the estate agent will sell:

(i) exactly 1 house,

(2 marks)

(ii) at least 2 houses but no more than 4 houses.

(3 marks)

b) Use a suitable approximation to find the probability that the estate agent will sell fewer than 52 houses over the next 26 weeks.

(6 marks)

4 The duration in minutes, X, of a car wash is a little erratic, but it is normally distributed with a mean of 8 minutes and a variance of 1.2 minutes. Find:

a) $P(X < 7.5)$, *(3 marks)*

b) the duration in minutes, d, such that there is no more than a 1% probability that the car wash will take longer than this duration. *(4 marks)*

c) The mean of 20 observations of X is denoted by $\overline{X}$.

(i) Write down the distribution of $\overline{X}$, giving the values of any parameters. *(2 marks)*

(ii) Find $P(\overline{X} > 8.5)$. *(2 marks)*

5 Past records suggest that 45% of the members of a gym use the swimming pool. The gym's manager thinks that the popularity of the swimming pool has decreased over recent months.

a) A random sample of 15 gym members is surveyed and it is found that 3 of them use the pool. Using a 5% level of significance, test whether there is evidence to suggest that the popularity of the pool has decreased. *(7 marks)*

b) The manager decides that the same test should be done again, but this time using a larger sample. He surveys a random sample of 30 members and carries out the test. He concludes that at the 5% level of significance there is evidence to suggest that the popularity of the pool has decreased. Find the maximum possible number of gym members in the sample of 30 who use the pool. *(4 marks)*

6 The continuous random variable X has the probability density function

$$f(x) = \begin{cases} \frac{kx}{2} & 0 \le x \le 4 \\ 0 & \text{otherwise} \end{cases}$$

where k is a positive constant.

a) Show that $k = 0.25$. *(3 marks)*

b) Calculate $E(X)$. *(3 marks)*

c) Find the median of X. *(3 marks)*

7 The speeds of the balls bowled by a cricketer are assumed to follow a normal distribution. The cricketer records the speeds, x mph, of 40 randomly selected balls. His results are summarised by the following:

$$\sum x = 3400 \quad \text{and} \quad \sum(x - \bar{x})^2 = 120$$

a) Calculate unbiased estimates for the mean and variance of the speeds of the balls he bowls. *(2 marks)*

b) Use your answers to part a) to estimate the probability that the speed of the next ball bowled by the cricketer will be less than 90 mph. *(2 marks)*

c) The mean of a random sample of 20 speeds is denoted by $\overline{X}$. Explain whether you would apply the Central Limit Theorem to calculate an estimate of $P(\overline{X} > 80)$.
(You should not attempt any calculations.) *(2 marks)*

8 The heights of the sunflowers in a particular field follow a normal distribution with a mean of 150 cm and a variance of 22. The heights of the sunflowers in a second field are assumed to follow an $N(\mu, 22)$ distribution, where μ is unknown. The heights, x cm, of a random sample of 10 of these sunflowers from the second field are recorded and the sample mean, $\overline{X}$, is calculated as 146 cm.

a) Test at the 5% level of significance whether the average height of the sunflowers in the second field is the same as the average height of the sunflowers in the first field. *(7 marks)*

The heights of the sunflowers in a third field are also assumed to follow an $N(\mu, 22)$ distribution, where μ is unknown. A significance test of the null hypothesis H_0: $\mu = 150$, against the alternative hypothesis H_1: $\mu < 150$, is carried out at the 5% significance level, based on the heights, y cm, of a sample of size 10.

b) Find the critical region for the above test, in terms of the sample mean $\overline{Y}$.
Give your answer to the nearest 0.1 cm. *(5 marks)*

c) It is discovered that many of the sunflowers in the third field are shaded by trees, meaning that the small group of flowers which aren't shaded are much taller than the rest.
Comment on what this suggests about the use of a normal distribution as a model for the heights. *(2 marks)*

General Certificate of Education
Advanced Subsidiary (AS) and Advanced Level

Statistics S2 — Practice Exam Two

Time Allowed: 1 hour 30 min

Graphical calculators may be used for this exam.

Give any non-exact numerical answers to 3 significant figures.

Statistical tables can be found on page 136.

There are 72 marks available for this paper.

1 A particular model of car is prone to developing a rattle in the first year after being made. The probability of any particular car developing this rattle is 0.65. A random sample of 200 cars of this model are selected.

Use a suitable approximation, which should be justified, to find the probability that exactly 140 of the cars have the rattle.

(7 marks)

2 A discrete random variable A follows a Poisson distribution with a mean of 40.
Use an appropriate approximation, which should be justified, to calculate $P(A > 35)$.

(6 marks)

3 A 'donkey-rides' business hires out donkeys for rides along the beach. The average rate at which customers want to hire a donkey on a weekday during the summer is 2 per hour.

a) Write down a suitable distribution to model the number of customers per hour.

(2 marks)

b) Find the probability that in one randomly selected hour:

(i) there are fewer than 3 customers

(1 mark)

(ii) there is exactly 1 customer

(2 marks)

On Saturdays during the summer, the 'donkey-rides' business is open for 6 hours a day.
On one randomly selected Saturday, there are 25 customers.

c) Test at the 1% level of significance whether there is evidence to suggest that there are more customers per hour on a Saturday than on a weekday.

(6 marks)

4 The number of seconds (T) that trained divers can hold their breath for may be modelled by a normal distribution with a mean of 132 seconds and a standard deviation of 40 seconds.

a) Find:

(i) $P(T > 160)$,

(3 marks)

(ii) $P(60 \leq T \leq 90)$.

(4 marks)

b) The mean of n observations of T is denoted by $\overline{T}$.
If $P(\overline{T} > 135) = 0.2266$, find the value of n.

(4 marks)

5 Jack runs judo classes at 'basic' and 'advanced' levels. He estimates that the proportion, p, of the people who attend who have done judo for at least two years is 0.2.

a) To test this, he plans to survey a random sample of 20 of the people who attend his classes.

(i) Give two properties of his survey method that will allow Jack to draw unbiased conclusions about p.

(2 marks)

(ii) Explain why it would be a bad idea for Jack to test his theory by surveying all the members in just one of his classes.

(2 marks)

b) Find the critical region for a two-tailed test of Jack's hypothesis at the 5% level of significance.

(5 marks)

c) What is the probability that this test results in a Type I error?

(2 marks)

d) Given that 7 of the surveyed class members say they have done judo for at least two years, carry out the test of Jack's hypothesis.

(2 marks)

6 The continuous random variable X has the probability density function:

$$f(x) = \begin{cases} 3x^2 & 0 \le x \le 1 \\ 0 & \text{otherwise} \end{cases}$$

a) Find the mean of X. *(3 marks)*

b) Calculate the variance of X. *(3 marks)*

c) Calculate the probability that a single observation of X lies between 0 and 0.5. *(2 marks)*

d) 50 observations of X are recorded. State the distribution of Y, where Y is the number of observations that lie between 0 and 0.5, giving the value(s) of any parameters. *(2 marks)*

7 Each roll of fabric used by a home furnishings manufacturer should be 5 metres long. The length of fabric, x cm, on 50 randomly selected rolls is measured, giving the following results:

$$\sum x = 24\,500 \quad \text{and} \quad \sum x^2 = 12\,011\,500$$

a) Calculate unbiased estimates of the mean length, μ, and the variance, σ^2, of the fabric on the rolls the manufacturer uses. *(3 marks)*

The manager claims that the mean length of fabric per roll is less than 5 metres.
He decides to test his theory at the 5% significance level, using the mean of the sample of 50 rolls.

b) Find the critical region for the test, in terms of the sample mean $\overline{X}$.
Give your answer to the nearest 0.1 cm. *(5 marks)*

c) Using the sample mean you calculated in part a), carry out the test of the manager's claim. *(2 marks)*

d) If the test were carried out on a new random sample of 50 rolls, calculate the probability that it would result in a Type II error, given that the mean length of fabric per roll is actually 496 cm. *(4 marks)*

Cumulative Poisson probabilities

λ	0.01	0.02	0.03	0.04	0.05	0.06	0.07	0.08	0.09
x = 0	0.9900	0.9802	0.9704	0.9608	0.9512	0.9418	0.9324	0.9231	0.9139
1	1.0000	0.9998	0.9996	0.9992	0.9988	0.9983	0.9977	0.9970	0.9962
2	1.0000	1.0000	1.0000	1.0000	1.0000	1.0000	0.9999	0.9999	0.9999
3	1.0000	1.0000	1.0000	1.0000	1.0000	1.0000	1.0000	1.0000	1.0000

λ	0.10	0.20	0.30	0.40	0.50	0.60	0.70	0.80	0.90
x = 0	0.9048	0.8187	0.7408	0.6703	0.6065	0.5488	0.4966	0.4493	0.4066
1	0.9953	0.9825	0.9631	0.9384	0.9098	0.8781	0.8442	0.8088	0.7725
2	0.9998	0.9989	0.9964	0.9921	0.9856	0.9769	0.9659	0.9526	0.9371
3	1.0000	0.9999	0.9997	0.9992	0.9982	0.9966	0.9942	0.9909	0.9865
4	1.0000	1.0000	1.0000	0.9999	0.9998	0.9996	0.9992	0.9986	0.9977
5	1.0000	1.0000	1.0000	1.0000	1.0000	1.0000	0.9999	0.9998	0.9997
6	1.0000	1.0000	1.0000	1.0000	1.0000	1.0000	1.0000	1.0000	1.0000

λ	1.00	1.10	1.20	1.30	1.40	1.50	1.60	1.70	1.80	1.90
x = 0	0.3679	0.3329	0.3012	0.2725	0.2466	0.2231	0.2019	0.1827	0.1653	0.1496
1	0.7358	0.6990	0.6626	0.6268	0.5918	0.5578	0.5249	0.4932	0.4628	0.4337
2	0.9197	0.9004	0.8795	0.8571	0.8335	0.8088	0.7834	0.7572	0.7306	0.7037
3	0.9810	0.9743	0.9662	0.9569	0.9463	0.9344	0.9212	0.9068	0.8913	0.8747
4	0.9963	0.9946	0.9923	0.9893	0.9857	0.9814	0.9763	0.9704	0.9636	0.9559
5	0.9994	0.9990	0.9985	0.9978	0.9968	0.9955	0.9940	0.9920	0.9896	0.9868
6	0.9999	0.9999	0.9997	0.9996	0.9994	0.9991	0.9987	0.9981	0.9974	0.9966
7	1.0000	1.0000	1.0000	0.9999	0.9999	0.9998	0.9997	0.9996	0.9994	0.9992
8	1.0000	1.0000	1.0000	1.0000	1.0000	1.0000	1.0000	0.9999	0.9999	0.9998
9	1.0000	1.0000	1.0000	1.0000	1.0000	1.0000	1.0000	1.0000	1.0000	1.0000

λ	2.00	2.10	2.20	2.30	2.40	2.50	2.60	2.70	2.80	2.90
x = 0	0.1353	0.1225	0.1108	0.1003	0.0907	0.0821	0.0743	0.0672	0.0608	0.0550
1	0.4060	0.3796	0.3546	0.3309	0.3084	0.2873	0.2674	0.2487	0.2311	0.2146
2	0.6767	0.6496	0.6227	0.5960	0.5697	0.5438	0.5184	0.4936	0.4695	0.4460
3	0.8571	0.8386	0.8194	0.7993	0.7787	0.7576	0.7360	0.7141	0.6919	0.6696
4	0.9473	0.9379	0.9275	0.9162	0.9041	0.8912	0.8774	0.8629	0.8477	0.8318
5	0.9834	0.9796	0.9751	0.9700	0.9643	0.9580	0.9510	0.9433	0.9349	0.9258
6	0.9955	0.9941	0.9925	0.9906	0.9884	0.9858	0.9828	0.9794	0.9756	0.9713
7	0.9989	0.9985	0.9980	0.9974	0.9967	0.9958	0.9947	0.9934	0.9919	0.9901
8	0.9998	0.9997	0.9995	0.9994	0.9991	0.9989	0.9985	0.9981	0.9976	0.9969
9	1.0000	0.9999	0.9999	0.9999	0.9998	0.9997	0.9996	0.9995	0.9993	0.9991
10	1.0000	1.0000	1.0000	1.0000	1.0000	0.9999	0.9999	0.9999	0.9998	0.9998
11	1.0000	1.0000	1.0000	1.0000	1.0000	1.0000	1.0000	1.0000	1.0000	0.9999
12	1.0000	1.0000	1.0000	1.0000	1.0000	1.0000	1.0000	1.0000	1.0000	1.0000

λ	3.00	3.10	3.20	3.30	3.40	3.50	3.60	3.70	3.80	3.90
x = 0	0.0498	0.0450	0.0408	0.0369	0.0334	0.0302	0.0273	0.0247	0.0224	0.0202
1	0.1991	0.1847	0.1712	0.1586	0.1468	0.1359	0.1257	0.1162	0.1074	0.0992
2	0.4232	0.4012	0.3799	0.3594	0.3397	0.3208	0.3027	0.2854	0.2689	0.2531
3	0.6472	0.6248	0.6025	0.5803	0.5584	0.5366	0.5152	0.4942	0.4735	0.4532
4	0.8153	0.7982	0.7806	0.7626	0.7442	0.7254	0.7064	0.6872	0.6678	0.6484
5	0.9161	0.9057	0.8946	0.8829	0.8705	0.8576	0.8441	0.8301	0.8156	0.8006
6	0.9665	0.9612	0.9554	0.9490	0.9421	0.9347	0.9267	0.9182	0.9091	0.8995
7	0.9881	0.9858	0.9832	0.9802	0.9769	0.9733	0.9692	0.9648	0.9599	0.9546
8	0.9962	0.9953	0.9943	0.9931	0.9917	0.9901	0.9883	0.9863	0.9840	0.9815
9	0.9989	0.9986	0.9982	0.9978	0.9973	0.9967	0.9960	0.9952	0.9942	0.9931
10	0.9997	0.9996	0.9995	0.9994	0.9992	0.9990	0.9987	0.9984	0.9981	0.9977
11	0.9999	0.9999	0.9999	0.9998	0.9998	0.9997	0.9996	0.9995	0.9994	0.9993
12	1.0000	1.0000	1.0000	1.0000	0.9999	0.9999	0.9999	0.9999	0.9998	0.9998
13	1.0000	1.0000	1.0000	1.0000	1.0000	1.0000	1.0000	1.0000	1.0000	0.9999
14	1.0000	1.0000	1.0000	1.0000	1.0000	1.0000	1.0000	1.0000	1.0000	1.0000

Cumulative Poisson probabilities (continued)

λ	4.00	4.10	4.20	4.30	4.40	4.50	4.60	4.70	4.80	4.90
x = 0	0.0183	0.0166	0.0150	0.0136	0.0123	0.0111	0.0101	0.0091	0.0082	0.0074
1	0.0916	0.0845	0.0780	0.0719	0.0663	0.0611	0.0563	0.0518	0.0477	0.0439
2	0.2381	0.2238	0.2102	0.1974	0.1851	0.1736	0.1626	0.1523	0.1425	0.1333
3	0.4335	0.4142	0.3954	0.3772	0.3594	0.3423	0.3257	0.3097	0.2942	0.2793
4	0.6288	0.6093	0.5898	0.5704	0.5512	0.5321	0.5132	0.4946	0.4763	0.4582
5	0.7851	0.7693	0.7531	0.7367	0.7199	0.7029	0.6858	0.6684	0.6510	0.6335
6	0.8893	0.8786	0.8675	0.8558	0.8436	0.8311	0.8180	0.8046	0.7908	0.7767
7	0.9489	0.9427	0.9361	0.9290	0.9214	0.9134	0.9049	0.8960	0.8867	0.8769
8	0.9786	0.9755	0.9721	0.9683	0.9642	0.9597	0.9549	0.9497	0.9442	0.9382
9	0.9919	0.9905	0.9889	0.9871	0.9851	0.9829	0.9805	0.9778	0.9749	0.9717
10	0.9972	0.9966	0.9959	0.9952	0.9943	0.9933	0.9922	0.9910	0.9896	0.9880
11	0.9991	0.9989	0.9986	0.9983	0.9980	0.9976	0.9971	0.9966	0.9960	0.9953
12	0.9997	0.9997	0.9996	0.9995	0.9993	0.9992	0.9990	0.9988	0.9986	0.9983
13	0.9999	0.9999	0.9999	0.9998	0.9998	0.9997	0.9997	0.9996	0.9995	0.9994
14	1.0000	1.0000	1.0000	1.0000	0.9999	0.9999	0.9999	0.9999	0.9999	0.9998
15	1.0000	1.0000	1.0000	1.0000	1.0000	1.0000	1.0000	1.0000	1.0000	0.9999
16	1.0000	1.0000	1.0000	1.0000	1.0000	1.0000	1.0000	1.0000	1.0000	1.0000

λ	5.00	5.50	6.00	6.50	7.00	7.50	8.00	8.50	9.00	9.50
x = 0	0.0067	0.0041	0.0025	0.0015	0.0009	0.0006	0.0003	0.0002	0.0001	0.0001
1	0.0404	0.0266	0.0174	0.0113	0.0073	0.0047	0.0030	0.0019	0.0012	0.0008
2	0.1247	0.0884	0.0620	0.0430	0.0296	0.0203	0.0138	0.0093	0.0062	0.0042
3	0.2650	0.2017	0.1512	0.1118	0.0818	0.0591	0.0424	0.0301	0.0212	0.0149
4	0.4405	0.3575	0.2851	0.2237	0.1730	0.1321	0.0996	0.0744	0.0550	0.0403
5	0.6160	0.5289	0.4457	0.3690	0.3007	0.2414	0.1912	0.1496	0.1157	0.0885
6	0.7622	0.6860	0.6063	0.5265	0.4497	0.3782	0.3134	0.2562	0.2068	0.1649
7	0.8666	0.8095	0.7440	0.6728	0.5987	0.5246	0.4530	0.3856	0.3239	0.2687
8	0.9319	0.8944	0.8472	0.7916	0.7291	0.6620	0.5925	0.5231	0.4557	0.3918
9	0.9682	0.9462	0.9161	0.8774	0.8305	0.7764	0.7166	0.6530	0.5874	0.5218
10	0.9863	0.9747	0.9574	0.9332	0.9015	0.8622	0.8159	0.7634	0.7060	0.6453
11	0.9945	0.9890	0.9799	0.9661	0.9467	0.9208	0.8881	0.8487	0.8030	0.7520
12	0.9980	0.9955	0.9912	0.9840	0.9730	0.9573	0.9362	0.9091	0.8758	0.8364
13	0.9993	0.9983	0.9964	0.9929	0.9872	0.9784	0.9658	0.9486	0.9261	0.8981
14	0.9998	0.9994	0.9986	0.9970	0.9943	0.9897	0.9827	0.9726	0.9585	0.9400
15	0.9999	0.9998	0.9995	0.9988	0.9976	0.9954	0.9918	0.9862	0.9780	0.9665
16	1.0000	0.9999	0.9998	0.9996	0.9990	0.9980	0.9963	0.9934	0.9889	0.9823
17	1.0000	1.0000	0.9999	0.9998	0.9996	0.9992	0.9984	0.9970	0.9947	0.9911
18	1.0000	1.0000	1.0000	0.9999	0.9999	0.9997	0.9993	0.9987	0.9976	0.9957
19	1.0000	1.0000	1.0000	1.0000	1.0000	0.9999	0.9997	0.9995	0.9989	0.9980
20	1.0000	1.0000	1.0000	1.0000	1.0000	1.0000	0.9999	0.9998	0.9996	0.9991
21	1.0000	1.0000	1.0000	1.0000	1.0000	1.0000	1.0000	0.9999	0.9998	0.9996
22	1.0000	1.0000	1.0000	1.0000	1.0000	1.0000	1.0000	1.0000	0.9999	0.9999
23	1.0000	1.0000	1.0000	1.0000	1.0000	1.0000	1.0000	1.0000	1.0000	0.9999
24	1.0000	1.0000	1.0000	1.0000	1.0000	1.0000	1.0000	1.0000	1.0000	1.0000

Cumulative Poisson probabilities (continued)

λ	10.00	11.00	12.00	13.00	14.00	15.00	16.00	17.00	18.00	19.00
x = 0	0.0000	0.0000	0.0000	0.0000	0.0000	0.0000	0.0000	0.0000	0.0000	0.0000
1	0.0005	0.0002	0.0001	0.0000	0.0000	0.0000	0.0000	0.0000	0.0000	0.0000
2	0.0028	0.0012	0.0005	0.0002	0.0001	0.0000	0.0000	0.0000	0.0000	0.0000
3	0.0103	0.0049	0.0023	0.0011	0.0005	0.0002	0.0001	0.0000	0.0000	0.0000
4	0.0293	0.0151	0.0076	0.0037	0.0018	0.0009	0.0004	0.0002	0.0001	0.0000
5	0.0671	0.0375	0.0203	0.0107	0.0055	0.0028	0.0014	0.0007	0.0003	0.0002
6	0.1301	0.0786	0.0458	0.0259	0.0142	0.0076	0.0040	0.0021	0.0010	0.0005
7	0.2202	0.1432	0.0895	0.0540	0.0316	0.0180	0.0100	0.0054	0.0029	0.0015
8	0.3328	0.2320	0.1550	0.0998	0.0621	0.0374	0.0220	0.0126	0.0071	0.0039
9	0.4579	0.3405	0.2424	0.1658	0.1094	0.0699	0.0433	0.0261	0.0154	0.0089
10	0.5830	0.4599	0.3472	0.2517	0.1757	0.1185	0.0774	0.0491	0.0304	0.0183
11	0.6968	0.5793	0.4616	0.3532	0.2600	0.1848	0.1270	0.0847	0.0549	0.0347
12	0.7916	0.6887	0.5760	0.4631	0.3585	0.2676	0.1931	0.1350	0.0917	0.0606
13	0.8645	0.7813	0.6815	0.5730	0.4644	0.3632	0.2745	0.2009	0.1426	0.0984
14	0.9165	0.8540	0.7720	0.6751	0.5704	0.4657	0.3675	0.2808	0.2081	0.1497
15	0.9513	0.9074	0.8444	0.7636	0.6694	0.5681	0.4667	0.3715	0.2867	0.2148
16	0.9730	0.9441	0.8987	0.8355	0.7559	0.6641	0.5660	0.4677	0.3751	0.2920
17	0.9857	0.9678	0.9370	0.8905	0.8272	0.7489	0.6593	0.5640	0.4686	0.3784
18	0.9928	0.9823	0.9626	0.9302	0.8826	0.8195	0.7423	0.6550	0.5622	0.4695
19	0.9965	0.9907	0.9787	0.9573	0.9235	0.8752	0.8122	0.7363	0.6509	0.5606
20	0.9984	0.9953	0.9884	0.9750	0.9521	0.9170	0.8682	0.8055	0.7307	0.6472
21	0.9993	0.9977	0.9939	0.9859	0.9712	0.9469	0.9108	0.8615	0.7991	0.7255
22	0.9997	0.9990	0.9970	0.9924	0.9833	0.9673	0.9418	0.9047	0.8551	0.7931
23	0.9999	0.9995	0.9985	0.9960	0.9907	0.9805	0.9633	0.9367	0.8989	0.8490
24	1.0000	0.9998	0.9993	0.9980	0.9950	0.9888	0.9777	0.9594	0.9317	0.8933
25	1.0000	0.9999	0.9997	0.9990	0.9974	0.9938	0.9869	0.9748	0.9554	0.9269
26	1.0000	1.0000	0.9999	0.9995	0.9987	0.9967	0.9925	0.9848	0.9718	0.9514
27	1.0000	1.0000	0.9999	0.9998	0.9994	0.9983	0.9959	0.9912	0.9827	0.9687
28	1.0000	1.0000	1.0000	0.9999	0.9997	0.9991	0.9978	0.9950	0.9897	0.9805
29	1.0000	1.0000	1.0000	1.0000	0.9999	0.9996	0.9989	0.9973	0.9941	0.9882
30	1.0000	1.0000	1.0000	1.0000	0.9999	0.9998	0.9994	0.9986	0.9967	0.9930
31	1.0000	1.0000	1.0000	1.0000	1.0000	0.9999	0.9997	0.9993	0.9982	0.9960
32	1.0000	1.0000	1.0000	1.0000	1.0000	1.0000	0.9999	0.9996	0.9990	0.9978
33	1.0000	1.0000	1.0000	1.0000	1.0000	1.0000	0.9999	0.9998	0.9995	0.9988
34	1.0000	1.0000	1.0000	1.0000	1.0000	1.0000	1.0000	0.9999	0.9998	0.9994
35	1.0000	1.0000	1.0000	1.0000	1.0000	1.0000	1.0000	1.0000	0.9999	0.9997
36	1.0000	1.0000	1.0000	1.0000	1.0000	1.0000	1.0000	1.0000	0.9999	0.9998
37	1.0000	1.0000	1.0000	1.0000	1.0000	1.0000	1.0000	1.0000	1.0000	0.9999
38	1.0000	1.0000	1.0000	1.0000	1.0000	1.0000	1.0000	1.0000	1.0000	1.0000

OCR S2 — STATISTICAL TABLES

The normal distribution function

The table below shows $\Phi(z) = P(Z \leq z)$, where $Z \sim N(0, 1)$.

For negative z, use: $\Phi(-z) = 1 - \Phi(z)$.

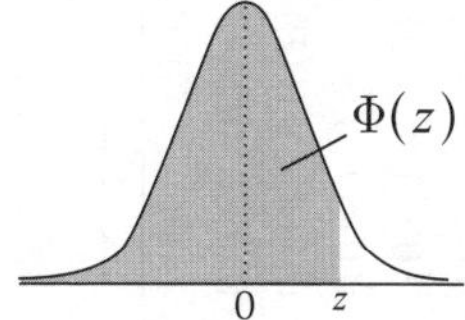

z	0	1	2	3	4	5	6	7	8	9	1	2	3	4	5 ADD	6	7	8	9
0.0	0.5000	0.5040	0.5080	0.5120	0.5160	0.5199	0.5239	0.5279	0.5319	0.5359	4	8	12	16	20	24	28	32	36
0.1	0.5398	0.5438	0.5478	0.5517	0.5557	0.5596	0.5636	0.5675	0.5714	0.5753	4	8	12	16	20	24	28	32	36
0.2	0.5793	0.5832	0.5871	0.5910	0.5948	0.5987	0.6026	0.6064	0.6103	0.6141	4	8	12	15	19	23	27	31	35
0.3	0.6179	0.6217	0.6255	0.6293	0.6331	0.6368	0.6406	0.6443	0.6480	0.6517	4	7	11	15	19	22	26	30	34
0.4	0.6554	0.6591	0.6628	0.6664	0.6700	0.6736	0.6772	0.6808	0.6844	0.6879	4	7	11	14	18	22	25	29	32
0.5	0.6915	0.6950	0.6985	0.7019	0.7054	0.7088	0.7123	0.7157	0.7190	0.7224	3	7	10	14	17	20	24	27	31
0.6	0.7257	0.7291	0.7324	0.7357	0.7389	0.7422	0.7454	0.7486	0.7517	0.7549	3	7	10	13	16	19	23	26	29
0.7	0.7580	0.7611	0.7642	0.7673	0.7704	0.7734	0.7764	0.7794	0.7823	0.7852	3	6	9	12	15	18	21	24	27
0.8	0.7881	0.7910	0.7939	0.7967	0.7995	0.8023	0.8051	0.8078	0.8106	0.8133	3	5	8	11	14	16	19	22	25
0.9	0.8159	0.8186	0.8212	0.8238	0.8264	0.8289	0.8315	0.8340	0.8365	0.8389	3	5	8	10	13	15	18	20	23
1.0	0.8413	0.8438	0.8461	0.8485	0.8508	0.8531	0.8554	0.8577	0.8599	0.8621	2	5	7	9	12	14	16	19	21
1.1	0.8643	0.8665	0.8686	0.8708	0.8729	0.8749	0.8770	0.8790	0.8810	0.8830	2	4	6	8	10	12	14	16	18
1.2	0.8849	0.8869	0.8888	0.8907	0.8925	0.8944	0.8962	0.8980	0.8997	0.9015	2	4	6	7	9	11	13	15	17
1.3	0.9032	0.9049	0.9066	0.9082	0.9099	0.9115	0.9131	0.9147	0.9162	0.9177	2	3	5	6	8	10	11	13	14
1.4	0.9192	0.9207	0.9222	0.9236	0.9251	0.9265	0.9279	0.9292	0.9306	0.9319	1	3	4	6	7	8	10	11	13
1.5	0.9332	0.9345	0.9357	0.9370	0.9382	0.9394	0.9406	0.9418	0.9429	0.9441	1	2	4	5	6	7	8	10	11
1.6	0.9452	0.9463	0.9474	0.9484	0.9495	0.9505	0.9515	0.9525	0.9535	0.9545	1	2	3	4	5	6	7	8	9
1.7	0.9554	0.9564	0.9573	0.9582	0.9591	0.9599	0.9608	0.9616	0.9625	0.9633	1	2	3	4	4	5	6	7	8
1.8	0.9641	0.9649	0.9656	0.9664	0.9671	0.9678	0.9686	0.9693	0.9699	0.9706	1	1	2	3	4	4	5	6	6
1.9	0.9713	0.9719	0.9726	0.9732	0.9738	0.9744	0.9750	0.9756	0.9761	0.9767	1	1	2	2	3	4	4	5	5
2.0	0.9772	0.9778	0.9783	0.9788	0.9793	0.9798	0.9803	0.9808	0.9812	0.9817	0	1	1	2	2	3	3	4	4
2.1	0.9821	0.9826	0.9830	0.9834	0.9838	0.9842	0.9846	0.9850	0.9854	0.9857	0	1	1	2	2	2	3	3	4
2.2	0.9861	0.9864	0.9868	0.9871	0.9875	0.9878	0.9881	0.9884	0.9887	0.9890	0	1	1	1	2	2	2	3	3
2.3	0.9893	0.9896	0.9898	0.9901	0.9904	0.9906	0.9909	0.9911	0.9913	0.9916	0	1	1	1	1	2	2	2	2
2.4	0.9918	0.9920	0.9922	0.9925	0.9927	0.9929	0.9931	0.9932	0.9934	0.9936	0	0	1	1	1	1	1	2	2
2.5	0.9938	0.9940	0.9941	0.9943	0.9945	0.9946	0.9948	0.9949	0.9951	0.9952	0	0	0	1	1	1	1	1	1
2.6	0.9953	0.9955	0.9956	0.9957	0.9959	0.9960	0.9961	0.9962	0.9963	0.9964	0	0	0	0	1	1	1	1	1
2.7	0.9965	0.9966	0.9967	0.9968	0.9969	0.9970	0.9971	0.9972	0.9973	0.9974	0	0	0	0	0	1	1	1	1
2.8	0.9974	0.9975	0.9976	0.9977	0.9977	0.9978	0.9979	0.9979	0.9980	0.9981	0	0	0	0	0	0	0	1	1
2.9	0.9981	0.9982	0.9982	0.9983	0.9984	0.9984	0.9985	0.9985	0.9986	0.9986	0	0	0	0	0	0	0	0	0

Critical values for the normal distribution

For $Z \sim N(0, 1)$, this table gives the value of z for which $P(Z \leq z) = p$.

p	0.75	0.90	0.95	0.975	0.99	0.995	0.9975	0.999	0.9995
z	0.674	1.282	1.645	1.960	2.326	2.576	2.807	3.090	3.291

Cumulative binomial probabilities

n = 5, p	0.05	0.1	0.15	1/6	0.2	0.25	0.3	1/3	0.35	0.4	0.45	0.5	0.55	0.6	0.65	2/3	0.7	0.75	0.8	5/6	0.85	0.9	0.95
x = 0	0.7738	0.5905	0.4437	0.4019	0.3277	0.2373	0.1681	0.1317	0.1160	0.0778	0.0503	0.0313	0.0185	0.0102	0.0053	0.0041	0.0024	0.0010	0.0003	0.0001	0.0001	0.0000	0.0000
1	0.9774	0.9185	0.8352	0.8038	0.7373	0.6328	0.5282	0.4609	0.4284	0.3370	0.2562	0.1875	0.1312	0.0870	0.0540	0.0453	0.0308	0.0156	0.0067	0.0033	0.0022	0.0005	0.0000
2	0.9988	0.9914	0.9734	0.9645	0.9421	0.8965	0.8369	0.7901	0.7648	0.6826	0.5931	0.5000	0.4069	0.3174	0.2352	0.2099	0.1631	0.1035	0.0579	0.0355	0.0266	0.0086	0.0012
3	1.0000	0.9995	0.9978	0.9967	0.9933	0.9844	0.9692	0.9547	0.9460	0.9130	0.8688	0.8125	0.7438	0.6630	0.5716	0.5391	0.4718	0.3672	0.2627	0.1962	0.1648	0.0815	0.0226
4	1.0000	1.0000	0.9999	0.9999	0.9997	0.9990	0.9976	0.9959	0.9947	0.9898	0.9815	0.9688	0.9497	0.9222	0.8840	0.8683	0.8319	0.7627	0.6723	0.5981	0.5563	0.4095	0.2262
5	1.0000	1.0000	1.0000	1.0000	1.0000	1.0000	1.0000	1.0000	1.0000	1.0000	1.0000	1.0000	1.0000	1.0000	1.0000	1.0000	1.0000	1.0000	1.0000	1.0000	1.0000	1.0000	1.0000

n = 6, p	0.05	0.1	0.15	1/6	0.2	0.25	0.3	1/3	0.35	0.4	0.45	0.5	0.55	0.6	0.65	2/3	0.7	0.75	0.8	5/6	0.85	0.9	0.95
x = 0	0.7351	0.5314	0.3771	0.3349	0.2621	0.1780	0.1176	0.0878	0.0754	0.0467	0.0277	0.0156	0.0083	0.0041	0.0018	0.0014	0.0007	0.0002	0.0001	0.0000	0.0000	0.0000	0.0000
1	0.9672	0.8857	0.7765	0.7368	0.6554	0.5339	0.4202	0.3512	0.3191	0.2333	0.1636	0.1094	0.0692	0.0410	0.0223	0.0178	0.0109	0.0046	0.0016	0.0007	0.0004	0.0001	0.0000
2	0.9978	0.9842	0.9527	0.9377	0.9011	0.8306	0.7443	0.6804	0.6471	0.5443	0.4415	0.3438	0.2553	0.1792	0.1174	0.1001	0.0705	0.0376	0.0170	0.0087	0.0059	0.0013	0.0001
3	0.9999	0.9987	0.9941	0.9913	0.9830	0.9624	0.9295	0.8999	0.8826	0.8208	0.7447	0.6563	0.5585	0.4557	0.3529	0.3196	0.2557	0.1694	0.0989	0.0623	0.0473	0.0159	0.0022
4	1.0000	0.9999	0.9996	0.9993	0.9984	0.9954	0.9891	0.9822	0.9777	0.9590	0.9308	0.8906	0.8364	0.7667	0.6809	0.6488	0.5798	0.4661	0.3446	0.2632	0.2235	0.1143	0.0328
5	1.0000	1.0000	1.0000	1.0000	0.9999	0.9998	0.9993	0.9986	0.9982	0.9959	0.9917	0.9844	0.9723	0.9533	0.9246	0.9122	0.8824	0.8220	0.7379	0.6651	0.6229	0.4686	0.2649
6	1.0000	1.0000	1.0000	1.0000	1.0000	1.0000	1.0000	1.0000	1.0000	1.0000	1.0000	1.0000	1.0000	1.0000	1.0000	1.0000	1.0000	1.0000	1.0000	1.0000	1.0000	1.0000	1.0000

n = 7, p	0.05	0.1	0.15	1/6	0.2	0.25	0.3	1/3	0.35	0.4	0.45	0.5	0.55	0.6	0.65	2/3	0.7	0.75	0.8	5/6	0.85	0.9	0.95
x = 0	0.6983	0.4783	0.3206	0.2791	0.2097	0.1335	0.0824	0.0585	0.0490	0.0280	0.0152	0.0078	0.0037	0.0016	0.0006	0.0005	0.0002	0.0001	0.0000	0.0000	0.0000	0.0000	0.0000
1	0.9556	0.8503	0.7166	0.6698	0.5767	0.4449	0.3294	0.2634	0.2338	0.1586	0.1024	0.0625	0.0357	0.0188	0.0090	0.0069	0.0038	0.0013	0.0004	0.0001	0.0001	0.0000	0.0000
2	0.9962	0.9743	0.9262	0.9042	0.8520	0.7564	0.6471	0.5706	0.5323	0.4199	0.3164	0.2266	0.1529	0.0963	0.0556	0.0453	0.0288	0.0129	0.0047	0.0020	0.0012	0.0002	0.0000
3	0.9998	0.9973	0.9879	0.9824	0.9667	0.9294	0.8740	0.8267	0.8002	0.7102	0.6083	0.5000	0.3917	0.2898	0.1998	0.1733	0.1260	0.0706	0.0333	0.0176	0.0121	0.0027	0.0002
4	1.0000	0.9998	0.9988	0.9980	0.9953	0.9871	0.9712	0.9547	0.9444	0.9037	0.8471	0.7734	0.6836	0.5801	0.4677	0.4294	0.3529	0.2436	0.1480	0.0958	0.0738	0.0257	0.0038
5	1.0000	1.0000	0.9999	0.9999	0.9996	0.9987	0.9962	0.9931	0.9910	0.9812	0.9643	0.9375	0.8976	0.8414	0.7662	0.7366	0.6706	0.5551	0.4233	0.3302	0.2834	0.1497	0.0444
6	1.0000	1.0000	1.0000	1.0000	1.0000	0.9999	0.9998	0.9995	0.9994	0.9984	0.9963	0.9922	0.9848	0.9720	0.9510	0.9415	0.9176	0.8665	0.7903	0.7209	0.6794	0.5217	0.3017
7	1.0000	1.0000	1.0000	1.0000	1.0000	1.0000	1.0000	1.0000	1.0000	1.0000	1.0000	1.0000	1.0000	1.0000	1.0000	1.0000	1.0000	1.0000	1.0000	1.0000	1.0000	1.0000	1.0000

n = 8, p	0.05	0.1	0.15	1/6	0.2	0.25	0.3	1/3	0.35	0.4	0.45	0.5	0.55	0.6	0.65	2/3	0.7	0.75	0.8	5/6	0.85	0.9	0.95
x = 0	0.6634	0.4305	0.2725	0.2326	0.1678	0.1001	0.0576	0.0390	0.0319	0.0168	0.0084	0.0039	0.0017	0.0007	0.0002	0.0002	0.0001	0.0000	0.0000	0.0000	0.0000	0.0000	0.0000
1	0.9428	0.8131	0.6572	0.6047	0.5033	0.3671	0.2553	0.1951	0.1691	0.1064	0.0632	0.0352	0.0181	0.0085	0.0036	0.0026	0.0013	0.0004	0.0001	0.0000	0.0000	0.0000	0.0000
2	0.9942	0.9619	0.8948	0.8652	0.7969	0.6785	0.5518	0.4682	0.4278	0.3154	0.2201	0.1445	0.0885	0.0498	0.0253	0.0197	0.0113	0.0042	0.0012	0.0004	0.0002	0.0000	0.0000
3	0.9996	0.9950	0.9786	0.9693	0.9437	0.8862	0.8059	0.7414	0.7064	0.5941	0.4770	0.3633	0.2604	0.1737	0.1061	0.0879	0.0580	0.0273	0.0104	0.0046	0.0029	0.0004	0.0000
4	1.0000	0.9996	0.9971	0.9954	0.9896	0.9727	0.9420	0.9121	0.8939	0.8263	0.7396	0.6367	0.5230	0.4059	0.2936	0.2586	0.1941	0.1138	0.0563	0.0307	0.0214	0.0050	0.0004
5	1.0000	1.0000	0.9998	0.9996	0.9988	0.9958	0.9887	0.9803	0.9747	0.9502	0.9115	0.8555	0.7799	0.6846	0.5722	0.5318	0.4482	0.3215	0.2031	0.1348	0.1052	0.0381	0.0058
6	1.0000	1.0000	1.0000	1.0000	0.9999	0.9996	0.9987	0.9974	0.9964	0.9915	0.9819	0.9648	0.9368	0.8936	0.8309	0.8049	0.7447	0.6329	0.4967	0.3953	0.3428	0.1869	0.0572
7	1.0000	1.0000	1.0000	1.0000	1.0000	1.0000	0.9999	0.9998	0.9998	0.9993	0.9983	0.9961	0.9916	0.9832	0.9681	0.9610	0.9424	0.8999	0.8322	0.7674	0.7275	0.5695	0.3366
8	1.0000	1.0000	1.0000	1.0000	1.0000	1.0000	1.0000	1.0000	1.0000	1.0000	1.0000	1.0000	1.0000	1.0000	1.0000	1.0000	1.0000	1.0000	1.0000	1.0000	1.0000	1.0000	1.0000

Cumulative binomial probabilities (continued)

$n = 9$, p	0.05	0.1	0.15	1/6	0.2	0.25	0.3	1/3	0.35	0.4	0.45	0.5	0.55	0.6	0.65	2/3	0.7	0.75	0.8	5/6	0.85	0.9	0.95
$x =$ 0	0.6302	0.3874	0.2316	0.1938	0.1342	0.0751	0.0404	0.0260	0.0207	0.0101	0.0046	0.0020	0.0008	0.0003	0.0001	0.0001	0.0000	0.0000	0.0000	0.0000	0.0000	0.0000	0.0000
1	0.9288	0.7748	0.5995	0.5427	0.4362	0.3003	0.1960	0.1431	0.1211	0.0705	0.0385	0.0195	0.0091	0.0038	0.0014	0.0010	0.0004	0.0001	0.0000	0.0000	0.0000	0.0000	0.0000
2	0.9916	0.9470	0.8591	0.8217	0.7382	0.6007	0.4628	0.3772	0.3373	0.2318	0.1495	0.0898	0.0498	0.0250	0.0112	0.0083	0.0043	0.0013	0.0003	0.0001	0.0000	0.0000	0.0000
3	0.9994	0.9917	0.9661	0.9520	0.9144	0.8343	0.7297	0.6503	0.6089	0.4826	0.3614	0.2539	0.1658	0.0994	0.0536	0.0424	0.0253	0.0100	0.0031	0.0011	0.0006	0.0001	0.0000
4	1.0000	0.9991	0.9944	0.9910	0.9804	0.9511	0.9012	0.8552	0.8283	0.7334	0.6214	0.5000	0.3786	0.2666	0.1717	0.1448	0.0988	0.0489	0.0196	0.0090	0.0056	0.0009	0.0000
5	1.0000	0.9999	0.9994	0.9989	0.9969	0.9900	0.9747	0.9576	0.9464	0.9006	0.8342	0.7461	0.6386	0.5174	0.3911	0.3497	0.2703	0.1657	0.0856	0.0480	0.0339	0.0083	0.0006
6	1.0000	1.0000	1.0000	0.9999	0.9997	0.9987	0.9957	0.9917	0.9888	0.9750	0.9502	0.9102	0.8505	0.7682	0.6627	0.6228	0.5372	0.3993	0.2618	0.1783	0.1409	0.0530	0.0084
7	1.0000	1.0000	1.0000	1.0000	1.0000	0.9999	0.9996	0.9990	0.9986	0.9962	0.9909	0.9805	0.9615	0.9295	0.8789	0.8569	0.8040	0.6997	0.5638	0.4573	0.4005	0.2252	0.0712
8	1.0000	1.0000	1.0000	1.0000	1.0000	1.0000	1.0000	0.9999	0.9999	0.9997	0.9992	0.9980	0.9954	0.9899	0.9793	0.9740	0.9596	0.9249	0.8658	0.8062	0.7684	0.6126	0.3698
9	1.0000	1.0000	1.0000	1.0000	1.0000	1.0000	1.0000	1.0000	1.0000	1.0000	1.0000	1.0000	1.0000	1.0000	1.0000	1.0000	1.0000	1.0000	1.0000	1.0000	1.0000	1.0000	1.0000

$n = 10$, p	0.05	0.1	0.15	1/6	0.2	0.25	0.3	1/3	0.35	0.4	0.45	0.5	0.55	0.6	0.65	2/3	0.7	0.75	0.8	5/6	0.85	0.9	0.95
$x =$ 0	0.5987	0.3487	0.1969	0.1615	0.1074	0.0563	0.0282	0.0173	0.0135	0.0060	0.0025	0.0010	0.0003	0.0001	0.0000	0.0000	0.0000	0.0000	0.0000	0.0000	0.0000	0.0000	0.0000
1	0.9139	0.7361	0.5443	0.4845	0.3758	0.2440	0.1493	0.1040	0.0860	0.0464	0.0233	0.0107	0.0045	0.0017	0.0005	0.0004	0.0001	0.0000	0.0000	0.0000	0.0000	0.0000	0.0000
2	0.9885	0.9298	0.8202	0.7752	0.6778	0.5256	0.3828	0.2991	0.2616	0.1673	0.0996	0.0547	0.0274	0.0123	0.0048	0.0034	0.0016	0.0004	0.0001	0.0000	0.0000	0.0000	0.0000
3	0.9990	0.9872	0.9500	0.9303	0.8791	0.7759	0.6496	0.5593	0.5138	0.3823	0.2660	0.1719	0.1020	0.0548	0.0260	0.0197	0.0106	0.0035	0.0009	0.0003	0.0001	0.0000	0.0000
4	0.9999	0.9984	0.9901	0.9845	0.9672	0.9219	0.8497	0.7869	0.7515	0.6331	0.5044	0.3770	0.2616	0.1662	0.0949	0.0766	0.0473	0.0197	0.0064	0.0024	0.0014	0.0001	0.0000
5	1.0000	0.9999	0.9986	0.9976	0.9936	0.9803	0.9527	0.9234	0.9051	0.8338	0.7384	0.6230	0.4956	0.3669	0.2485	0.2131	0.1503	0.0781	0.0328	0.0155	0.0099	0.0016	0.0001
6	1.0000	1.0000	0.9999	0.9997	0.9991	0.9965	0.9894	0.9803	0.9740	0.9452	0.8980	0.8281	0.7340	0.6177	0.4862	0.4407	0.3504	0.2241	0.1209	0.0697	0.0500	0.0128	0.0010
7	1.0000	1.0000	1.0000	1.0000	0.9999	0.9996	0.9984	0.9966	0.9952	0.9877	0.9726	0.9453	0.9004	0.8327	0.7384	0.7009	0.6172	0.4744	0.3222	0.2248	0.1798	0.0702	0.0115
8	1.0000	1.0000	1.0000	1.0000	1.0000	1.0000	0.9999	0.9996	0.9995	0.9983	0.9955	0.9893	0.9767	0.9536	0.9140	0.8960	0.8507	0.7560	0.6242	0.5155	0.4557	0.2639	0.0861
9	1.0000	1.0000	1.0000	1.0000	1.0000	1.0000	1.0000	1.0000	1.0000	0.9999	0.9997	0.9990	0.9975	0.9940	0.9865	0.9827	0.9718	0.9437	0.8926	0.8385	0.8031	0.6513	0.4013
10	1.0000	1.0000	1.0000	1.0000	1.0000	1.0000	1.0000	1.0000	1.0000	1.0000	1.0000	1.0000	1.0000	1.0000	1.0000	1.0000	1.0000	1.0000	1.0000	1.0000	1.0000	1.0000	1.0000

$n = 12$, p	0.05	0.1	0.15	1/6	0.2	0.25	0.3	1/3	0.35	0.4	0.45	0.5	0.55	0.6	0.65	2/3	0.7	0.75	0.8	5/6	0.85	0.9	0.95
$x =$ 0	0.5404	0.2824	0.1422	0.1122	0.0687	0.0317	0.0138	0.0077	0.0057	0.0022	0.0008	0.0002	0.0001	0.0000	0.0000	0.0000	0.0000	0.0000	0.0000	0.0000	0.0000	0.0000	0.0000
1	0.8816	0.6590	0.4435	0.3813	0.2749	0.1584	0.0850	0.0540	0.0424	0.0196	0.0083	0.0032	0.0011	0.0003	0.0001	0.0000	0.0000	0.0000	0.0000	0.0000	0.0000	0.0000	0.0000
2	0.9804	0.8891	0.7358	0.6774	0.5583	0.3907	0.2528	0.1811	0.1513	0.0834	0.0421	0.0193	0.0079	0.0028	0.0008	0.0005	0.0002	0.0000	0.0000	0.0000	0.0000	0.0000	0.0000
3	0.9978	0.9744	0.9078	0.8748	0.7946	0.6488	0.4925	0.3931	0.3467	0.2253	0.1345	0.0730	0.0356	0.0153	0.0056	0.0039	0.0017	0.0004	0.0001	0.0000	0.0000	0.0000	0.0000
4	0.9998	0.9957	0.9761	0.9636	0.9274	0.8424	0.7237	0.6315	0.5833	0.4382	0.3044	0.1938	0.1117	0.0573	0.0255	0.0188	0.0095	0.0028	0.0006	0.0002	0.0001	0.0000	0.0000
5	1.0000	0.9995	0.9954	0.9921	0.9806	0.9456	0.8822	0.8223	0.7873	0.6652	0.5269	0.3872	0.2607	0.1582	0.0846	0.0664	0.0386	0.0143	0.0039	0.0013	0.0007	0.0001	0.0000
6	1.0000	0.9999	0.9993	0.9987	0.9961	0.9857	0.9614	0.9336	0.9154	0.8418	0.7393	0.6128	0.4731	0.3348	0.2127	0.1777	0.1178	0.0544	0.0194	0.0079	0.0046	0.0005	0.0000
7	1.0000	1.0000	0.9999	0.9998	0.9994	0.9972	0.9905	0.9812	0.9745	0.9427	0.8883	0.8062	0.6956	0.5618	0.4167	0.3685	0.2763	0.1576	0.0726	0.0364	0.0239	0.0043	0.0002
8	1.0000	1.0000	1.0000	1.0000	0.9999	0.9996	0.9983	0.9961	0.9944	0.9847	0.9644	0.9270	0.8655	0.7747	0.6533	0.6069	0.5075	0.3512	0.2054	0.1252	0.0922	0.0256	0.0022
9	1.0000	1.0000	1.0000	1.0000	1.0000	1.0000	0.9998	0.9995	0.9992	0.9972	0.9921	0.9807	0.9579	0.9166	0.8487	0.8189	0.7472	0.6093	0.4417	0.3226	0.2642	0.1109	0.0196
10	1.0000	1.0000	1.0000	1.0000	1.0000	1.0000	1.0000	1.0000	0.9999	0.9997	0.9989	0.9968	0.9917	0.9804	0.9576	0.9460	0.9150	0.8416	0.7251	0.6187	0.5565	0.3410	0.1184
11	1.0000	1.0000	1.0000	1.0000	1.0000	1.0000	1.0000	1.0000	1.0000	1.0000	0.9999	0.9998	0.9992	0.9978	0.9943	0.9923	0.9862	0.9683	0.9313	0.8878	0.8578	0.7176	0.4596
12	1.0000	1.0000	1.0000	1.0000	1.0000	1.0000	1.0000	1.0000	1.0000	1.0000	1.0000	1.0000	1.0000	1.0000	1.0000	1.0000	1.0000	1.0000	1.0000	1.0000	1.0000	1.0000	1.0000

Cumulative binomial probabilities (continued)

$n = 14$ p	0.05	0.1	0.15	1/6	0.2	0.25	0.3	1/3	0.35	0.4	0.45	0.5	0.55	0.6	0.65	2/3	0.7	0.75	0.8	5/6	0.85	0.9	0.95
$x =$ 0	0.4877	0.2288	0.1028	0.0779	0.0440	0.0178	0.0068	0.0034	0.0024	0.0008	0.0002	0.0001	0.0000	0.0000	0.0000	0.0000	0.0000	0.0000	0.0000	0.0000	0.0000	0.0000	0.0000
1	0.8470	0.5846	0.3567	0.2960	0.1979	0.1010	0.0475	0.0274	0.0205	0.0081	0.0029	0.0009	0.0003	0.0001	0.0000	0.0000	0.0000	0.0000	0.0000	0.0000	0.0000	0.0000	0.0000
2	0.9699	0.8416	0.6479	0.5795	0.4481	0.2811	0.1608	0.1053	0.0839	0.0398	0.0170	0.0065	0.0022	0.0006	0.0001	0.0001	0.0000	0.0000	0.0000	0.0000	0.0000	0.0000	0.0000
3	0.9958	0.9559	0.8535	0.8063	0.6982	0.5213	0.3552	0.2612	0.2205	0.1243	0.0632	0.0287	0.0114	0.0039	0.0011	0.0007	0.0002	0.0000	0.0000	0.0000	0.0000	0.0000	0.0000
4	0.9996	0.9908	0.9533	0.9310	0.8702	0.7415	0.5842	0.4755	0.4227	0.2793	0.1672	0.0898	0.0426	0.0175	0.0060	0.0040	0.0017	0.0003	0.0000	0.0000	0.0000	0.0000	0.0000
5	1.0000	0.9985	0.9885	0.9809	0.9561	0.8883	0.7805	0.6898	0.6405	0.4859	0.3373	0.2120	0.1189	0.0583	0.0243	0.0174	0.0083	0.0022	0.0004	0.0001	0.0000	0.0000	0.0000
6	1.0000	0.9998	0.9978	0.9959	0.9884	0.9617	0.9067	0.8505	0.8164	0.6925	0.5461	0.3953	0.2586	0.1501	0.0753	0.0576	0.0315	0.0103	0.0024	0.0007	0.0003	0.0000	0.0000
7	1.0000	1.0000	0.9997	0.9993	0.9976	0.9897	0.9685	0.9424	0.9247	0.8499	0.7414	0.6047	0.4539	0.3075	0.1836	0.1495	0.0933	0.0383	0.0116	0.0041	0.0022	0.0002	0.0000
8	1.0000	1.0000	1.0000	0.9999	0.9996	0.9978	0.9917	0.9826	0.9757	0.9417	0.8811	0.7880	0.6627	0.5141	0.3595	0.3102	0.2195	0.1117	0.0439	0.0191	0.0115	0.0015	0.0000
9	1.0000	1.0000	1.0000	1.0000	1.0000	0.9997	0.9983	0.9960	0.9940	0.9825	0.9574	0.9102	0.8328	0.7207	0.5773	0.5245	0.4158	0.2585	0.1298	0.0690	0.0467	0.0092	0.0004
10	1.0000	1.0000	1.0000	1.0000	1.0000	1.0000	0.9998	0.9993	0.9989	0.9961	0.9886	0.9713	0.9368	0.8757	0.7795	0.7388	0.6448	0.4787	0.3018	0.1937	0.1465	0.0441	0.0042
11	1.0000	1.0000	1.0000	1.0000	1.0000	1.0000	1.0000	0.9999	0.9999	0.9994	0.9978	0.9935	0.9830	0.9602	0.9161	0.8947	0.8392	0.7189	0.5519	0.4205	0.3521	0.1584	0.0301
12	1.0000	1.0000	1.0000	1.0000	1.0000	1.0000	1.0000	1.0000	1.0000	0.9999	0.9997	0.9991	0.9971	0.9919	0.9795	0.9726	0.9525	0.8990	0.8021	0.7040	0.6433	0.4154	0.1530
13	1.0000	1.0000	1.0000	1.0000	1.0000	1.0000	1.0000	1.0000	1.0000	1.0000	1.0000	0.9999	0.9998	0.9992	0.9976	0.9966	0.9932	0.9822	0.9560	0.9221	0.8972	0.7712	0.5123
14	1.0000	1.0000	1.0000	1.0000	1.0000	1.0000	1.0000	1.0000	1.0000	1.0000	1.0000	1.0000	1.0000	1.0000	1.0000	1.0000	1.0000	1.0000	1.0000	1.0000	1.0000	1.0000	1.0000

$n = 16$ p	0.05	0.1	0.15	1/6	0.2	0.25	0.3	1/3	0.35	0.4	0.45	0.5	0.55	0.6	0.65	2/3	0.7	0.75	0.8	5/6	0.85	0.9	0.95
$x =$ 0	0.4401	0.1853	0.0743	0.0541	0.0281	0.0100	0.0033	0.0015	0.0010	0.0003	0.0001	0.0000	0.0000	0.0000	0.0000	0.0000	0.0000	0.0000	0.0000	0.0000	0.0000	0.0000	0.0000
1	0.8108	0.5147	0.2839	0.2272	0.1407	0.0635	0.0261	0.0137	0.0098	0.0033	0.0010	0.0003	0.0001	0.0000	0.0000	0.0000	0.0000	0.0000	0.0000	0.0000	0.0000	0.0000	0.0000
2	0.9571	0.7892	0.5614	0.4868	0.3518	0.1971	0.0994	0.0594	0.0451	0.0183	0.0066	0.0021	0.0006	0.0001	0.0000	0.0000	0.0000	0.0000	0.0000	0.0000	0.0000	0.0000	0.0000
3	0.9930	0.9316	0.7899	0.7291	0.5981	0.4050	0.2459	0.1659	0.1339	0.0651	0.0281	0.0106	0.0035	0.0009	0.0002	0.0001	0.0000	0.0000	0.0000	0.0000	0.0000	0.0000	0.0000
4	0.9991	0.9830	0.9209	0.8866	0.7982	0.6302	0.4499	0.3391	0.2892	0.1666	0.0853	0.0384	0.0149	0.0049	0.0013	0.0008	0.0003	0.0000	0.0000	0.0000	0.0000	0.0000	0.0000
5	0.9999	0.9967	0.9765	0.9622	0.9183	0.8103	0.6598	0.5469	0.4900	0.3288	0.1976	0.1051	0.0486	0.0191	0.0062	0.0040	0.0016	0.0003	0.0000	0.0000	0.0000	0.0000	0.0000
6	1.0000	0.9995	0.9944	0.9899	0.9733	0.9204	0.8247	0.7374	0.6881	0.5272	0.3660	0.2272	0.1241	0.0583	0.0229	0.0159	0.0071	0.0016	0.0002	0.0000	0.0000	0.0000	0.0000
7	1.0000	0.9999	0.9989	0.9979	0.9930	0.9729	0.9256	0.8735	0.8406	0.7161	0.5629	0.4018	0.2559	0.1423	0.0671	0.0500	0.0257	0.0075	0.0015	0.0004	0.0002	0.0000	0.0000
8	1.0000	1.0000	0.9998	0.9996	0.9985	0.9925	0.9743	0.9500	0.9329	0.8577	0.7441	0.5982	0.4371	0.2839	0.1594	0.1265	0.0744	0.0271	0.0070	0.0021	0.0011	0.0001	0.0000
9	1.0000	1.0000	1.0000	1.0000	0.9998	0.9984	0.9929	0.9841	0.9771	0.9417	0.8759	0.7728	0.6340	0.4728	0.3119	0.2626	0.1753	0.0796	0.0267	0.0101	0.0056	0.0005	0.0000
10	1.0000	1.0000	1.0000	1.0000	1.0000	0.9997	0.9984	0.9960	0.9938	0.9809	0.9514	0.8949	0.8024	0.6712	0.5100	0.4531	0.3402	0.1897	0.0817	0.0378	0.0235	0.0033	0.0001
11	1.0000	1.0000	1.0000	1.0000	1.0000	1.0000	0.9997	0.9992	0.9987	0.9951	0.9851	0.9616	0.9147	0.8334	0.7108	0.6609	0.5501	0.3698	0.2018	0.1134	0.0791	0.0170	0.0009
12	1.0000	1.0000	1.0000	1.0000	1.0000	1.0000	1.0000	0.9999	0.9998	0.9991	0.9965	0.9894	0.9719	0.9349	0.8661	0.8341	0.7541	0.5950	0.4019	0.2709	0.2101	0.0684	0.0070
13	1.0000	1.0000	1.0000	1.0000	1.0000	1.0000	1.0000	1.0000	1.0000	0.9999	0.9994	0.9979	0.9934	0.9817	0.9549	0.9406	0.9006	0.8029	0.6482	0.5132	0.4386	0.2108	0.0429
14	1.0000	1.0000	1.0000	1.0000	1.0000	1.0000	1.0000	1.0000	1.0000	1.0000	0.9999	0.9997	0.9990	0.9967	0.9902	0.9863	0.9739	0.9365	0.8593	0.7728	0.7161	0.4853	0.1892
15	1.0000	1.0000	1.0000	1.0000	1.0000	1.0000	1.0000	1.0000	1.0000	1.0000	1.0000	1.0000	0.9999	0.9997	0.9990	0.9985	0.9967	0.9900	0.9719	0.9459	0.9257	0.8147	0.5599
16	1.0000	1.0000	1.0000	1.0000	1.0000	1.0000	1.0000	1.0000	1.0000	1.0000	1.0000	1.0000	1.0000	1.0000	1.0000	1.0000	1.0000	1.0000	1.0000	1.0000	1.0000	1.0000	1.0000

OCR S2 — STATISTICAL TABLES

Cumulative binomial probabilities (continued)

$n = 18$ p	0.05	0.1	0.15	1/6	0.2	0.25	0.3	1/3	0.35	0.4	0.45	0.5	0.55	0.6	0.65	2/3	0.7	0.75	0.8	5/6	0.85	0.9	0.95
$x =$ 0	0.3972	0.1501	0.0536	0.0376	0.0180	0.0056	0.0016	0.0007	0.0004	0.0001	0.0000	0.0000	0.0000	0.0000	0.0000	0.0000	0.0000	0.0000	0.0000	0.0000	0.0000	0.0000	0.0000
1	0.7735	0.4503	0.2241	0.1728	0.0991	0.0395	0.0142	0.0068	0.0046	0.0013	0.0003	0.0001	0.0000	0.0000	0.0000	0.0000	0.0000	0.0000	0.0000	0.0000	0.0000	0.0000	0.0000
2	0.9419	0.7338	0.4797	0.4027	0.2713	0.1353	0.0600	0.0326	0.0236	0.0082	0.0025	0.0007	0.0001	0.0000	0.0000	0.0000	0.0000	0.0000	0.0000	0.0000	0.0000	0.0000	0.0000
3	0.9891	0.9018	0.7202	0.6479	0.5010	0.3057	0.1646	0.1017	0.0783	0.0328	0.0120	0.0038	0.0010	0.0002	0.0000	0.0000	0.0000	0.0000	0.0000	0.0000	0.0000	0.0000	0.0000
4	0.9985	0.9718	0.8794	0.8318	0.7164	0.5187	0.3327	0.2311	0.1886	0.0942	0.0411	0.0154	0.0049	0.0013	0.0003	0.0001	0.0000	0.0000	0.0000	0.0000	0.0000	0.0000	0.0000
5	0.9998	0.9936	0.9581	0.9347	0.8671	0.7175	0.5344	0.4122	0.3550	0.2088	0.1077	0.0481	0.0183	0.0058	0.0014	0.0009	0.0003	0.0000	0.0000	0.0000	0.0000	0.0000	0.0000
6	1.0000	0.9988	0.9882	0.9794	0.9487	0.8610	0.7217	0.6085	0.5491	0.3743	0.2258	0.1189	0.0537	0.0203	0.0062	0.0039	0.0014	0.0002	0.0000	0.0000	0.0000	0.0000	0.0000
7	1.0000	0.9998	0.9973	0.9947	0.9837	0.9431	0.8593	0.7767	0.7283	0.5634	0.3915	0.2403	0.1280	0.0576	0.0212	0.0144	0.0061	0.0012	0.0002	0.0000	0.0000	0.0000	0.0000
8	1.0000	1.0000	0.9995	0.9989	0.9957	0.9807	0.9404	0.8924	0.8609	0.7368	0.5778	0.4073	0.2527	0.1347	0.0597	0.0433	0.0210	0.0054	0.0009	0.0002	0.0001	0.0000	0.0000
9	1.0000	1.0000	0.9999	0.9998	0.9991	0.9946	0.9790	0.9567	0.9403	0.8653	0.7473	0.5927	0.4222	0.2632	0.1391	0.1076	0.0596	0.0193	0.0043	0.0011	0.0005	0.0000	0.0000
10	1.0000	1.0000	1.0000	1.0000	0.9998	0.9988	0.9939	0.9856	0.9788	0.9424	0.8720	0.7597	0.6085	0.4366	0.2717	0.2233	0.1407	0.0569	0.0163	0.0053	0.0027	0.0002	0.0000
11	1.0000	1.0000	1.0000	1.0000	1.0000	0.9998	0.9986	0.9961	0.9938	0.9797	0.9463	0.8811	0.7742	0.6257	0.4509	0.3915	0.2783	0.1390	0.0513	0.0206	0.0118	0.0012	0.0000
12	1.0000	1.0000	1.0000	1.0000	1.0000	1.0000	0.9997	0.9991	0.9986	0.9942	0.9817	0.9519	0.8923	0.7912	0.6450	0.5878	0.4656	0.2825	0.1329	0.0653	0.0419	0.0064	0.0002
13	1.0000	1.0000	1.0000	1.0000	1.0000	1.0000	1.0000	0.9999	0.9997	0.9987	0.9951	0.9846	0.9589	0.9058	0.8114	0.7689	0.6673	0.4813	0.2836	0.1682	0.1206	0.0282	0.0015
14	1.0000	1.0000	1.0000	1.0000	1.0000	1.0000	1.0000	1.0000	1.0000	0.9998	0.9990	0.9962	0.9880	0.9672	0.9217	0.8983	0.8354	0.6943	0.4990	0.3521	0.2798	0.0982	0.0109
15	1.0000	1.0000	1.0000	1.0000	1.0000	1.0000	1.0000	1.0000	1.0000	1.0000	0.9999	0.9993	0.9975	0.9918	0.9764	0.9674	0.9400	0.8647	0.7287	0.5973	0.5203	0.2662	0.0581
16	1.0000	1.0000	1.0000	1.0000	1.0000	1.0000	1.0000	1.0000	1.0000	1.0000	1.0000	0.9999	0.9997	0.9987	0.9954	0.9932	0.9858	0.9605	0.9009	0.8272	0.7759	0.5497	0.2265
17	1.0000	1.0000	1.0000	1.0000	1.0000	1.0000	1.0000	1.0000	1.0000	1.0000	1.0000	1.0000	1.0000	0.9999	0.9996	0.9993	0.9984	0.9944	0.9820	0.9624	0.9464	0.8499	0.6028
18	1.0000	1.0000	1.0000	1.0000	1.0000	1.0000	1.0000	1.0000	1.0000	1.0000	1.0000	1.0000	1.0000	1.0000	1.0000	1.0000	1.0000	1.0000	1.0000	1.0000	1.0000	1.0000	1.0000

$n = 20$ p	0.05	0.1	0.15	1/6	0.2	0.25	0.3	1/3	0.35	0.4	0.45	0.5	0.55	0.6	0.65	2/3	0.7	0.75	0.8	5/6	0.85	0.9	0.95
$x =$ 0	0.3585	0.1216	0.0388	0.0261	0.0115	0.0032	0.0008	0.0003	0.0002	0.0000	0.0000	0.0000	0.0000	0.0000	0.0000	0.0000	0.0000	0.0000	0.0000	0.0000	0.0000	0.0000	0.0000
1	0.7358	0.3917	0.1756	0.1304	0.0692	0.0243	0.0076	0.0033	0.0021	0.0005	0.0001	0.0000	0.0000	0.0000	0.0000	0.0000	0.0000	0.0000	0.0000	0.0000	0.0000	0.0000	0.0000
2	0.9245	0.6769	0.4049	0.3287	0.2061	0.0913	0.0355	0.0176	0.0121	0.0036	0.0009	0.0002	0.0000	0.0000	0.0000	0.0000	0.0000	0.0000	0.0000	0.0000	0.0000	0.0000	0.0000
3	0.9841	0.8670	0.6477	0.5665	0.4114	0.2252	0.1071	0.0604	0.0444	0.0160	0.0049	0.0013	0.0003	0.0000	0.0000	0.0000	0.0000	0.0000	0.0000	0.0000	0.0000	0.0000	0.0000
4	0.9974	0.9568	0.8298	0.7687	0.6296	0.4148	0.2375	0.1515	0.1182	0.0510	0.0189	0.0059	0.0015	0.0003	0.0000	0.0000	0.0000	0.0000	0.0000	0.0000	0.0000	0.0000	0.0000
5	0.9997	0.9887	0.9327	0.8982	0.8042	0.6172	0.4164	0.2972	0.2454	0.1256	0.0553	0.0207	0.0064	0.0016	0.0003	0.0002	0.0000	0.0000	0.0000	0.0000	0.0000	0.0000	0.0000
6	1.0000	0.9976	0.9781	0.9629	0.9133	0.7858	0.6080	0.4793	0.4166	0.2500	0.1299	0.0577	0.0214	0.0065	0.0015	0.0009	0.0003	0.0000	0.0000	0.0000	0.0000	0.0000	0.0000
7	1.0000	0.9996	0.9941	0.9887	0.9679	0.8982	0.7723	0.6615	0.6010	0.4159	0.2520	0.1316	0.0580	0.0210	0.0060	0.0037	0.0013	0.0002	0.0000	0.0000	0.0000	0.0000	0.0000
8	1.0000	0.9999	0.9987	0.9972	0.9900	0.9591	0.8867	0.8095	0.7624	0.5956	0.4143	0.2517	0.1308	0.0565	0.0196	0.0130	0.0051	0.0009	0.0001	0.0000	0.0000	0.0000	0.0000
9	1.0000	1.0000	0.9998	0.9994	0.9974	0.9861	0.9520	0.9081	0.8782	0.7553	0.5914	0.4119	0.2493	0.1275	0.0532	0.0376	0.0171	0.0039	0.0006	0.0001	0.0000	0.0000	0.0000
10	1.0000	1.0000	1.0000	0.9999	0.9994	0.9961	0.9829	0.9624	0.9468	0.8725	0.7507	0.5881	0.4086	0.2447	0.1218	0.0919	0.0480	0.0139	0.0026	0.0006	0.0002	0.0000	0.0000
11	1.0000	1.0000	1.0000	1.0000	0.9999	0.9991	0.9949	0.9870	0.9804	0.9435	0.8692	0.7483	0.5857	0.4044	0.2376	0.1905	0.1133	0.0409	0.0100	0.0028	0.0013	0.0001	0.0000
12	1.0000	1.0000	1.0000	1.0000	1.0000	0.9998	0.9987	0.9963	0.9940	0.9790	0.9420	0.8684	0.7480	0.5841	0.3990	0.3385	0.2277	0.1018	0.0321	0.0113	0.0059	0.0004	0.0000
13	1.0000	1.0000	1.0000	1.0000	1.0000	1.0000	0.9997	0.9991	0.9985	0.9935	0.9786	0.9423	0.8701	0.7500	0.5834	0.5207	0.3920	0.2142	0.0867	0.0371	0.0219	0.0024	0.0000
14	1.0000	1.0000	1.0000	1.0000	1.0000	1.0000	1.0000	0.9998	0.9997	0.9984	0.9936	0.9793	0.9447	0.8744	0.7546	0.7028	0.5836	0.3828	0.1958	0.1018	0.0673	0.0113	0.0003
15	1.0000	1.0000	1.0000	1.0000	1.0000	1.0000	1.0000	1.0000	1.0000	0.9997	0.9985	0.9941	0.9811	0.9490	0.8818	0.8485	0.7625	0.5852	0.3704	0.2313	0.1702	0.0432	0.0026
16	1.0000	1.0000	1.0000	1.0000	1.0000	1.0000	1.0000	1.0000	1.0000	1.0000	0.9997	0.9987	0.9951	0.9840	0.9556	0.9396	0.8929	0.7748	0.5886	0.4335	0.3523	0.1330	0.0159
17	1.0000	1.0000	1.0000	1.0000	1.0000	1.0000	1.0000	1.0000	1.0000	1.0000	1.0000	0.9998	0.9991	0.9964	0.9879	0.9824	0.9645	0.9087	0.7939	0.6713	0.5951	0.3231	0.0755
18	1.0000	1.0000	1.0000	1.0000	1.0000	1.0000	1.0000	1.0000	1.0000	1.0000	1.0000	1.0000	0.9999	0.9995	0.9979	0.9967	0.9924	0.9757	0.9308	0.8696	0.8244	0.6083	0.2642
19	1.0000	1.0000	1.0000	1.0000	1.0000	1.0000	1.0000	1.0000	1.0000	1.0000	1.0000	1.0000	1.0000	1.0000	0.9998	0.9997	0.9992	0.9968	0.9885	0.9739	0.9612	0.8784	0.6415
20	1.0000	1.0000	1.0000	1.0000	1.0000	1.0000	1.0000	1.0000	1.0000	1.0000	1.0000	1.0000	1.0000	1.0000	1.0000	1.0000	1.0000	1.0000	1.0000	1.0000	1.0000	1.0000	1.0000

Cumulative binomial probabilities (continued)

$n = 25$ p	0.05	0.1	0.15	1/6	0.2	0.25	0.3	1/3	0.35	0.4	0.45	0.5	0.55	0.6	0.65	2/3	0.7	0.75	0.8	5/6	0.85	0.9	0.95
$x =$ 0	0.2774	0.0718	0.0172	0.0105	0.0038	0.0008	0.0001	0.0000	0.0000	0.0000	0.0000	0.0000	0.0000	0.0000	0.0000	0.0000	0.0000	0.0000	0.0000	0.0000	0.0000	0.0000	0.0000
1	0.6424	0.2712	0.0931	0.0629	0.0274	0.0070	0.0016	0.0005	0.0003	0.0001	0.0000	0.0000	0.0000	0.0000	0.0000	0.0000	0.0000	0.0000	0.0000	0.0000	0.0000	0.0000	0.0000
2	0.8729	0.5371	0.2537	0.1887	0.0982	0.0321	0.0090	0.0035	0.0021	0.0004	0.0001	0.0000	0.0000	0.0000	0.0000	0.0000	0.0000	0.0000	0.0000	0.0000	0.0000	0.0000	0.0000
3	0.9659	0.7636	0.4711	0.3816	0.2340	0.0962	0.0332	0.0149	0.0097	0.0024	0.0005	0.0001	0.0000	0.0000	0.0000	0.0000	0.0000	0.0000	0.0000	0.0000	0.0000	0.0000	0.0000
4	0.9928	0.9020	0.6821	0.5937	0.4207	0.2137	0.0905	0.0462	0.0320	0.0095	0.0023	0.0005	0.0001	0.0000	0.0000	0.0000	0.0000	0.0000	0.0000	0.0000	0.0000	0.0000	0.0000
5	0.9988	0.9666	0.8385	0.7720	0.6167	0.3783	0.1935	0.1120	0.0826	0.0294	0.0086	0.0020	0.0004	0.0001	0.0000	0.0000	0.0000	0.0000	0.0000	0.0000	0.0000	0.0000	0.0000
6	0.9998	0.9905	0.9305	0.8908	0.7800	0.5611	0.3407	0.2215	0.1734	0.0736	0.0258	0.0073	0.0016	0.0003	0.0000	0.0000	0.0000	0.0000	0.0000	0.0000	0.0000	0.0000	0.0000
7	1.0000	0.9977	0.9745	0.9553	0.8909	0.7265	0.5118	0.3703	0.3061	0.1536	0.0639	0.0216	0.0058	0.0012	0.0002	0.0001	0.0000	0.0000	0.0000	0.0000	0.0000	0.0000	0.0000
8	1.0000	0.9995	0.9920	0.9843	0.9532	0.8506	0.6769	0.5376	0.4668	0.2735	0.1340	0.0539	0.0174	0.0043	0.0008	0.0004	0.0001	0.0000	0.0000	0.0000	0.0000	0.0000	0.0000
9	1.0000	0.9999	0.9979	0.9953	0.9827	0.9287	0.8106	0.6956	0.6303	0.4246	0.2424	0.1148	0.0440	0.0132	0.0029	0.0016	0.0005	0.0000	0.0000	0.0000	0.0000	0.0000	0.0000
10	1.0000	1.0000	0.9995	0.9988	0.9944	0.9703	0.9022	0.8220	0.7712	0.5858	0.3843	0.2122	0.0960	0.0344	0.0093	0.0056	0.0018	0.0002	0.0000	0.0000	0.0000	0.0000	0.0000
11	1.0000	1.0000	0.9999	0.9997	0.9985	0.9893	0.9558	0.9082	0.8746	0.7323	0.5426	0.3450	0.1827	0.0778	0.0255	0.0164	0.0060	0.0009	0.0001	0.0000	0.0000	0.0000	0.0000
12	1.0000	1.0000	1.0000	0.9999	0.9996	0.9966	0.9825	0.9585	0.9396	0.8462	0.6937	0.5000	0.3063	0.1538	0.0604	0.0415	0.0175	0.0034	0.0004	0.0001	0.0000	0.0000	0.0000
13	1.0000	1.0000	1.0000	1.0000	0.9999	0.9991	0.9940	0.9836	0.9745	0.9222	0.8173	0.6550	0.4574	0.2677	0.1254	0.0918	0.0442	0.0107	0.0015	0.0003	0.0001	0.0000	0.0000
14	1.0000	1.0000	1.0000	1.0000	1.0000	0.9998	0.9982	0.9944	0.9907	0.9656	0.9040	0.7878	0.6157	0.4142	0.2288	0.1780	0.0978	0.0297	0.0056	0.0012	0.0005	0.0000	0.0000
15	1.0000	1.0000	1.0000	1.0000	1.0000	1.0000	0.9995	0.9984	0.9971	0.9868	0.9560	0.8852	0.7576	0.5754	0.3697	0.3044	0.1894	0.0713	0.0173	0.0047	0.0021	0.0001	0.0000
16	1.0000	1.0000	1.0000	1.0000	1.0000	1.0000	0.9999	0.9996	0.9992	0.9957	0.9826	0.9461	0.8660	0.7265	0.5332	0.4624	0.3231	0.1494	0.0468	0.0157	0.0080	0.0005	0.0000
17	1.0000	1.0000	1.0000	1.0000	1.0000	1.0000	1.0000	0.9999	0.9998	0.9988	0.9942	0.9784	0.9361	0.8464	0.6939	0.6297	0.4882	0.2735	0.1091	0.0447	0.0255	0.0023	0.0000
18	1.0000	1.0000	1.0000	1.0000	1.0000	1.0000	1.0000	1.0000	1.0000	0.9997	0.9984	0.9927	0.9742	0.9264	0.8266	0.7785	0.6593	0.4389	0.2200	0.1092	0.0695	0.0095	0.0002
19	1.0000	1.0000	1.0000	1.0000	1.0000	1.0000	1.0000	1.0000	1.0000	0.9999	0.9996	0.9980	0.9914	0.9706	0.9174	0.8880	0.8065	0.6217	0.3833	0.2280	0.1615	0.0334	0.0012
20	1.0000	1.0000	1.0000	1.0000	1.0000	1.0000	1.0000	1.0000	1.0000	1.0000	0.9999	0.9995	0.9977	0.9905	0.9680	0.9538	0.9095	0.7863	0.5793	0.4063	0.3179	0.0980	0.0072
21	1.0000	1.0000	1.0000	1.0000	1.0000	1.0000	1.0000	1.0000	1.0000	1.0000	1.0000	0.9999	0.9995	0.9976	0.9903	0.9851	0.9668	0.9038	0.7660	0.6184	0.5289	0.2364	0.0341
22	1.0000	1.0000	1.0000	1.0000	1.0000	1.0000	1.0000	1.0000	1.0000	1.0000	1.0000	1.0000	0.9999	0.9996	0.9979	0.9965	0.9910	0.9679	0.9018	0.8113	0.7463	0.4629	0.1271
23	1.0000	1.0000	1.0000	1.0000	1.0000	1.0000	1.0000	1.0000	1.0000	1.0000	1.0000	1.0000	1.0000	0.9999	0.9997	0.9995	0.9984	0.9930	0.9726	0.9371	0.9069	0.7288	0.3576
24	1.0000	1.0000	1.0000	1.0000	1.0000	1.0000	1.0000	1.0000	1.0000	1.0000	1.0000	1.0000	1.0000	1.0000	1.0000	1.0000	0.9999	0.9992	0.9962	0.9895	0.9828	0.9282	0.7226
25	1.0000	1.0000	1.0000	1.0000	1.0000	1.0000	1.0000	1.0000	1.0000	1.0000	1.0000	1.0000	1.0000	1.0000	1.0000	1.0000	1.0000	1.0000	1.0000	1.0000	1.0000	1.0000	1.0000

Cumulative binomial probabilities (continued)

$n = 30$ p	0.05	0.1	0.15	1/6	0.2	0.25	0.3	1/3	0.35	0.4	0.45	0.5	0.55	0.6	0.65	2/3	0.7	0.75	0.8	5/6	0.85	0.9	0.95
x = 0	0.2146	0.0424	0.0076	0.0042	0.0012	0.0002	0.0000	0.0000	0.0000	0.0000	0.0000	0.0000	0.0000	0.0000	0.0000	0.0000	0.0000	0.0000	0.0000	0.0000	0.0000	0.0000	0.0000
1	0.5535	0.1837	0.0480	0.0295	0.0105	0.0020	0.0003	0.0001	0.0000	0.0000	0.0000	0.0000	0.0000	0.0000	0.0000	0.0000	0.0000	0.0000	0.0000	0.0000	0.0000	0.0000	0.0000
2	0.8122	0.4114	0.1514	0.1028	0.0442	0.0106	0.0021	0.0007	0.0003	0.0000	0.0000	0.0000	0.0000	0.0000	0.0000	0.0000	0.0000	0.0000	0.0000	0.0000	0.0000	0.0000	0.0000
3	0.9392	0.6474	0.3217	0.2396	0.1227	0.0374	0.0093	0.0033	0.0019	0.0003	0.0000	0.0000	0.0000	0.0000	0.0000	0.0000	0.0000	0.0000	0.0000	0.0000	0.0000	0.0000	0.0000
4	0.9844	0.8245	0.5245	0.4243	0.2552	0.0979	0.0302	0.0122	0.0075	0.0015	0.0002	0.0000	0.0000	0.0000	0.0000	0.0000	0.0000	0.0000	0.0000	0.0000	0.0000	0.0000	0.0000
5	0.9967	0.9268	0.7106	0.6164	0.4275	0.2026	0.0766	0.0355	0.0233	0.0057	0.0011	0.0002	0.0000	0.0000	0.0000	0.0000	0.0000	0.0000	0.0000	0.0000	0.0000	0.0000	0.0000
6	0.9994	0.9742	0.8474	0.7765	0.6070	0.3481	0.1595	0.0838	0.0586	0.0172	0.0040	0.0007	0.0001	0.0000	0.0000	0.0000	0.0000	0.0000	0.0000	0.0000	0.0000	0.0000	0.0000
7	0.9999	0.9922	0.9302	0.8863	0.7608	0.5143	0.2814	0.1668	0.1238	0.0435	0.0121	0.0026	0.0004	0.0000	0.0000	0.0000	0.0000	0.0000	0.0000	0.0000	0.0000	0.0000	0.0000
8	1.0000	0.9980	0.9722	0.9494	0.8713	0.6736	0.4315	0.2860	0.2247	0.0940	0.0312	0.0081	0.0016	0.0002	0.0000	0.0000	0.0000	0.0000	0.0000	0.0000	0.0000	0.0000	0.0000
9	1.0000	0.9995	0.9903	0.9803	0.9389	0.8034	0.5888	0.4317	0.3575	0.1763	0.0694	0.0214	0.0050	0.0009	0.0001	0.0000	0.0000	0.0000	0.0000	0.0000	0.0000	0.0000	0.0000
10	1.0000	0.9999	0.9971	0.9933	0.9744	0.8943	0.7304	0.5848	0.5078	0.2915	0.1350	0.0494	0.0138	0.0029	0.0004	0.0002	0.0000	0.0000	0.0000	0.0000	0.0000	0.0000	0.0000
11	1.0000	1.0000	0.9992	0.9980	0.9905	0.9493	0.8407	0.7239	0.6548	0.4311	0.2327	0.1002	0.0334	0.0083	0.0014	0.0007	0.0002	0.0000	0.0000	0.0000	0.0000	0.0000	0.0000
12	1.0000	1.0000	0.9998	0.9995	0.9969	0.9784	0.9155	0.8340	0.7802	0.5785	0.3592	0.1808	0.0714	0.0212	0.0045	0.0025	0.0006	0.0001	0.0000	0.0000	0.0000	0.0000	0.0000
13	1.0000	1.0000	1.0000	0.9999	0.9991	0.9918	0.9599	0.9102	0.8737	0.7145	0.5025	0.2923	0.1356	0.0481	0.0124	0.0072	0.0021	0.0002	0.0000	0.0000	0.0000	0.0000	0.0000
14	1.0000	1.0000	1.0000	1.0000	0.9998	0.9973	0.9831	0.9565	0.9348	0.8246	0.6448	0.4278	0.2309	0.0971	0.0301	0.0188	0.0064	0.0008	0.0001	0.0000	0.0000	0.0000	0.0000
15	1.0000	1.0000	1.0000	1.0000	0.9999	0.9992	0.9936	0.9812	0.9699	0.9029	0.7691	0.5722	0.3552	0.1754	0.0652	0.0435	0.0169	0.0027	0.0002	0.0000	0.0000	0.0000	0.0000
16	1.0000	1.0000	1.0000	1.0000	1.0000	0.9998	0.9979	0.9928	0.9876	0.9519	0.8644	0.7077	0.4975	0.2855	0.1263	0.0898	0.0401	0.0082	0.0009	0.0001	0.0000	0.0000	0.0000
17	1.0000	1.0000	1.0000	1.0000	1.0000	0.9999	0.9994	0.9975	0.9955	0.9788	0.9286	0.8192	0.6408	0.4215	0.2198	0.1660	0.0845	0.0216	0.0031	0.0005	0.0002	0.0000	0.0000
18	1.0000	1.0000	1.0000	1.0000	1.0000	1.0000	0.9998	0.9993	0.9986	0.9917	0.9666	0.8998	0.7673	0.5689	0.3452	0.2761	0.1593	0.0507	0.0095	0.0020	0.0008	0.0000	0.0000
19	1.0000	1.0000	1.0000	1.0000	1.0000	1.0000	1.0000	0.9998	0.9996	0.9971	0.9862	0.9506	0.8650	0.7085	0.4922	0.4152	0.2696	0.1057	0.0256	0.0067	0.0029	0.0001	0.0000
20	1.0000	1.0000	1.0000	1.0000	1.0000	1.0000	1.0000	1.0000	0.9999	0.9991	0.9950	0.9786	0.9306	0.8237	0.6425	0.5683	0.4112	0.1966	0.0611	0.0197	0.0097	0.0005	0.0000
21	1.0000	1.0000	1.0000	1.0000	1.0000	1.0000	1.0000	1.0000	1.0000	0.9998	0.9984	0.9919	0.9688	0.9060	0.7753	0.7140	0.5685	0.3264	0.1287	0.0506	0.0278	0.0020	0.0000
22	1.0000	1.0000	1.0000	1.0000	1.0000	1.0000	1.0000	1.0000	1.0000	1.0000	0.9996	0.9974	0.9879	0.9565	0.8762	0.8332	0.7186	0.4857	0.2392	0.1137	0.0698	0.0078	0.0001
23	1.0000	1.0000	1.0000	1.0000	1.0000	1.0000	1.0000	1.0000	1.0000	1.0000	0.9999	0.9993	0.9960	0.9828	0.9414	0.9162	0.8405	0.6519	0.3930	0.2235	0.1526	0.0258	0.0006
24	1.0000	1.0000	1.0000	1.0000	1.0000	1.0000	1.0000	1.0000	1.0000	1.0000	1.0000	0.9998	0.9989	0.9943	0.9767	0.9645	0.9234	0.7974	0.5725	0.3836	0.2894	0.0732	0.0033
25	1.0000	1.0000	1.0000	1.0000	1.0000	1.0000	1.0000	1.0000	1.0000	1.0000	1.0000	1.0000	0.9998	0.9985	0.9925	0.9878	0.9698	0.9021	0.7448	0.5757	0.4755	0.1755	0.0156
26	1.0000	1.0000	1.0000	1.0000	1.0000	1.0000	1.0000	1.0000	1.0000	1.0000	1.0000	1.0000	1.0000	0.9997	0.9981	0.9967	0.9907	0.9626	0.8773	0.7604	0.6783	0.3526	0.0608
27	1.0000	1.0000	1.0000	1.0000	1.0000	1.0000	1.0000	1.0000	1.0000	1.0000	1.0000	1.0000	1.0000	1.0000	0.9997	0.9993	0.9979	0.9894	0.9558	0.8972	0.8486	0.5886	0.1878
28	1.0000	1.0000	1.0000	1.0000	1.0000	1.0000	1.0000	1.0000	1.0000	1.0000	1.0000	1.0000	1.0000	1.0000	1.0000	0.9999	0.9997	0.9980	0.9895	0.9705	0.9520	0.8163	0.4465
29	1.0000	1.0000	1.0000	1.0000	1.0000	1.0000	1.0000	1.0000	1.0000	1.0000	1.0000	1.0000	1.0000	1.0000	1.0000	1.0000	1.0000	0.9998	0.9988	0.9958	0.9924	0.9576	0.7854
30	1.0000	1.0000	1.0000	1.0000	1.0000	1.0000	1.0000	1.0000	1.0000	1.0000	1.0000	1.0000	1.0000	1.0000	1.0000	1.0000	1.0000	1.0000	1.0000	1.0000	1.0000	1.0000	1.0000

Discrete Groups of Particles in 1 Dimension

Welcome to the Centre of Mass. No, not your local Catholic church...

For Particles in a Line — Combine Moments about the Origin

1) The weight of an object is considered to act at its centre of mass.
A group of objects also has a centre of mass, which isn't necessarily in the same position as any one of the objects.

2) It's often convenient to model these objects as particles (point masses) since the position of a particle is the position of its centre of mass. If a group of particles all lie in a horizontal line, then the centre of mass of the group will lie somewhere on the same line.

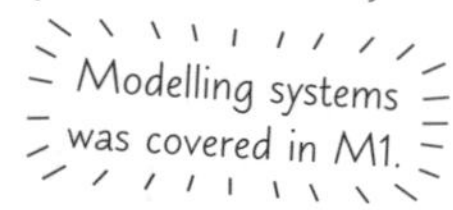

3) The moment (turning effect) of a particle from a fixed point is:

weight (mass × gravity)	×	perpendicular distance from point (x)

This is mgx if the fixed point and the particle are horizontally aligned.

Moments are covered in Section 2 (p. 154-155). Flick ahead for a sneak preview.

4) The moment of a group of particles in a horizontal line about a point in the horizontal line can be found by adding together all the individual moments about the point — Σmgx.

5) This has the same effect as the combined weight (Σmg) acting at the centre of mass of the whole group ($\bar{x}$).

Writing this as a formula:

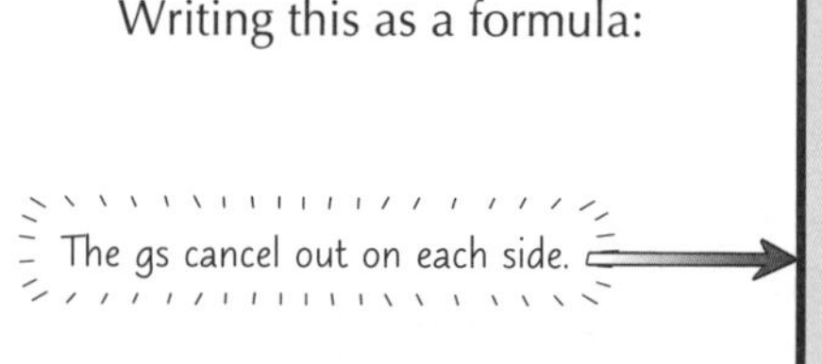

$$\Sigma mgx = \bar{x}\Sigma mg$$

e.g. for 3 particles in a horizontal line:

$$m_1gx_1 + m_2gx_2 + m_3gx_3 = \bar{x}(m_1g + m_2g + m_3g)$$

$$\Rightarrow m_1x_1 + m_2x_2 + m_3x_3 = \bar{x}(m_1 + m_2 + m_3)$$

$$\Rightarrow \Sigma mx = \bar{x}\Sigma m$$

Use this simplified formula to find the centre of mass, $\bar{x}$, of a group of objects in a horizontal line.

EXAMPLE Three particles are placed at positions along the x-axis as shown. Find the coordinates of the centre of mass of the group of particles.

m_1 = 3 kg (-2, 0); 0; m_2 = 1.5 kg (3, 0); m_3 = 0.5 kg (5, 0)

1) Use the formula $\Sigma mx = \bar{x}\Sigma m$ and put in what you know:
$m_1x_1 + m_2x_2 + m_3x_3 = \bar{x}(m_1 + m_2 + m_3)$
$\Rightarrow (3 \times -2) + (1.5 \times 3) + (0.5 \times 5) = \bar{x}(3 + 1.5 + 0.5)$
$\Rightarrow 1 = 5\bar{x} \quad \Rightarrow \quad \bar{x} = 0.2$

Negative coordinates go in the formula just as they are.

2) So the centre of mass of the group has the coordinates (0.2, 0)

Use $\bar{y}$ for Particles in a Vertical Line

It's the same for particles arranged in a vertical line. The centre of mass has the coordinate (0, $\bar{y}$).

$$\Sigma my = \bar{y}\Sigma m$$

EXAMPLE A light vertical rod AB has particles attached at various positions, as shown. At what height is the centre of mass of the rod?

A light rod has length but no width or depth, and no mass (as it's light).

B; m_4 = 2 kg; 1 m; m_3 = 1 kg; 2 m; m_2 = 4 kg; 1 m; m_1 = 3 kg; 1 m; A

1) First, work out the positions of all the particles relative to a single point or 'origin'.
Since you're asked for the vertical height, pick point A at the bottom of the rod:
$y_1 = 1$, $y_2 = 2$, $y_3 = 4$, $y_4 = 5$.

2) Plug the numbers into the formula:
$\Sigma my = \bar{y}\Sigma m \quad \Rightarrow \quad m_1y_1 + m_2y_2 + m_3y_3 + m_4y_4 = \bar{y}(m_1 + m_2 + m_3 + m_4)$
$\Rightarrow (3 \times 1) + (4 \times 2) + (1 \times 4) + (2 \times 5) = \bar{y} \times (3 + 4 + 1 + 2)$
$\Rightarrow 25 = \bar{y} \times 10 \quad \Rightarrow \quad \bar{y} = 25 \div 10 = 2.5.$

3) Make sure you've answered the question — $\bar{y}$ is the vertical coordinate from the 'origin' which we took as the bottom of the rod. So the vertical height of the centre of mass is 2.5 m.

Take a moment to understand the basics...

Once you've got your head around what's going on with a system of particles, the number crunching is the easy part. You'll often have to tackle wordy problems where you first have to model a situation using rods and particles and things — you should be more than familiar with doing this from M1, and there's more practice to come later in the section.

Discrete Groups of Particles in 2 Dimensions

Let's face it, in the 'real world', you'll rarely come across a group in a perfectly orderly line (think of queuing up in the sales — madness). Luckily, the same principles apply in two dimensions — it's no harder than the stuff on the last page.

For Centre of Mass of a Group on a Plane, Find each Coordinate Separately

At some point you may need to find the centre of mass of a group of particles on a plane (i.e. in 2 dimensions, x and y, rather than just in a line). The easiest way to do this is to just find each coordinate of the centre of mass separately:

EXAMPLE Find the coordinates of the centre of mass of the system of particles shown in the diagram.

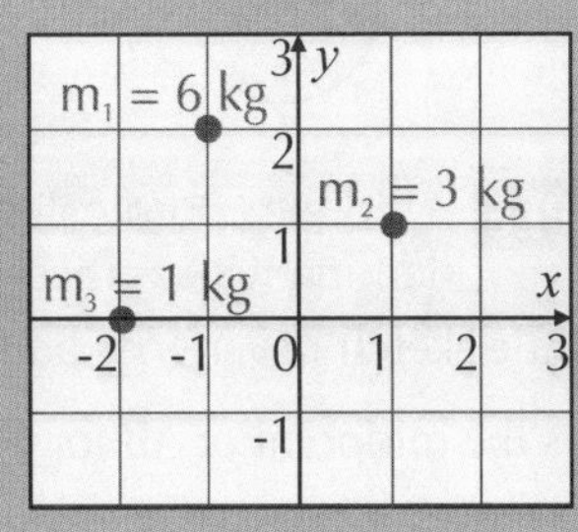

1) Find the x coordinate of the centre of mass first (pretend the particles are in a horizontal line...)
$x_1 = -1$, $x_2 = 1$, $x_3 = -2$, so:
$m_1x_1 + m_2x_2 + m_3x_3 = \bar{x}(m_1 + m_2 + m_3)$
$\Rightarrow\ (6 \times -1) + (3 \times 1) + (1 \times -2) = \bar{x}(6 + 3 + 1)$
$\Rightarrow \bar{x} = -\frac{5}{10} = \underline{-0.5}$.
2) Now find the y coordinate in the same way: $y_1 = 2$, $y_2 = 1$, $y_3 = 0$, so:
$m_1y_1 + m_2y_2 + m_3y_3 = \bar{y}(m_1 + m_2 + m_3)$
$\Rightarrow\ (6 \times 2) + (3 \times 1) + (1 \times 0) = \bar{y}(6 + 3 + 1)$
$\Rightarrow \bar{y} = \frac{15}{10} = \underline{1.5}$.
3) So the centre of mass has the coordinates (−0.5, 1.5).

Sometimes you'll be able to use symmetry to help you find one coordinate — see the next page.

The Formula works for finding Unknown Masses and Locations

You won't always be asked to find the centre of mass of a system. You could be given the position of the centre of mass and asked to work out something else, like the mass or coordinates of a particle in the system. Use the same formula.

A lamina is just a flat (2D) shape.

EXAMPLE The diagram shows the position of the centre of mass (COM) of a system of three particles attached to the corners of a light rectangular lamina. Find m_1 and m_2.

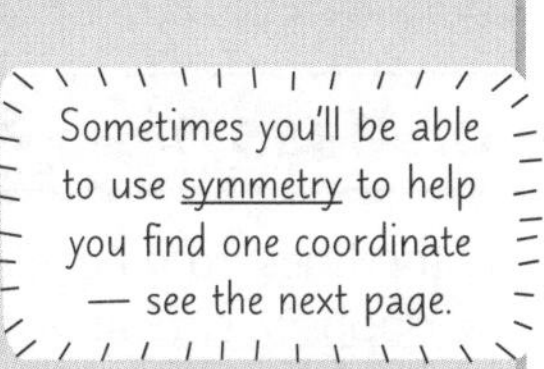

1) First of all, pick your origin — bottom left looks as good as anywhere — and define all your coordinates from this point:
$(x_1, y_1) = (0, 4)$; $(x_2, y_2) = (6, 4)$; $(x_3, y_3) = (6, 0)$; COM, $(\bar{x}, \bar{y})$ is at (3, 3.5).
2) First, consider only the x-coordinates and fill in what you know in the formula:
$m_1x_1 + m_2x_2 + m_3x_3 = \bar{x}(m_1 + m_2 + m_3)$
$\Rightarrow\ (m_1 \times 0) + (m_2 \times 6) + (2 \times 6) = 3(m_1 + m_2 + 2)$
$\Rightarrow\ 6m_2 + 12 = 3m_1 + 3m_2 + 6 \Rightarrow m_2 = m_1 - 2$ — call this **Eqn 1**
3) Now, consider only the y-coordinates and again, fill in what you know in the formula:
$m_1y_1 + m_2y_2 + m_3y_3 = \bar{y}(m_1 + m_2 + m_3)$
$\Rightarrow\ (m_1 \times 4) + (m_2 \times 4) + (2 \times 0) = 3.5(m_1 + m_2 + 2)$
$\Rightarrow\ 4m_1 + 4m_2 = 3.5m_1 + 3.5m_2 + 7 \Rightarrow m_1 + m_2 = 14$ — call this **Eqn 2**
4) You've now got a pair of simultaneous equations, which you can solve to find m_1 and m_2:
Sub Eqn 1 into Eqn 2: $m_1 + (m_1 - 2) = 14 \Rightarrow m_1 = \mathbf{8\ kg}$
Now use this value of m_1 in Eqn 1 to find $m_2 = 8 - 2 = \mathbf{6\ kg}$. Bang — and the maths is done.

2D or not 2D — that is the question...

Well actually the question's more likely to be 'Find the centre of mass of the following system of particles...', but then I doubt that would have made Hamlet quite such a gripping tale. Make sure you can do this stuff with your eyes shut because you'll need it again later on, and there's also a new compulsory blindfolded section to the M2 exam this year...

Standard Uniform Laminas

A page full of shapes for you to learn, just like in little school. However, you need to be able to find the centres of mass of these uniform plane laminas, not just colour them in. Even if you can do it neatly inside the lines.

Use Lines of Symmetry with Regular and Standard Shapes

Uniform laminas have evenly spread mass, so the centre of mass is in the centre of the shape, on all the lines of symmetry. So for shapes with more than one line of symmetry, the centre of mass is where the lines of symmetry intersect.

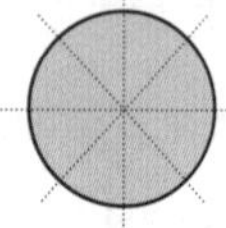

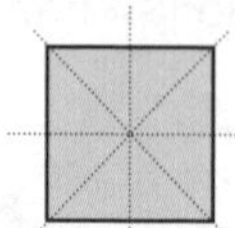

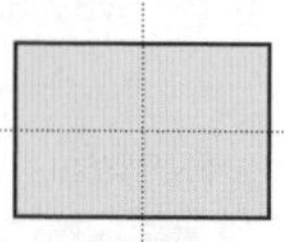

EXAMPLE Find the coordinates of the centre of mass of a uniform rectangular lamina with vertices A(−4, 7), B (2, 7), C(−4, −3) and D(2, −3).

1) A little sketch never goes amiss...
2) $\bar{x}$ is the midpoint of AB (or CD), i.e. $(-4 + 2) \div 2 = -1$.
3) $\bar{y}$ is the midpoint of AC (or BD), i.e. $(7 + -3) \div 2 = 2$.
4) So the centre of mass is at (−1, 2). Easy peasy lemon squeezy*.

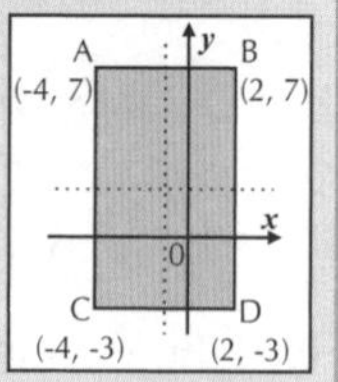

The Centre of Mass of a Triangle is the Centroid

1) In any triangle, the lines from each vertex to the midpoint of the opposite side are called medians.

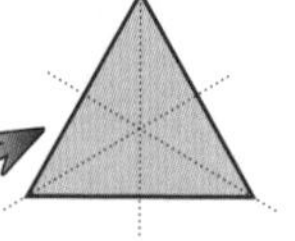

In an equilateral triangle, the medians are lines of symmetry.

2) If you draw in the medians on any triangle, the point where they meet will be two thirds of the way up each median from each vertex. This point is the centroid, and it's the centre of mass in a uniform triangle.

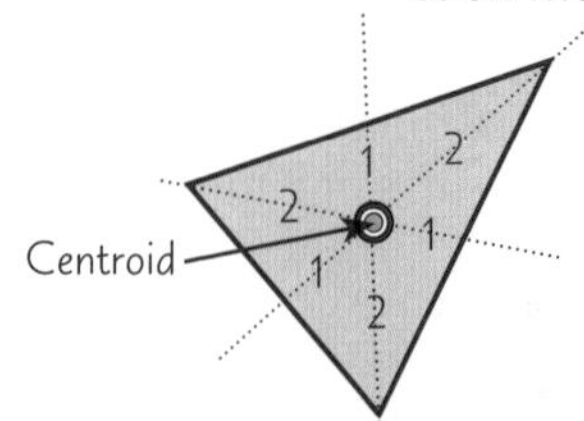

3) There's a formula for finding the coordinates of the centroid:

> For a triangle with vertices at (x_1, y_1), (x_2, y_2) and (x_3, y_3):
>
> **Centre of Mass $(\bar{x}, \bar{y})$ is at $\left(\frac{x_1 + x_2 + x_3}{3}, \frac{y_1 + y_2 + y_3}{3}\right)$**
>
> (i.e. the mean x coordinate and mean y coordinate)

The 'two thirds' fact will be on the formula sheet but you need to know how to use it.

Use the Formula to find the COM of a Sector of a Circle

Finding the centre of mass of a sector of a circle is a bit harder, so the formula is given to you in the exam:

> For a uniform circle sector, radius r and angle 2α radians:
>
> **Centre of Mass is at $\frac{2r\sin\alpha}{3\alpha}$ from the centre of the circle on the axis of symmetry.**

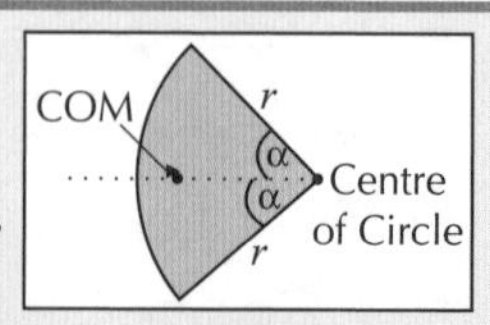

EXAMPLE A sector is cut from a uniform circle of radius 3 cm, centre P. The sector is an eighth of the whole circle. How far along the axis of symmetry is the centre of mass of the sector from P?

1) The angle of the sector is an eighth of the whole circle, so $2\alpha = \frac{2\pi}{8} \Rightarrow \alpha = \frac{\pi}{8}$.
2) Using the formula $\frac{2r\sin\alpha}{3\alpha}$, with $r = 3$ cm:

   Centre of Mass $= \dfrac{2 \times 3 \times \sin\frac{\pi}{8}}{\frac{3\pi}{8}} = 1.9489... =$ 1.95 cm from P (to 3 s.f.)

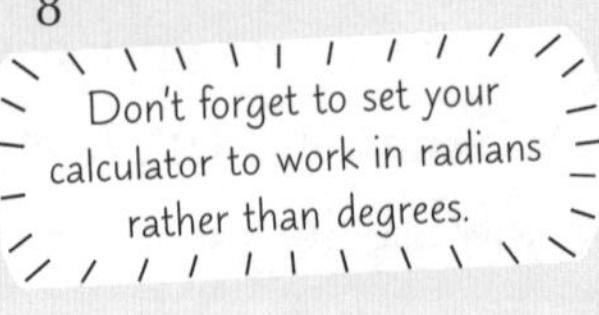

I love a lamina in uniform...

A nice easy page with lots of pretty shapes and colours. Before you start unleashing your inner toddler and demanding sweets and afternoon naps, make sure you fully understand what's been said on this page, because the tough stuff is coming right up. There's plenty of time for sweets and afternoon naps when the exams are over. Trust me...

*Squeezing lemons is actually quite tricky so I'm not sure where this saying comes from.

Composite Shapes

It's time to combine all the things covered so far in the section into one lamina lump. Yay.

For a *Composite Shape* — Find each COM *Individually* then *Combine*

A composite shape is one that can be broken up into standard parts such as triangles, rectangles and circles. Once you've found the COM of a part, imagine replacing it with a particle of the same mass in the position of the COM. Do this for each part, then find the COM of the group of 'particles' — this is the COM of the composite shape.

EXAMPLE A house-shaped lamina is cut from a single piece of card, with dimensions as shown. Find the location of the centre of mass of the shape in relation to the point O.

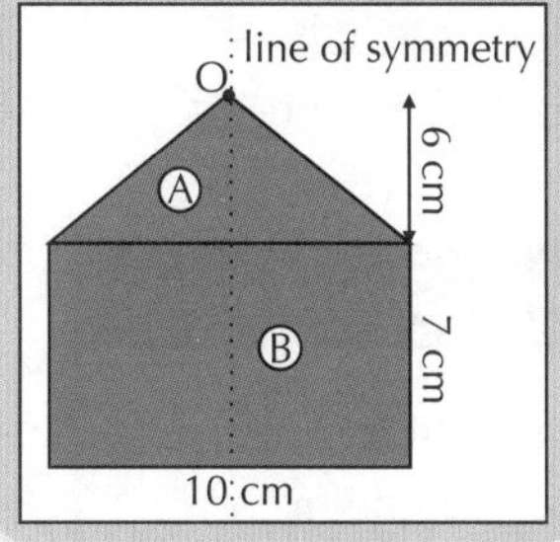

1) First, split up the shape into a triangle (A) and rectangle (B). As both bits are made of the same material, the masses of A and B are in proportion to their areas, so we can say $m_A = \frac{1}{2} \times 10 \times 6 = 30$, and $m_B = 10 \times 7 = 70$.

2) The shape has a line of symmetry, so the centre of mass must be on that line, directly below the point O.

3) Next find the vertical position of the centres of mass of both A and B individually:

   $y_A = \frac{2}{3}$ of the distance down from O $= \frac{2}{3} \times 6$ cm $= 4$ cm from O
   (since A is a triangle and the vertical line of symmetry from O is a median of the triangle — p.148)

   $y_B = 6$ cm $+ (7$ cm $\div 2) = 9.5$ cm from O
   (since B has a horizontal line of symmetry halfway down, but is 6 cm below O to start with)

Use symmetry where you can — but make sure you explain what you've done.

4) Treat the shapes as two particles positioned at the centres of mass of each shape, and use the formula from p.146:
   $\Sigma my = \bar{y}\Sigma m \Rightarrow m_A y_A + m_B y_B = \bar{y}(m_A + m_B)$
   $\Rightarrow (30 \times 4) + (70 \times 9.5) = \bar{y}(30 + 70) \Rightarrow 785 = 100\bar{y} \Rightarrow \bar{y} = 785 \div 100 = 7.85$ cm.

5) Make sure you've answered the question —
   The centre of mass of the whole shape is 7.85 cm vertically below O on the line of symmetry. Job done.

You can use the *Removal Method* for *Some Shapes*

You may have a shape that looks like a 'standard' shape with other standard shapes 'removed' rather than stuck together. The removal method is like the one above, except the individual centres of mass are subtracted rather than added.

EXAMPLE A section of a uniform triangular lamina is removed, as shown. Find the centre of mass of the resulting shape.

1) Let's call the 'whole' triangle A and the 'chunk' that's been removed B.

2) First find the COM of A using the formula from page 148:
   A has vertices at (1, 1), (9, 1) and (2, 7), so COM $(\bar{x}, \bar{y})$ is at:
   $\left(\frac{1+9+2}{3}, \frac{1+1+7}{3}\right) = (4, 3)$.

3) By symmetry, you can read off the COM of B as (3.5, 2.5).

4) As in the example above, the masses of A and B are proportional to their areas.
   So, $m_A = \frac{1}{2} \times 8 \times 6 = 24$, and $m_B = 3$.

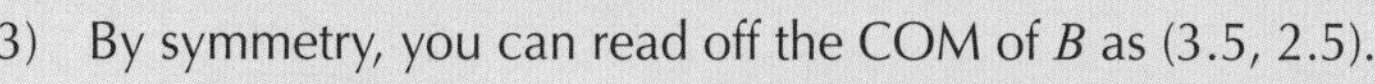

You can read the area of B straight off the graph, by 'counting squares'.

   Now you can use the 'Removal Method' to find the COM of the resulting shape.
   As ever, find each coordinate of the COM separately:

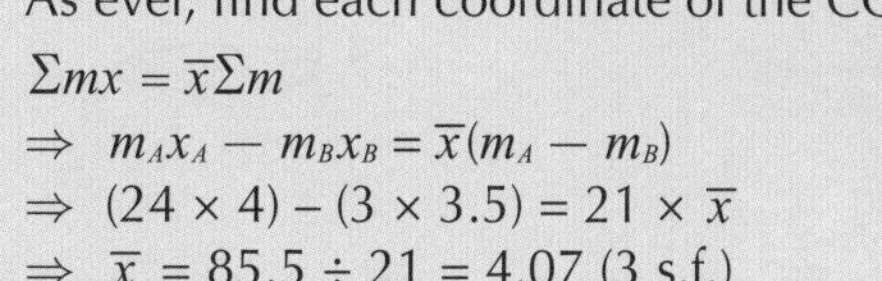

$\Sigma mx = \bar{x}\Sigma m$
$\Rightarrow m_A x_A - m_B x_B = \bar{x}(m_A - m_B)$
$\Rightarrow (24 \times 4) - (3 \times 3.5) = 21 \times \bar{x}$
$\Rightarrow \bar{x} = 85.5 \div 21 = 4.07$ (3 s.f.)

$\Sigma my = \bar{y}\Sigma m$
$\Rightarrow m_A y_A - m_B y_B = \bar{y}(m_A - m_B)$
$\Rightarrow (24 \times 3) - (3 \times 2.5) = 21 \times \bar{y}$
$\Rightarrow \bar{y} = 64.5 \div 21 = 3.07$ (3 s.f.)

5) So the COM of the resulting shape is at (4.07, 3.07) to 3 significant figures.

Waxing is another effective removal method...

Now you've got all you need to find the centre of mass of any lamina shape, so long as you can spot how it breaks up into circles, triangles, etc. Quite arty-farty this. Set out your working neatly though, especially for the more complicated shapes.

Centres of Mass in 3 Dimensions

I know how much you must have enjoyed this centre of mass stuff so far. But if you're anything like me, you'll be hungry for more. MORE. So, I present to you today's special — Centres of Mass in 3 Dimensions. Delicious.

Use **Symmetry** to find the COM of a **Uniform 3D Shape**

Remember — uniform means that the mass is evenly distributed.

1) As you've seen on the previous few pages, using the symmetry of a shape makes finding the COM tonnes easier.
2) This is just as true for uniform 3D shapes as it is for laminas.
3) For example, spheres, cubes, cylinders and cuboids all have their centre of mass right slap bang in the centre.
4) In fact, for any uniform 3D shape, the COM will be at the point where all the planes of symmetry intersect.
5) So, for a shape with an axis of rotational symmetry, the centre of mass will be somewhere on that axis.
6) Luckily, there's only a few shapes you're likely to get asked about on your exam, and for each one there's a formula telling you where the centre of mass is. Even better — they'll all be on the formula sheet in the exam.

COM of Uniform Solids

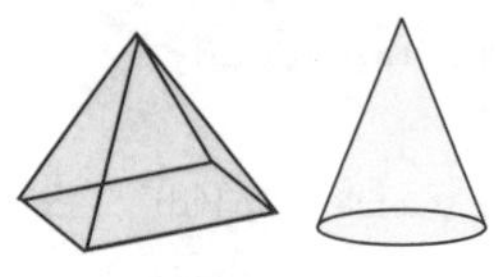

Pyramid or **cone**, height h:
$\frac{1}{4}h$ above base on line from centre of base to vertex

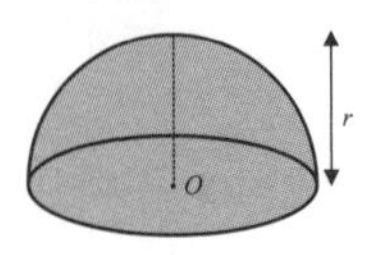

Hemisphere, radius r and centre O:
$\frac{3}{8}r$ from O on axis of symmetry

COM of Uniform Shells

Conical Shell, height h:
$\frac{1}{3}h$ above 'base' on line from centre of 'base' to vertex

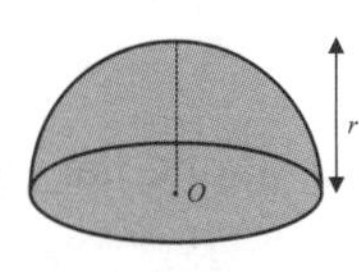

Hemispherical shell, radius r and centre O:
$\frac{1}{2}r$ from O on axis of symmetry

You also need to know how to find the centre of mass for a sphere, cube, cylinder and cuboid. But they is like well easy.

A shell is basically a solid with all the insides scooped out. And with no base.

Use the same method for **Composite Shapes in 3D** as in 2D

Just find the centre of mass for each shape individually, then combine.

EXAMPLE

A toy rocket, R, is made up of a solid uniform cone, A, of height 4 cm and mass 0.5 kg and a solid uniform cylinder, B, of height 12 cm and mass 1 kg. A and B are joined so that the base of A coincides with one of the plane faces of B, as shown below. Find the position of the rocket's centre of mass in relation to O, the centre of its base.

1) The rocket has an axis of symmetry running through O and the vertex of A, so the centres of mass of A, B and R will all lie somewhere on this line.

This simplifies the question to particles in a vertical line. Just like p. 146.

2) Find the vertical position of centres of mass of A and B individually:

$y_A = \frac{1}{4}(4) + 12 = 1 + 12 = 13$ cm above O

(using the formula for the centre of mass of a solid uniform cone and the fact that the base of A is 12 cm above O to start with)

$y_B = \frac{1}{2}h_B = \frac{1}{2}(12) = 6$ cm from O

(since the cylinder has a horizontal plane of symmetry halfway up)

3) Now, just like you did in 2D, treat the shapes as two particles positioned at the centre of mass of each shape and use the formula from p. 146. to find the centre of mass of R:

$\Sigma my = \bar{y}\Sigma m \Rightarrow m_A y_A + m_B y_B = m_R y_R$

$\Rightarrow 0.5(13) + 1(6) = 1.5y_R \Rightarrow y_R = 12.5 \div 1.5 = 8\frac{1}{3}$ cm.

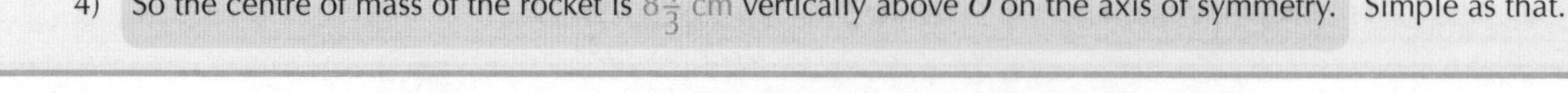

4) So the centre of mass of the rocket is $8\frac{1}{3}$ cm vertically above O on the axis of symmetry. Simple as that.

'Centres of Mass 3D' — the must-miss movie of the year...

...contact your local cinema for details. Or, if that's not your thing, then spend some time practising centre of mass questions.

Laminas in Equilibrium

This is what the whole section's been working up to. The raison d'être for centres of mass, if you'll pardon my French. The position of the centre of mass will tell you what happens when you hang it up or tilt it. Très intéressant, non?

Laminas **Hang** with the Centre of Mass **Directly Below** the **Pivot**

When you suspend a shape, either from a point on its edge or from a pivot point within the shape, it will hang in equilibrium so that the centre of mass is vertically below the suspension point.

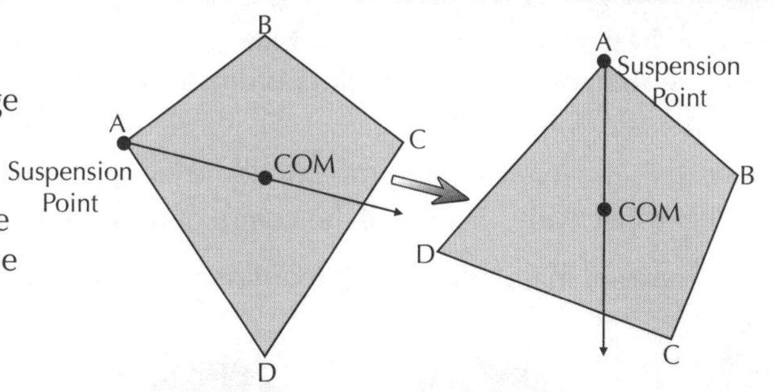

Knowing where the centre of mass lies will let you work out the angle that the shape hangs at.

EXAMPLE In the shape above, A is at (0, 6), C is at (8, 6), and the COM is at (4, 5). Find, in radians to 3 s.f., the angle AC makes with the vertical when the shape is suspended from A.

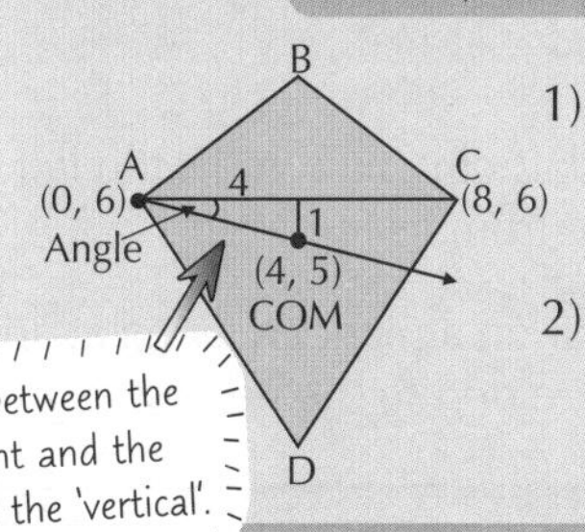

1) Do a little sketch of the shape showing the lengths you know. Draw in the line representing the vertical from the suspension point to the COM and label the angle you need to find.

2) The angle should now be an easy piece of trig away:
Angle = $\tan^{-1}\frac{1}{4}$ = 0.245 radians to 3 s.f.

A straight line between the suspension point and the COM represents the 'vertical'.

In an exam question, you'll usually have to find the position of the centre of mass first and THEN do this bit to finish.

Shapes **Topple** if the COM is not **Directly Above** the **Bottom Edge**

SAFE

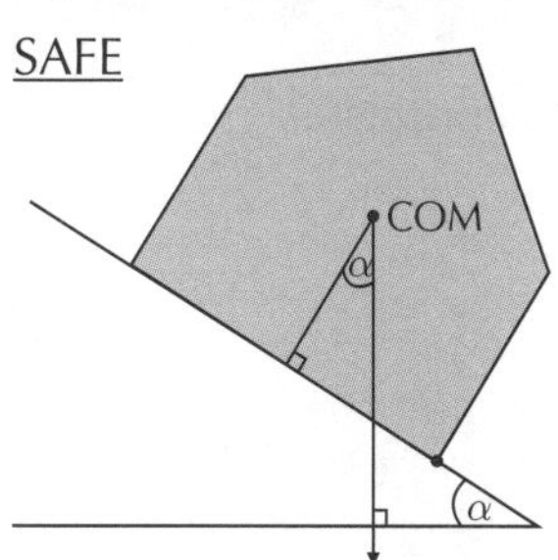

MORTAL PERIL

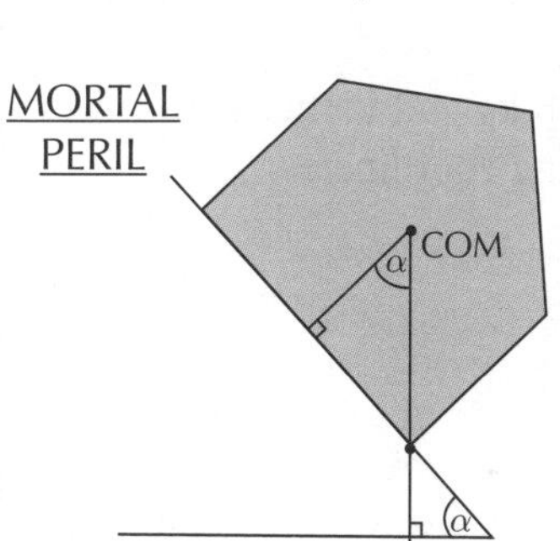

Tilting a shape on an inclined plane will make it topple over eventually (assuming there's enough friction to stop it sliding).

To make it fall over, you need to incline the plane above an angle, α, where the centre of mass is vertically above the bottom corner or edge of the shape, as shown in the pictures on the left.

EXAMPLE The house-shaped lamina from p. 149 is in equilibrium on a plane inclined at an angle α. Find the value of α at the point where the shape is about to topple (in rads to 3 s.f.).

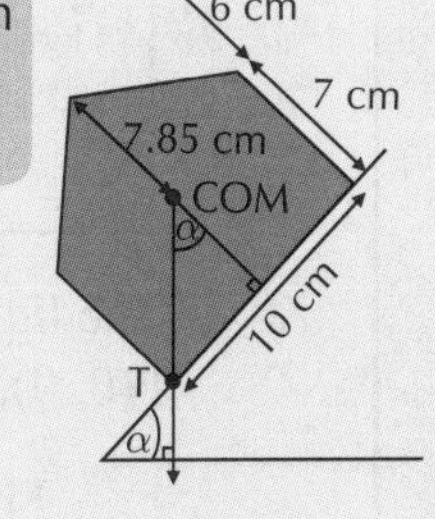

1) Draw in a line between the COM and the corner point (T) of the shape — this line will be vertical at the tipping point.

Use what you know about the position of the COM to draw a right-angled triangle containing α.
Height of COM from bottom edge = 7 + 6 – 7.85 = 5.15 cm.
COM is also halfway along the bottom edge, i.e. 10 ÷ 2 = 5 cm from T.

2) Use basic trig to work out the size of the angle:
$\alpha = \tan^{-1}\left(\frac{5}{5.15}\right)$ = 0.771 rads to 3 s.f.

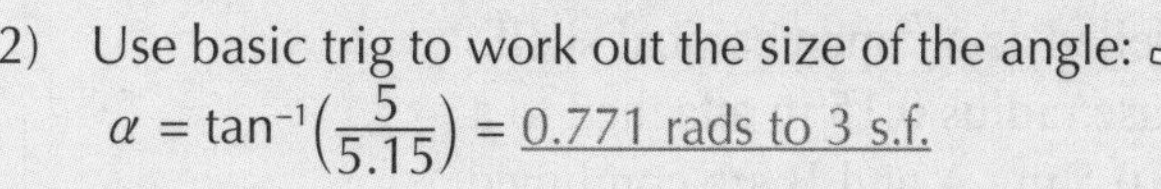

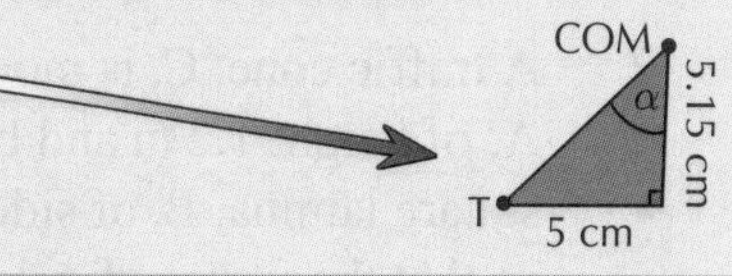

You might get a question about a solid 3D object standing on an inclined plane. You go about solving it in exactly the same way.

Don't hang around — get practising or you're heading for a fall...

This page may seem deceptively easy because in both examples it's assumed you've already found the centre of mass (that's what all the other pages were about in case you'd forgotten). In the exam you'll more than likely have to find the COM first and then work out the hanging or toppling angles. Luckily, there's plenty of practice at doing this on the next two pages...

M2 Section 1 — Practice Questions

Hurrah and huzzah — it's time to put your slick Section 1 skills (try saying that in a hurry) to the test. As with all strenuous exercise, you need to warm up properly — and as if by chance, look what we have here...

Warm-up Questions

1) Three particles have mass $m_1 = 1$ kg, $m_2 = 2$ kg, and $m_3 = 3$ kg.
Find the centre of mass of the system of particles if their coordinates are, respectively:
a) (1, 0), (2, 0), (3, 0) b) (0, 3), (0, 2), (0, 1) c) (3, 4), (3, 1), (1, 0)

2) A system of particles located at coordinates A(0, 0), B(0, 4), C(5, 4) and D(5, 0) have masses m kg, $2m$ kg, $3m$ kg and 12 kg respectively. Find m, if the centre of mass of the system is at (3.5, 2).

3) Find the coordinates of the centres of mass of each of the uniform laminas shown below.

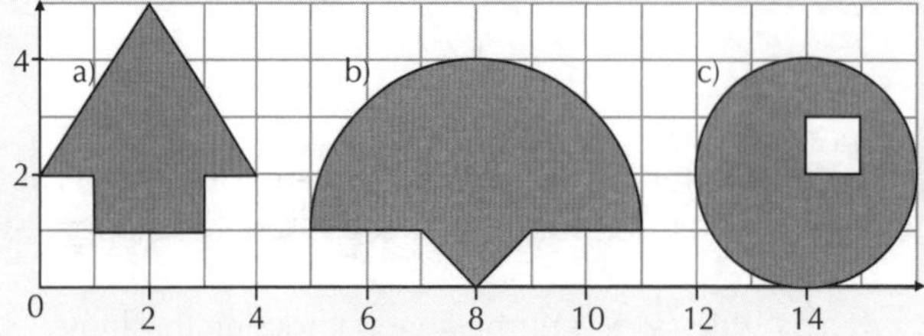

4) A square uniform lamina of width 10 cm has a smaller square of width 2 cm cut from its top left corner. Find the distance of the centre of mass of the remaining shape from its top edge.

5) A solid uniform cylinder, P, of height 6 cm and radius 2.5 cm is placed on a plane inclined at an angle α to the horizontal. If P is on the point of toppling, find the value of α to the nearest degree.

The universe is full of seemingly unanswerable questions to ponder. Fortunately for those not particularly inclined towards philosophy there are some perfectly good answerable ones here. Enjoy.

Exam Questions

1 The diagram below shows three particles attached to a light rectangular lamina at coordinates A(1, 3), B(5, 1) and C(4, y).

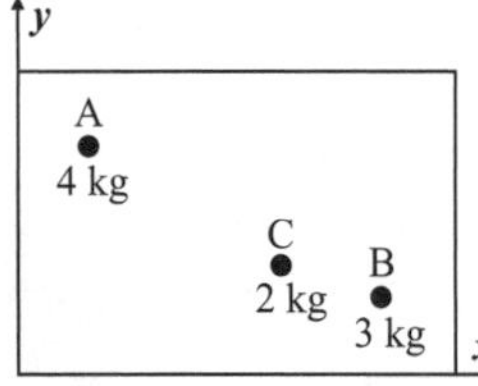

The centre of mass of the system is at $(\bar{x}, 2)$.

a) Show that $y = 1.5$. *(3 marks)*

b) Show that $\bar{x} = 3$. *(3 marks)*

The light lamina is replaced with a uniform rectangle PQRS, having a mass of 6 kg and vertices at P(0, 0), Q(0, 5), R(7, 5) and S(7, 0). Particles A, B and C remain at their existing coordinates.

c) Find the coordinates of the new centre of mass of the whole system. *(6 marks)*

2 A traffic cone, C, is modelled as an open conical shell, A, of height 1.2 m and base radius 0.15 m attached to a square lamina, B, of side 0.5 m. A and B are combined so that the vertex of A is vertically above the centre of B, the point O. It is assumed that A and B are made from the same uniform material.

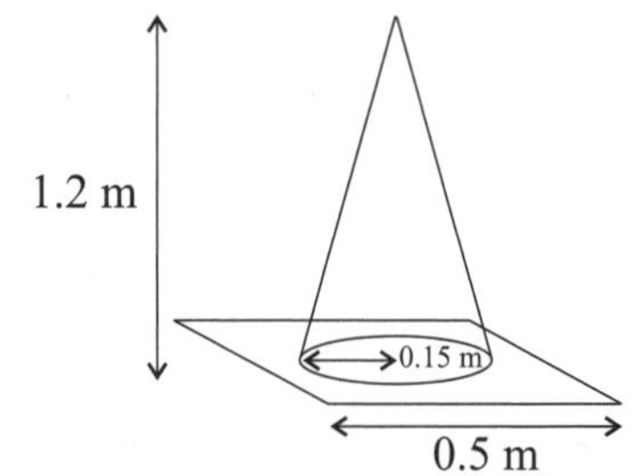

Find the position of the centre of mass of the cone in relation to O.
Use the fact that the curved surface of a cone has area πrl, where l is the length of the sloped edge. *(6 marks)*

M2 Section 1 — Practice Questions

3 A cardboard 'For Sale' sign is modelled as a uniform lamina consisting of two squares and an isosceles triangle. The line of symmetry through the triangle coincides with that of the larger square, as shown.

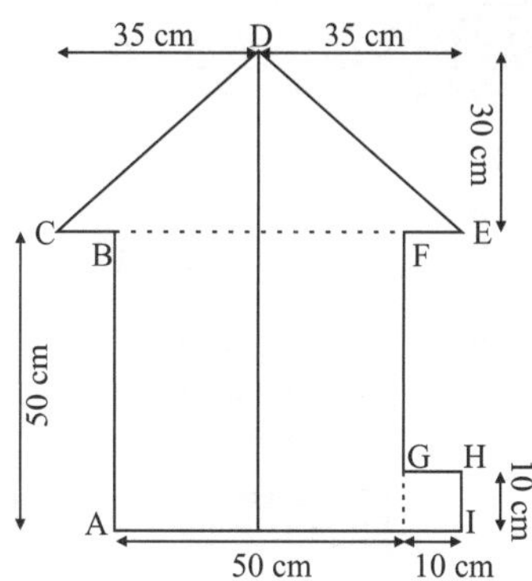

a) Show that the centre of mass of the sign, to 3 s.f., is 25.8 cm from AB and 34.5 cm from AI. *(8 marks)*

The sign, with a mass of 1 kg, is suspended from the point D, and hangs in equilibrium, at an angle. A small weight, modelled as a particle, is attached at A, so that the sign hangs with AI horizontal.

b) Find the mass of the particle needed to make the sign hang in this way. Give your answer in kg to 3 s.f. *(3 marks)*

4 A stencil is made from a uniform sheet of metal by removing a quarter of a circle with centre at the point O.

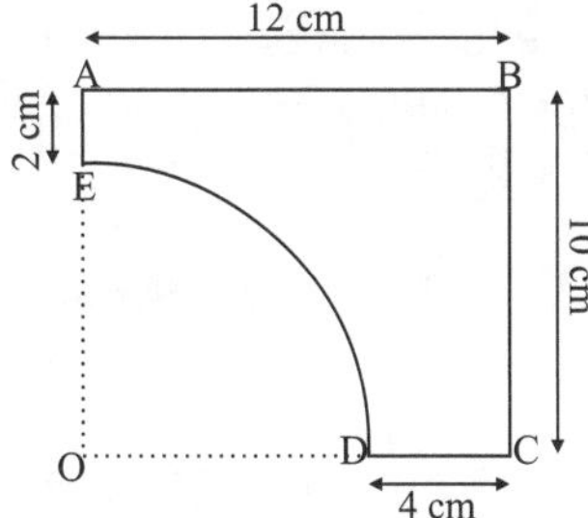

a) Taking the point O as the origin, find the coordinates of the centre of mass of the stencil, to 3 s.f. Assume the stencil can be modelled as a lamina. *(7 marks)*

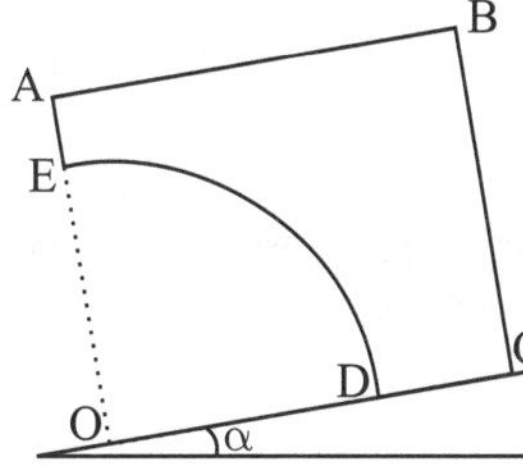

Particles are added to the stencil to adjust the centre of mass so that it now acts at coordinates (9, 6) from O. The stencil rests in equilibrium on a rough inclined plane, as shown. The angle of incline is increased until the shape is just about to fall over, balanced on the point D.

b) Find the angle of incline above which the shape will topple. Give your answer in radians to 3 s.f. *(3 marks)*

5 A piece of jewellery is made by cutting a triangle from a thin circle of metal, as shown. P is the centre of the circle, which has a radius of 2 cm. Triangle PQR is right-angled and isosceles. The shape can be modelled as a uniform lamina.

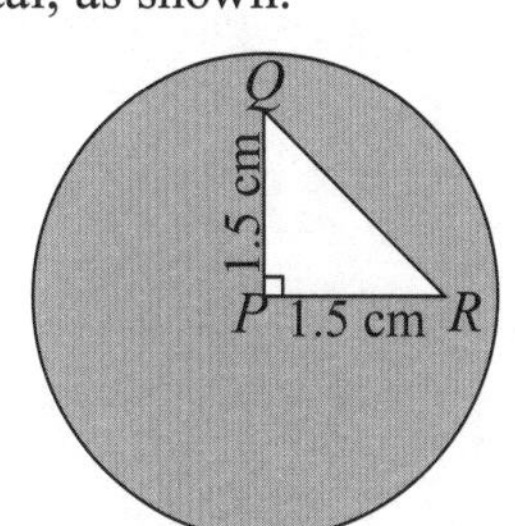

a) Show that the centre of mass of the shape is 0.070 cm from P, to 3 decimal places. *(5 marks)*

The shape hangs in equilibrium from a pin at point Q, about which it is able to freely rotate. The pin can be modelled as a smooth peg.

b) Find the angle that PQ makes with the vertical. Give your answer in degrees, to 1 decimal place. *(3 marks)*

Moments

In this lifetime there are moments — moments of joy and of sorrow, and those moments where you have to answer questions on moments in exams.

Moment = Force × Perpendicular Distance from the force's Line of Action

A '<u>moment</u>' is the <u>turning effect</u> a force has <u>around a point</u>. The <u>larger the force</u>, and the <u>greater the distance</u> from the point, then the <u>larger the moment</u>.

Moment = Force × Perpendicular Distance from Line of Action

Often, you'll be given a distance between the point and the force, but this distance won't be <u>perpendicular</u> to the force's '<u>line of action</u>'. You'll need to <u>resolve</u> to find the <u>perpendicular distance</u>.

EXAMPLE Find the sum of the moments of the forces shown about the point A.

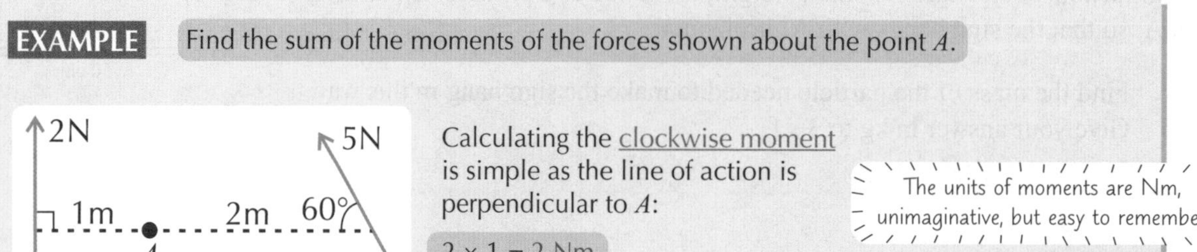

Calculating the <u>clockwise moment</u> is simple as the line of action is perpendicular to A:

$2 \times 1 = 2$ Nm

The units of moments are Nm, unimaginative, but easy to remember.

The <u>anticlockwise moment</u> is trickier as the line of action of the force <u>isn't perpendicular</u> to A. There are two ways to go about finding the moment — by finding the <u>perpendicular distance</u> or finding the <u>perpendicular component</u> of the force.

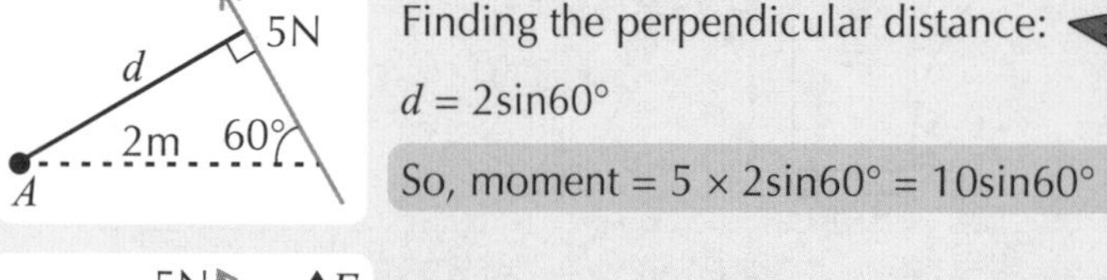

Finding the perpendicular distance:

$d = 2\sin 60°$

So, moment $= 5 \times 2\sin 60° = 10\sin 60° = 5\sqrt{3}$ Nm

Both methods give the same moment. Just choose whichever you find simplest — and be sure to show your workings.

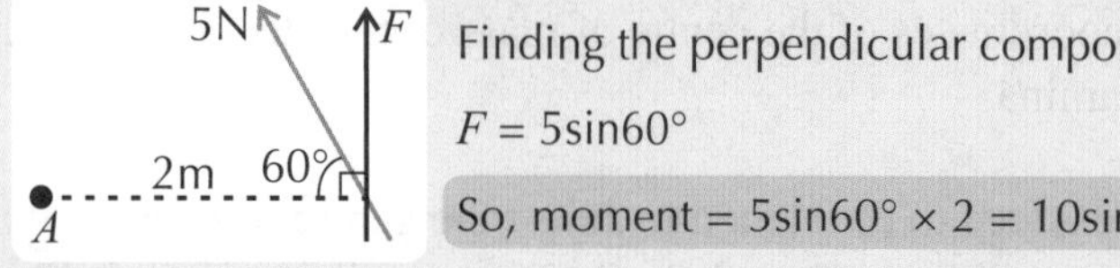

Finding the perpendicular component of the force:

$F = 5\sin 60°$

So, moment $= 5\sin 60° \times 2 = 10\sin 60° = 5\sqrt{3}$ Nm

We can now find the sum of the moments (in this case, taking anticlockwise as negative):

Clockwise + anticlockwise moments $= 2 + (-5\sqrt{3}) = -6.66$ Nm (3 s.f.) $= 6.66$ Nm anticlockwise

In Equilibrium Moments total Zero around Any Point

If a system is in equilibrium, the moments about <u>any</u> point total zero — so <u>anticlockwise moments = clockwise moments</u> about any point.

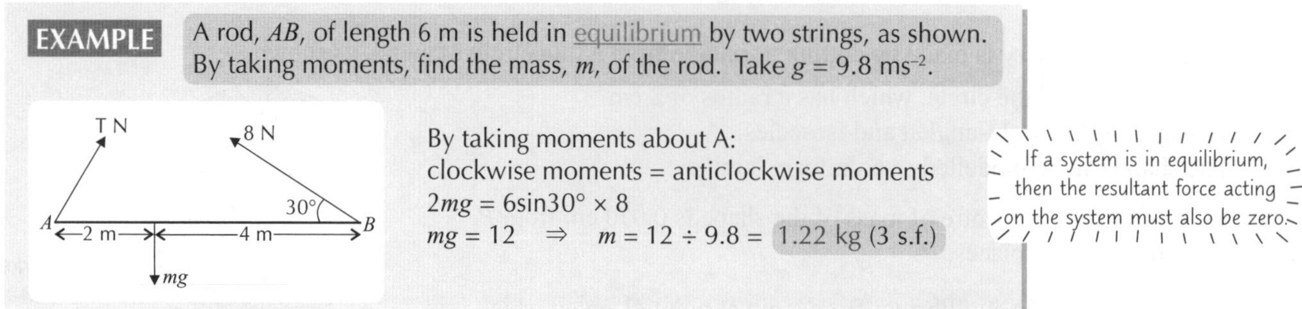

EXAMPLE A rod, AB, of length 6 m is held in <u>equilibrium</u> by two strings, as shown. By taking moments, find the mass, m, of the rod. Take $g = 9.8$ ms^{-2}.

By taking moments about A:
clockwise moments = anticlockwise moments
$2mg = 6\sin 30° \times 8$
$mg = 12 \Rightarrow m = 12 \div 9.8 =$ 1.22 kg (3 s.f.)

If a system is in equilibrium, then the resultant force acting on the system must also be zero.

Although you <u>can</u> take moments about <u>any point</u> (even one <u>not</u> on the rod), it's always easier to take moments about a point that has an <u>unknown force</u> going through it (as in the example above).

Resolve the force, Luke — use the perpendicular distance...

Why do I want to write a musical every time I read a page about moments? Clearly a sci-fi epic would be more appropriate.

Moments

When taking moments, you often need to know where an object's weight acts.
For an object other than a particle, all the weight is considered to act at the centre of mass (see page 146).

The Weight acts at the Centre of a Uniform rod

Often, you'll be dealing with rods. A model rod has negligible thickness, so you only need to consider where along its length the centre of mass lies. If the rod is uniform then the weight acts at the centre of the rod.

EXAMPLE A uniform rod, AB, of length l m and mass m kg is suspended in horizontal equilibrium by two inextensible wires, with tensions as shown. Find m.

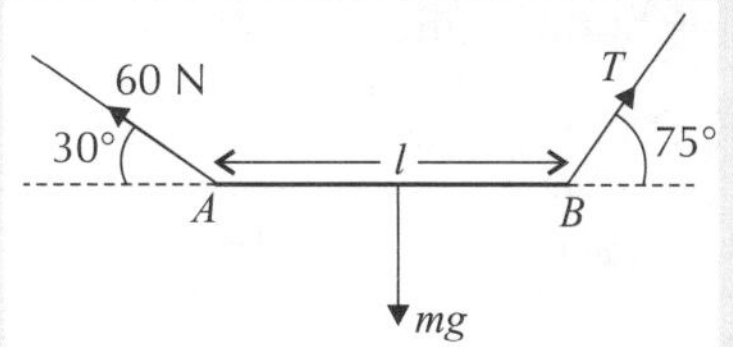

Moments about B:

$60\sin 30° \times l = mg \times \frac{1}{2}l$

so $m = \frac{60l}{gl} = \frac{60}{g} = 6.12$ kg (3 s.f.)

You can pick any point to take moments about, but it makes sense to choose B, because that eliminates the unknown force, T.

You can Calculate the Centre of Mass for Non-Uniform rods

If the weight acts at an unknown point along a rod, the point can be found in the usual way — by taking moments. You might also have to resolve the forces horizontally or vertically to find some missing information.

EXAMPLE A plank of mass 5 kg is supported by a vertical string attached at a point B, as shown. One end of the plank, A, rests upon a pole. The tension in the string is T and the normal reaction at the pole is 70 N. A particle, P, of mass 9 kg rests on the plank 2 m from A, as shown. Find T and the distance, x, between A and the centre of mass of the plank.

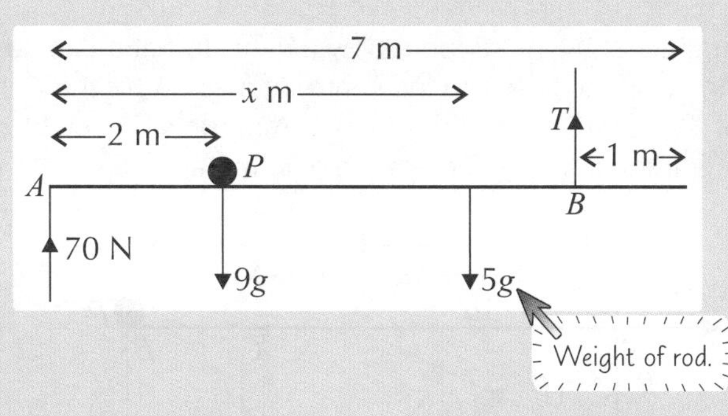

Resolve vertically:
upward forces = downward forces:

$T + 70 = 9g + 5g$

so, $T = 137.2 - 70 = 67.2$ N

Moments about A:
clockwise moments = anticlockwise moments:

$(9g \times 2) + (5g \times x) = 67.2 \times 6$

$49x = 403.2 - 176.4$

so $x = \frac{226.8}{49} = 4.63$ m (3 s.f.)

These statements are only (and always) true at equilibrium.

EXAMPLE A non-uniform rod, AB, of mass 2 kg and length 1 m, is suspended in equilibrium at an angle of θ to the vertical by two vertical strings, as shown. The tensions in the strings are T N and 12 N respectively. Find the distance, x, from A to the rod's centre of mass.

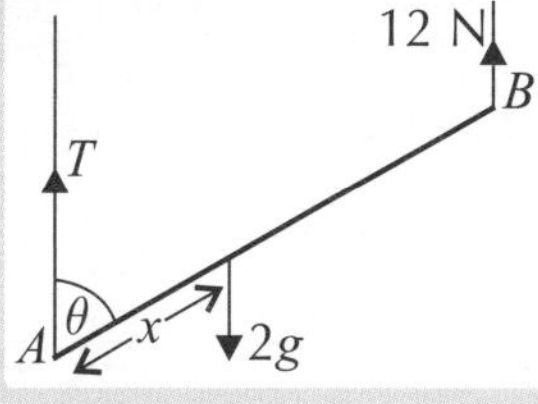

Taking moments about A: clockwise moments = anticlockwise moments

$2g\sin\theta \times x = 12\sin\theta \times 1$

$2\sin\theta$ cancels, so:

$gx = 6$

$x = 0.612$ m (3 s.f.)

There's a diagram I really wanted to put on this page...

...but I couldn't make it fit.
To make it up to you I've put it down here — it's about modelling non-uniform rods.
Don't get bogged down worrying that the models used in Mechanics aren't that realistic — it's the ability to do the maths (and pass those exams) that counts. Anyway, you can worry about real life when you're done with school (when there'll be fewer exams).

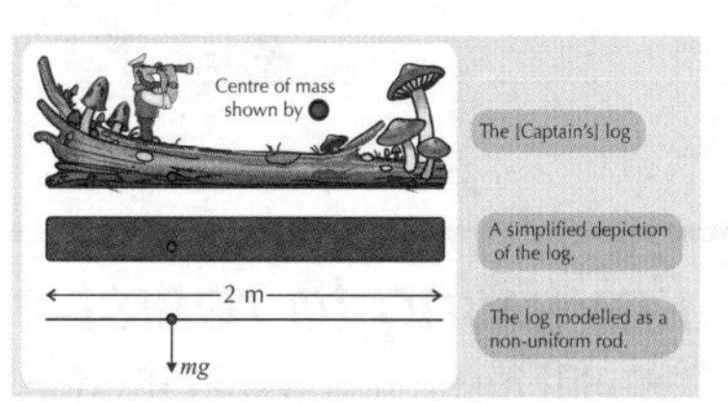

Rigid Bodies

If reactions are at a weird angle, rather than horizontal, vertical or perpendicular to something else, then it's easier to think of them as two components — in two nice, convenient perpendicular directions.

Reactions can have *Horizontal and Vertical Components*

If a rod is connected to a plane (such as a wall) by a hinge or pivot and the forces holding it in equilibrium aren't parallel, then the reaction at the wall won't be perpendicular to the wall. Don't panic though, components are super-helpful here.

EXAMPLE A uniform rod, AB, is freely hinged on a vertical wall at A. The rod is held in horizontal equilibrium by a light inextensible string attached at a point C, 0.4 m from the end B at an angle of 45° to the rod, as shown. Given that the rod is 1.2 m long and has mass 2 kg, find the tension in the string and the magnitude of the reaction at the wall.

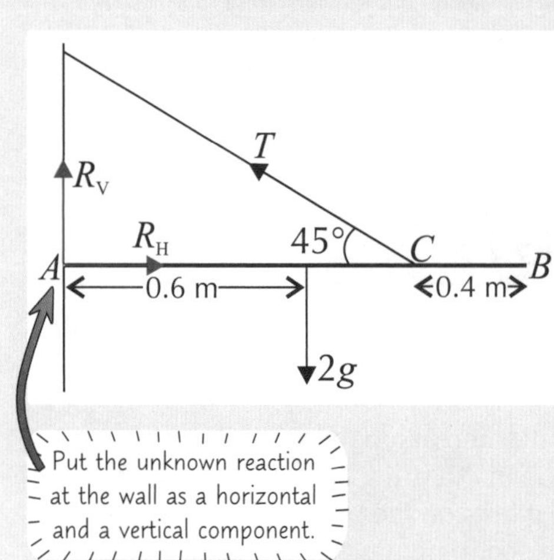

Put the unknown reaction at the wall as a horizontal and a vertical component.

Moments about A:
$T\sin 45° \times (1.2 - 0.4) = 2g \times 0.6$
so, $T\sin 45° = 14.7$
and $T = 20.788... = 20.8$ N (3 s.f.)

Choose A so that you can ignore the unknown reaction components while finding T.

Resolving horizontally:
$R_H = T\cos 45° = 20.788... \times \cos 45°$
so, $R_H = 14.7$ N

The rod is in equilibrium, so the resultant force in any direction is zero.

Resolving vertically:
$R_V + T\sin 45° = 2g$
so $R_V = 4.9$ N

Magnitude of reaction:
$|R| = \sqrt{R_H^2 + R_V^2} = \sqrt{14.7^2 + 4.9^2}$
so $|R| = 15.5$ N (3 s.f.)

EXAMPLE A non-uniform rod, AB, of length $6a$ and mass 4 kg is supported by a light strut at an angle of 70° to a vertical wall, as shown. The distance from A to the centre of mass, X, of the rod is xa m. The strut exerts a thrust of 16 N at the centre of the rod. A particle of weight 2 N is placed at B. Find x, and the magnitude and direction of the reaction at A.

Moments about A:
$16\cos 70° \times 3a = (4g \times xa) + (2 \times 6a)$
so $4gxa = 4.4169... \times a$
and $x = 0.113$ (3 s.f.)

Resolving horizontally:
$R_H = 16\sin 70°$
$\Rightarrow R_H = 15.04$ N (4 s.f.)

Resolving vertically:
$R_V + 4g + 2 = 16\cos 70°$
so $R_V = 16\cos 70° - 39.2 - 2 \Rightarrow R_V = -35.73$ N (4 s.f.)

Don't worry if you're not sure which directions the reaction components act in. You'll just get negative numbers if you're wrong (the magnitude will be the same).

Magnitude of reaction:
$|R| = \sqrt{R_H^2 + R_V^2} = \sqrt{15.04^2 + 35.73^2}$
so $|R| = 38.8$ N (3 s.f.)

R_V is negative — so it must go upwards instead of downwards.

Direction of reaction:

$\tan\theta = \dfrac{15.04}{35.73}$

so $\theta = 22.8°$ (3 s.f.) to the wall

I'm trying to resist making a pun about rigor mortis...

...so I'll just tell you that it's due to irreversible muscular contraction caused by a shortage of adenosine triphosphate. Nice.

Rigid Bodies and Friction

Where would we be without friction? Well, using a ladder would certainly be trickier. Before getting too distracted by that thought you should really revise this page instead — ladders are featured, I promise.

Friction lets you assume the *Reaction is Perpendicular*

From the previous page, you know that a rod attached to a wall has a reaction at the wall with a horizontal and vertical component. If the rod is held by friction instead, then the frictional force 'replaces' the vertical component.

EXAMPLE A rod, AB, rests against a rough vertical wall and is held in limiting equilibrium perpendicular to the wall by a light inextensible string attached at B at an angle of θ, as shown, where $\tan\theta = \frac{7}{17}$. The tension in the string is 42 N. The length AB is 5.5 m and the centre of mass is located 3.8 m from B. Find the mass of the rod, m, and the coefficient of friction, μ, between the wall and the rod.

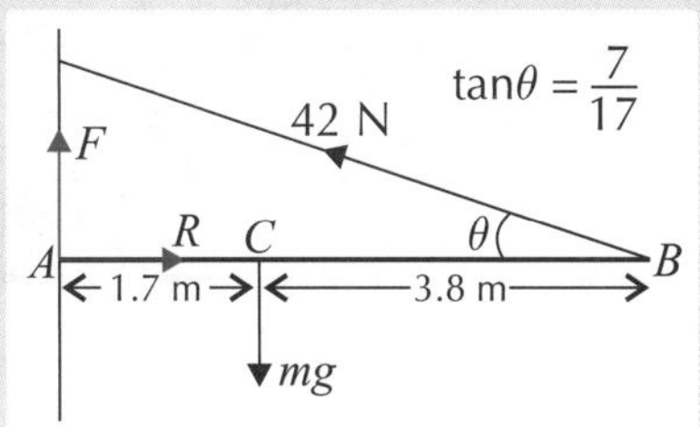

First take moments about A so you can find mg while ignoring the unknowns F and R.

Moments about A: $mg \times 1.7 = 42\sin\theta \times 5.5$
so $mg = 51.737...$ N
and $m = 5.28$ kg (3 s.f.)

Now take moments about a different point to find F. I've taken them about C, but you could have used B.

Moments about C: $1.7 \times F = 3.8 \times 42\sin\theta$
so $F = 35.7$ N (3 s.f.)

Now you know F, you only need to find R before you can find μ.

Resolving horizontally:
$R = 42\cos\theta$
$R = 38.8$ N (3 s.f.)

Limiting equilibrium, so $F = \mu R$:
$35.7 = 38.8\mu$
so $\mu = 0.92$ (2 s.f.)

Limiting equilibrium showed up in M1 — it means that the body is on the point of moving.

Multiple Surfaces can exert a *Frictional Force*

'Ladder' questions, where a rod rests at an angle against the ground and a wall, are common in M2 exams. Often, the ground is modelled as rough and the wall as smooth. Can't take these things for granted though...

The 4 possible combinations of surfaces for 'ladder' questions:

Most common in exams

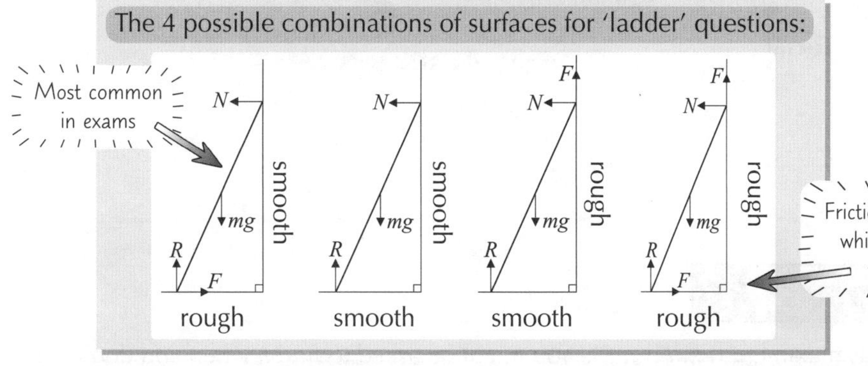

Friction acts to prevent motion — so think about which way the ladder would slip and draw the frictional force in the opposite direction.

EXAMPLE A ladder rests against a smooth wall at an angle of 65° to the rough ground, as shown. The ladder has mass 1.3 kg and length $5x$ m. A cat of mass 4.5 kg sits on the ladder at C, $4x$ m from the base. The ladder is in limiting equilibrium. Model the ladder as a uniform rod and the cat as a particle. Find the coefficient of friction between the ground and the ladder.

R is the normal reaction of the ground and N is the normal reaction of the wall.

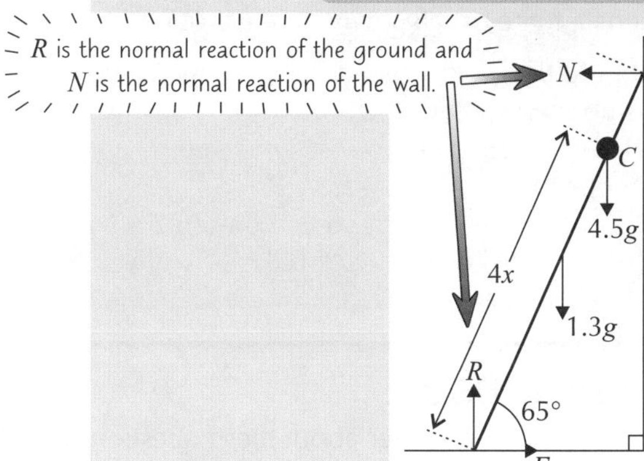

Resolving horizontally: $F = N$

Take moments about the base of the ladder to find N:
$N\sin65° \times 5x = (1.3g\cos65° \times 2.5x) + (4.5g\cos65° \times 4x)$
$4.532xN = 13.46x + 74.55x$
so, $N = \frac{88.01x}{4.532x} = 19.4$ N (3 s.f.)

Resolve vertically to find R:
$R = 1.3g + 4.5g$
$\Rightarrow R = 56.84$ N

The ladder is in limiting equilibrium, so $F = \mu R$:
Resolving horizontally shows $F = N$, so, $19.4 = 56.84\mu$
and $\mu = 0.34$ (2 s.f.)

Rigid Bodies and Friction

A Reaction is always Perpendicular to the Surface

Sometimes a body may be leaning against a surface that isn't vertical. This blows my mind.

EXAMPLE A uniform ladder of length 3 m rests against a smooth wall slanted at 10° to the vertical, as shown. The ladder is at an angle of 60° to the ground. The magnitude of the normal reaction of the wall is 18 N. Find the mass of the ladder.

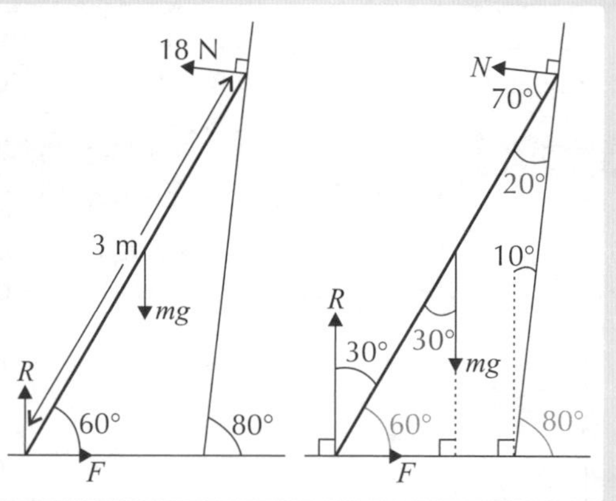

If the wall was vertical then the angles shown in red would be identical as both the weight and the wall would be perpendicular to the ground. Simple. However, the reaction at the wall, N, is perpendicular to the wall, so be careful when resolving forces relative to the ladder.

Moments about the base of the ladder:
$mg\sin30° \times 1.5 = 18\sin70° \times 3$
so $m = 6.90$ kg (3 s.f.)

Bodies can be Supported Along Their Lengths

If a rod is resting on something along its length then the reaction is perpendicular to the rod.

EXAMPLE A uniform rod, AB, rests with end A on rough ground and upon a smooth peg at C, 0.9 m from B. The rod has length 3.3 m and weight 10 N. A particle, P, with weight 25 N is placed at B. Given that the rod is in limiting equilibrium find the magnitude of the normal reaction, N, at the peg and the friction, F, between the rod and the ground.

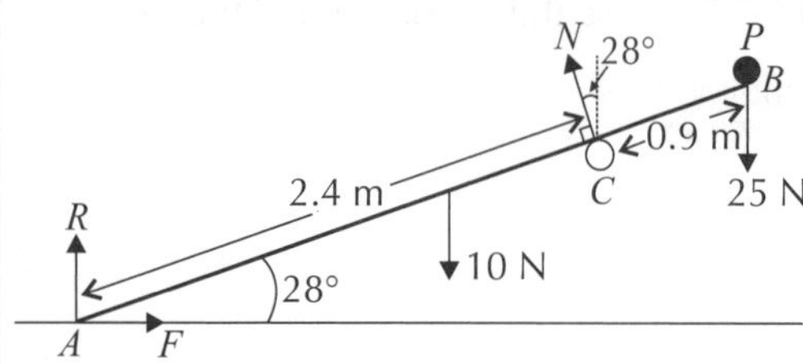

It's a uniform rod, so its mass acts in the middle.

Moments about A:
$2.4N = (10\cos28° \times 1.65) + (25\cos28° \times 3.3)$
so $N = 36.421... = 36.4$ N (3 s.f.)

Resolving horizontally:
$F = N\sin28° = 36.421... \times \sin28°$
$\Rightarrow F = 17.1$ N (3 s.f.)

If equilibrium isn't limiting, $F \leq \mu R$

In limiting equilibrium, friction is at its maximum (i.e. $F = \mu R$). You might be asked to find μ when you don't know if equilibrium is limiting. Just find it in the same way as if equilibrium was limiting, but replace $F = \mu R$ with $F \leq \mu R$.

EXAMPLE A rough peg supports a rod at a point B, 0.2 m from one end of the rod, as shown. The other end of the rod, A, rests on a smooth horizontal plane. The rod is 1.5 m long, with its centre of mass located 1.2 m from A at point C. Given that the rod is in equilibrium at an angle of 15° to the horizontal plane and that the friction at the peg exerts a force of 8 N, show that $\mu \geq 0.3$.

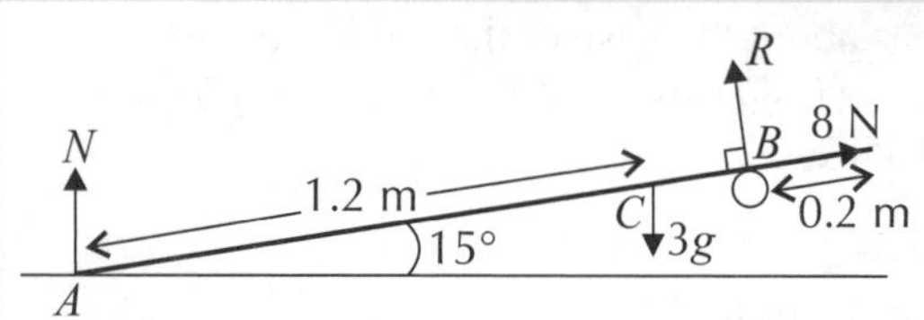

You know F, but to find μ you also need to know R.
Take moments about A to find R:
$R \times (1.5 - 0.2) = 3g\cos15° \times 1.2$
so $R = 26.2$ N (3 s.f.)

$F \leq \mu R$
so $\mu \geq 8 \div 26.2$
$\mu \geq 0.3$

A body can also be supported along its length by a bed...

... but rough ground and a smooth peg sound much more comfortable. The thing to remember about these questions is to keep an eye on whether the points of contact are rough or smooth — that tells you whether or not you need to worry about friction. It's a bit of a pain, but you've just got to take the rough with the smooth I guess...

Laminas and Moments

I'm getting a bit fed up with thin rods and beams — I'm ready to take it to another dimension. Pay close attention.

*Remember to measure to the **Line of Action** of a Force*

You probably don't need me to tell you again that to find the moment of a force about a point, you need to use the perpendicular distance from the point to the line of action of the force. Well, it's that 'line of action' bit that starts to become more important when you're dealing with 2D shapes:

EXAMPLE A uniform lamina, $ABCD$, of weight 8 N is freely hinged to the corner of a wall at A. The lamina is held in equilibrium by a vertical force F acting at point C as shown. Find the value of F by taking moments about A.

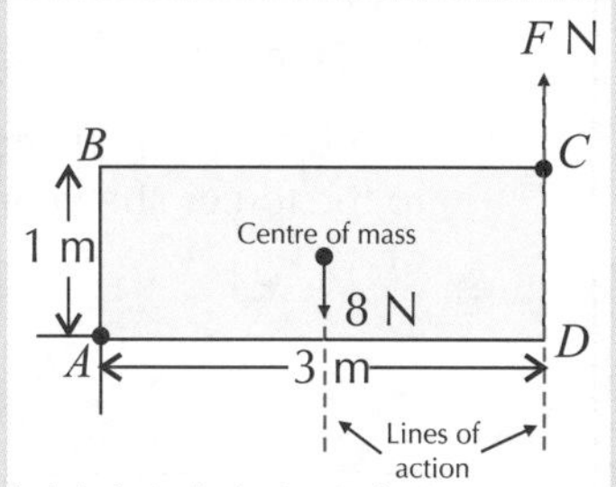

1) The lamina is uniform, so the mass acts at the centre. The perpendicular distance from A to the line of action of the lamina's weight is the horizontal distance from AB to the centre of mass (1.5 m).
2) The force F also acts vertically and the perpendicular distance from A to the line of action of the force is 3 m.
3) So, taking moments about A: $8 \times 1.5 = F \times 3 \Rightarrow F = 4$ N

The vertical distances between A and the forces don't matter. Because both forces are only acting vertically, you only need to use the horizontal distance to work out the moments.

*Split **Angled forces** into **Perpendicular components**, then take **Moments***

1) When you've got a lamina held in equilibrium at a funny angle, the easiest thing to do is just split each force acting on the lamina into two perpendicular components.
2) Then, when you take moments, just use the perpendicular distance to the line of action of each component.
3) And remember — when you take moments about a point on a 2D shape, you need to look for forces acting in all directions. (With 1D shapes like rods, you can ignore any forces acting parallel to the rod when taking moments.)

EXAMPLE A house-shaped lamina of mass 8 kg is smoothly pivoted at point P and is supported in equilibrium by a light, inextensible vertical wire at point Q, as shown. The base of the lamina makes an angle of 15° with the horizontal. Find the tension, T, in the wire.

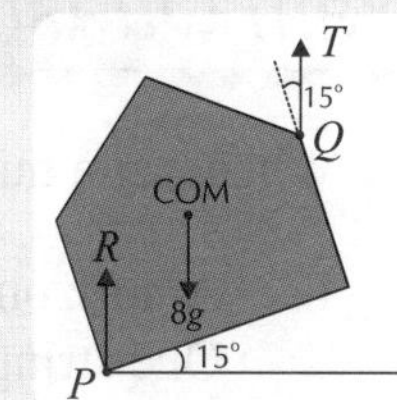

This is the house-shaped lamina from page 149. On page 149, the centre of mass of the shape was found to be 7.85 cm below the vertex of the triangle, on the line of symmetry.

Split the forces acting on the shape into components acting parallel and perpendicular to the base of the lamina:

You have to calculate this length because it's measured from a different point than on p. 149. It's 13 – 7.85 = 5.15 cm from P.

Now take moments about P (so R can be ignored):

- Total clockwise moment = $(8g\cos 15° \times 5) + (T\sin 15° \times 7)$
- Total anticlockwise moment = $(8g\sin 15° \times 5.15) + (T\cos 15° \times 10)$

The lamina is in equilibrium, so:

$(8g\cos 15° \times 5) + (T\sin 15° \times 7) = (8g\sin 15° \times 5.15) + (T\cos 15° \times 10)$

$\Rightarrow 7T\sin 15° - 10T\cos 15° = (8g\sin 15° \times 5.15) - (8g\cos 15° \times 5)$

$$\Rightarrow T = \frac{(8g\sin 15° \times 5.15) - (8g\cos 15° \times 5)}{7\sin 15° - 10\cos 15°} = 34.9 \text{ N (3 s.f.)}$$

Let's take a moment to resolve the issue...

You don't have to split the forces into perpendicular components first — you could just take moments straight away. But more often than not, that leads to tricky Pythagoras and trig to get the distances right. I reckon this way makes it a bit easier.

M2 Section 2 — Practice Questions

Time to make like a tree and leaf leave sway gently in the breeze. Darn it, that analogy wasn't really working... Anyway, time to be a dedicated student and practise your statics know-how. Ace.

Warm-up Questions

Whenever a numerical value of g is required in the following questions, take $g = 9.8\ \text{ms}^{-2}$.

1) A 60 kg uniform beam AE of length 14 m is in equilibrium, supported by two vertical ropes attached to B and D as shown. Find the tensions in the ropes to 1 d.p.

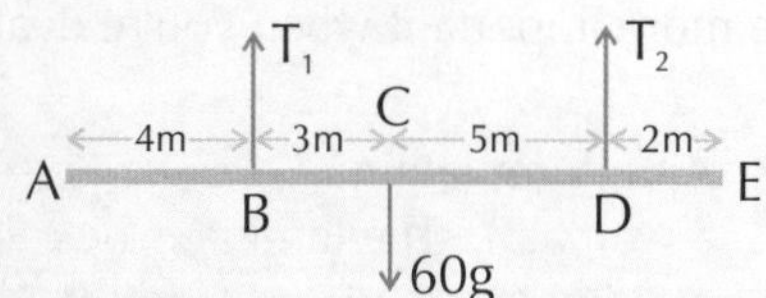

2) Calculate the perpendicular distance from the particle, P, to the forces shown in the diagrams below:

a)

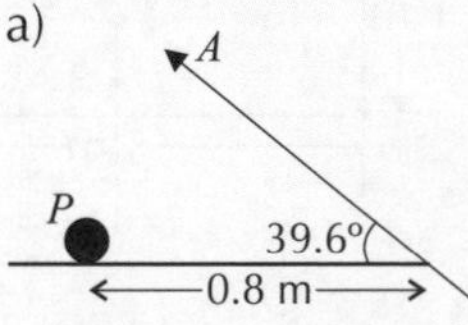

b)

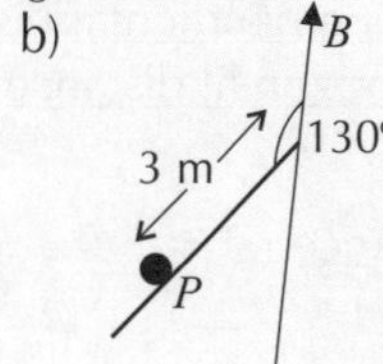

c)

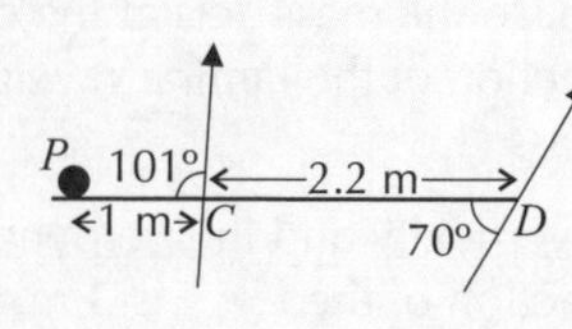

3) What is meant by a 'non-uniform rod'?

4) Given that the beam shown is in equilibrium,
   a) calculate the magnitude of T.
   b) find the value of x.

T, 128.3°, 28 N, 120°, xy, y, 42 N

5) A uniform ladder, of length l m, is placed on rough horizontal ground and rests against a smooth vertical wall at an angle of 20° to the wall. Draw a diagram illustrating this system with forces labelled. State what assumptions you would make.

Those practice questions should've been a doddle. Time to step it up a notch with some questions more like those you'll get in the exam. In the words of a fictional dance-squad commander, "don't let me down".

Exam Questions

Whenever a numerical value of g is required in the following questions, take $g = 9.8\ \text{ms}^{-2}$.

1 A horizontal uniform beam with length x and weight 18 N is held in equilibrium by two vertical strings. One string is attached to one end of the beam and the other at point A, 3 m from the first string. The tension in the string at point A is 12 N. Show that $x = 4$ m.

(3 marks)

2 A shape is made up of a uniform square lamina and a uniform rectangular lamina as shown. The centre of mass of the shape is located 2 m from AB and 2.28 m from AC.

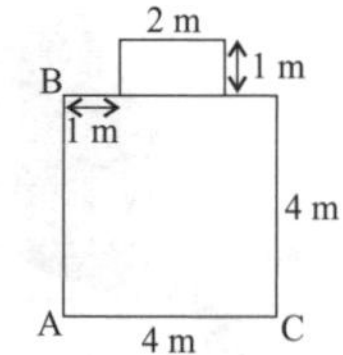

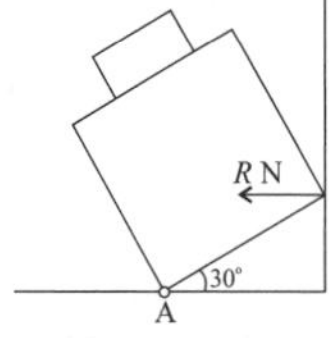

The shape is smoothly pivoted at A and rests in equilibrium against a smooth vertical wall, as shown. The angle between AC and the horizontal ground is 30°. Given that the weight of the shape is 4 N, find the magnitude of the reaction force, R, of the wall on the shape.

(4 marks)

M2 Section 2 — Practice Questions

If the previous question was a struggle, then you know what to do — go back a few pages and have another look. These questions will still be here while you're gone. Lurking.

3 A uniform rod, AB, is held in limiting horizontal equilibrium against a rough wall by an inextensible string connected to the rod at point C and the wall at point D, as shown. A particle of mass m kg rests at point B. The magnitude of the normal reaction of the wall at A is 72.5 N. The mass of the rod is 3 kg.

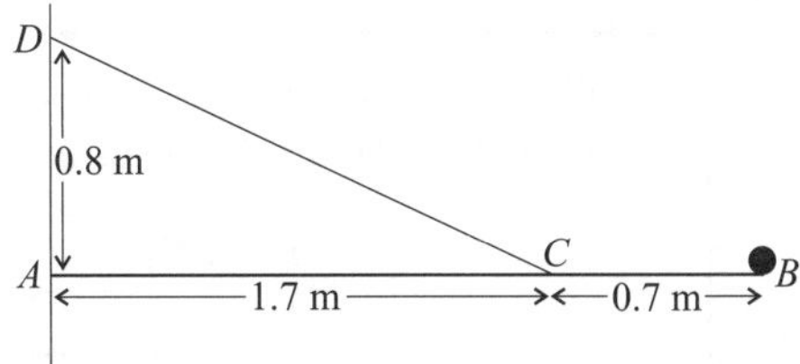

a) Find the tension, T, in the string.

(4 marks)

b) Find m.

(3 marks)

c) Find the magnitude of the frictional force, F, between the wall and the rod.

(3 marks)

4 A non-uniform rod, AB, is freely hinged at a vertical wall. It is held in horizontal equilibrium by a beam attached to the wall at C at an angle of 55°. The tension in the beam is 30 N, as shown. The rod has mass 2 kg, centred 0.4 m from A. The total length of the rod is x m.

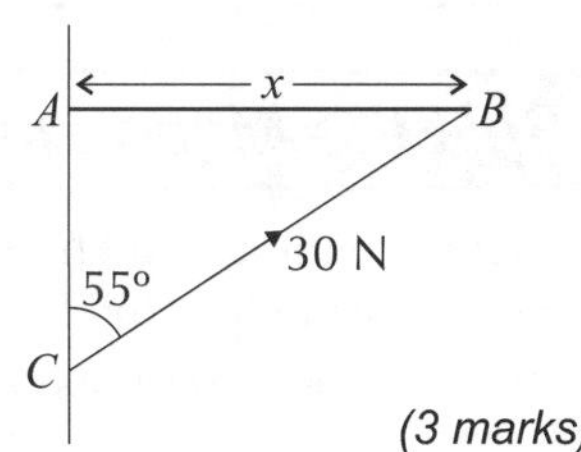

a) Find the length of the rod, x.

(3 marks)

b) Find the magnitude and direction of the reaction at A.

(5 marks)

5 A uniform ladder, AB, is positioned against a smooth vertical wall and rests upon rough horizontal ground at an angle of θ, as shown. Clive stands on the ladder at point C, two-thirds of the way along the ladder's length from A. The ladder is 4.2 m long and weighs 180 N. The normal reaction at A is 490 N. The ladder rests in limiting equilibrium. Model Clive as a particle and find:

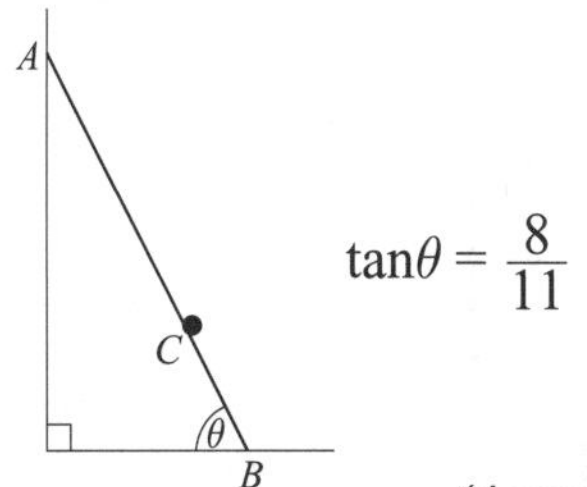

$\tan\theta = \frac{8}{11}$

a) the mass of Clive, m, to the nearest kg.

(4 marks)

b) the coefficient of friction, μ, between the ground and the ladder.

(5 marks)

6 A 6 m long uniform beam of mass 20 kg is in equilibrium. One end is resting on a vertical pole, and the other end is held up by a vertical wire attached to that end so that the beam rests horizontally. There are two 10 kg weights attached to the beam, situated 2 m from either end.

a) Draw a diagram of the beam including all the forces acting on it.

(2 marks)

Find, in terms of g:

b) T, the tension in the wire.

(3 marks)

c) R, the normal reaction at the pole.

(2 marks)

Projectiles

A 'projectile' is just any old object that's been lobbed through the air. When you're doing projectile questions you'll have to model the motion of particles in two dimensions whilst ignoring air resistance.

Split Velocity of Projection into Two Components

A particle projected with a speed u at an angle α to the horizontal has two components of initial velocity — one horizontal (parallel to the x-axis) and one vertical (parallel to the y-axis).
These are called x and y components, and they make projectile questions dead easy to deal with:

Here's the same information in a diagram:

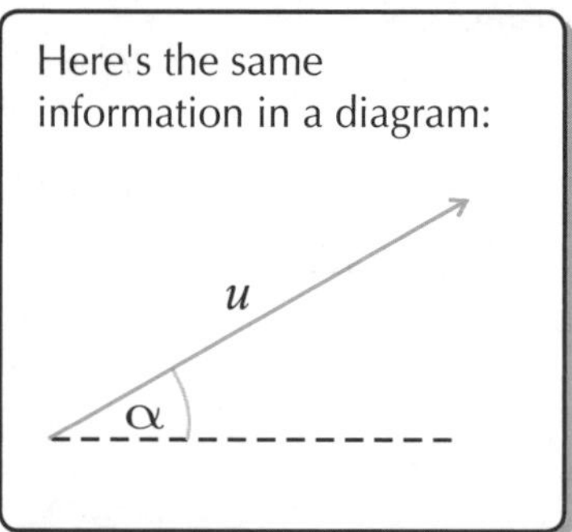

Split the velocity into its x and y components:

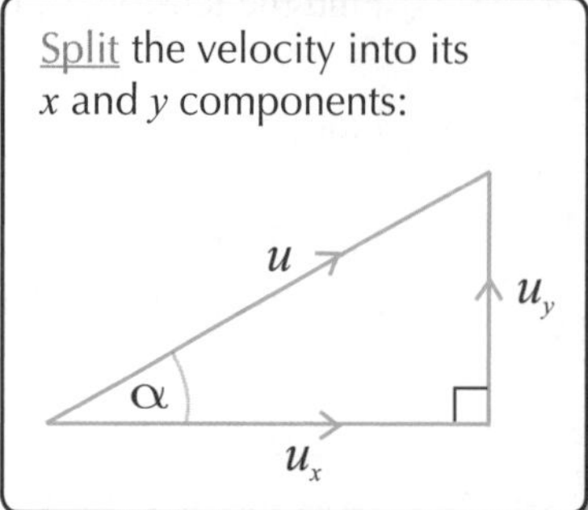

Finally, work out the values of the components using trigonometry:

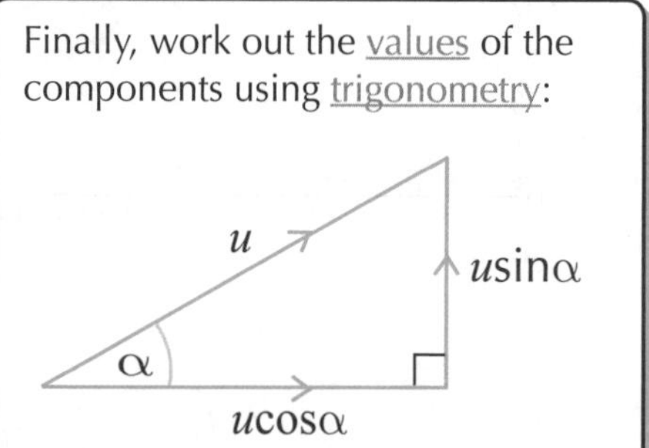

Split the Motion into Horizontal and Vertical Components too

Split everything you know about the motion into horizontal and vertical components too. Then you can deal with them separately using the 'uvast' equations from M1. The only thing that's the same in both directions is time — so this connects the two directions. Remember that the only acceleration is due to gravity — so horizontal acceleration is zero.

EXAMPLE

A stone is thrown horizontally with speed 10 ms^{-1} from a height of 2 m above the horizontal ground. Find the time taken for the stone to hit the ground and the horizontal distance travelled before impact. Find also the speed and direction of the stone after 0.5 s.

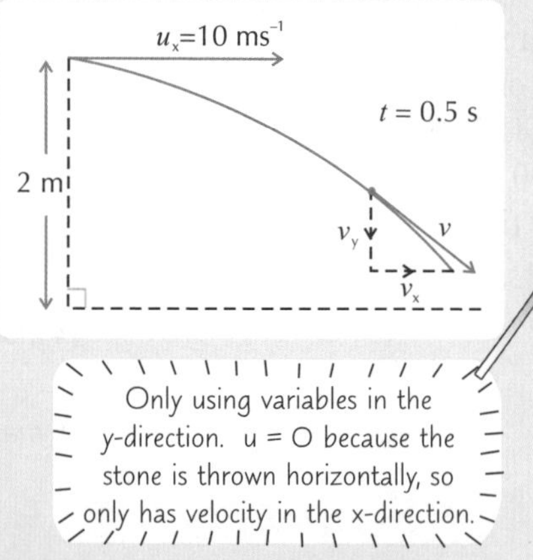

Only using variables in the y-direction. u = 0 because the stone is thrown horizontally, so only has velocity in the x-direction.

Resolving vertically (take down as +ve):

$u = u_y = 0 \quad s = 2$
$a = 9.8 \quad t = ?$

$s = ut + \frac{1}{2}at^2$

$2 = 0 \times t + \frac{1}{2} \times 9.8 \times t^2$

$t = 0.639$ s (to 3 s.f.)
i.e. the stone lands after 0.639 seconds

Resolving horizontally (take right as +ve):

The same as for the vertical motion.

$u = u_x = 10 \quad s = ?$
$a = 0 \quad t = 0.6389$

$s = ut + \frac{1}{2}at^2$

$= 10 \times 0.6389 + \frac{1}{2} \times 0 \times 0.6389^2$

$= 6.39$ m (to 3 s.f.)

i.e. the stone has gone 6.39 m horizontally when it lands.

Now find the velocity after 0.5 s — again, keep the vertical and horizontal bits separate.

Unless you're told otherwise, always take $g = 9.8$ ms^{-2}.

$v = u + at$

$v_y = 0 + 9.8 \times 0.5$

$= 4.9$ ms^{-1}

$v = u + at$

$v_x = 10 + 0 \times \frac{1}{2}$

$= 10$ ms^{-1}

v_x is always equal to u_x when there's no horizontal acceleration.

Now you can find the speed and direction...

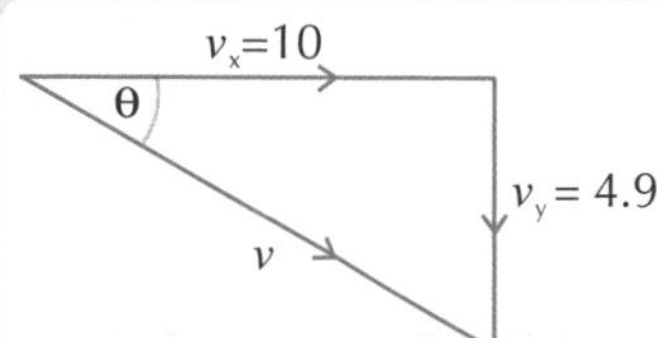

$v = \sqrt{4.9^2 + 10^2} = 11.1$ ms^{-1} (3 s.f.)

$\tan\theta = \frac{4.9}{10}$

So $\theta = 26.1°$ below horizontal

Projectiles

EXAMPLE A cricket ball is projected with a speed of 30 ms^{-1} at an angle of 25° to the horizontal. Assume the ground is horizontal and the ball is struck from a point 1.5 m above the ground. Find:

a) the maximum height the ball reaches (h),

b) the horizontal distance travelled by the ball before it hits the ground (r),

c) the length of time the ball is at least 5 m above the ground,

d) the horizontal distance of the ball from the point of projection at the instant when it is moving downwards at an angle of 15° to the horizontal.

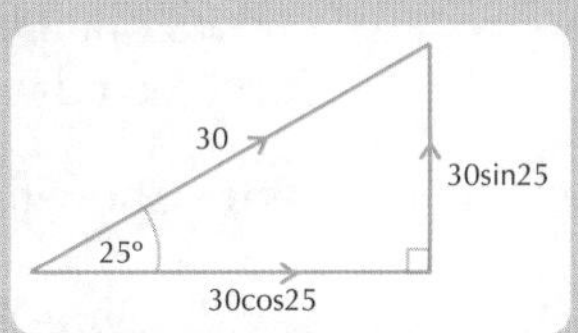

a) **Resolving vertically** (take up as +ve):

$u = 30\sin25°$ $\quad v = 0$
$a = -9.8$ $\quad s = ?$

The ball will momentarily stop moving vertically when it reaches its maximum height.

$$v^2 = u^2 + 2as$$
$$0 = (30\sin 25°)^2 + 2(-9.8 \times s)$$
$$s = 8.201\text{m (4 s.f.)}$$
$$\text{h} = 8.201\text{m} + 1.5\text{m} = 9.70\text{m (3 s.f.)}$$

Don't forget to add the height from which the ball is hit.

b) **Resolving vertically** (take up as +ve):

$s = -1.5$
$a = -9.8$
$u = 30\sin25°$
$t = ?$

$$s = ut + \frac{1}{2}at^2$$
$$-1.5 = (30\sin 25°)t - \frac{1}{2}(9.8)t^2$$
$$t^2 - 2.587t - 0.3061 = 0$$
$$t = -0.1113 \text{ or } \mathbf{t = 2.701\,s}$$

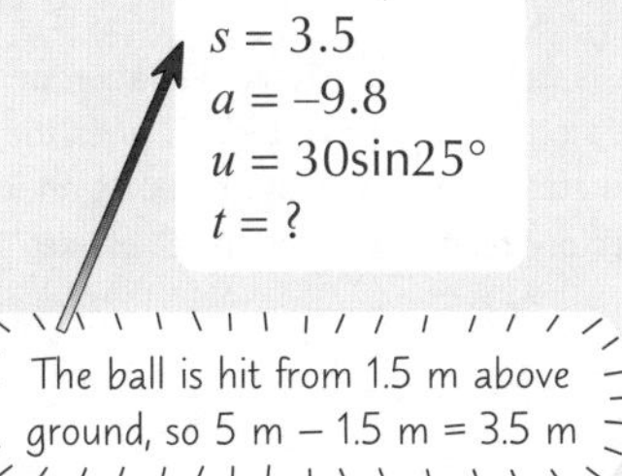

Resolving horizontally (take right as +ve):

$s = \text{r}$ $\quad u = 30\cos25°$
$t = 2.701$ $\quad a = 0$

$$s = ut + \frac{1}{2}at^2$$
$$\text{r} = 30\cos 25° \times 2.701 + \frac{1}{2} \times 0 \times 2.701^2$$
$$= 73.4\text{m (3 s.f.)}$$

c) **Resolving vertically** (take up as +ve):

$s = 3.5$
$a = -9.8$
$u = 30\sin25°$
$t = ?$

The ball is hit from 1.5 m above ground, so 5 m – 1.5 m = 3.5 m

$$s = ut + \frac{1}{2}at^2$$
$$3.5 = (30\sin 25°)t - \frac{1}{2}(9.8)t^2$$
$$t^2 - 2.587t + 0.7143 = 0$$
$$t = 0.3142\text{ s or } t = 2.273\text{ s}$$

These are the two times when the ball is 5 m above the ground.

So, length of time at least 5 m above the ground:

2.273 s – 0.3142 s = 1.96 s (3 s.f.)

d) Use trig to find the vertical component of velocity when the ball is moving at this angle:

$$\tan 15° = \frac{V}{30\cos 25°}$$
$$\Rightarrow V = 30\cos 25° \tan 15° = 7.285\,\text{ms}^{-1}\text{(4 s.f.)}$$

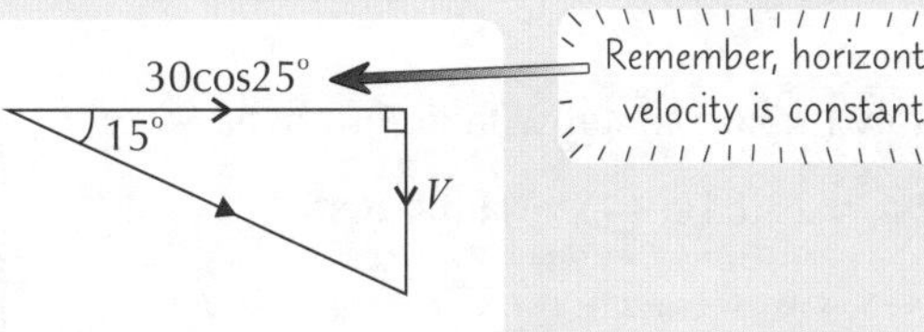

Now **resolving vertically** (take up as +ve):

$a = -9.8$ $\quad v = -V = -7.285$
$u = 30\sin25°$ $\quad t = ?$

The ball is moving downwards, so the vertical component of its velocity is negative.

$$v = u + at$$
$$\Rightarrow t = \frac{v-u}{a} = \frac{-7.285 - 30\sin 25}{-9.8}$$

So $t = 2.037$ s (4 s.f.)

And **resolving horizontally** (take right as +ve):

$s = ?$ $\quad u = 30\cos25°$
$t = 2.037$ $\quad a = 0$

$$s = ut + \frac{1}{2}at^2$$
$$s = 30\cos 25° \times 2.037 + \frac{1}{2} \times 0 \times 2.037^2$$
$$= 55.4\text{m (3 s.f.)}$$

Projectiles

Just one last example of projectile motion. But boy is it a beauty...

EXAMPLE

A golf ball is struck from a point A on a horizontal plane. When the ball has moved a horizontal distance x, its height above the plane is y. The ball is modelled as a particle projected with initial speed u ms^{-1} at an angle α.

a) Show that $y = x\tan\alpha - \dfrac{gx^2}{2u^2\cos^2\alpha}$.

The ball just passes over the top of a 10 m tall tree, which is 45 m away. Given that $\alpha = 45°$,

b) find the speed of the ball as it passes over the tree.

a) Displacement, acceleration and initial velocity are the only variables in the formula, so use these. Also use time, because that's the variable which connects the two components of motion. The formula includes motion in both directions (x and y), so form two equations and substitute one into the other:

Resolving horizontally (taking right as +ve):

$u_x = u\cos\alpha$ $\quad a = 0$

$s = x$ $\quad t = t$

Using $s = ut + \frac{1}{2}at^2$:

$x = u\cos\alpha \times t$

Rearrange to make t the subject:

$t = \dfrac{x}{u\cos\alpha}$ — call this **equation 1**

When you're using these variables, this is the obvious equation to use.

t doesn't appear in the final formula, so by making it the subject you can eliminate it.

Resolving vertically (taking up as +ve):

$u_y = u\sin\alpha$ $\quad a = -g$

$s = y$ $\quad t = t$

Using $s = ut + \frac{1}{2}at^2$:

$y = (u\sin\alpha \times t) - \frac{1}{2}gt^2$ — call this **equation 2**

It would be a massive pain to make t the subject here, so do it with the other equation.

t is the same horizontally and vertically, so you can substitute the expression for t from **equation 1** into **equation 2** and eliminate t:

$$y = u\sin\alpha \times \frac{x}{u\cos\alpha} - \frac{1}{2}g\left(\frac{x}{u\cos\alpha}\right)^2 = x\frac{\sin\alpha}{\cos\alpha} - \frac{1}{2}g\left(\frac{x^2}{u^2\cos^2\alpha}\right)$$

$$= x\tan\alpha - \frac{gx^2}{2u^2\cos^2\alpha}$$ — as required.

$\dfrac{\sin\theta}{\cos\theta} = \tan\theta$

This is called the 'Cartesian equation of the trajectory of a projectile'. It gives the coordinates of an object at any point on its trajectory relative to a given set of axes.

b) Using the result from a), and substituting $x = 45$, $y = 10$ and $\alpha = 45°$:

$$10 = 45\tan 45° - \frac{9.8 \times 45^2}{2u^2 \times \cos^2 45°} = 45 - \frac{19\,845}{u^2}$$

Rearrange to find the speed of projection, u: $35u^2 = 19\,845 \Rightarrow$ $\mathbf{u = 23.81\,ms^{-1}}$

Now resolve to find the components of the ball's velocity as it passes over the tree:

Resolving horizontally (taking right as +ve):

$v_x = u_x = 23.81\cos 45 =$ **16.84 ms^{-1}**

Remember — with projectiles there's no horizontal acceleration, so v_x always equals u_x.

Resolving vertically (taking up as +ve):

$u_y = 23.81\sin 45$ $\quad a = -g$

$s = 10$ $\quad v_y = ?$

Using $v^2 = u^2 + 2as$:

$v_y^2 = 283.46 - 2 \times 9.8 \times 10 =$ **87.46**

Don't bother finding the square root, as you need v_y^2 in the next step. Sneaky.

Now you can find the speed: $\quad v = \sqrt{v_x^2 + v_y^2} = 19.3\,\text{ms}^{-1}$ (3 s.f.)

Projectiles — they're all about throwing up. Or across. Or slightly down...

You've used the equations of motion before, in M1, and there isn't much different here. The main thing to remember is that horizontal acceleration is zero — great news because it makes half the calculations as easy as a log-falling beginner's class.

M2 Section 3 — Practice Questions

Well that wasn't such a bad section. Before you crack on with more mechanical delights, I reckon it's time for some practice questions to make sure you've made sense of everything you've just read. And because I'm nice, I'll start you off with some nice easy warm-up questions...

Warm-up Questions

1) A particle is projected with initial velocity u ms^{-1} at an angle α to the horizontal. What is the initial velocity of the particle in the direction parallel to the horizontal in terms of u and α?
2) A rifle fires a bullet horizontally at 120 ms^{-1}. The target is hit at a horizontal distance of 60 m from the end of the rifle. Find how far the target is vertically below the end of the rifle. Take $g = 9.8$ ms^{-2}.
3) A golf ball takes 4 seconds to land after being hit with a golf club from a point on the horizontal ground. If it leaves the club with a speed of 22 ms^{-1}, at an angle of α to the horizontal, find α. Take $g = 9.8$ ms^{-2}.

Right, now you're warmed up and there's absolutely no danger of you pulling a maths muscle, it's time to get down to the serious business of practice exam questions.

Exam Questions

Whenever a numerical value of g is required in the questions below, take $g = 9.8$ ms^{-2}.

1 A stationary football is kicked with a speed of 20 ms^{-1}, at an angle of 30° to the horizontal, towards a goal 30 m away. The crossbar is 2.5 m above the level ground. Assuming the path of the ball is not impeded, determine whether the ball passes above or below the crossbar. What assumptions does your model make?

(6 marks)

2

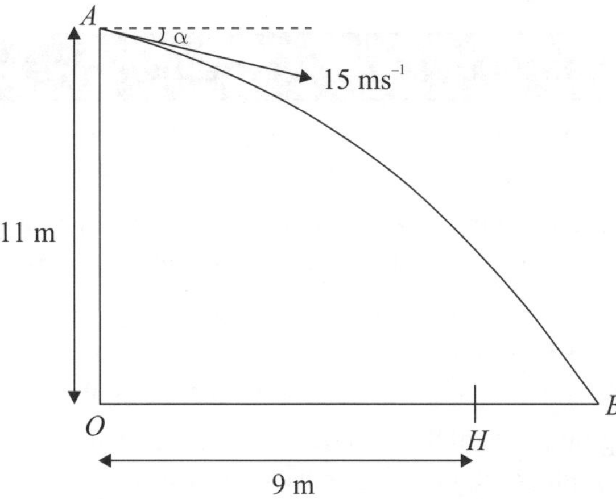

A stone is thrown from point A on the edge of a cliff, towards a point H, which is on horizontal ground. The point O is on the ground, 11 m vertically below the point of projection. The stone is thrown with speed 15 ms^{-1} at an angle α below the horizontal, where $\tan\alpha = \frac{3}{4}$.

The horizontal distance from O to H is 9 m.

The stone misses the point H and hits the ground at point B, as shown above. Find:

a) the time taken by the stone to reach the ground. *(5 marks)*

b) the horizontal distance the stone misses H by. *(3 marks)*

c) the speed of projection which would have ensured that the stone landed at H. *(5 marks)*

Circular Motion

Things often move in circular paths — and it's a whole new world of motion to sink your teeth into.

Angular Speed is Measured in Radians per Second

1) You can measure the speed of a particle travelling in a circle in two different ways — linear speed and angular speed:

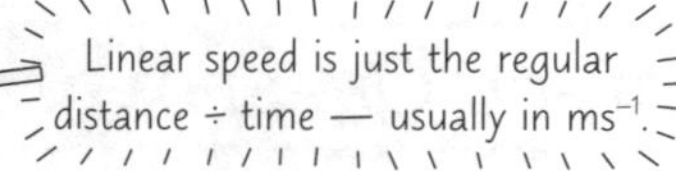

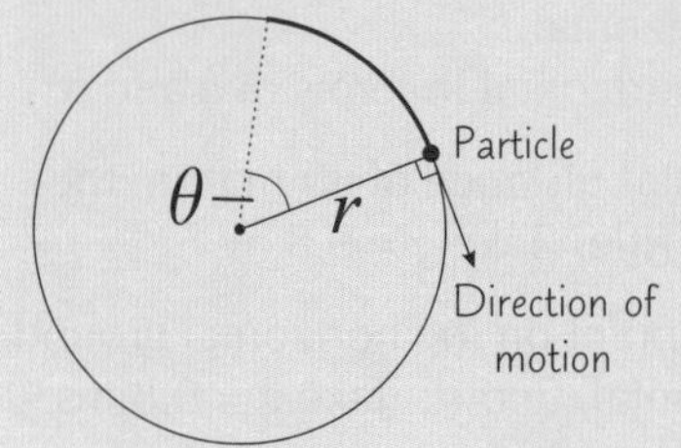

The angular speed, ω, is how quickly the radius, r, is turning — or the rate of change of θ. There's a formula for working it out:

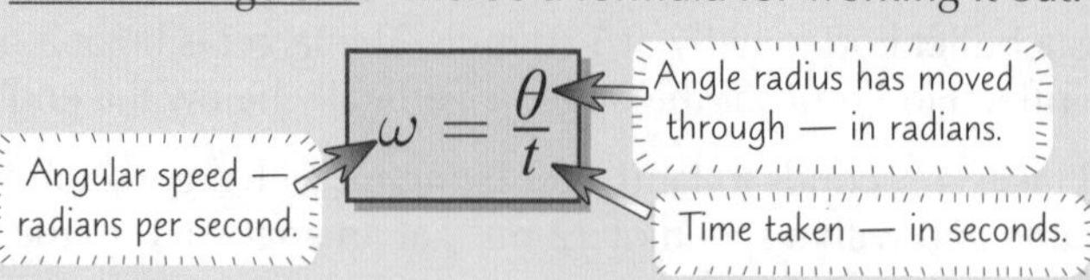

$$\omega = \frac{\theta}{t}$$

You need to learn the angular speed formula. Make sure you do.

2) It's really important to measure the angle in RADIANS, or this lovely equation linking angular and linear speed won't work:

Linear speed = radius × angular speed
(ms^{-1}) (m) (radians s^{-1})

$$v = r\omega$$

3) You might have to convert from units such as revolutions per minute to radians per second, so learn these:

360° = 2π radians = 1 revolution

EXAMPLE A particle moves in a horizontal circle, completing 600 revolutions per minute. What is its angular speed?

Find θ: 600 revolutions = 600 × 2π radians = 1200π radians.

Now find ω: $\omega = \frac{\theta}{t} = \frac{1200\pi}{60} = 20\pi$ radians s^{-1}

The time must be in seconds.

Direction is Always Changing, so the Velocity is Changing too

1) The direction of something moving in a circle is always parallel to the tangent of the circle — so it's constantly changing. Velocity has magnitude and direction, so changing direction means changing velocity.

2) If something's velocity is changing, it must be accelerating. So even if a particle is moving in a circle with a constant speed, it will still be accelerating.

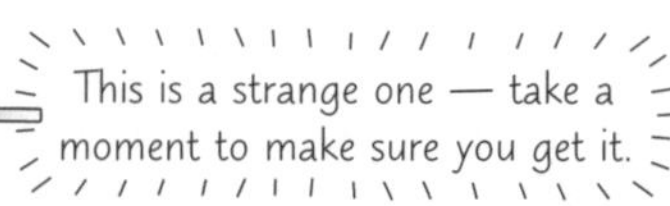

3) The acceleration is always directed towards the centre of the circle, perpendicular to the direction of motion. It's called radial acceleration and there's a couple of formulas to learn:

One using angular speed... $a = r\omega^2$

...and one using linear speed. $a = \frac{v^2}{r}$

4) There must be a force acting on the particle to produce the acceleration. And there is. It's called the centripetal force, it always acts towards the centre of the circle, and you just use the old $F = ma$ formula to find it.

EXAMPLE A particle moves with an angular speed of 20π rad s^{-1} around a horizontal circle of radius 0.25 m.
a) Find the magnitude of its acceleration.

$$a = r\omega^2 = 0.25 \times (20\pi)^2 = 100\pi^2 \text{ ms}^{-2}$$

In the case of a particle on a string, the centripetal force is provided by the tension in the string.

b) A light string connects the particle above to the centre of the circle. Find the tension in the string if the particle's mass is 3 kg.

Resolving horizontally:
$F = ma \Rightarrow T = mr\omega^2$
$= 3 \times 100\pi^2 = 300\pi^2$ N

I propose the motion that we stop going round in circles and move on...

You need to learn all the formulas on this page — you won't be given them in the exam. Remember that θ should be in radians when you're calculating ω and remember to use the radial acceleration in $F = ma$ to find the centripetal force.

Conical Pendulums

Conical pendulum questions aren't as tricky as they look — they're usually just a case of resolving a force and then plonking things into the equations on the previous page.

Resolve Tension in a Conical Pendulum into Components

1) If you dangle an object at the end of a string, then twirl it round so the weight moves in a horizontal circle, you've made a conical pendulum.
2) There are only two forces acting on the object — its weight and the tension in the string.
3) The vertical component of the tension in the string supports the weight of the object, and the horizontal component is the centripetal force causing the radial acceleration.

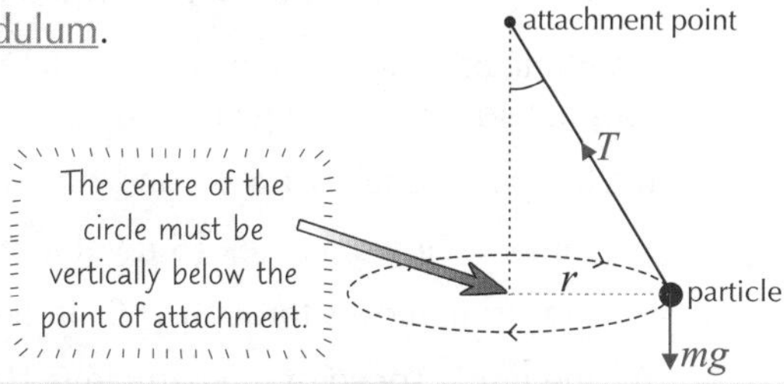

EXAMPLE One end of a light, inextensible string is attached to a point X and the other end to a particle of mass 5 kg. The particle moves with an angular speed of 4π radians s^{-1} in a horizontal circle as shown.

X 40°

Remember, light means the string has no weight, and inextensible means it can't be stretched.

a) Find the tension in the string.

Resolving vertically:

$T\cos 40° = 5 \times 9.8$

$T = 64.0$ N (to 3 s.f.)

40° T 5g

b) Find the radius of the circle.

Resolving horizontally:

$T\sin 40° = ma = mr\omega^2$

$64.0\sin 40° = 5 \times r \times (4\pi)^2$

$r = 0.052$ m (to 2 s.f.)

Use $F_{net} = mr\omega^2$ because you're given the angular speed.

Don't be Confused by Slight Variations in Questions

Circular motion exam questions come in a variety of different shapes and sizes. Examiners have a little stash of special pendulums that they sometimes like to throw in to spice things up. The little tinkers.

The particle on a plane:
You have to include the normal reaction, R, of the plane on the particle, as well as the tension.

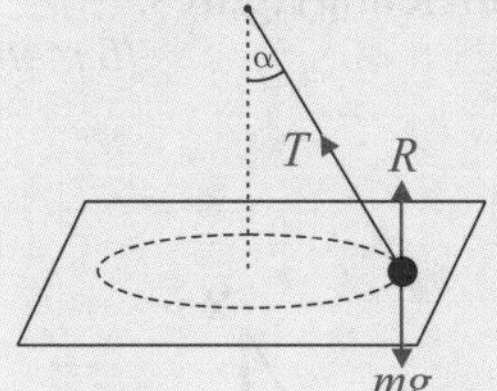

e.g. Resolving vertically:
$T\cos\alpha + R = mg$

You might even get a particle on a curved surface. Mental.

The two string pendulum:
Each string has a separate tension. You have to include the horizontal or vertical components of both strings when resolving forces,

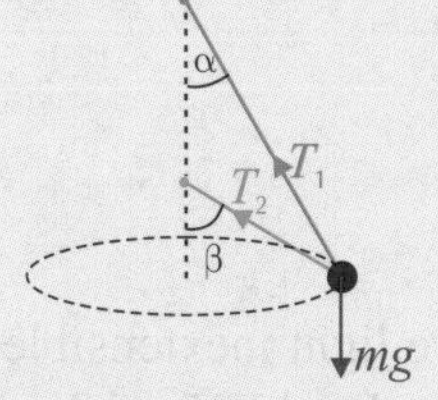

e.g. Resolving vertically:
$T_1\cos\alpha + T_2\cos\beta = mg$

The second string might be horizontal — that makes life easier, cos there'll be no vertical component of tension. Brilliant.

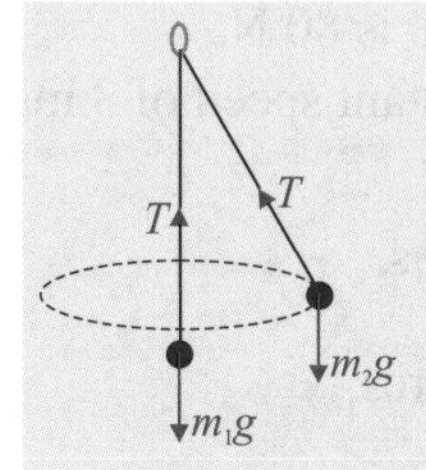

The single string through a smooth ring:

The tension in both parts of the string is the same — and it's equal to the weight of the particle hanging vertically:

$T = m_1g$

A big deep breath... And... resolve...

You might have to use radians and degrees in the same question — so stay alert. You'll need angles in radians for finding the angular speed, but in degrees for finding the components of forces. It's not too tricky but it's easy to get wrong. Perfect.

M2 Section 4 — Practice Questions

When you design your own fairground, you'll need to know about <u>circular motion</u> — so it really is a vital life skill. It'll also be handy for the M2 exam, in which you're virtually guaranteed one, if not two, questions on it.

Warm-up Questions

Whenever a numerical value of g is required in the following questions, take $g = 9.8 \text{ ms}^{-2}$.

1) A particle attached to one end of a light, inextensible string moves in a horizontal circle of radius 3 m with constant speed. Leaving your answers in terms of π, find the particle's angular speed and its acceleration if:
   a) the particle takes 1.5 seconds to complete 1 revolution,
   b) the particle completes 15 revolutions in one minute,
   c) the string moves through 160° in one second,
   d) the linear speed of the particle is 10 ms^{-1}.

2) A particle with mass 2 kg moves in a horizontal circle of radius 0.4 m with constant speed. Find the centripetal force acting on the particle if:
   a) the particle's angular speed is 10π radians s^{-1},
   b) the particle's linear speed is 4 ms^{-1}.

3) For the conical pendulum shown on the right, find:
   a) the tension in the string (which is light and inextensible),
   b) the radius of the circle described by the pendulum given that the particle has a speed of v ms^{-1}.

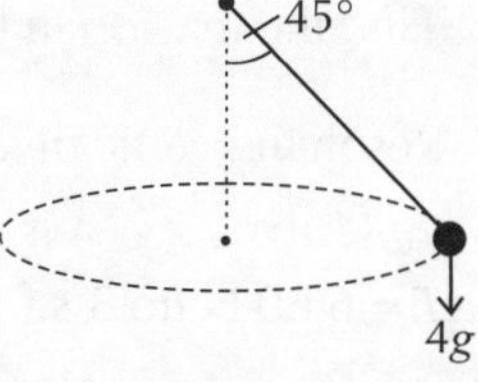

More on the merry-go-round of M2 maths magic...

Exam Questions

Whenever a numerical value of g is required in the following questions, take $g = 9.8 \text{ ms}^{-2}$.

1 A quad bike of mass 500 kg is travelling with constant speed around a horizontal circular track with a radius of 30 m. A frictional force acts towards the centre of the track, and there is no resistance to motion. If the coefficient of friction between the quad bike and the track is 0.5, find the greatest speed the quad bike can go round the track without slipping. Give your answer to 3 significant figures.

(5 marks)

2 Particle P is attached to two light inextensible strings. The other end of each string is attached to a vertical rod XY, as shown in the diagram. The tension in string PX is 55 N, and the tension in string PY is 80 N. The particle moves in a horizontal circle about Y with a constant speed of 3 ms^{-1}. Find:

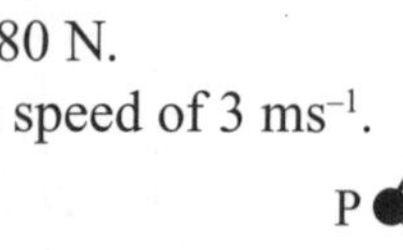

   a) the mass of particle P, correct to three significant figures,

   (2 marks)

   b) the length of string PY, correct to three significant figures,

   (3 marks)

   c) the number of revolutions the particle will make in one minute.

   (3 marks)

M2 Section 4 — Practice Questions

3

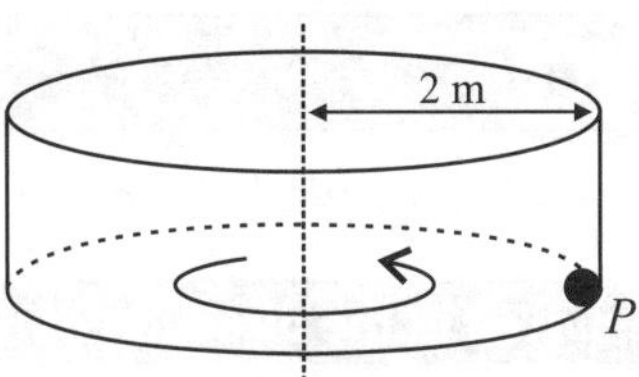

A particle, P, moves on the inside of a smooth hollow cylinder such that P remains in contact with both the base and curved surface of the cylinder at all times, as shown. The mass of P is 0.1 kg, the radius of the cylinder is 2 m and P moves through an angle of π radians every second.

a) Calculate the force exerted on P by the curved surface of the cylinder. *(2 marks)*

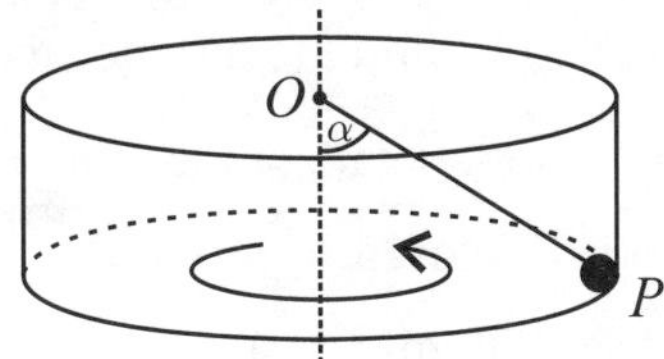

P is now attached to one end of a light, inextensible string, the other end of which is fixed at point O, at the centre of the top face of the cylinder, as shown. P continues to move with circular motion, remaining in contact with the base and curved surface of the cylinder, and moving through an angle of π radians every second.

b) Given that the force exerted on P by the curved surface of the cylinder is now 1.7 N and the force exerted on P by the base of the cylinder is 0.75 N, find the tension in the string and the angle, α, that the string makes with the vertical. *(7 marks)*

4

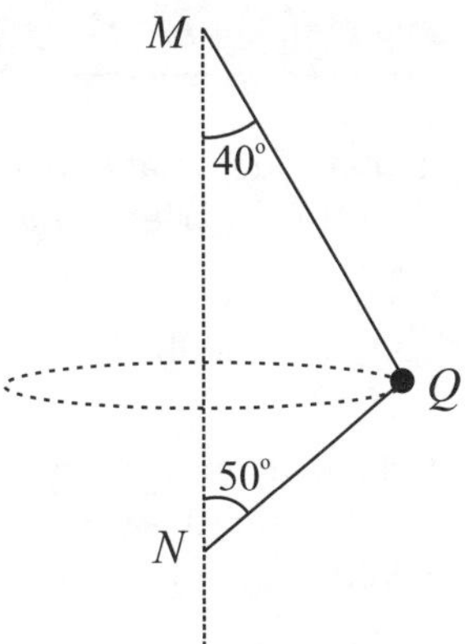

A particle, Q, of mass 1.5 kg is attached to one end of each of two light, inextensible strings. The other end of the longer string is attached to a fixed point M and the other end of the shorter string is attached to a fixed point N, vertically below M, as shown. The strings MQ and NQ are inclined at angles of 40° and 50° to the vertical, and MQ has length 0.5 m. Q moves in a horizontal circle with angular speed 2π rad s^{-1}.

a) Find the tensions in the two strings. *(8 marks)*

String NQ is on the point of becoming slack, and Q now moves with constant angular speed ω rad s^{-1}.

b) Find the kinetic energy of Q. *(4 marks)*

Work Done

Hello, good evening, welcome to Section 5 — where energy, work and power are tonight's chef's specials...

You Can Find the **Work Done** by a Force Over a Certain **Distance**

When a force is acting on a particle, you can work out the work done by the force using the formula:

Work done = force (F) × distance moved in the direction of the force (s)

For F in newtons, and s in metres, the unit of work done is joules (J).

E.g. if an object is pushed 4 m across a horizontal floor by a force of magnitude 12 N acting horizontally, the work done by the force will be 12 × 4 = 48 J

EXAMPLE A rock is dragged across horizontal ground by a rope attached to the rock at an angle of 25° to the horizontal. Given that the work done by the force is 470 J and the tension in the rope is 120 N, find the distance the rock is moved.

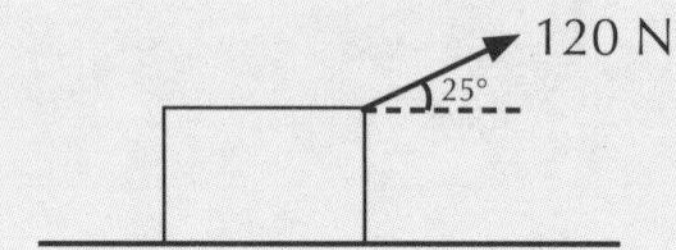

Work = horizontal component of force × s

$470 = 120\cos25 \times s$

$s = 4.32$ m (3 s.f.)

Because the force and the distance moved have to be in the same direction.

EXAMPLE A sack of flour of mass m kg is attached to a vertical rope and raised h m at a constant speed. Show that the work done against gravity by the tension in the rope, T, can be expressed as mgh.

T N

mg N

Resolve vertically:
$F = ma$
$T - mg = m \times 0$
$\Rightarrow T = mg$

Work done = Fs
$= T \times h$
$= mgh$

Work and gravity

You can always use the formula mgh to find the work done by a force against gravity.

A Particle Moving **Up a Rough Slope** does Work against **Friction and Gravity**

EXAMPLE A block of mass 3 kg is pulled 9 m up a rough plane inclined at an angle of 20° to the horizontal by a force, T. The block moves at a constant speed. The work done by T against friction is 154 J.

Find: a) the work done by T against gravity
b) the coefficient of friction between the block and the plane.

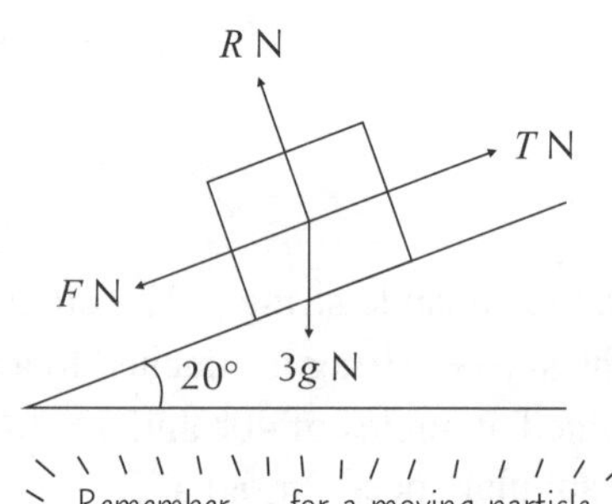

Remember — for a moving particle, F = μR, where μ is the coefficient of friction and R is the normal reaction.

a) Work done against gravity = mgh
$= 3g \times 9\sin20$
$=$ **90.5 J** (3 s.f.)

You need to use the vertical height, because it's only vertically that T does work against gravity.

b) Resolve perpendicular to the slope to find R:
$R - 3g\cos20 = m \times 0$
$\Rightarrow R = 3g\cos20$

Particle is moving, so:
$F = \mu R$
$= \mu \times 3g\cos20$

Work done by T against friction
$= F \times s = 154$
So, $\mu \times 3g\cos20 \times 9 = 154$
$\mu =$ **0.619** (3 s.f.)

The bit of T that is working against friction must be equal to F as the block is moving with constant speed (i.e. a = 0), so you can just use F here.

My work done = coffee × flapjack...

The really important thing to remember from this page is that the distance moved must be in the same direction as the force. Also, don't forget that a particle moving at constant velocity has no resultant force acting on it — this makes resolving forces easy.

Kinetic and Potential Energy

Here are couple of jokers you might remember from GCSE Science. I know, I know — Science. This means we're skirting dangerously close to the real world here. :| Don't be too afraid though — it's not as scary as you might think...

A Moving Particle Possesses Kinetic Energy

Any particle that is moving has kinetic energy (K.E.). You can find the kinetic energy of a particle using the formula:

$$\text{K.E.} = \frac{1}{2}mv^2$$

You need to learn this formula — you won't be given it in the exam.

If mass, m, is measured in kg and velocity, v, in ms^{-1}, then kinetic energy is measured in joules.

EXAMPLE

An ice skater of mass 60 kg is moving at a constant velocity of 8 ms^{-1}. Find the ice skater's kinetic energy.

$$\text{Kinetic energy} = \frac{1}{2}mv^2$$
$$= \frac{1}{2} \times 60 \times 8^2 = 1920 \text{ J}$$

Work Done is related to Kinetic Energy

The work done by a resultant force to change the velocity of a particle moving horizontally is equal to the change in that particle's kinetic energy:

Work done = change in kinetic energy

$$\text{Work done} = \frac{1}{2}mv^2 - \frac{1}{2}mu^2 = \frac{1}{2}m(v^2 - u^2)$$

EXAMPLE

A particle P of mass 6 kg is pulled along a rough horizontal plane by a force of 40 N, acting parallel to the plane. The particle travels 4 m in a straight line between two points on the plane, A and B. The coefficient of friction between P and the plane is 0.35.

a) Find the work done against friction in moving P from A to B.

At B, P has a speed of 8 ms^{-1}.

b) Calculate the speed of P at A.

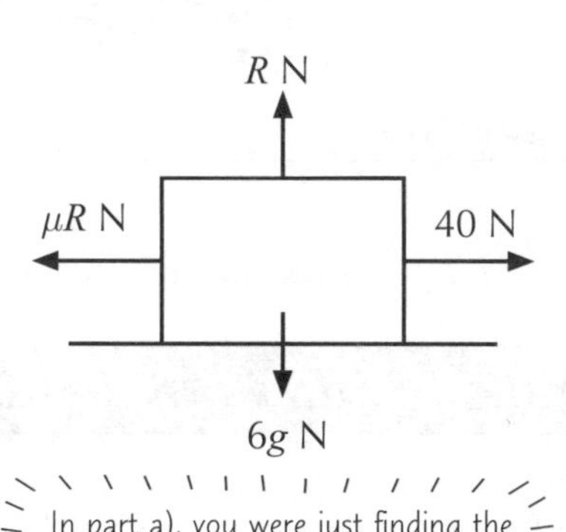

a) $R - 6g = 0$
$\Rightarrow R = 6g.$

There's no acceleration perpendicular to the plane, so use F = ma with a = 0 to find R.

$F = \mu R$
$= 0.35 \times 6 \times g = 20.58$ N

Work against friction $= Fs$
$= 20.58 \times 4$
$= 82.3$ J (3 s.f.)

b) $\text{Work done} = \frac{1}{2}mv^2 - \frac{1}{2}mu^2$

$(40 - \mu R) \times 4 = \frac{1}{2} \times 6 \times 8^2 - \frac{1}{2} \times 6 \times u^2$

$77.68 = 192 - 3u^2$

$u^2 = 38.11$

So, speed of P at A, $u = 6.17 \text{ ms}^{-1}$ (3 s.f.)

In part a), you were just finding the work done against friction. Here, you want the work done by the resultant force, so multiply the resultant force acting on P by the distance moved.

Kinetic and Potential Energy

Gravitational Potential Energy is all about a Particle's *Height*

The gravitational potential energy (G.P.E.) of a particle can be found using the formula:

G.P.E. = mgh ← You need to learn this formula as well.

If mass (m) is measured in kg, acceleration due to gravity (g) in ms^{-2} and the vertical height above some base level (h) in m, then G.P.E. is measured in joules.

The greater the height of a particle above the 'base level', the greater that particle's gravitational potential energy.

EXAMPLE

A lift and its occupants have a combined mass of 750 kg. The lift moves vertically from the ground to the first floor of a building, 6.1 m above the ground. After pausing, it moves vertically to the 17th floor, 64.9 m above the ground. Find the gravitational potential energy gained by the lift and its occupants in moving:

a) from the ground floor to the first floor,

b) from the first floor to the 17th floor.

a) G.P.E. gained = $mg \times$ increase in height
$= 750 \times 9.8 \times 6.1$
$= 44\ 800$ J (3 s.f)

b) G.P.E. gained = $mg \times$ increase in height
$= 750 \times 9.8 \times (64.9 - 6.1)$
$= 432\ 000$ J (3 s.f.)

Gravitational Potential Energy Always uses the Vertical Height

When you're working out the gravitational potential energy of a particle, the value of h you use should always, always, always be the vertical height above the 'base level'. This means that for a particle moving on a slope, it's only the vertical component of the distance you're interested in:

EXAMPLE A skateboarder and her board have a combined mass of 65 kg. The skateboarder starts from rest at a point X and freewheels down a slope inclined at 15° to the horizontal. She travels 40 m down the line of greatest slope. Find the gravitational potential energy lost by the skateboarder.

The skateboarder has moved a distance of 40 m down the slope, so this is a vertical distance of: 40sin15° m.

G.P.E. = mgh
$= 65 \times 9.8 \times 40\sin 15°$
$= 6590$ J = 6.59 kJ (both to 3 s.f.)

Mechanical Energy is the *Sum* of a Particle's *Kinetic and Potential Energies*

Over the next couple of pages, you're going to see a fair bit about 'mechanical energy'.
This is nothing to freak out about — it's just the sum of the kinetic and potential energies of a particle:

Total Mechanical Energy = Kinetic Energy + Gravitational Potential Energy

Strictly speaking, it also includes Elastic Potential Energy, but you don't need to know about that in M2 — hooray!

Particle P has so much potential — if only he could apply himself...

There shouldn't be anything earth-shattering on these two pages — I'd bet my completed 1994-95 Premier League sticker album that you've seen both of these types of energy before*. Still, it's worth refreshing yourself for what comes next.

*I won't though, it's too dear to me. Ahh, shinies...

The Work-Energy Principle

Those pages refreshing your memory on potential and kinetic energy weren't just for fun and giggles. Behold...

Learn the *Principle of Conservation of Mechanical Energy...*

The principle of conservation of mechanical energy says that:

If there are no external forces doing work on an object, the total mechanical energy of the object will remain constant.

An external force is any force other than the weight of the object, e.g. friction, air resistance, tension in a rope, etc.
This means that the sum of potential and kinetic energies remains the same throughout an object's motion.
This is a pretty useful bit of knowledge:

EXAMPLE

A BASE jumper with mass 88 kg jumps from a ledge on a building, 150 m above the ground. He falls with an initial velocity of 6 ms^{-1} towards the ground. He releases his parachute at a point 60 m above the ground.

a) Find the initial kinetic energy of the jumper in kJ.

b) Use the principle of conservation of mechanical energy to find the jumper's kinetic energy and speed at the point where he releases his parachute.

c) State one assumption you have made in modelling this situation.

a) Initial K.E. $= \frac{1}{2}mu^2 = \frac{1}{2} \times 88 \times (6)^2$
$= 1584 = 1.58$ kJ (3 s.f.)

b) Decrease in G.P.E. as he falls:
$mgh = 88 \times 9.8 \times (150 - 60)$
$= 77\,616$ J

You can just use the change in height here, as it's the change in P.E. that you're interested in.

Using conservation of mechanical energy: Increase in K.E. = Decrease in G.P.E.

So, K.E. when parachute released – Initial K.E. = Decrease in G.P.E.

$\frac{1}{2}mv^2$ = Decrease in G.P.E. + Initial K.E.
$= 77616 + 1584 = 79.2$ kJ

Rearrange $\frac{1}{2}mv^2 = 79\,200$ to find the speed of the jumper when parachute is released:

$$v = \sqrt{\frac{79\,200}{\frac{1}{2} \times 88}} = 42.4 \text{ ms}^{-1} \text{ (3 s.f.)}$$

If you don't assume this, then you can't use the principle of conservation of energy.

c) That the only force acting on the jumper is his weight.

...and the *Work-Energy Principle*

1) As you saw above, if there are no external forces doing work on an object, then the total mechanical energy of the object remains constant.

2) So, if there *is* an external force doing work on an object, then the total mechanical energy of the object must change.

3) This leads to the work-energy principle:

The work done on an object by external forces is equal to the change in the total mechanical energy of that object.

4) The work-energy principle is pretty similar to the result on page 171. It's generally more useful though, because you can use it for objects moving in any direction — not just horizontally.

Turn the page for a **HOT** and **SEXY** example...

The Work-Energy Principle

As promised, a lovely example of the work-energy principle...

Example

A particle of mass 3 kg is projected up a rough plane inclined at an angle θ to the horizontal, where $\tan\theta = \frac{5}{12}$. The particle moves through a point A at a speed of 11 ms^{-1}.
The particle continues to move up the line of greatest slope and comes to rest at a point B before sliding back down the plane. The coefficient of friction between the particle and the slope is $\frac{1}{3}$.

a) Use the work-energy principle to find the distance AB.

b) Find the speed of the particle when it returns to A.

a) Call the distance AB x.

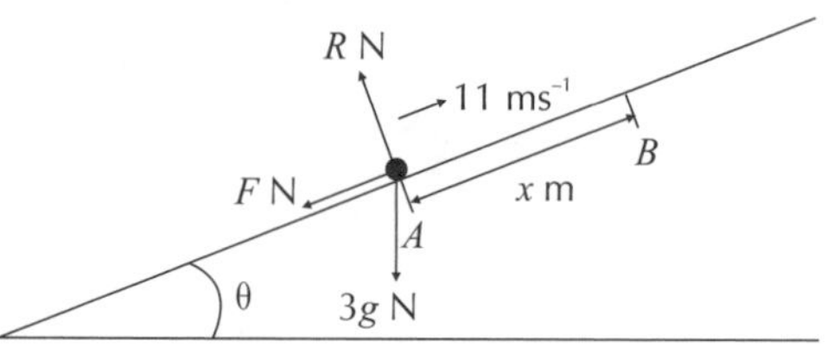

You're told to use the work-energy principle, so first find the change in total mechanical energy:

Change in K.E. of the particle = Final K.E. – Initial K.E.

$$= \frac{1}{2}mv^2 - \frac{1}{2}mu^2 = 0 - \left(\frac{1}{2} \times 3 \times 11^2\right) = \mathbf{-181.5\ J}$$

Change in P.E. of the particle = mg × (change in height)

$$= 3gx\sin\theta = 3gx \times \frac{5}{13} = \mathbf{\frac{15gx}{13}\ J}$$

$\tan\theta = \frac{5}{12} \Rightarrow \sin\theta = \frac{5}{13}$

So, change in total mechanical energy

$$= \mathbf{-181.5 + \frac{15gx}{13}}$$

The only external force doing work on the particle is the frictional force, F. So you need to find the work done by F.

First, resolve perpendicular to slope:

$$R - 3g\cos\theta = 0 \Rightarrow R = 3g \times \frac{12}{13} = \frac{36g}{13}$$

$$F = \mu R = \frac{1}{3} \times \frac{36g}{13} = \frac{12g}{13}$$

$\tan\theta = \frac{5}{12} \Rightarrow \cos\theta = \frac{12}{13}$

Displacement is negative because the particle is moving in the opposite direction to F.

Work done by $F = Fs = \frac{12g}{13} \times -x = \mathbf{-\frac{12gx}{13}}$

Using the work-energy principle:
Change in total mechanical energy = Work done by F

$$\text{So: } -181.5 + \frac{15gx}{13} = -\frac{12gx}{13}$$

$$\frac{27gx}{13} = 181.5$$

$$x = \frac{181.5 \times 13}{27g} = 8.92 \text{ m (3 s.f.)}$$

b) The particle moves from A, up to B and back down to A, so overall change in P.E. = 0

So, the change in total mechanical energy between the first and second time the particle is at A is just the change in Kinetic Energy, i.e. Final K.E. – Initial K.E. = $\frac{1}{2}mv^2 - \frac{1}{2}mu^2$

Work done on the particle = $Fs = F \times -2x$

$$= \frac{12g}{13} \times -2(8.917) = \mathbf{-161.3}$$

The particle has travelled the distance AB twice and is always moving in the opposite direction to the frictional force.

Using the work-energy principle:

$$\frac{1}{2} \times 3 \times v^2 - \frac{1}{2} \times 3 \times 11^2 = -161.3$$

u = 11 ms^{-1}, as this is the speed of the particle when it's first at A.

$$\frac{3}{2}v^2 = 181.5 - 161.3 \quad \Rightarrow \quad v = 3.67 \text{ ms}^{-1} \text{ (3 s.f.)}$$

Does this mean we can save energy by doing less work...

There are a few different ways you could tackle part b). You could just look at the motion back down the slope and look at the K.E. gained and the G.P.E. lost. Or you could resolve parallel to the slope, work out the acceleration and use $v^2 = u^2 + 2as$.
If the question doesn't tell you what method to use, you'll get marks for using any correct method. Correct being the key word.

Power

Right, last couple of pages of learnin' in this section. They're good 'uns as well.
And just think: after this — practice questions. Get in.

Power is the Rate at which Work is done on an Object

Power is a measure of the rate a force does work on an object.
The unit for power is the watt, where 1 watt (1 W) = 1 joule per second.

So $\text{Power} = \frac{\text{Work Done}}{\text{Time}}$

For an engine producing a driving force of F newtons, and moving a vehicle at a speed of v ms^{-1}, the power in watts can be found using the formula:

Power = $F \times v$

$\text{Power} = \frac{\text{Work Done}}{\text{Time}} = \frac{\text{Force} \times \text{Distance}}{\text{Time}} = \text{Force} \times \text{Velocity}$

This is the formula you'll end up using most of the time — those examiners can't resist a question about engines.
But don't forget what power means, just in case they throw you a curveball — it's the rate of doing work.

EXAMPLE

A train of mass 500 000 kg is travelling along a straight horizontal track with a constant speed of 20 ms^{-1}. The train experiences a constant resistance to motion of magnitude 275 000 N.

a) Find the rate at which the train's engine is working. Give your answer in kW.

b) The train now moves up a hill inclined at 2° to the horizontal. If the engine continues to work at the same rate and the magnitude of the non-gravitational resistance to motion remains the same, find the new constant speed of the train.

a) Call the driving force of the train T N and the speed of the train u ms^{-1}.
Resolve horizontally to find T:
$T - 275\,000 = m \times 0$
So $T = 275\,000$ N
Power $= T \times u = 275\,000 \times 20 = 5500$ kW.

b) Call the new driving force T' and resolve parallel to the slope:
$T' - 275\,000 - 500\,000g\sin 2° = m \times 0$
$\Rightarrow T' = 275\,000 + 500\,000g\sin 2°$ N $= 446\,008$ N
Power $= T' \times v$
$5\,500\,000 = 446\,008 \times v \quad \Rightarrow \quad v = \frac{5\,500\,000}{446\,008} = 12.3$ ms^{-1} (3 s.f.)

EXAMPLE

A tractor of mass 3000 kg is moving down a hill inclined at an angle of θ to the horizontal, where $\sin\theta = \frac{1}{24}$. The acceleration of the tractor is 1.5 ms^{-2} and its engine is working at a constant rate of 30 kW. Find the magnitude of the non-gravitational resistance to motion at the instant when the tractor is travelling at a speed of 8 ms^{-1}.

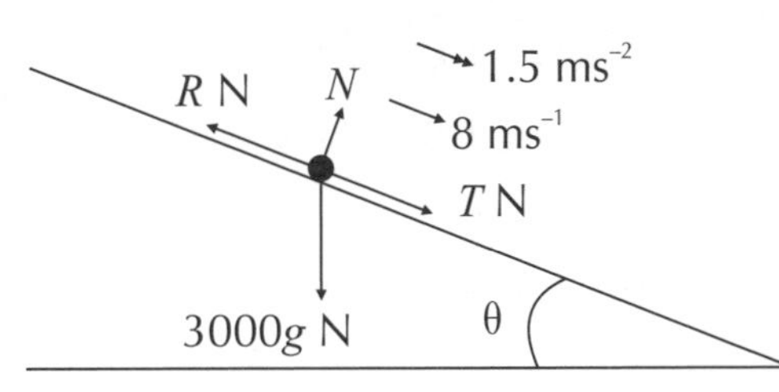

Use Power = $F \times v$ to find T:
$30\,000 = T \times 8 \Rightarrow T = 3750$ N
Resolve parallel to the slope: $T + mg\sin\theta - R = ma$
$3750 + (3000 \times 9.8 \times \frac{1}{24}) - R = 3000 \times 1.5$
$R = 3750 + 1225 - 4500$
$R = 475$ N

Add the component of weight, as the tractor is moving down the slope.

There is acceleration here, so this term doesn't disappear for once.

All together now — Watt's the unit for power...

Nearly there now. Make sure you understand this page before you move on — it's about to get a teeny bit more complicated...

Power

Be prepared for a **Variable Resistive Force**

There's a good chance you'll get a power question where the resistive force isn't constant — it'll be dependent on the velocity of whatever's moving. Like the examples on the previous page, these questions require resolving of forces and the careful use of $F = ma$.

EXAMPLE

A car of mass 1200 kg travels on a straight horizontal road. It experiences a resistive force of magnitude $30v$ N, where v is the car's speed in ms^{-1}. The maximum speed of the car on this road is 70 ms^{-1}. Find:

a) the car's maximum power,

b) the car's maximum possible acceleration when its speed is 40 ms^{-1}.

a) When the car is travelling at its maximum speed, its acceleration is zero, and so the driving force of the car, T, must be equal to the resistive force, i.e. $T = 30v$.

Now use Power = Force × Velocity to give $P = 30v^2 = 30 \times 70^2 = 147$ kW.

b) Call the new driving force of the car F.

Power = Force × Velocity $\Rightarrow F = \frac{147\,000}{40} = 3675$ N

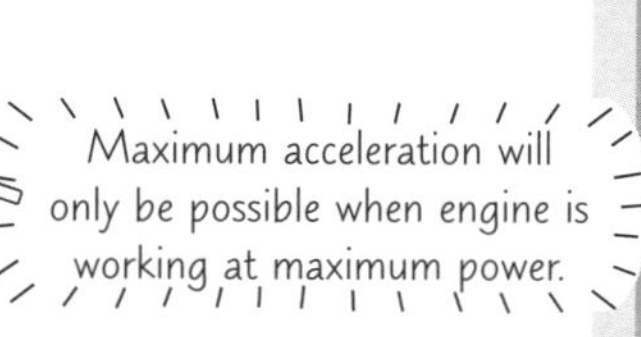

Resolve forces horizontally:

$3675 - 30v = ma$

$3675 - (30 \times 40) = 1200a \Rightarrow a = 2.06\ \text{ms}^{-2}$ (3 s.f.).

EXAMPLE

A van of mass 1500 kg moves up a road inclined at an angle of 5° to the horizontal. The van's engine works at a constant rate of 25 kW and the van experiences a resistive force of magnitude kv N, where k is a constant and v is the van's speed in ms^{-1}. At the point where the van has speed 8 ms^{-1}, its acceleration is 0.5 ms^{-2}.

a) Show that $k = 137$ to 3 s.f.

b) Using $k = 137$, show that U, the maximum speed of the van up this road, satisfies the equation: $U^2 + 9.35U - 182 = 0$, where the coefficients are given to 3 s.f.

a) Use Power = $T \times v$, to find T, the driving force of the van's engine:

$T = \frac{\text{Power}}{v} = \frac{25\,000}{8} = 3125$ N

Resolve forces parallel to the slope: $T - kv - mg\sin 5° = ma$

So: $3125 - 8k - (1500 \times 9.8 \times \sin 5°) = 1500 \times 0.5$

And rearrange: $k = \frac{1}{8}(3125 - (1500 \times 9.8 \times \sin 5°) - (1500 \times 0.5)) = 137$ (3 s.f.)

b) From Power = Fv, the driving force of the van's engine at speed U is $\frac{25\,000}{U}$ N.

Again, resolve forces parallel to the slope: $\frac{25\,000}{U} - 137U - mg\sin 5° = 0$

The van is travelling at maximum speed, so acceleration is zero.

Multiply throughout by U: $25\,000 - 137U^2 - (mg\sin 5° \times U) = 0$

Rearrange and simplify (to 3 s.f.) to give: $U^2 + 9.35U - 182 = 0$ — as required.

The Power of Love — a Variable Resistive Force from Above...

Well that pretty much wraps up this section on work and energy. Plenty of formulas to learn and plenty of fun force diagrams to draw. If you're itching for some practice at all this then turn over and crack on. Even if you're not, do it anyway.

M2 Section 5 — Practice Questions

I don't know about you, but I enjoyed that section. Lots of engines and energy and blocks moving on slopes and GRRRRR look how manly I am as I do work against friction.
Ahem sorry about that. Right-oh — practice questions...

Warm-up Questions

1) A crate is pushed across a smooth horizontal floor by a force of 250 N, acting in the direction of motion. Find the work done in pushing the crate 3 m.

2) A crane lifts a concrete block 12 m vertically at constant speed. If the crane does 34 kJ of work against gravity, find the mass of the concrete block. Take $g = 9.8$ ms^{-1}.

3) A horse of mass 450 kg is cantering at a speed of 13 ms^{-1}. Find the horse's kinetic energy.

4) An ice skater of mass 65 kg sets off from rest. After travelling 40 m in a straight line across horizontal ice, she has done 800 J of work. Find the speed of the ice skater at this point.

5) A particle of mass 0.5 kg is projected upwards from ground level and reaches a maximum height of 150 m above the ground. Find the increase in the particle's gravitational potential energy. Take $g = 9.8$ ms^{-2}.

6) State the principle of conservation of mechanical energy.
Explain why you usually need to model an object as a particle if you are using this principle.

7) A jubilant cowboy throws his hat vertically upwards with a velocity of 5 ms^{-1}. Use conservation of energy to find the maximum height the hat reaches above the point of release. Take $g = 9.8$ ms^{-2}.

8) State the work-energy principle. Explain what is meant by an 'external force'.

9) A car's engine is working at a rate of 350 kW. If the car is moving with speed 22 ms^{-1}, find the driving force of the engine.

Well those warm-up questions should have got your maths juices flowing, and you should now be eager to move on to something a bit more exam-like.

It's probably best not to ask what maths juice is.

Exam Questions

Whenever a numerical value of g is required in the questions below, take $g = 9.8$ ms^{-2}.

1 A cyclist is riding up a road at a constant speed of 4 ms^{-1}. The road is inclined at an angle α to the horizontal. The cyclist is working at a rate of 250 W and experiences a constant non-gravitational resistance to motion of magnitude 35 N. The cyclist and his bike have a combined mass of 88 kg.

a) Find the angle of the slope, α. *(4 marks)*

b) The cyclist now increases his work rate to 370 W. If all resistances to motion remain unchanged, find the cyclist's acceleration when his speed is 4 ms^{-1}. *(4 marks)*

M2 Section 5 — Practice Questions

I hope you've got the energy to power through all this work. I don't want to have to force you...

2

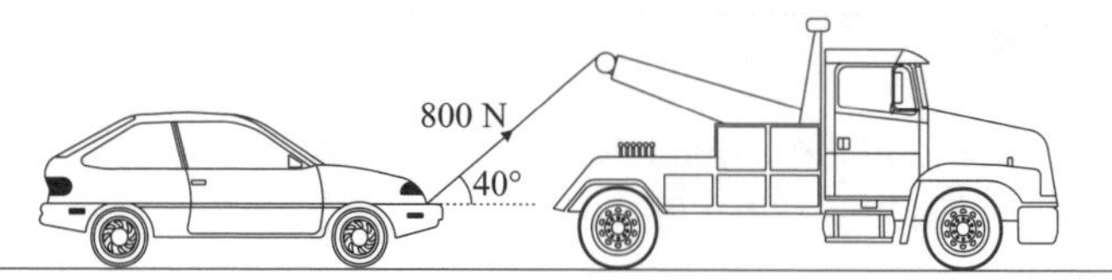

A car of mass 1500 kg is towed 320 m along a straight horizontal road by a rope attached to a pick-up truck. The rope is attached to the car at an angle of 40° to the horizontal and the tension in the rope is 800 N. The car experiences a constant resistance to motion from friction.

a) Find the work done by the towing force. *(3 marks)*

b) Over the 320 m, the car increases in speed from 11 ms^{-1} to 16 ms^{-1}. Assuming that the magnitude of the towing force remains constant at 800 N, find the coefficient of friction between the car and the road. *(4 marks)*

3 A van of mass 2700 kg is travelling at a constant speed of 16 ms^{-1} up a road inclined at an angle of 12° to the horizontal. The non-gravitational resistance to motion is modelled as a single force of magnitude of 800 N.

a) Find the rate of work of the engine. *(4 marks)*

When the van passes a point A, still travelling at 16 ms^{-1}, the engine is switched off and the van comes to rest without braking, a distance x m from A. If all resistance to motion remains constant, find:

b) the distance x, *(4 marks)*

c) the time taken for the van to come to rest. *(4 marks)*

4 A stone of mass 0.3 kg is dropped down a well. The stone hits the surface of the water in the well with a speed of 20 ms^{-1}.

a) Calculate the kinetic energy of the stone as it hits the water. *(2 marks)*

b) By modelling the stone as a particle and using conservation of energy, find the height above the surface of the water from which the stone was dropped. *(3 marks)*

c) When the stone hits the water, it begins to sink vertically and experiences a constant resistive force of 23 N. Use the work-energy principle to find the depth the stone has sunk to when the speed of the stone is reduced to 1 ms^{-1}. *(5 marks)*

M2 Section 5 — Practice Questions

Encore encore, more more more...

5 A car of mass 1000 kg experiences a resistive force of magnitude kv N, where k is a constant and v ms^{-1} is the car's speed. The car travels up a slope inclined at an angle of $\theta°$ to the horizontal, where $\sin\theta = 0.1$. The power generated by the car is 20 kW and its speed up the slope remains constant at 10 ms^{-1}.

a) Show that $k = 102$.

(3 marks)

b) The car's maximum power output is 50 kW.

(i) Show that, going up this slope, the car's maximum possible speed, u, satisfies the equation

$$102u^2 + 980u - 50\,000 = 0.$$

(4 marks)

(ii) Hence find the car's maximum possible speed up this slope.

(2 marks)

The car reaches the top of the slope and begins travelling on a flat horizontal road. The power increases to 21 kW and the resistive force remains at kv N.

c) Find the acceleration of the car when its speed is 12 ms^{-1}.

(3 marks)

6

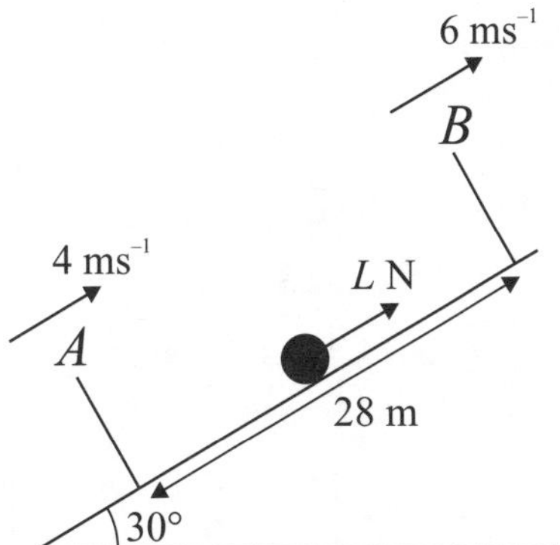

A skier is pulled up a sloping plane by a force, L, acting parallel to the plane which is inclined at an angle of 30° to the horizontal. The skier and his skis have a combined mass of 90 kg and he experiences a constant frictional force of 66 N as he moves up the slope. The skier passes through two gates, A and B, which are 28 m apart. His speed at gate A is 4 ms^{-1}. At gate B, his speed has increased to 6 ms^{-1}. Find:

a) the increase in the skier's total mechanical energy as he moves from gate A to gate B, *(5 marks)*

b) the magnitude of the force, L, pulling the skier up the slope. *(3 marks)*

Impulse

An impulse changes the momentum of a particle in the direction of motion.

In case you've forgotten — momentum is the measure of how much 'umph' an object has. You can find an object's momentum using the formula Momentum = Mass × Velocity.

Impulse is Change in Momentum

To work out the impulse that's acted on an object, just subtract the object's initial momentum from its final momentum. Impulse is measured in newton seconds (Ns).

$$\text{Impulse} = mv - mu$$

EXAMPLE

A body of mass 500 g is travelling in a straight line. Find the magnitude of the impulse needed to increase its velocity from 2 ms^{-1} to 5 ms^{-1}.

Impulse = Change in momentum

$= mv - mu$

$= (0.5 \times 5) - (0.5 \times 2)$

$= 1.5$ Ns

This is called the impulse-momentum principle. Ooooh, aaaaaah.

EXAMPLE

A 20 g ball is dropped 1 m onto horizontal ground. Immediately after rebounding the ball has a speed of 2 ms^{-1}. Find the impulse given to the ball by the ground. How high does the ball rebound? Take $g = 9.8$ ms^{-2}.

Take 'down' as positive.

First you need to work out the ball's speed as it reaches the ground:

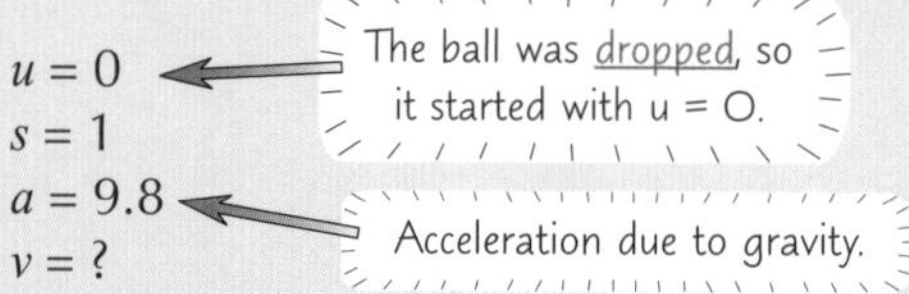

List the variables you're given: $u = 0$, $s = 1$, $a = 9.8$, $v = ?$

The ball was dropped, so it started with u = 0.

Acceleration due to gravity.

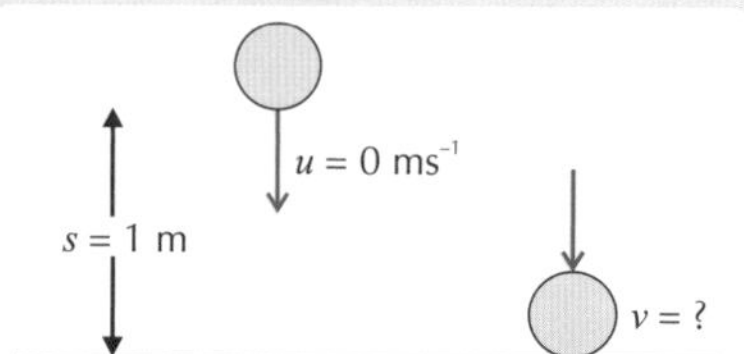

Choose an equation containing u, s, a and v:

$v^2 = u^2 + 2as$

$v^2 = 0^2 + (2 \times 9.8 \times 1)$

$\mathbf{v = 4.43}$ **ms^{-1}** (3 s.f.)

The sign is really important. Make sure that down is positive throughout this part of the question.

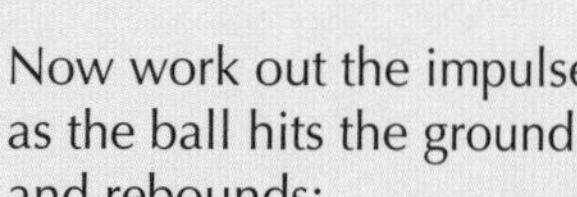

Now work out the impulse as the ball hits the ground and rebounds:

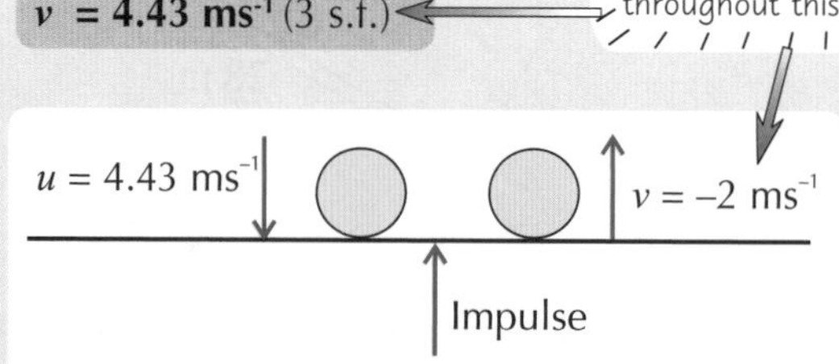

Impulse $= mv - mu$

$= (0.02 \times -2) - (0.02 \times 4.43)$

$= -0.129$ Ns (to 3 s.f.)

The impulse is negative, which means it's acting upwards (as down was taken as positive).

Finally you need to use a new equation of motion to find s (the greatest height the ball reaches after the bounce). This time take 'up' as positive:

List the variables: $u = 2$, $v = 0$, $a = -9.8$, $s = ?$

$v = 0$ at the ball's greatest height.

a is negative because the ball is decelerating.

$v^2 = u^2 + 2as$

$0^2 = 2^2 + (2 \times -9.8 \times s)$

$s = 0.204$ m (to 3 s.f.)

Impulse

*Impulses always **Balance in Collisions***

During impact between particles A and B, the impulse that A gives to B is the same as the impulse that B gives to A, but in the opposite direction.

These calculations use the principle of conservation of momentum, which you learnt in M1, and which states that the total momentum of a system is the same before and after a collision.

EXAMPLE

A mass of 2 kg moving at 2 ms^{-1} collides with a mass of 3 kg which is moving in the same direction at 1 ms^{-1}. The 2 kg mass continues to move in the same direction at 1 ms^{-1} after impact. Find the impulse given by the 2 kg mass to the other mass.

Using "conservation of momentum":

$(2 \times 2) + (3 \times 1) = (2 \times 1) + 3v$

So $v = 1\frac{2}{3}$ ms^{-1}

Before

A (2kg) 2 ms^{-1} → B (3kg) 1 ms^{-1} →

After

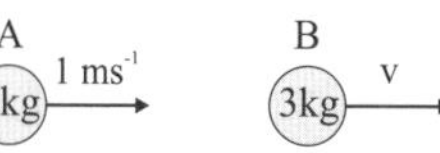

Impulse (on B) = $mv - mu$ (for B)

$= (3 \times 1\frac{2}{3}) - (3 \times 1)$

$= 2$ Ns

The impulse B gives to A is $(2 \times 1) - (2 \times 2) = $ **–2 Ns**. Aside from the different direction, you can see it's the same — so you didn't actually need to find v for this question.

EXAMPLE

Two snooker balls A and B have a mass of 0.6 kg and 0.9 kg respectively. The balls are initially at rest on a snooker table. Ball A is given an impulse of magnitude 4.5 Ns towards ball B. Modelling the snooker table as a smooth horizontal plane, find the speed of ball A before it collides with B.

Impulse = $mv - mu$

$\Rightarrow 4.5 = (0.6 \times v) - (0.6 \times 0) = 0.6v$

$\Rightarrow v = \frac{4.5}{0.6} = 7.5$ ms^{-1}

The balls collide and move away in the direction A was travelling before the collision. Find the speed of ball A after the collision, given that the speed of ball B is 4 ms^{-1}.

Using conservation of momentum:

$(0.6 \times 7.5) + (0.9 \times 0) = 0.6v + (0.9 \times 4)$

So, $v = 1.5$ ms^{-1}

EXAMPLE

Particles A and B, of masses m kg and M kg respectively, move towards each other on a smooth horizontal plane, as shown. A has speed 4 ms^{-1} and B has speed 1 ms^{-1}. When A and B collide, an impulse of magnitude 10 Ns brings A to rest. Immediately following the collision, B has the same speed as before the collision, but its direction has been reversed. Find m and M.

Before

A (m kg) 4 ms^{-1} → ← 1 ms^{-1} B (M kg)

After

Impulse (on A) = $mv - mu$ (for A)

$-10 = (m \times 0) - (m \times 4)$

$\Rightarrow -10 = -4m$

$\Rightarrow m = 2.5$ kg.

The impulse is acting in the opposite direction to A's motion, so (taking left to right as +ve), the impulse must be negative.

Using "conservation of momentum":

$(m \times 4) + (M \times -1) = (m \times 0) + (M \times 1)$

$\Rightarrow 4m - M = M$

$\Rightarrow M = 2m = 5$ kg.

You could also use impulse here, as the impulse A gives to B must be +10 Ns. $10 = (M \times 1) - (M \times -1) \Rightarrow M = 5$ kg.

The perils of internet shopping — the midnight impulse buy...

Not a bad little topic, impulse. You should remember most of the maths on these pages from M1 — and there's just the one new formula to get to know. As always, drawing a diagram is a good way to understand what's going on in these questions.

Collisions

Oh yes, you've not seen the last of those colliding particles. If you like things loud and dramatic, think demolition balls and high speed crashes. If you're anything like me though you'll be picturing a nice sedate game of snooker.

The Coefficient of Restitution is always between 0 and 1

When two particles collide in a direct impact (i.e. they're moving on the same straight line), the speeds they bounce away at depend on the coefficient of restitution, e. This is known as Newton's Law of Restitution, and looks like this:

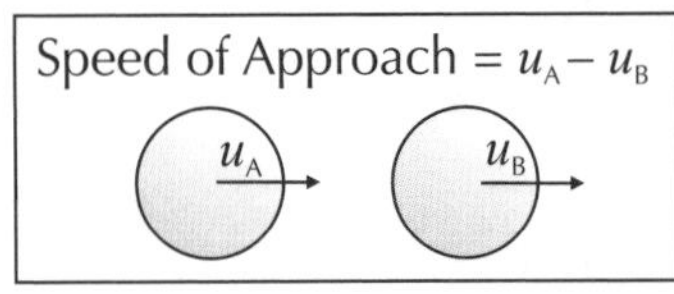

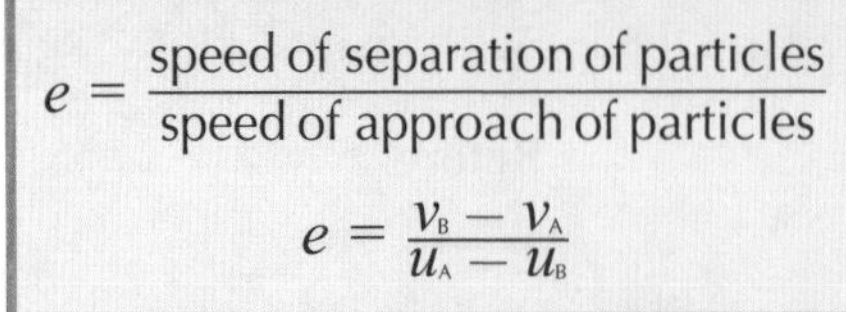

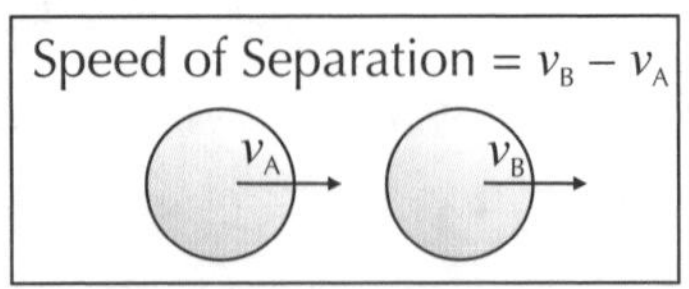

1) The value of e depends on the material that the particles are made of.
2) e always lies between 0 and 1.
3) When $e = 0$ the particles are called 'inelastic', and they'll coalesce.
4) When $e = 1$ the particles are 'perfectly elastic' and they'll bounce apart with no loss of speed.

Balls of modelling clay would be near the $e = 0$ end of the scale, while ping pong balls are nearer to $e = 1$.

EXAMPLE Two particles collide as shown. Find the coefficient of restitution.

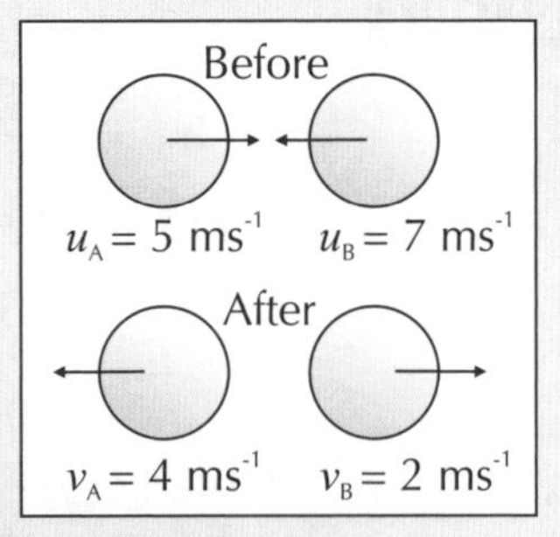

1) Firstly, work out the speeds of approach and separation, taking care with positives and negatives:
Speed of approach $= u_A - u_B = 5 - (-7) = 12$ ms^{-1}.
Speed of separation $= v_B - v_A = 2 - (-4) = 6$ ms^{-1}.

Think of 'left to right' as positive, and so particles travelling 'right to left' will have a negative speed.

2) Use $e = \frac{\text{speed of separation of particles}}{\text{speed of approach of particles}}$:

$e = \frac{6}{12} = 0.5$. So the coefficient of restitution is 0.5.

For Two Unknown Speeds — use Momentum Conservation too

Often you'll be given the value of e and asked to find the velocities of both particles either before or after impact. As there are two unknowns, you'll need to use the formula for conservation of momentum along with the Law of Restitution to form simultaneous equations.

EXAMPLE Two particles, A and B, are moving in opposite directions in the same straight line, as shown. If $e = \frac{1}{3}$, find the velocities of both particles after impact.

$m_A = 4$ kg $\quad m_B = 12$ kg

$u_A = 10$ ms^{-1} $\quad u_B = 2$ ms^{-1}

1) Use $e = \frac{v_B - v_A}{u_A - u_B}$ to get the first equation:

$\frac{1}{3} = \frac{v_B - v_A}{10 - (-2)} \Rightarrow v_B - v_A = 4$. Call this **equation 1**.

2) Use $m_Au_A + m_Bu_B = m_Av_A + m_Bv_B$ to get the second equation:
$(4 \times 10) + (12 \times -2) = 4v_A + 12v_B$
$\Rightarrow 16 = 4v_A + 12v_B \Rightarrow v_A + 3v_B = 4$. Call this **equation 2**.

3) **Equation 1** + **equation 2** gives:
$4v_B = 8$, so $v_B = 2$ ms^{-1} (i.e. 2 ms^{-1} going left to right).

4) Substituting in **equation 1** gives:
$2 - v_A = 4$, so $v_A = -2$ ms^{-1} (i.e. 2 ms^{-1} going right to left).

Collisions

There's a saying in Stoke-on-Trent that goes: 'cost kick a bo againt a wo till it bosses?'*
Well, that's kinda what this next bit's about, a.k.a. 'the collision of a particle with a plane surface'.

The **Law of Restitution** also works with a **Smooth Plane Surface**

Particles don't just collide with each other. They can collide with a fixed flat surface — such as when a ball is kicked against a vertical wall, or dropped onto a horizontal floor.

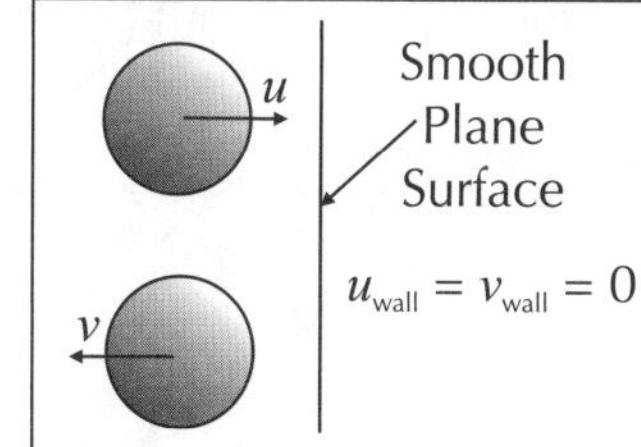

As long as the surface can be modelled as smooth (i.e. no friction) and perpendicular to the motion of the particle, the law can be simplified to:

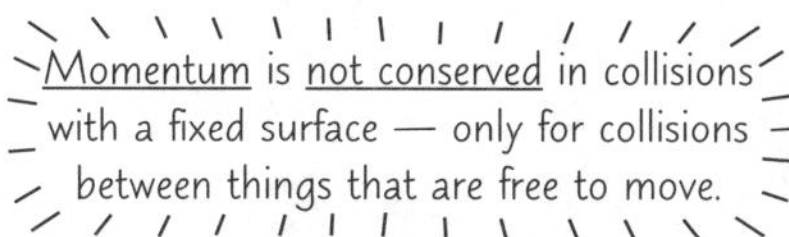

$$e = \frac{\text{speed of rebound of particle}}{\text{speed of approach of particle}} = \frac{v}{u}$$

EXAMPLE A ball rolling along a smooth horizontal floor at 6 ms⁻¹ hits a smooth vertical wall, with a coefficient of restitution $e = 0.65$. Find the speed of the ball as it rebounds.

BEFORE

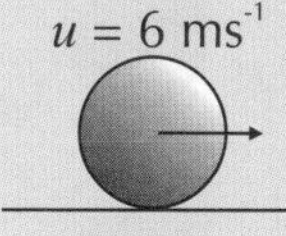

AFTER

v

Using $e = \frac{v}{u}$:

$0.65 = \frac{v}{6} \Rightarrow v = 0.65 \times 6 = 3.9$ ms^{-1}.

So the ball rebounds at a speed of 3.9 ms^{-1}. Piece of cake.

Use the **Laws of Motion** for things being **Dropped**

Things get a tiny bit trickier when a particle is dropped onto a horizontal surface because acceleration under gravity comes into play. You should be pretty nifty with equations of motion now though — just remember to use them here.

EXAMPLE A basketball is dropped vertically from rest at a height of 1.4 m onto a horizontal floor. It rebounds to a height of 0.9 m. Find e for the impact with the floor.

1) Assuming the ball is a particle, and the floor is smooth, we can use $e = \frac{v}{u}$.
For the diagram shown, this would be $e = \frac{u_2}{v_1}$, as we need the velocity just before the impact (v_1) and the velocity just after (u_2).

2) Using $v^2 = u^2 + 2as$ before the impact with the floor (where $a = g \approx 9.8$ ms^{-2}):
$v_1^2 = 0 + 2 \times 9.8 \times 1.4 = 27.44$
$\Rightarrow v_1 = 5.238$ ms^{-1} to 4 s.f.

3) Using $v^2 = u^2 + 2as$ after the impact with the floor (where $a = -g$ since the motion is against gravity):
$0 = u_2^2 + 2 \times -9.8 \times 0.9$
$\Rightarrow u_2 = 4.2$ ms^{-1}.

4) Finally, we can find e: $e = \frac{u_2}{v_1} = \frac{4.2}{5.238} = 0.802$ to 3 s.f.

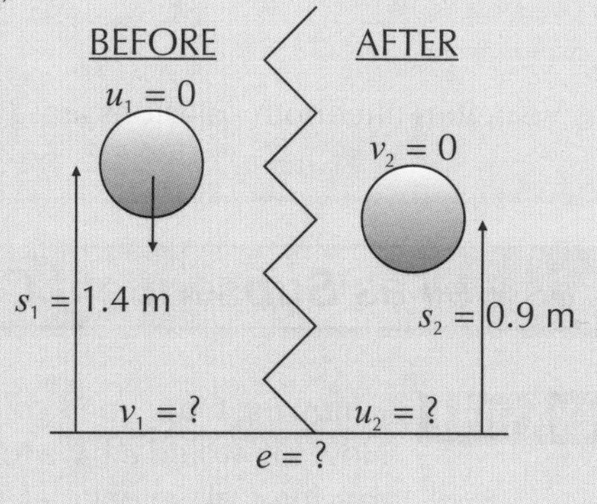

Dating Tip #107 — Avoid them if they're on the rebound...

Just when you were thinking collisions were a load of balls, along come walls and floors to shake things up a bit. The Law of Restitution is a pretty straightforward formula, but chances are there'll be added complications in the exam questions. Learn how to tackle the four types of question on these two pages and you'll be laughing.

*For those unfamiliar with Potteries dialect, this means 'Can you kick a ball against a wall until it bursts?'

Complex Collisions

You've had an easy ride so far this section, but now it's time to fasten your seatbelt, don your crash helmet, and prepare for some pretty scary collisions. Don't say I didn't warn you...

Solve ***Successive*** Collisions ***Step by Step...***

Think of this as a multi-particle pile-up. One particle collides with another, which then shoots off to collide with a third. No extra maths required, but quite a bit of extra thinking.

EXAMPLE Particles P, Q and R are travelling at different speeds along the same smooth straight line, as shown. Particles P and Q collide first ($e = 0.6$), then Q goes on to collide with R ($e = 0.2$). What are the velocities of P, Q and R after the second collision?

0.1 kg, P, 20 ms⁻¹ → ; 0.4 kg, Q, 5 ms⁻¹ → ; 2 kg, R, ← 1 ms⁻¹

1) Take things step by step. Forget about R for the moment and concentrate on the first collision — the one between P and Q:

Use $e = \frac{v_{Q1} - v_{P1}}{u_{P1} - u_{Q1}}$ first: $0.6 = \frac{v_{Q1} - v_{P1}}{20 - 5}$

$\Rightarrow v_{Q1} - v_{P1} = 9$ (**equation 1**).

There are lots of velocities to find here so label them clearly — e.g. v_{Q1} is the final velocity of Q after collision 1, etc.

Then use $m_P u_{P1} + m_Q u_{Q1} = m_P v_{P1} + m_Q v_{Q1}$:

$(0.1 \times 20) + (0.4 \times 5) = 0.1v_{P1} + 0.4v_{Q1}$

$\Rightarrow 4 = 0.1v_{P1} + 0.4v_{Q1} \quad \Rightarrow \quad v_{P1} + 4v_{Q1} = 40$ (**equation 2**).

Equation 1 + **equation 2** gives:

$5v_{Q1} = 49 \quad \Rightarrow \quad v_{Q1} = 9.8 \text{ ms}^{-1}$.

Substituting in **equation 1** gives:

$9.8 - v_{P1} = 9 \quad \Rightarrow \quad v_{P1} = 9.8 - 9 = 0.8 \text{ ms}^{-1}$.

Before 1st Collision: 0.1 kg P 20 ms⁻¹ → ; 0.4 kg Q 5 ms⁻¹ → ; $e = 0.6$

After 1st Collision: P 0.8 ms⁻¹ → ; Q 9.8 ms⁻¹ →

2) For the second collision, which is between Q and R: $e = \frac{v_{R2} - v_{Q2}}{u_{Q2} - u_{R2}}$.

u_{Q2} is the same as the velocity of Q after the first collision — you found this above (9.8 ms⁻¹), so:

$0.2 = \frac{v_{R2} - v_{Q2}}{9.8 - (-1)} \quad \Rightarrow \quad v_{R2} - v_{Q2} = 2.16$ (**equation 3**).

Then $m_Q u_{Q2} + m_R u_{R2} = m_Q v_{Q2} + m_R v_{R2}$:

$(0.4 \times 9.8) + (2 \times -1) = 0.4v_{Q2} + 2v_{R2}$

$\Rightarrow 1.92 = 0.4v_{Q2} + 2v_{R2} \quad \Rightarrow \quad 0.2v_{Q2} + v_{R2} = 0.96$ (**equation 4**).

Equation 4 – **equation 3** gives:

$1.2v_{Q2} = -1.2 \quad \Rightarrow \quad v_{Q2} = -1 \text{ ms}^{-1}$.

Substituting in **equation 3** gives:

$v_{R2} - (-1) = 2.16 \quad \Rightarrow \quad v_{R2} = 2.16 - 1 = 1.16 \text{ ms}^{-1}$.

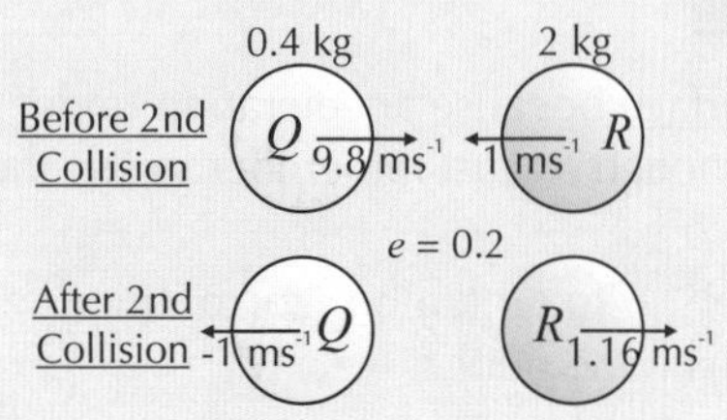

3) Velocities after both collisions are: $P = 0.8 \text{ ms}^{-1}$, $Q = -1 \text{ ms}^{-1}$ and $R = 1.16 \text{ ms}^{-1}$:

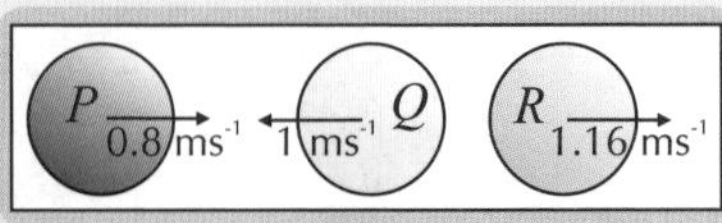

... as well as ***Subsequent Collisions*** with a ***Plane Surface***

EXAMPLE Following the second collision, P is removed and R hits a smooth vertical wall at a right angle. How big would e have to be for this impact to allow R to collide again with Q, assuming Q is moving with velocity –1 ms⁻¹?

1) Think things through carefully. Q is currently going at 1 ms⁻¹ in the opposite direction. To hit it again, R needs to bounce off the wall with a rebound speed higher than 1 ms⁻¹, so it can 'catch up'. So $v_{R3} > 1$.

2) For the impact with the wall, $e = \frac{v_{R3}}{u_{R3}} \quad \Rightarrow \quad v_{R3} = eu_{R3}$, and so $eu_{R3} > 1$.

3) From the example above, $u_{R3} = v_{R2} = 1.16 \text{ ms}^{-1}$, so $1.16e > 1 \quad \Rightarrow \quad e > \frac{1}{1.16} \quad \Rightarrow \quad e > 0.8620...$

4) So, to 3 s.f., e must be higher than 0.862 for R to collide again with Q.

Collisions and Energy

Almost the end of the section, and I guess your energy might be waning. Most things lose kinetic energy when they collide — you need to know how to work out how much. It's enough to make you want a quiet lie down...

Kinetic Energy is only Conserved in Perfectly Elastic Collisions

For any collision where $e < 1$, some kinetic energy will be lost (it changes into things like heat and sound). The formula for working out how much has been lost is fairly straightforward:

The units of K.E. are joules, if mass is given in kg and speed in ms^{-1}.

$$\text{Loss of K.E. on Impact} = \text{Total K.E. before} - \text{Total K.E. after} = (\tfrac{1}{2}m_1u_1^2 + \tfrac{1}{2}m_2u_2^2) - (\tfrac{1}{2}m_1v_1^2 + \tfrac{1}{2}m_2v_2^2)$$

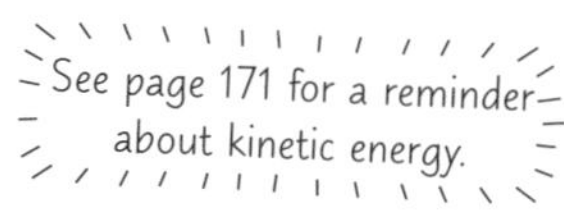

The tricky bit is finding the u's and v's to put in the formula...

EXAMPLE A tiny cannon fires a ball in a straight line across a smooth horizontal table, as shown. The ball collides directly with another, stationary, ball with $e = 0.7$, and moves away from this collision at 7.5 ms^{-1}.

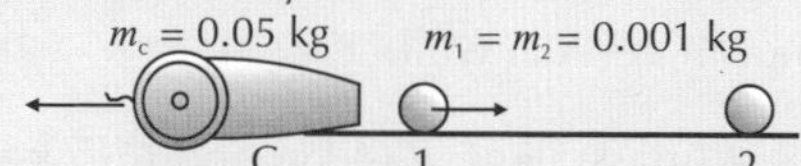

a) Find the loss of K.E. when the balls collide.

1) We first need to find u_1 (the speed of the fired ball before it hits the other) and v_2 (the final speed of the other ball). Use the law of restitution and conservation of momentum (as on p. 182) where $e = 0.7$, $v_1 = 7.5$, and $u_2 = 0$.

2) $e = \frac{v_2 - v_1}{u_1 - u_2} \Rightarrow 0.7 = \frac{v_2 - 7.5}{u_1 - 0} \Rightarrow v_2 - 0.7u_1 = 7.5$ (**eqn 1**).

$m_1u_1 + m_2u_2 = m_1v_1 + m_2v_2$ and since $m_1 = m_2$, they cancel:
$u_1 + 0 = 7.5 + v_2 \Rightarrow u_1 - v_2 = 7.5$ (**eqn 2**).

Eqn 1 + **eqn 2**: $0.3u_1 = 15 \Rightarrow u_1 = 50$ ms^{-1}.

Sub in **eqn 2**: $50 - v_2 = 7.5 \Rightarrow v_2 = 50 - 7.5 = 42.5$ ms^{-1}.

3) Finally, putting all the values in the K.E. formula:

$$\begin{aligned}\text{Loss of K.E.} &= (\tfrac{1}{2}m_1u_1^2 + \tfrac{1}{2}m_2u_2^2) - (\tfrac{1}{2}m_1v_1^2 + \tfrac{1}{2}m_2v_2^2)\\ &= \tfrac{1}{2}m[(u_1^2 + u_2^2) - (v_1^2 + v_2^2)]\\ &= \tfrac{1}{2} \times 0.001 \times [(50^2 + 0^2) - (7.5^2 + 42.5^2)]\\ &= 0.31875 = 0.319 \text{ J to 3 s.f.}\end{aligned}$$

b) Find the K.E. gained by firing the cannon.

1) Since both the cannon and the ball are stationary before firing, there is no initial K.E. The gain in K.E. is simply $\frac{1}{2}m_cv_c^2 + \frac{1}{2}m_1v_1^2$, where v_1 is the speed of the ball after firing, i.e. 50 ms^{-1}, as calculated in part a). You need to work out the velocity of the cannon (v_c) though.

2) Momentum is conserved so:
$m_cu_c + m_1u_1 = m_cv_c + m_1v_1$
$\Rightarrow 0 + 0 = 0.05v_c + (0.001 \times 50)$
$\Rightarrow v_c = -(0.001 \times 50) \div 0.05 = -1$ ms^{-1}.
(i.e. the cannon moves backwards at 1 ms^{-1}).

3) Gain in K.E. $= \frac{1}{2}m_cv_c^2 + \frac{1}{2}m_1v_1^2$
$= (\frac{1}{2} \times 0.05 \times (-1)^2) + (\frac{1}{2} \times 0.001 \times 50^2)$
$= 1.275 = 1.28$ J to 3 s.f.

An Impulse will cause a Change in K.E.

EXAMPLE A fly of mass 0.002 kg is moving in a straight line at a velocity of 2 ms^{-1} when it is swatted with an impulse of 0.006 Ns in the direction of its motion. How much kinetic energy is gained by the fly following the impulse?

1) Using the impulse formula from p. 180: $I = mv - mu$, so:
$0.006 = 0.002v - 0.002 \times 2 \Rightarrow 0.002v = 0.006 + 0.004 = 0.01$
$\Rightarrow \mathbf{v} = 0.01 \div 0.002 = 5$ ms^{-1}.

2) Increase in K.E. $= \frac{1}{2}mv^2 - \frac{1}{2}mu^2$
$= (\frac{1}{2} \times 0.002 \times 5^2) - (\frac{1}{2} \times 0.002 \times 2^2)$
$= 0.021$ J

The formula's been tweaked to suit the situation — there's only one 'particle', and there will be an increase rather than a loss in K.E.

I'm not lazy — I'm just conserving my kinetic energy...

There are plenty of different situations where you could be asked to find a change in kinetic energy — but they all use pretty much the same formula, and no doubt require you to calculate some speeds. Just think it through logically to decide whether K.E. will go up or down or whatever. Now make yourself a quick bevvy and a light snack — it's practice time...

M2 Section 6 — Practice Questions

Well that's been a crash course in collisions (ho ho). Don't just sit and hope that you've understood it all — come and have a go. Have a practice lap first...

Warm-up Questions

1) An impulse of 2 Ns acts against a ball of mass 300 g moving with a velocity of 5 ms^{-1}. Find the ball's new velocity.

2) A particle of mass 450 g is dropped 2 m onto a floor. It rebounds to two thirds of its original height. Find the impulse given to the particle by the ground.

3) Two particles travelling directly towards each other at the same speed collide. The impact causes one particle to stop, and the other to go in the opposite direction at half its original speed. Find the value of e.

4) A particle of mass 1 kg travelling at 10 ms^{-1} on a horizontal plane has a collision, where $e = 0.4$. Find the particle's rebound speed if it collides head-on with:

   a) a smooth vertical wall,

   b) a particle of mass 2 kg travelling at 12 ms^{-1} towards it.

5) Particles A (mass 1 kg), B (4 kg) and C (5 kg) travel in the same line at speeds of $3u$, $2u$ and u, respectively. If A collides with B first ($e = \frac{1}{4}$), then B with C ($e = \frac{1}{3}$), determine whether A and B will collide again.

6) Find the loss in kinetic energy when a particle of mass 2 kg travelling at 3 ms^{-1} collides with a stationary particle of mass 3 kg on a smooth horizontal plane surface, where $e = 0.3$.

Ready to notch it up a gear? Think you're the Stig of M2?
Well rev her up and let rip — just watch out for those hairpin bends.

Exam Questions

1 A marble of mass 0.02 kg, travelling at 2 ms^{-1}, collides directly with another, stationary, marble of mass 0.06 kg. Both can be modelled as smooth spheres on a smooth horizontal plane.
If the collision is perfectly elastic, find the speed of each marble immediately after the collision.

(4 marks)

2 Particles P (of mass $2m$) and Q (of mass m), travelling in a straight line towards each other at the same speed (u) on a smooth horizontal plane surface, collide with a coefficient of restitution of $\frac{3}{4}$.

a) Show that the collision reverses the direction of both particles, with Q having eight times the rebound speed of P.

(6 marks)

Following the collision, Q goes on to collide with a smooth vertical wall, perpendicular to its path. The coefficient of restitution for the impact with the wall is e_{wall}.
Q goes on to collide with P again on the rebound from the wall.

b) Show that $e_{\text{wall}} > \frac{1}{8}$.

(3 marks)

c) Suppose that $e_{\text{wall}} = \frac{3}{5}$. If after the second collision with P, Q continues to move away from the wall, but with a speed of 0.22 ms^{-1}, find the value of u, the initial speed of both particles, in ms^{-1}.

(7 marks)

M2 Section 6 — Practice Questions

3 A particle of mass $2m$, travelling at a speed of $3u$ on a smooth horizontal plane, collides directly with a particle of mass $3m$ travelling at $2u$ in the same direction. The coefficient of restitution is $\frac{1}{4}$.

a) Find expressions for the speeds of both particles after the collision.
Give your answers in terms of u.

(4 marks)

b) Show that the amount of kinetic energy lost in the collision is $\frac{9mu^2}{16}$. *(4 marks)*

4 Particles A (mass m), B (mass $2m$) and C (mass $4m$) lie on a straight line, as shown:

m $4u$ → (A) (B) $2m$ (C) $4m$, distance d between B and C

B and C are initially stationary when A collides with B at a speed of $4u$ ($u > 0$), causing B to collide with C. The coefficient of restitution between B and C is $2e$, where e is the coefficient of restitution between A and B.

a) Show that the collision between A and B does not reverse the direction of A. *(7 marks)*

By the time B and C collide, A has travelled a distance of $\frac{d}{4}$ since the first collision.

b) Show that $e = \frac{1}{3}$. *(3 marks)*

c) Hence find, in terms of u, the speed of C following its collision with B. *(5 marks)*

5 Two particles, P and Q, of mass 4 kg and 6 kg respectively, are at rest on a smooth plane.
P is given an impulse of 8 Ns towards Q and then strikes Q directly. Given that the coefficient of restitution between P and Q is 0.25, find the speeds of P and Q after the collision.

(8 marks)

6 Two spheres of the same radius, A (mass 3 kg) and B (mass 4 kg), collide directly, and the kinetic energy lost in the collision is 96 J. Immediately following the collision,
A and B move away from each other with speeds 1 ms^{-1} and 2 ms^{-1} respectively.
Find the speed and direction of both A and B before the collision.

(12 marks)

General Certificate of Education
Advanced Subsidiary (AS) and Advanced Level

Mechanics M2 — Practice Exam One

Time Allowed: 1 hour 30 min

Graphical calculators may be used for this exam.

Unless told otherwise, whenever a numerical value of g is required, take $g = 9.8 \text{ ms}^{-2}$.

Unless told otherwise, give any non-exact numerical answers to 3 significant figures.

There are 72 marks available for this paper.

1 A fireman of mass 80 kg slides down a smooth pole. He sets off at rest from the top of the pole, and reaches the bottom of the pole with a speed of 11 ms^{-1}. Find:

a) the fireman's kinetic energy when he reaches the bottom of the pole, *(2 marks)*

b) the height of the pole. *(3 marks)*

2 A particle, P, of mass 2 kg is attached to two light, inextensible strings. The other ends of the strings are attached to fixed points A and B, where A is vertically above B, as shown. P moves in a horizontal circle with uniform speed.

The tension, T, in the string BP is half the tension in the string AP.

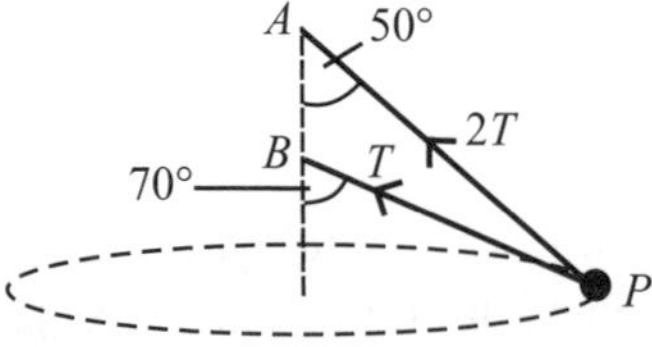

a) The particle completes 100 revolutions per minute.
Find the particle's angular speed in terms of π. *(2 marks)*

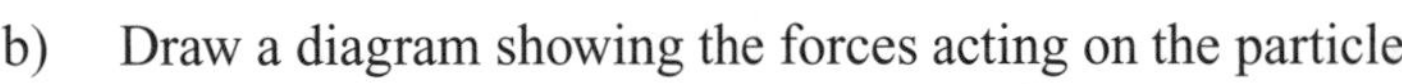

b) Draw a diagram showing the forces acting on the particle. *(1 mark)*

c) Show that $T = 12.0$ N, correct to 3 significant figures. *(3 marks)*

3 A car of mass 1300 kg has a maximum speed of 70 ms^{-1}. It travels in a straight line along a horizontal road with speed $v \text{ ms}^{-1}$, experiencing a total resistive force of magnitude $40v$ N.

a) Find the maximum power of the car's engine. *(3 marks)*

The car now ascends a hill of constant slope α to the horizontal, where $\sin \alpha = 0.4$.
The car travels with constant speed and the resistance to motion remains at $40v$ N.

b) Given that the car's engine is working at a rate of 40 kW,
calculate the driving force of the engine. *(7 marks)*

4 Particle A moves with speed $5u$ ms^{-1} in a straight line on a smooth, horizontal surface. It collides with a stationary particle, B. The collision reverses the direction of A's travel, and reduces its speed to u ms^{-1}. Particle A has a mass of 1 kg. The coefficient of restitution for the collision is $\frac{4}{5}$. Find:

a) the speed of B after the collision, in terms of u, *(3 marks)*

b) the value of M, the mass of particle B, *(3 marks)*

c) the impulse given to B during the collision, in terms of u. *(2 marks)*

Particle B goes on to collide with a smooth vertical wall, perpendicular to its direction of travel. The coefficient of restitution between B and the wall is e.

d) Find the range of values of e that would allow B to collide again with particle A. *(3 marks)*

5

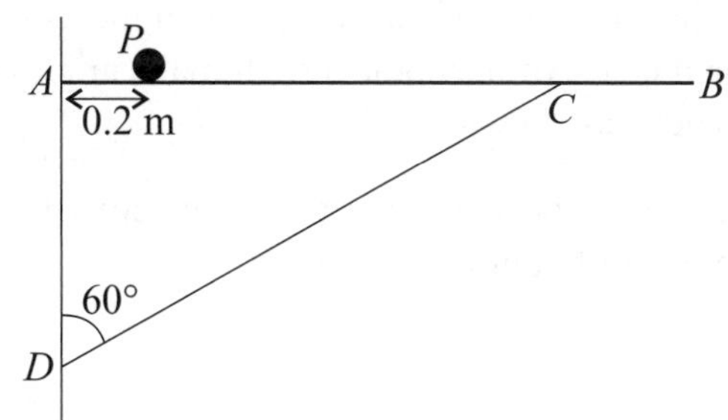

A freely-hinged beam, AB, attached to a vertical wall is held in equilibrium perpendicular to the wall by a strut attached to the beam at C. The strut is fastened to the wall at point D, making an angle of 60° with the wall, as shown. A particle, P, with a mass of 1.8 kg rests upon the beam at a point 0.2 m from A. The weight of the beam acts at point C. The distance from A to the centre of mass of the beam is 1.1 m.

a) Find the magnitude of the vertical component of the reaction at A. *(3 marks)*

Given that the magnitude of the horizontal component of the reaction at A is 35 N, find:

b) the magnitude and direction of the reaction at A, *(3 marks)*

c) the tension in the strut, *(3 marks)*

d) the mass of the beam. *(3 marks)*

6

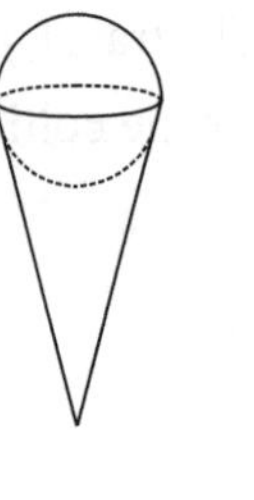

Fig. 1 Fig. 2

An ice cream is modelled as a uniform conical shell of mass 0.02 kg attached to a uniform solid sphere of mass 0.4 kg, as shown in Fig. 1. The conical shell has height 12 cm and the centre of the sphere, A, lies 12 cm directly above the vertex of the conical shell, O, as shown in Fig. 2.

a) Show that the centre of mass of the ice cream is 11.8 cm directly above O, correct to 3 significant figures. *(4 marks)*

A three-dimensional model is made of the ice cream, to be put on display in an ice-cream parlour. The total mass of the model is 2 kg and it has the same dimensions and centre of mass as the ice cream in part a). The model is smoothly pivoted at O and held in equilibrium by a light, inextensible wire attached at point B, where the base edge of the conical shell meets the sphere, as shown in Fig. 3. The slant edges of the conical shell make angles of 25° with the horizontal and vertical, as shown.

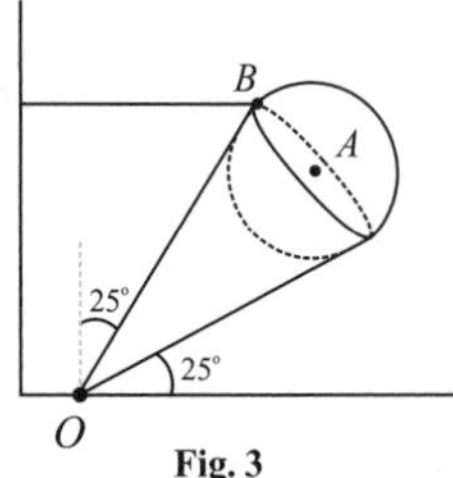

Fig. 3

b) By taking moments about O, show that $T = 14.1$ N, where T is the magnitude of the tension in the wire, correct to 3 significant figures. *(8 marks)*

7

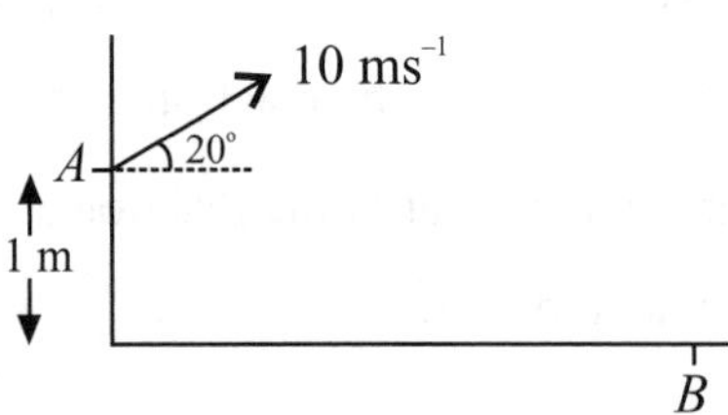

A stone is thrown from A, at a height of 1 m above the ground. The stone's initial velocity is 10 ms^{-1} at an angle of 20° above the horizontal. The stone lands on the horizontal ground at B. Find:

a) the maximum height the stone reaches during its flight, *(3 marks)*

b) the time it takes the stone to travel from A to B. *(4 marks)*

When the stone is at its highest point, a second stone is thrown from A.

c) Given that the second stone lands a horizontal distance of 9 m from A at the same time that the first stone lands at B, find the angle of projection and the initial speed of the second stone. *(9 marks)*

General Certificate of Education
Advanced Subsidiary (AS) and Advanced Level

Mechanics M2 — Practice Exam Two

Time Allowed: 1 hour 30 min

Graphical calculators may be used for this exam.

Unless told otherwise, whenever a numerical value of g is required, take g = 9.8 ms^{-2}.

Unless told otherwise, give any non-exact numerical answers to 3 significant figures.

There are 72 marks available for this paper.

1 A ball is dropped from a height of 5 m above smooth, horizontal ground. It hits the ground and rebounds vertically upwards. The coefficient of restitution between the ball and the ground is 0.7. Ignoring air resistance, calculate the speed of the ball immediately following its impact with the ground.

(4 marks)

2

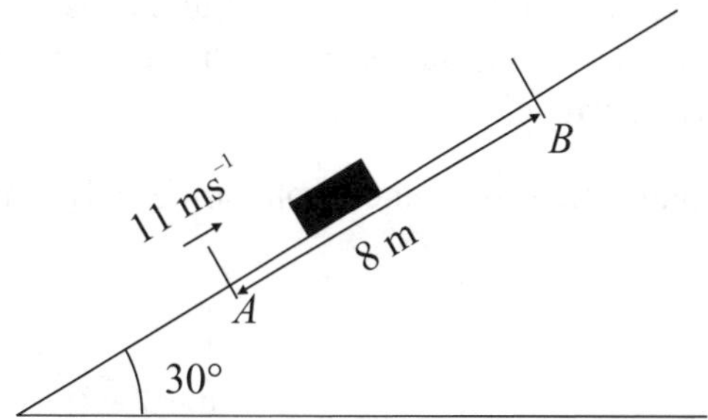

A particle of mass 9 kg is projected from a point A up a rough plane inclined at an angle of 30° to the horizontal. The speed of projection of the particle is 11 ms^{-1}. The particle travels 8 m up the line of greatest slope of the plane, before coming to instantaneous rest at point B.

Calculate the work done by friction in bringing the particle to rest.

(6 marks)

3 A bus of mass 13 000 kg is travelling along a straight, horizontal road at a constant speed of 14 ms^{-1}. The bus experiences a constant resistance to motion from non-gravitational forces which is modelled as a single force of magnitude 4500 N.

a) Find the rate at which the engine of the bus is working. Give your answer in kW.

(3 marks)

The bus now moves up a hill inclined at an angle, α, to the horizontal, where $\sin\alpha = \frac{1}{35}$. The engine in the bus now works at a rate of 72 kW.

b) Assuming that the non-gravitational resistance to motion remains constant at 4500 N, find the acceleration of the bus when the speed of the bus is 12 ms^{-1}.

(4 marks)

4 A piece of jewellery is made by combining a thin rectangle of metal $PQRS$ and a circle of the same material, as shown:

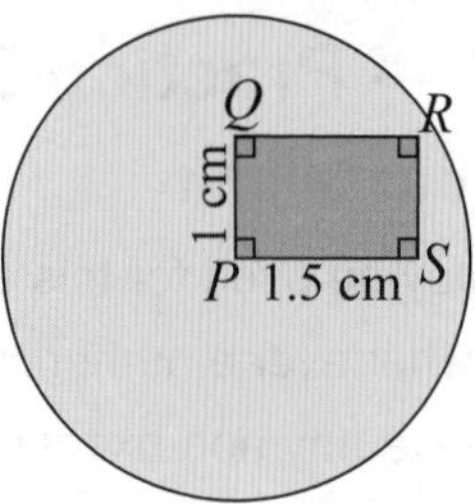

P is attached to the centre of the circle, which has radius 2 cm. The shapes can be modelled as uniform laminas.

a) Show that the centre of mass of the shape is 0.0961 cm from P. *(5 marks)*

The shape hangs in equilibrium from a pin at point Q, about which it is able to freely rotate. The pin can be modelled as a smooth peg.

b) Find the angle that PQ makes with the vertical. Give your answer in degrees. *(3 marks)*

5 A uniform beam, AB, rests with A on rough horizontal ground and B against a smooth vertical wall to make a ramp. The beam has length 3 m and mass 8 kg, and makes an angle of θ with the horizontal, where $\tan\theta = 0.45$. A woman of mass 60 kg stands at C, a distance of l m from B, as shown. The woman may be modelled as a particle.

The beam is on the point of slipping, and is prevented from doing so by a frictional force of magnitude 199 N.

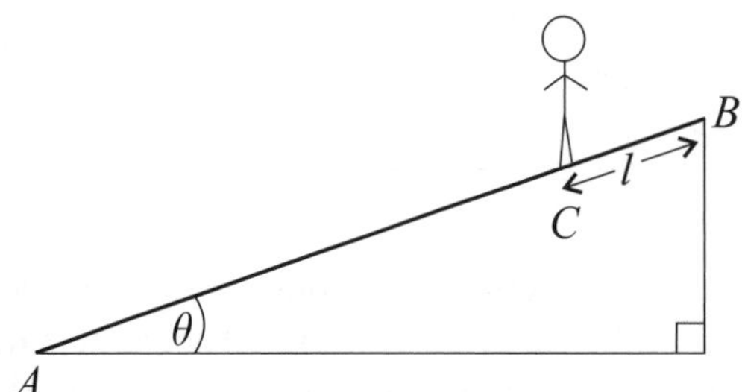

a) Show that μ, the coefficient of friction between the ground and the beam, is 0.3 to 1 significant figure. *(3 marks)*

b) Find l. *(5 marks)*

6 Three stationary particles, P, Q and R, lie in a line on a smooth horizontal surface. The particles have masses of 0.2 kg, 0.6 kg and 0.7 kg respectively. Particle P is projected towards Q at a speed of 5 ms^{-1}, and collides directly with the particle, with a coefficient of restitution of 0.65. Find:

a) the velocities of P and Q immediately after their collision, *(4 marks)*

b) the total kinetic energy lost in the collision. *(2 marks)*

Particle Q then collides directly with R. Q is brought to rest by the collision.

c) Find the size of the coefficient of restitution between Q and R. *(4 marks)*

7 A particle, A, is attached to one end of a light, inextensible string. The string passes through a smooth, fixed ring, O, and a second particle, B, is attached to the other end of the string. Particle A has mass 6 kg and hangs at rest vertically below the ring. Particle B moves in a horizontal circle with speed v ms^{-1}.

The angle between OB and OA is 30°.

a) Show that the mass of particle B is 5.20 kg, correct to three significant figures. *(3 marks)*

b) Given that the radius of the horizontal circle is 0.3 m, find v. *(3 marks)*

The string is now passed through a small, smooth hole in the vertex of a conical shell. Particle A hangs in equilibrium vertically below the hole and particle B moves in a horizontal circle of radius r m on the inside of the conical shell with angular speed 3π rad s^{-1}. The angle of the vertex of the conical shell is 60°, as shown.

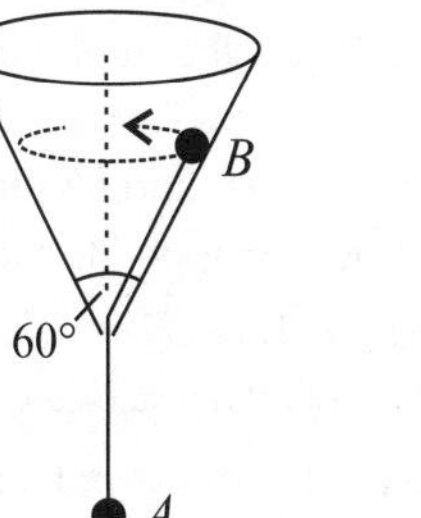

c) Find r. *(7 marks)*

8 A particle is projected from a height of 0.5 m vertically above a point O on horizontal ground with initial velocity U at an angle α° above the horizontal. The particle lands on horizontal ground at point P, as shown.

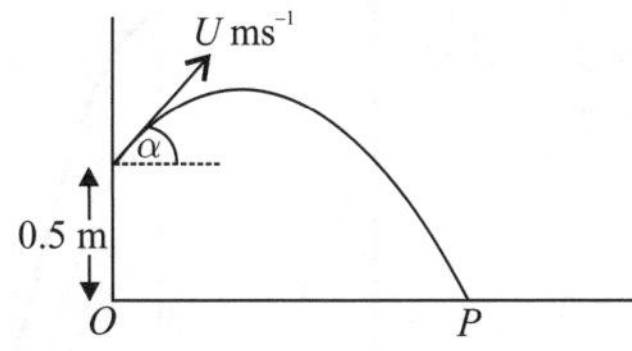

a) Show that the particle reaches maximum height $h = \dfrac{g + U^2\sin^2\alpha}{2g}$ m above the ground, where g is the acceleration due to gravity. *(4 marks)*

b) Show that V, the speed of the particle when it lands at P, is $V = \sqrt{U^2 + g}$ ms^{-1}. *(5 marks)*

The horizontal and vertical displacements of the particle from O at time t seconds are x m and y m respectively.

c) Given that $\alpha = 45°$, express x and y in terms of t and hence show that the Cartesian equation of the path of the particle is

$$y = \frac{1}{2} + x - \frac{gx^2}{U^2},$$

(4 marks)

You are also given that the horizontal range of the particle is 0.5 m.

d) Using your answer to part c), or otherwise, find U, the initial velocity of the particle. *(3 marks)*

Answers

C3 Section 1 — Algebra and Functions
Warm-up Questions

1) a) Range $f(x) \geq -16$. This is a function, and it's one-to-one (the domain is restricted so every x-value is mapped to only one value of $f(x)$).

b) To find the range of this function, you need to find the minimum point of $x^2 - 7x + 10$ — do this by completing the square: $x^2 - 7x + 10 = (x - 3.5)^2 - 12.25 + 10$
$= (x - 3.5)^2 - 2.25$.
As $(x - 3.5)^2 \geq 0$ the minimum value of $x^2 - 7x + 10$ is -2.25, so the range is $f(x) \geq -2.25$.
This is a function, and it's many-to-one (as more than one x-value is mapped to the same value of $f(x)$).

You could also have found the minimum point by differentiating, setting the derivative equal to 0 and solving for x.

c) Range $f(x) \geq 0$. This is not a function as $f(x)$ doesn't exist for $x < 0$.

d) Sketch the graph for this one:

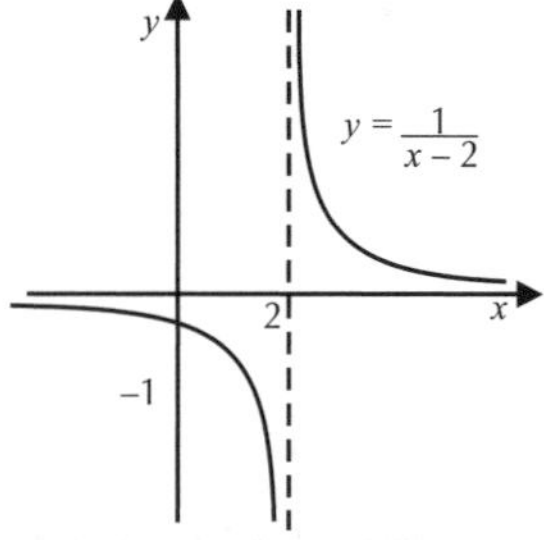

From the graph, the range is $f(x) \in \mathbb{R}$, $f(x) \neq 0$.
This is not a function as it's not defined for $x = 2$.

If you're not sure about any of the domains or ranges for the other parts, draw the graphs and see if that helps you figure it out.

2) a) $fg(2) = f(2(2) + 3) = f(7) = 3/7$.
$gf(1) = g(3/1) = g(3) = 2(3) + 3 = 9$.
$fg(x) = f(2x + 3) = \dfrac{3}{2x+3}$.

b) $fg(2) = f(2 + 4) = f(6) = 3(6^2) = 3 \times 36 = 108$.
$gf(1) = g(3(1^2)) = g(3) = 3 + 4 = 7$.
$fg(x) = f(x + 4) = 3(x + 4)^2$.

3) f is a one-to-one function so it has an inverse. The domain of the inverse is the range of the function and vice versa, so the domain of $f^{-1}(x)$ is $x \geq 3$ and the range is $f^{-1}(x) \in \mathbb{R}$.

4) Let $y = f(x)$. Then $y = \sqrt{2x - 4}$

$$y^2 = 2x - 4$$
$$y^2 + 4 = 2x$$
$$x = \frac{y^2 + 4}{2} = \frac{y^2}{2} + 2$$

Writing in terms of x and $f^{-1}(x)$ gives the inverse function as $f^{-1}(x) = \frac{x^2}{2} + 2$, which has domain $x \geq 0$ (as the range of $f(x) \geq 0$) and range $f^{-1}(x) \geq 2$.

5) a) b)

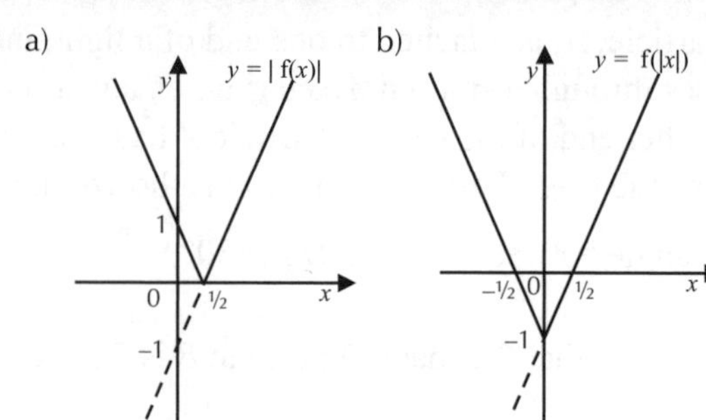

6)

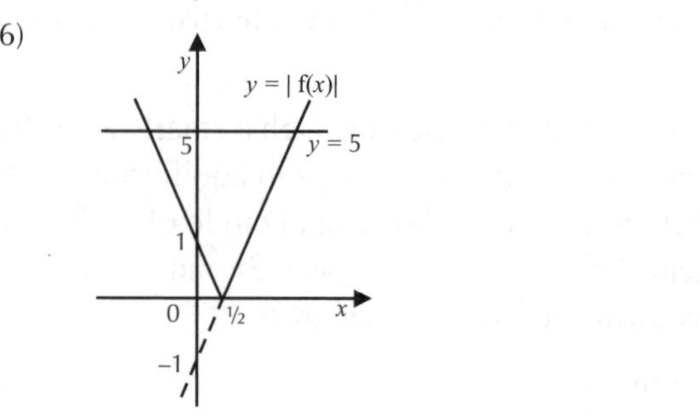

From the graph, $|2x - 1| = 5$ has 2 solutions, one where $2x - 1 = 5$ (so $x = 3$) and one where $-(2x - 1) = 5$ (so $x = -2$).

7) First, square both sides: $(2x + 1)^2 = (x + 4)^2$

$$4x^2 + 4x + 1 = x^2 + 8x + 16$$
$$3x^2 - 4x - 15 = 0$$
$$(3x + 5)(x - 3) = 0.$$

So $x = -\frac{5}{3}$ or $x = 3$.

You could have solved this one by sketching the graphs instead, then solving the equations $2x + 1 = x + 4$ and $-(2x + 1) = x + 4$.

8)

Exam Questions

1 a)

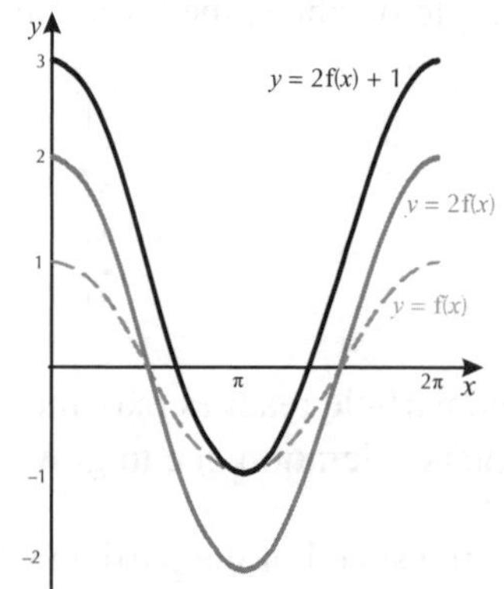

[3 marks available — 1 mark for $y = |2x|$ (touching axes at (0, 0)), 2 marks for $y = |x - 1|$ (1 mark for reflection in x-axis for $x < 1$, 1 mark for crossing y-axis at $y = 1$)]

Answers

b) First square both sides: $(2x)^2 = (x-1)^2$

$$4x^2 = x^2 - 2x + 1 \quad \textbf{[1 mark]}$$
$$3x^2 + 2x - 1 = 0 \quad \textbf{[1 mark]}$$
$$(3x-1)(x+1) = 0$$

So $x = \frac{1}{3}$ or $x = -1$ ***[1 mark]***.

You could also have solved the equations $-(2x) = -(x-1)$ and $2x = -(x-1)$ — you'd have got the same solutions.

c) $|2x| \le |x-1|$ when $y = |2x|$ is equal to or underneath $y = |x-1|$ ***[1 mark]***. From the graph, this occurs between the solutions in b), i.e. $-1 \le x \le \frac{1}{3}$ ***[1 mark]***.

2 To transform the curve $y = x^3$ into $y = (x-1)^3$, move it 1 unit ***[1 mark]*** horizontally to the right ***[1 mark]***. To transform this into the curve $y = 2(x-1)^3$, stretch it vertically ***[1 mark]*** by a scale factor of 2 ***[1 mark]***. Finally, to transform into the curve $y = 2(x-1)^3 + 4$, the whole curve is moved 4 units ***[1 mark]*** upwards ***[1 mark]***.

3 a) $gf(x) = g(x^2 - 3)$ ***[1 mark]*** $= \frac{1}{x^2 - 3}$ ***[1 mark]***

b) $\frac{1}{x^2-3} = \frac{1}{6} \Rightarrow x^2 - 3 = 6 \Rightarrow x^2 = 9 \Rightarrow x = 3, x = -3$

[3 marks available — 1 mark for rearranging to solve equation, 1 mark for each correct solution]

4 a) $fg(6) = f(\sqrt{(3 \times 6) - 2}) = f(\sqrt{16})$ ***[1 mark]***

$= f(4) = 2^4 = 16$ ***[1 mark]***

b) $gf(2) = g(2^2) = g(4)$ ***[1 mark]***

$= \sqrt{(3 \times 4) - 2} = \sqrt{10}$ ***[1 mark]***

c) (i) First, write $y = g(x)$ and rearrange to make x the subject:

$$y = \sqrt{3x - 2}$$
$$\Rightarrow y^2 = 3x - 2$$
$$\Rightarrow y^2 + 2 = 3x$$
$$\Rightarrow \frac{y^2 + 2}{3} = x \quad \textbf{[1 mark]}$$

Then replace x with $g^{-1}(x)$ and y with x: $g^{-1}(x) = \frac{x^2 + 2}{3}$ ***[1 mark]***.

(ii) $fg^{-1}(x) = f\left(\frac{x^2+2}{3}\right)$ ***[1 mark]***

$= 2^{\frac{x^2+2}{3}}$ ***[1 mark]***

5 a) The range of f is $f(x) > 0$ ***[1 mark]***.

b) (i) Let $y = f(x)$. Then $y = \frac{1}{x+5}$.

Rearrange this to make x the subject:

$$y(x+5) = 1$$
$$\Rightarrow x + 5 = \frac{1}{y} \quad \textbf{[1 mark]}$$
$$\Rightarrow x = \frac{1}{y} - 5 \quad \textbf{[1 mark]}$$

Finally, write out in terms of x and $f^{-1}(x)$:

$f^{-1}(x) = \frac{1}{x} - 5$ ***[1 mark]***.

(ii) The domain of the inverse is the same as the range of the function, so $x > 0$ ***[1 mark]***. The range of the inverse is the same as the domain of the function, so $f^{-1}(x) > -5$ ***[1 mark]***.

c)

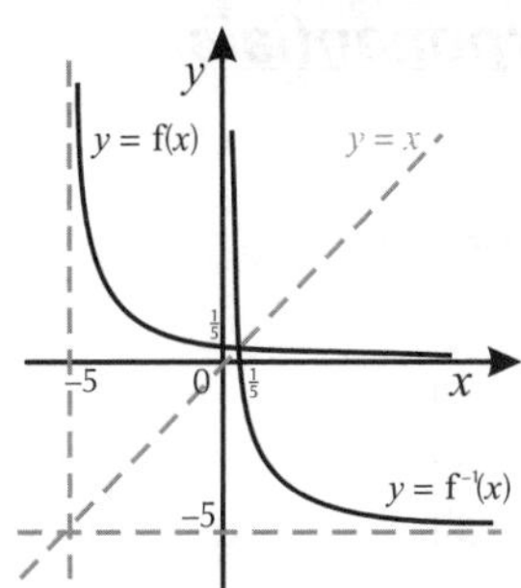

[2 marks available — 1 mark for each correct curve, each with correct intersections and asymptotes as shown]

6 a)

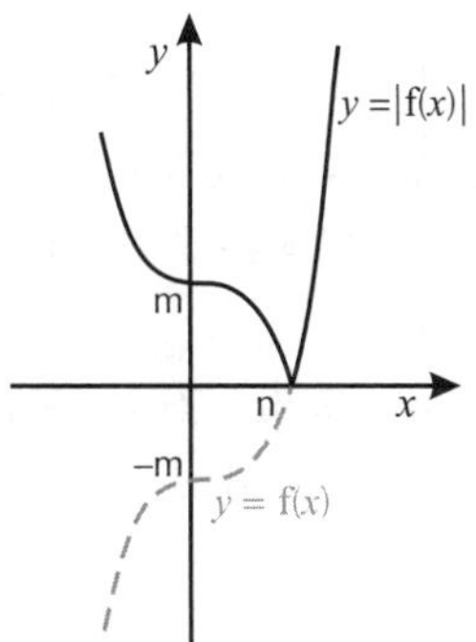

[2 marks available — 1 mark for reflecting in x-axis at x = n, 1 mark for crossing y-axis at y = m]

b)

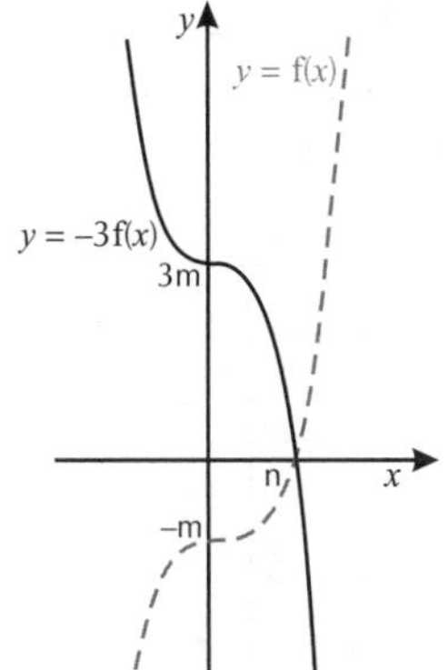

[2 marks available — 1 mark for reflecting in x-axis and 1 mark for crossing y-axis at y = 3m (due to stretch by scale factor 3)]

c)

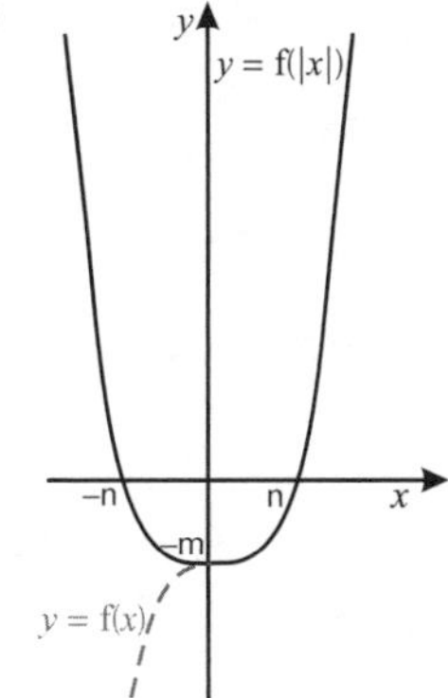

[2 marks available — 1 mark for reflecting in y-axis and 1 mark for crossing the x-axis at −n]

Answers

C3 Section 2 — Exponentials and Logarithms

Warm-up Questions

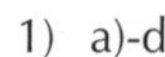

1) a)-d)

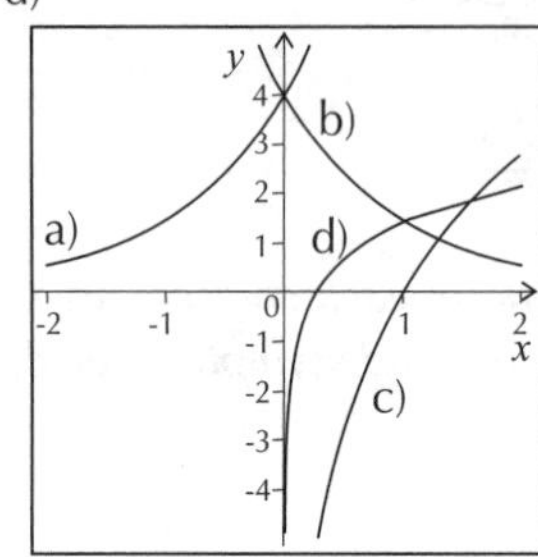

2) a) $e^{2x} = 6 \Rightarrow 2x = \ln 6 \Rightarrow x = \ln 6 \div 2 = 0.8959$ to 4 d.p.

   b) $\ln (x + 3) = 0.75 \Rightarrow x + 3 = e^{0.75} \Rightarrow x = e^{0.75} - 3$
   $= -0.8830$ to 4 d.p.

   c) $3e^{-4x+1} = 5 \Rightarrow e^{-4x+1} = \frac{5}{3} \Rightarrow e^{4x-1} = \frac{3}{5} \Rightarrow 4x - 1 = \ln \frac{3}{5}$
   $\Rightarrow x = (\ln \frac{3}{5} + 1) \div 4 = 0.1223$ to 4 d.p.

   d) $\ln x + \ln 5 = \ln 4 \Rightarrow \ln (5x) = \ln 4 \Rightarrow 5x = 4$
   $\Rightarrow x = 0.8000$ to 4 d.p.

3) a) $\ln (2x - 7) + \ln 4 = -3 \Rightarrow \ln (4(2x - 7)) = -3$
   $\Rightarrow 8x - 28 = e^{-3} \Rightarrow x = \frac{e^{-3} + 28}{8}$ or $\frac{1}{8e^3} + \frac{7}{2}$.

   b) $2e^{2x} + e^x = 3$, so if $y = e^x$, $2y^2 + y - 3 = 0$,
   which will factorise to: $(2y + 3)(y - 1) = 0$,
   so $e^x = -1.5$ (not possible), and $e^x = 1$,
   so $x = 0$ is the only solution.

4) a) $y = 2 - e^{x+1}$

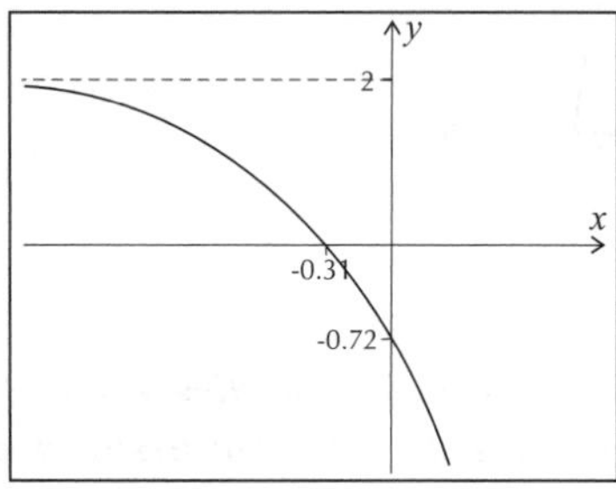

   Goes through (0, −0.72) and (−0.31, 0), with asymptote at $y = 2$.

   b) $y = 5e^{0.5x} + 5$

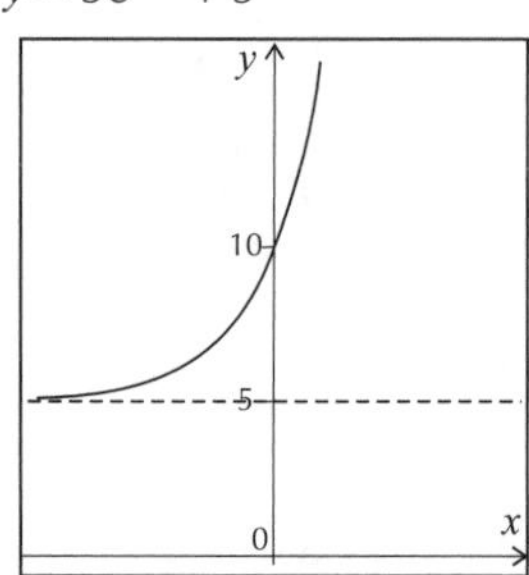

   Goes through (0, 10), with asymptote at $y = 5$.

   c) $y = \ln (2x) + 1$

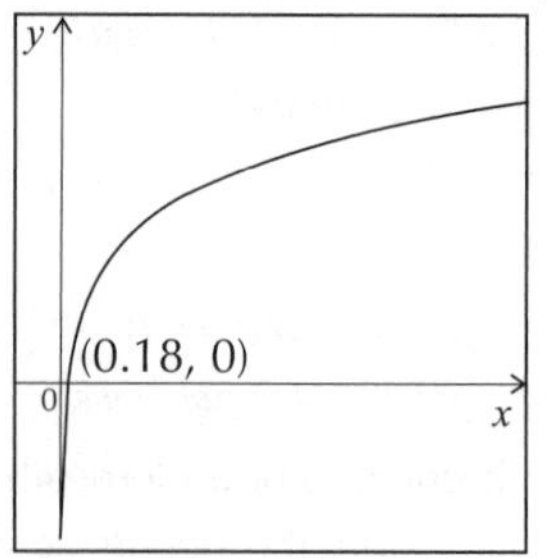

   Goes through (0.18, 0), with asymptote at $x = 0$.

   d) $y = \ln (x + 5)$

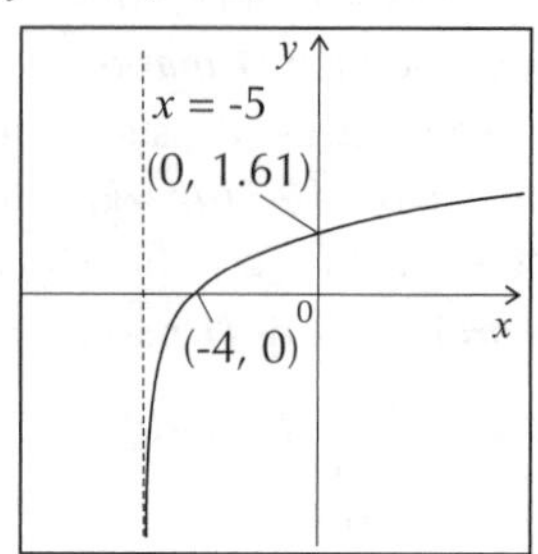

   Goes through (0, 1.61) and (−4, 0), with asymptote at $x = -5$.

   You can use your 'graph transformation' skills to work out what they'll look like, e.g. d) is just y = ln x shifted 5 to the left.

5) a) $V = 7500k^{-0.2t}$, so when $t = 0$, $V = 7500 \times k^0 = £7500$.

   b) $3000 = 7500k^{-0.2\times5} \Rightarrow 0.4 = k^{-1} \Rightarrow k = 2.5$.

   c) $V = 7500 \times 2.5^{(-0.2 \times 10)} = £1200$.

   d) When $V = 500$, $500 = 7500(2.5)^{-0.2t}$
   $\Rightarrow 2.5^{-0.2t} = \frac{500}{7500} \Rightarrow 2.5^{0.2t} = \frac{7500}{500} = 15$
   $\Rightarrow 0.2t\ln 2.5 = \ln 15$
   $\Rightarrow t = 2.9554... \div 0.2 = 14.777...$ years.
   So it will be 14.8 years old before the value falls below £500.

Exam Questions

1 a) $6e^x = 3 \Rightarrow e^x = 0.5$ ***[1 mark]*** $\Rightarrow x = \ln 0.5$ ***[1 mark]***.

  b) $e^{2x} - 8e^x + 7 = 0$.
  This looks like a quadratic, so use $y = e^x$.
  If $y = e^x$, then $y^2 - 8y + 7 = 0$. This will factorise to give:
  $(y - 7)(y - 1) = 0 \Rightarrow y = 7$ and $y = 1$.
  So $e^x = 7 \Rightarrow x = \ln 7$, and $e^x = 1 \Rightarrow x = \ln 1 = 0$.
  [4 marks available — 1 mark for factorisation of a quadratic, 1 mark for both solutions for e^x, and 1 mark for each correct solution for x.]

  c) $4 \ln x = 3 \Rightarrow \ln x = 0.75$ ***[1 mark]*** $\Rightarrow x = e^{0.75}$ ***[1 mark]***.

  d) $\ln x + \frac{24}{\ln x} = 10$
  You need to get rid of that fraction, so multiply through by $\ln x$.
  $(\ln x)^2 + 24 = 10 \ln x$
  $\Rightarrow (\ln x)^2 - 10 \ln x + 24 = 0$
  which looks like a quadratic, so use $y = \ln x$.

Answers

$y^2 - 10y + 24 = 0 \Rightarrow (y - 6)(y - 4) = 0$
$\Rightarrow y = 6$ or $y = 4$.
So $\ln x = 6 \Rightarrow x = e^6$, or $\ln x = 4 \Rightarrow x = e^4$.

[4 marks available — 1 mark for factorisation of a quadratic, 1 mark for both solutions for ln x, and 1 mark for each correct solution for x.]

2 $y = e^{ax} + b$

The sketch shows that when $x = 0$, $y = -6$, so:
$-6 = e^0 + b$ ***[1 mark]***
$-6 = 1 + b \Rightarrow b = -7$ ***[1 mark]***.

The sketch also shows that when $y = 0$, $x = \frac{1}{4}\ln 7$, so:
$0 = e^{(\frac{a}{4}\ln 7)} - 7$ ***[1 mark]***
$\Rightarrow e^{(\frac{a}{4}\ln 7)} = 7$
$\Rightarrow \frac{a}{4}\ln 7 = \ln 7 \Rightarrow \frac{a}{4} = 1 \Rightarrow a = 4$ ***[1 mark]***.
The asymptote occurs as $x \to -\infty$, so $e^{4x} \to 0$, and since $y = e^{4x} - 7$, $y \to -7$.
So the equation of the asymptote is $y = -7$ ***[1 mark]***.

3 a) When $t = 0$ (i.e. when the mink were introduced to the habitat) $M = 74 \times e^0 = 74$, so there were 74 mink originally ***[1 mark]***.

b) After 3 years, $M = 74 \times e^{0.6 \times 3}$ ***[1 mark]*** = 447 mink ***[1 mark]***.

You can't round up here as there are only 447 whole mink.

c) For $M = 10\,000$:
$10\,000 = 74e^{0.6t}$
$\Rightarrow e^{0.6t} = 10\,000 \div 74 = 135.1351$
$\Rightarrow 0.6t = \ln 135.1351 = 4.9063$ ***[1 mark]***
$\Rightarrow t = 4.9063 \div 0.6 = 8.2$ years to reach 10 000, so it would take 9 complete years for the population to exceed 10 000 ***[1 mark]***.

d)

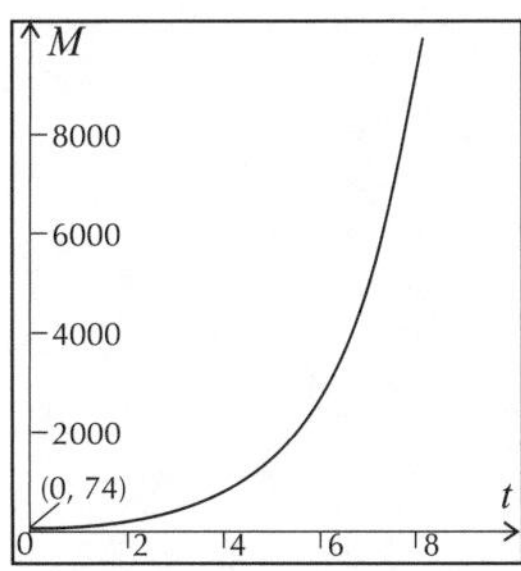

[2 marks available — 1 mark for correct shape of graph, 1 mark for (0, 74) as a point on the graph.]

4 a) $y = \ln(4x - 3)$, and $x = a$ when $y = 1$.
$1 = \ln(4a - 3) \Rightarrow e^1 = 4a - 3$ ***[1 mark]***
$\Rightarrow a = (e^1 + 3) \div 4 = 1.43$ to 2 d.p. ***[1 mark]***.

b) The curve can only exist when $4x - 3 > 0$ ***[1 mark]*** so $x > 3 \div 4$, $x > 0.75$. If $x > b$, then $b = 0.75$ ***[1 mark]***.

c)

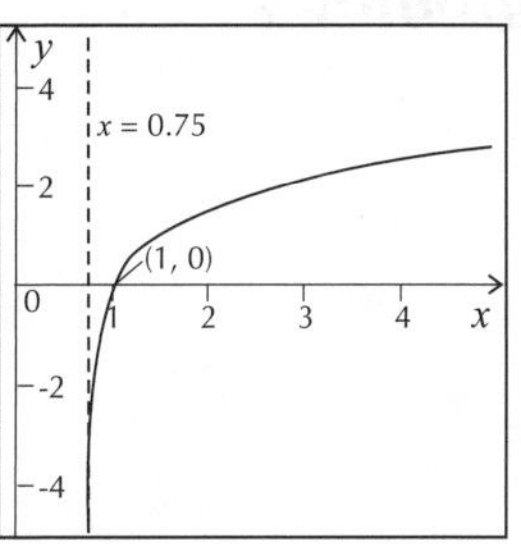

When $y = 0$, $4x - 3 = e^0 = 1$, so $x = 1$.
As $x \to \infty$, $y \to \infty$ gradually.
From (b), there will be an asymptote at $x = 0.75$.

[2 marks available — 1 mark for correct shape including asymptote at x = 0.75, 1 mark for (1, 0) as a point on the graph.]

5 a) $2e^x + 18e^{-x} = 20$
Multiply through by e^x to remove the e^{-x}, since $e^x \times e^{-x} = 1$.
$2e^{2x} + 18 = 20e^x$
$\Rightarrow 2e^{2x} - 20e^x + 18 = 0 \Rightarrow e^{2x} - 10e^x + 9 = 0$
This now looks like a quadratic equation, so use $y = e^x$ to simplify.
$y^2 - 10y + 9 = 0$
$\Rightarrow (y - 1)(y - 9) = 0 \Rightarrow y = 1$ or $y = 9$.
So $e^x = 1 \Rightarrow x = 0$
or $e^x = 9 \Rightarrow x = \ln 9$.

[4 marks available — 1 mark for factorisation of a quadratic, 1 mark for both solutions for eˣ, and 1 mark for each correct exact solution for x.]

b) $2\ln x - \ln 3 = \ln 12$
$\Rightarrow 2\ln x = \ln 12 + \ln 3$
Use the log laws to simplify at this point:
$\Rightarrow \ln x^2 = \ln 36$ ***[1 mark]***
$\Rightarrow x^2 = 36$ ***[1 mark]***
$\Rightarrow x = 6$ ***[1 mark]***

x must be positive as ln (–6) does not exist.

6 a) B is the value of A when $t = 0$.
From the table, $B = 50$ ***[1 mark]***.

b) Substitute $t = 5$ and $A = 42$ into $A = 50e^{-kt}$:
$42 = 50e^{-5k} \Rightarrow e^{-5k} = \frac{42}{50} \Rightarrow e^{5k} = \frac{50}{42}$ ***[1 mark]***
$\Rightarrow 5k = \ln(\frac{50}{42}) = 0.17435$
$\Rightarrow k = 0.17435 \div 5 = 0.0349$ to 3 s.f. ***[1 mark]***.

c) $A = 50e^{-0.0349t}$ (using values from (a) and (b)), so when $t = 10$, $A = 50 \times e^{-0.0349 \times 10}$ ***[1 mark]***
= 35 to the nearest whole ***[1 mark]***.

d) The half-life will be the value of t when A reaches half of the original value of 50, i.e. when $A = 25$.
$25 = 50e^{-0.0349t}$
$\Rightarrow \frac{25}{50} = e^{-0.0349t} \Rightarrow \frac{50}{25} = e^{0.0349t} \Rightarrow e^{0.0349t} = 2$ ***[1 mark]***.
$0.0349t = \ln 2$ ***[1 mark]***
$\Rightarrow t = \ln 2 \div 0.0349 = 20$ days to the nearest day ***[1 mark]***.

Answers

C3 Section 3 — Trigonometry

Warm-up Questions

1) a) $\sin^{-1}\frac{1}{\sqrt{2}} = \frac{\pi}{4}$

b) $\cos^{-1}0 = \frac{\pi}{2}$

c) $\tan^{-1}\sqrt{3} = \frac{\pi}{3}$

2) See p15.

3) a) cosec 30° = 2 (since sin 30° = 0.5)

b) sec 30° = $\frac{2}{\sqrt{3}}$ (since cos 30° = $\frac{\sqrt{3}}{2}$)

c) cot 30° = $\sqrt{3}$ (since tan 30° = $\frac{1}{\sqrt{3}}$)

4) See p16.

5) Divide the whole identity by $\cos^2\theta$ to get:

$\frac{\cos^2\theta}{\cos^2\theta} + \frac{\sin^2\theta}{\cos^2\theta} \equiv \frac{1}{\cos^2\theta}$

$\Rightarrow 1 + \tan^2\theta \equiv \sec^2\theta$

(as sin/cos ≡ tan and 1/cos ≡ sec)

6) Using the identities $\text{cosec}^2\theta \equiv 1 + \cot^2\theta$ and $\sin^2\theta + \cos^2\theta \equiv 1$, the LHS becomes:

$(\text{cosec}^2\theta - 1) + (1 - \cos^2\theta) \equiv \text{cosec}^2\theta - \cos^2\theta$,

which is the same as the RHS.

7) $\cos 2\theta \equiv \cos^2\theta - \sin^2\theta$

$\cos 2\theta \equiv 2\cos^2\theta - 1$

$\cos 2\theta \equiv 1 - 2\sin^2\theta$

8) $\sin 2\theta = -\sqrt{3}\sin\theta \Rightarrow \sin 2\theta + \sqrt{3}\sin\theta = 0$

$2\sin\theta\cos\theta + \sqrt{3}\sin\theta = 0$

$\sin\theta(2\cos\theta + \sqrt{3}) = 0$

So either $\sin\theta = 0$, so θ = 0°, 180°, 360° or

$2\cos\theta + \sqrt{3} = 0 \Rightarrow \cos\theta = -\frac{\sqrt{3}}{2}$

so θ = 150° or 210°. The set of values for θ is 0°, 150°, 180°, 210°, 360°.

If you don't know where the 180°, 360°, 210° etc. came from, you need to go back over your C2 notes...

9) $\frac{\pi}{12} = \frac{\pi}{3} - \frac{\pi}{4}$, so use the addition formula for cos(A – B):

$\cos\frac{\pi}{12} = \cos\left(\frac{\pi}{3} - \frac{\pi}{4}\right) = \cos\frac{\pi}{3}\cos\frac{\pi}{4} + \sin\frac{\pi}{3}\sin\frac{\pi}{4}$

As $\cos\frac{\pi}{3} = \frac{1}{2}$, $\cos\frac{\pi}{4} = \frac{1}{\sqrt{2}}$, $\sin\frac{\pi}{3} = \frac{\sqrt{3}}{2}$ and $\sin\frac{\pi}{4} = \frac{1}{\sqrt{2}}$, putting these values into the equation gives:

$\cos\frac{\pi}{3}\cos\frac{\pi}{4} + \sin\frac{\pi}{3}\sin\frac{\pi}{4} = \left(\frac{1}{2}\cdot\frac{1}{\sqrt{2}}\right) + \left(\frac{\sqrt{3}}{2}\cdot\frac{1}{\sqrt{2}}\right)$

$= \frac{1}{2\sqrt{2}} + \frac{\sqrt{3}}{2\sqrt{2}} = \frac{1+\sqrt{3}}{2\sqrt{2}} = \frac{\sqrt{2}(1+\sqrt{3})}{4} = \frac{\sqrt{2}+\sqrt{6}}{4}$

You could also have used $\frac{\pi}{12} = \frac{\pi}{4} - \frac{\pi}{6}$ in your answer.

10) sin(A + B) = sin A cos B + cos A sin B.

As $\sin A = \frac{4}{5}$, $\cos A = \frac{3}{5}$ (from the right-angled triangle with sides of length 3, 4 and 5) and as $\sin B = \frac{7}{25}$, $\cos B = \frac{24}{25}$ (from the right-angled triangle with sides of length 7, 24 and 25). Putting these values into the equation gives:

$\sin A\cos B + \cos A\sin B = \left(\frac{4}{5}\cdot\frac{24}{25}\right) + \left(\frac{3}{5}\cdot\frac{7}{25}\right)$

$= \frac{96}{125} + \frac{21}{125} = \frac{117}{125}$ (= 0.936)

11) $a\cos\theta + b\sin\theta = R\cos(\theta - \alpha)$ or

$b\sin\theta + a\cos\theta = R\sin(\theta + \alpha)$

12) $5\sin\theta - 6\cos\theta = R\sin(\theta - \alpha)$

$= R\sin\theta\cos\alpha - R\cos\theta\sin\alpha$ (using the addition rule for sin).

Equating coefficients of $\sin\theta$ and $\cos\theta$ gives:

1. $R\cos\alpha = 5$ and 2. $R\sin\alpha = 6$.

Dividing 2. by 1. to find α: $\frac{R\sin\alpha}{R\cos\alpha} = \tan\alpha$, so $\frac{6}{5} = \tan\alpha$

Solving this gives α = 50.19°.

To find R, square equations 1. and 2., then square root:

$R = \sqrt{5^2 + 6^2} = \sqrt{25 + 36} = \sqrt{61}$, so

$5\sin\theta - 6\cos\theta = \sqrt{61}\sin(\theta - 50.19°)$.

13) Use the sin addition formulas:

$\sin(x + y) \equiv \sin x\cos y + \cos x\sin y$

$\sin(x - y) \equiv \sin x\cos y - \cos x\sin y$

Take the second away from the first:

$\sin(x + y) - \sin(x - y) \equiv 2\cos x\sin y$.

Let $A = x + y$ and $B = x - y$, so that $x = ½(A + B)$ and $y = ½(A - B)$. Then

$\sin A - \sin B = 2\cos\left(\frac{A+B}{2}\right)\sin\left(\frac{A-B}{2}\right)$.

Hint: to get the formulas for x and y in terms of A and B, you need to treat A = x + y and B = x − y as a pair of simultaneous equations.

14) Start by putting the LHS over a common denominator:

$\frac{\cos\theta}{\sin\theta} + \frac{\sin\theta}{\cos\theta} \equiv \frac{\cos\theta\cos\theta}{\sin\theta\cos\theta} + \frac{\sin\theta\sin\theta}{\sin\theta\cos\theta}$

$\equiv \frac{\cos^2\theta + \sin^2\theta}{\sin\theta\cos\theta} \equiv \frac{1}{\sin\theta\cos\theta}$

(using the identity $\sin^2\theta + \cos^2\theta \equiv 1$).

Now, $\sin 2\theta \equiv 2\sin\theta\cos\theta$, so $\sin\theta\cos\theta = ½\sin 2\theta$.

So $\frac{1}{\sin\theta\cos\theta} \equiv \frac{1}{½\sin 2\theta} \equiv 2\,\text{cosec}\,2\theta$, which is the same as the RHS.

Exam Questions

1 a)

[3 marks available — 1 mark for n-shaped curve in third quadrant and u-shaped curve in first quadrant, 1 mark for asymptotes at 0 and ±π and 1 mark for max/min points of the curves at −1 and 1]

b) If $\text{cosec}\,x = \frac{5}{4} \Rightarrow \frac{1}{\sin x} = \frac{5}{4} \Rightarrow \sin x = \frac{4}{5}$ ***[1 mark].***

Solving this for x gives x = 0.927, 2.21

[1 mark for each solution, lose a mark if answers aren't given to 3 s.f.].

Answers

The second solution can be found by sketching y = sin x:

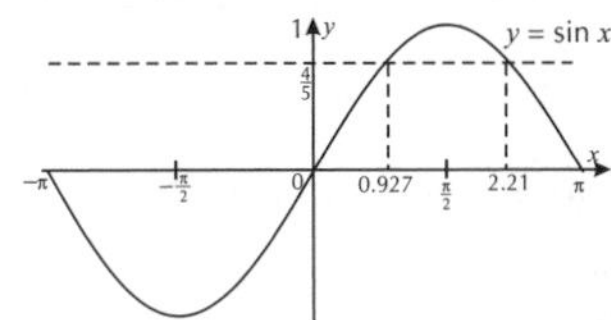

You can see that there are two solutions, one at 0.927, and the other at π – 0.927 = 2.21.

c) $\operatorname{cosec} x = 3\sec x \Rightarrow \frac{1}{\sin x} = \frac{3}{\cos x} \Rightarrow \frac{\cos x}{\sin x} = 3$

$\Rightarrow \frac{1}{\tan x} = 3$ so $\tan x = \frac{1}{3}$

Solving for x gives $x = -2.82, 0.322$, ***[1 mark for appropriate rearranging, 1 mark for each solution.]***.

Again, you need to sketch a graph to find the second solution:

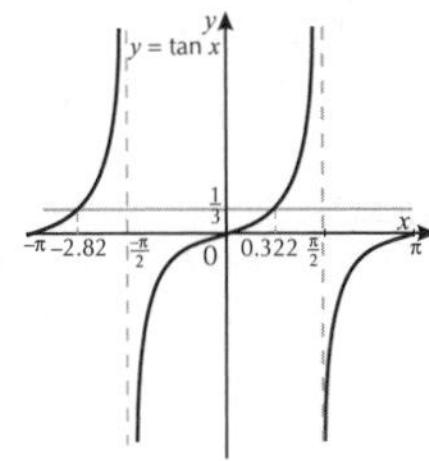

You can see that there are two solutions in the given range, one at 0.322 (this is the one you get from your calculator) and one at −π + 0.322 = −2.82.

2 a) $9\sin\theta + 12\cos\theta \equiv R\sin(\theta + \alpha)$. Using the sin addition formula, $9\sin\theta + 12\cos\theta \equiv R\sin\theta\cos\alpha + R\cos\theta\sin\alpha$.
Equating coefficients of $\sin\theta$ and $\cos\theta$ gives:
$R\cos\alpha = 9$ and $R\sin\alpha = 12$ ***[1 mark]***.
$\frac{R\sin\alpha}{R\cos\alpha} = \tan\alpha$, so $\tan\alpha = \frac{12}{9} = \frac{4}{3}$
Solving this gives $\alpha = 0.927$ ***[1 mark — no other solutions in given range]***.
$R = \sqrt{9^2 + 12^2} = \sqrt{81 + 144} = \sqrt{225} = 15$ ***[1 mark]***,
so $9\sin\theta + 12\cos\theta = 15\sin(\theta + 0.927)$.

b) If $9\sin\theta + 12\cos\theta = 3$, then from part a), $15\sin(\theta + 0.927) = 3$, so $\sin(\theta + 0.927) = 0.2$. The range for θ is $0 \le \theta \le 2\pi$, which becomes $0.927 \le \theta + 0.927 \le 7.210$. Solving the equation gives $(\theta + 0.927) = 0.201$ ***[1 mark]***.
As this is outside the range, use a sketch to find values that are in the range:

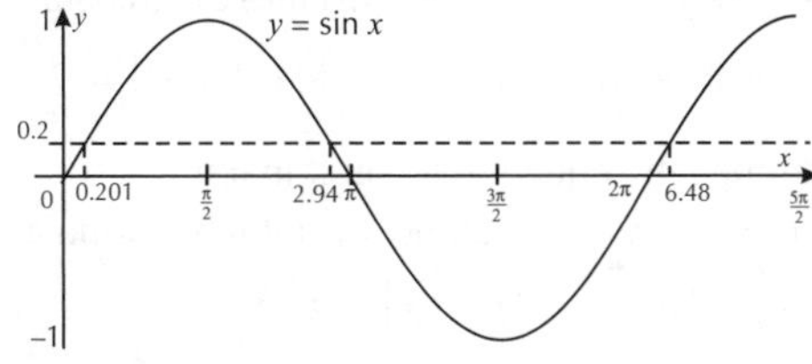

From the graph, it is clear that there are solutions at $\pi - 0.201 = 2.94$ and at $2\pi + 0.201 = 6.48$, so $(\theta + 0.927) = 2.940, 6.48$ ***[1 mark for each value]***,
so $\theta = 2.01, 5.56$ ***[1 mark for each solution]***.

Be careful with the range — if you hadn't extended the range to 2π + 0.927, you would have missed one of the solutions.

3 $\sin 3x \equiv \sin(2x + x) \equiv \sin 2x\cos x + \cos 2x\sin x$ ***[1 mark]***
$\equiv (2\sin x\cos x)\cos x + (1 - 2\sin^2 x)\sin x$ ***[1 mark]***
$\equiv 2\sin x\cos^2 x + \sin x - 2\sin^3 x$
$\equiv 2\sin x(1 - \sin^2 x) + \sin x - 2\sin^3 x$ ***[1 mark]***
$\equiv 2\sin x - 2\sin^3 x + \sin x - 2\sin^3 x$
$\equiv 3\sin x - 4\sin^3 x$ ***[1 mark]***

4 a) The start and end points of the cos curve (with restricted domain) are $(0, 1)$ and $(\pi, -1)$, so the coordinates of the start point of $\cos^{-1}$ (point A) are $(-1, \pi)$ ***[1 mark]*** and the coordinates of the end point (point B) are $(1, 0)$ ***[1 mark]***.

b) $y = \cos^{-1}x$, so $x = \cos y$ ***[1 mark]***.

c) $\cos^{-1}x = 2$, so $x = \cos 2$ ***[1 mark]*** $\Rightarrow x = -0.416$ ***[1 mark]***.

5 a) $\frac{2\sin x}{1 - \cos x} - \frac{2\cos x}{\sin x} \equiv \frac{2\sin^2 x - 2\cos x + 2\cos^2 x}{\sin x(1 - \cos x)}$ ***[1 mark]***
$\equiv \frac{2 - 2\cos x}{\sin x(1 - \cos x)}$ ***[1 mark]***
$\equiv \frac{2(1 - \cos x)}{\sin x(1 - \cos x)}$ ***[1 mark]***
$\equiv \frac{2}{\sin x} \equiv 2\operatorname{cosec} x$ ***[1 mark]***

b) $2\operatorname{cosec} x = 4$
$\operatorname{cosec} x = 2$ <u>OR</u> $\sin x = \frac{1}{2}$ ***[1 mark]***
$x = \frac{\pi}{6}$ ***[1 mark]***, $x = \frac{5\pi}{6}$ ***[1 mark]***.

6 a) $5\cos\theta + 12\sin\theta \equiv R\cos(\theta - \alpha)$. Using the cos addition formula, $5\cos\theta + 12\sin\theta \equiv R\cos\theta\cos\alpha + R\sin\theta\sin\alpha$.
Equating coefficients gives:
$R\cos\alpha = 5$ and $R\sin\alpha = 12$ ***[1 mark]***.
$\frac{R\sin\alpha}{R\cos\alpha} = \tan\alpha$, so $\tan\alpha = \frac{12}{5}$ ***[1 mark]***.
Solving this gives $\alpha = 67.38°$ ***[1 mark]***.
$R = \sqrt{5^2 + 12^2} = \sqrt{25 + 144} = \sqrt{169} = 13$ ***[1 mark]***,
so $5\cos\theta + 12\sin\theta = 13\cos(\theta - 67.38°)$.

b) From part (a), if $5\cos\theta + 12\sin\theta = 2$, that means $13\cos(\theta - 67.38°) = 2$, so $\cos(\theta - 67.38°) = \frac{2}{13}$ ***[1 mark]***. The range for θ is $0 \le \theta \le 360°$, which becomes $-67.38° \le \theta - 67.38° \le 292.62°$ ***[1 mark]***. Solving the equation gives $\theta - 67.38 = 81.15, 278.85$ ***[1 mark]***,
so $\theta = 148.53°, 346.23°$ ***[1 mark for each value]***.

Look at the cos graph to get the second solution of θ − 67.38°:

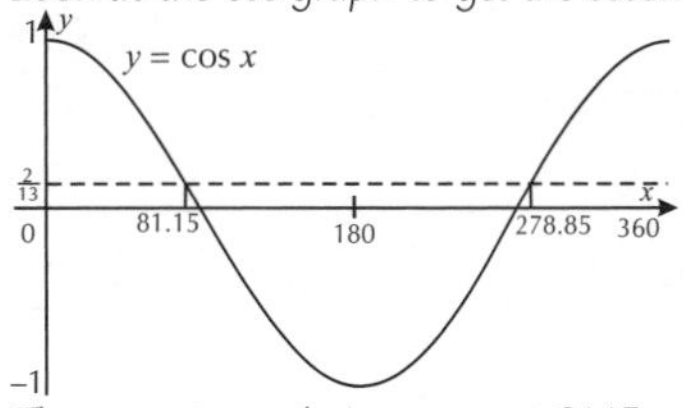

There are two solutions, one at 81.15°, and the other at 360 – 81.15 = 278.85°.

c) The minimum points of the cos curve have a value of –1, so as $5\cos\theta + 12\sin\theta = 13\cos(\theta - 67.38°)$, the minimum value of $5\cos\theta + 12\sin\theta$ is -13 ***[1 mark]***. Hence the minimum value of $(5\cos\theta + 12\sin\theta)^3$ is $(-13)^3 = -2197$ ***[1 mark]***.

7 a) (i) Rearrange the identity $\sec^2\theta \equiv 1 + \tan^2\theta$ to get $\sec^2\theta - 1 \equiv \tan^2\theta$, then replace $\tan^2\theta$ in the equation:
$3\tan^2\theta - 2\sec\theta = 5$
$3(\sec^2\theta - 1) - 2\sec\theta - 5 = 0$ ***[1 mark]***
$3\sec^2\theta - 3 - 2\sec\theta - 5 = 0$
so $3\sec^2\theta - 2\sec\theta - 8 = 0$ ***[1 mark]***

Answers

(ii) To factorise this, let $y = \sec\theta$, so the equation becomes $3y^2 - 2y - 8 = 0$, so $(3y + 4)(y - 2) = 0$ ***[1 mark]***. Solving for y gives $y = -\frac{4}{3}$ or $y = 2$. As $y = \sec\theta$, this means that $\sec\theta = -\frac{4}{3}$ or $\sec\theta = 2$ ***[1 mark]***. $\sec\theta = \frac{1}{\cos\theta}$, so $\cos\theta = -\frac{3}{4}$ or $\cos\theta = \frac{1}{2}$ ***[1 mark]***.

b) Let $\theta = 2x$. From above, we know that the solutions to $3\tan^2\theta - 2\sec\theta = 5$ satisfy $\cos\theta = -\frac{3}{4}$ or $\cos\theta = \frac{1}{2}$. The range for x is $0 \le x \le 180°$, so as $\theta = 2x$, the range for θ is $0 \le \theta \le 360°$ ***[1 mark]***. Solving these equations for θ gives $\theta = 138.59°$, $221.41°$ and $\theta = 60°$, $300°$ ***[1 mark]***. So, as $\theta = 2x$, $x = \frac{1}{2}\theta$, so $x = 69.30°$, $110.70°$, $30°$, $150°$ ***[1 mark]***.

Once you have the values 60° and 138.59°, you can sketch the graph to find the other values:

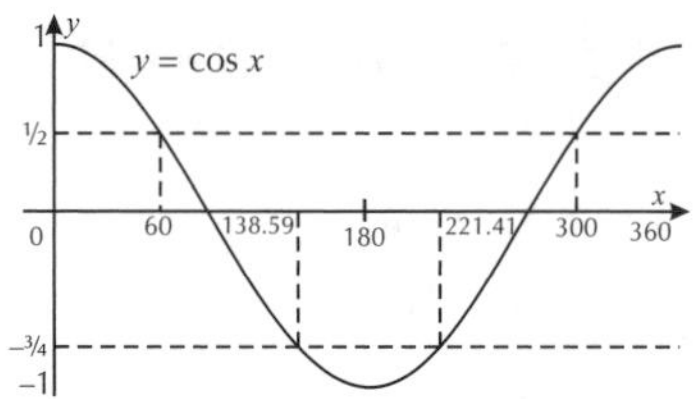

There is a solution at 360 – 60 = 300°, and another at 360 – 138.59 = 221.41°. Don't be fooled by the 2x in this question — you don't need to use the double angle formulas for this one.

C3 Section 4 — Differentiation and Integration Warm-up Questions

1) a) $y = u^{\frac{1}{2}} \Rightarrow \frac{dy}{du} = \frac{1}{2}u^{-\frac{1}{2}} = \frac{1}{2\sqrt{u}} = \frac{1}{2\sqrt{x^3 + 2x^2}}$

$u = x^3 + 2x^2 \Rightarrow \frac{du}{dx} = 3x^2 + 4x$

$\Rightarrow \frac{dy}{dx} = \frac{3x^2 + 4x}{2\sqrt{x^3 + 2x^2}}$.

b) $y = u^{-\frac{1}{2}} \Rightarrow \frac{dy}{du} = -\frac{1}{2}u^{-\frac{3}{2}} = -\frac{1}{2(\sqrt{u})^3} = -\frac{1}{2(\sqrt{x^3 + 2x^2})^3}$

$u = x^3 + 2x^2 \Rightarrow \frac{du}{dx} = 3x^2 + 4x$

$\Rightarrow \frac{dy}{dx} = -\frac{3x^2 + 4x}{2(\sqrt{x^3 + 2x^2})^3}$.

c) $y = e^u \Rightarrow \frac{dy}{du} = e^u = e^{5x^2}$.

$u = 5x^2 \Rightarrow \frac{du}{dx} = 10x$

$\Rightarrow \frac{dy}{dx} = 10xe^{5x^2}$.

d) $y = \ln u \Rightarrow \frac{dy}{du} = \frac{1}{u} = \frac{1}{(6 - x^2)}$

$u = 6 - x^2 \Rightarrow \frac{du}{dx} = -2x$

$\Rightarrow \frac{dy}{dx} = -\frac{2x}{(6 - x^2)}$.

2) a) $x = 2e^y \Rightarrow \frac{dx}{dy} = 2e^y \Rightarrow \frac{dy}{dx} = \frac{1}{2e^y}$.

b) $x = \ln u$ where $u = 2y + 3$

$\frac{dx}{du} = \frac{1}{u} = \frac{1}{2y + 3}$ and $\frac{du}{dy} = 2 \Rightarrow \frac{dx}{dy} = \frac{2}{2y + 3}$

$\Rightarrow \frac{dy}{dx} = \frac{2y + 3}{2} = y + 1.5$.

3) For $y = e^{2x}(x^2 - 3)$, use the product rule:

$u = e^{2x} \Rightarrow \frac{du}{dx} = 2e^{2x}$ (from the chain rule),

$v = x^2 - 3 \Rightarrow \frac{dv}{dx} = 2x$.

$\frac{dy}{dx} = u\frac{dv}{dx} + v\frac{du}{dx} = 2xe^{2x} + 2e^{2x}(x^2 - 3) = 2e^{2x}(x^2 + x - 3)$.

When $x = 0$, $\frac{dy}{dx} = 2e^0(0 + 0 - 3) = 2 \times 1 \times -3 = -6$.

4) For $y = \frac{6x^2 + 3}{4x^2 - 1}$, use the quotient rule:

$u = 6x^2 + 3 \Rightarrow \frac{du}{dx} = 12x$,

$v = 4x^2 - 1 \Rightarrow \frac{dv}{dx} = 8x$.

$\frac{dy}{dx} = \frac{v\frac{du}{dx} - u\frac{dv}{dx}}{v^2} = \frac{12x(4x^2 - 1) - 8x(6x^2 + 3)}{(4x^2 - 1)^2}$.

At (1, 3), $x = 1$ and so gradient =

$\frac{dy}{dx} = \frac{12(4 - 1) - 8(6 + 3)}{(4 - 1)^2} = \frac{36 - 72}{9} = -4$.

Equation of a straight line is:

$y - y_1 = m(x - x_1)$, where m is the gradient.

So the equation of the tangent at (1, 3) is:

$y - 3 = -4(x - 1) \Rightarrow y = -4x + 7$ (or equivalent).

5) $A = 2(x)(2x) + 2(x)(3x) + 2(2x)(3x)$

$= 4x^2 + 6x^2 + 12x^2$

$= 22x^2$

So $\frac{dA}{dx} = 44x$

$V = (x)(2x)(3x) = 6x^3$

So $\frac{dV}{dx} = 18x^2$

By the chain rule:

$\frac{dA}{dt} = \frac{dA}{dx} \times \frac{dx}{dt} = 44x \times \frac{dx}{dt}$

To find $\frac{dx}{dt}$, use the chain rule again:

$\frac{dx}{dt} = \frac{dx}{dV} \times \frac{dV}{dt} = \frac{1}{\left(\frac{dV}{dx}\right)} \times \frac{dV}{dt} = \frac{1}{18x^2} \times 3 = \frac{1}{6x^2}$

So $\frac{dA}{dt} = 44x \times \frac{1}{6x^2} = \frac{22}{3x}$

6) $2e^{2x} + C$

7) Let $u = 3x - 5$. Then $\frac{du}{dx} = 3$, and $dx = \frac{du}{3}$. Putting this into the integral gives $\int \frac{1}{3}e^u du = \frac{1}{3}e^{3x-5} + C$.

8) $\frac{2}{3}\ln|x| + C$

9) Let $u = 2x + 1$. Then $\frac{du}{dx} = 2$, and $dx = \frac{du}{2}$. Putting this into the integral gives $\int 2\frac{1}{2}\frac{1}{u}du = \ln|2x + 1| + C$.

10) If $y = \frac{1}{x}$ then $y^2 = \frac{1}{x^2}$. Putting this into the integral gives:

$V = \pi\int_2^4 \frac{1}{x^2}dx = \pi\left[-\frac{1}{x}\right]_2^4 = \pi\left[\left(-\frac{1}{4}\right) - \left(-\frac{1}{2}\right)\right] = \frac{\pi}{4}$.

11) First, rearrange the equation to get it in terms of x^2:

$y = x^2 + 1 \Rightarrow x^2 = y - 1$. Putting this into the formula:

$V = \pi\int_1^3 y - 1\,dy = \pi\left[\frac{1}{2}y^2 - y\right]_1^3$

$= \pi\left[\left(\frac{1}{2}(9) - 3\right) - \left(\frac{1}{2}(1) - 1\right)\right] = 2\pi$.

Exam Questions

1 $-\frac{1}{2}e^{(5-6x)} + C$

[1 mark for answer in the form $ke^{(5-6x)}$, 1 mark for the correct value of k]

Answers

2 a) For $x = \sqrt{y^2 + 3y}$, find $\frac{dx}{dy}$ first (using the chain rule):

$x = u^{\frac{1}{2}}$ where $u = y^2 + 3y$.

$\frac{dx}{du} = \frac{1}{2}u^{-\frac{1}{2}} = \frac{1}{2\sqrt{u}} = \frac{1}{2\sqrt{y^2+3y}}$ ***[1 mark]***.

$\frac{du}{dy} = 2y + 3$ ***[1 mark]***.

So $\frac{dx}{dy} = \frac{2y+3}{2\sqrt{y^2+3y}}$ ***[1 mark]***.

Now, flip the fraction upside down for dy/dx.

$\frac{dy}{dx} = \frac{2\sqrt{y^2+3y}}{2y+3}$ ***[1 mark]***.

At the point (2, 1), $y = 1$, so:

$\frac{dy}{dx} = \frac{2\sqrt{1^2+3}}{2+3} = \frac{4}{5} = 0.8$ ***[1 mark]***.

b) Equation of a straight line is:

$y - y_1 = m(x - x_1)$, where m is the gradient.

For the tangent at (2, 1), $y_1 = 1$, $x_1 = 2$, and $m = \frac{dy}{dx} = 0.8$.

So the equation is:

$y - 1 = 0.8(x - 2) \Rightarrow y = 0.8x - 0.6$ (or equivalent fractions)

[2 marks available — 1 mark for correct substitution of (2, 1) and gradient from (a), and 1 mark for final answer.]

3 For $y = \frac{e^x + x}{e^x - x}$, use the quotient rule:

$u = e^x + x \Rightarrow \frac{du}{dx} = e^x + 1$.

$v = e^x - x \Rightarrow \frac{dv}{dx} = e^x - 1$.

$\frac{dy}{dx} = \frac{v\frac{du}{dx} - u\frac{dv}{dx}}{v^2} = \frac{(e^x - x)(e^x + 1) - (e^x + x)(e^x - 1)}{(e^x - x)^2}$.

When $x = 0$, $e^x = 1$, and $\frac{dy}{dx} = \frac{(1-0)(1+1) - (1+0)(1-1)}{(1-0)^2}$

$= \frac{2-0}{1^2} = 2$.

[3 marks available — 1 mark for finding u, v and their derivatives, 1 mark for dy/dx (however rearranged), and 1 mark for dy/dx = 2 when x = 0.]

4 a) For $y = \sqrt{e^x + e^{2x}}$, use the chain rule:

$y = u^{\frac{1}{2}}$ where $u = e^x + e^{2x}$.

$\frac{dy}{du} = \frac{1}{2}u^{-\frac{1}{2}} = \frac{1}{2\sqrt{u}} = \frac{1}{2\sqrt{e^x + e^{2x}}}$ ***[1 mark]***.

$\frac{du}{dx} = e^x + 2e^{2x}$ ***[1 mark]***.

So $\frac{dy}{dx} = \frac{e^x + 2e^{2x}}{2\sqrt{e^x + e^{2x}}}$ ***[1 mark]***.

b) For $y = 3e^{2x+1} - \ln(1 - x^2) + 2x^3$, use the chain rule for the first 2 parts separately:

For $y = 3e^{2x+1}$, $y = 3e^u$ where $u = 2x + 1$, so $\frac{dy}{du} = 3e^u = 3e^{2x+1}$

and $\frac{du}{dx} = 2$, so $\frac{dy}{dx} = 6e^{2x+1}$ ***[1 mark]***.

For $y = \ln(1 - x^2)$, $y = \ln u$ where $u = 1 - x^2$,

so $\frac{dy}{du} = \frac{1}{u} = \frac{1}{(1-x^2)}$ and $\frac{du}{dx} = -2x$, so $\frac{dy}{dx} = -\frac{2x}{(1-x^2)}$

[1 mark].

So overall: $\frac{dy}{dx} = 6e^{2x+1} + \frac{2x}{(1-x^2)} + 6x^2$ ***[1 mark]***.

5 a) For $f(x) = 4\ln 3x$, use the chain rule:

$y = 4\ln u$ where $u = 3x$, so $\frac{dy}{du} = \frac{4}{u} = \frac{4}{3x}$, and $\frac{du}{dx} = 3$

[1 mark for both], so $f'(x) = \frac{dy}{dx} = \frac{12}{3x} = \frac{4}{x}$ ***[1 mark]***.

So for $x = 1$, $f'(1) = 4$ ***[1 mark]***.

b) Equation of a straight line is:

$y - y_1 = m(x - x_1)$, where m is the gradient.

For the tangent at $x_1 = 1$, $y_1 = 4\ln 3$, and $m = \frac{dy}{dx} = 4$.

So the equation is:

$y - 4\ln 3 = 4(x - 1) \Rightarrow y = 4(x - 1 + \ln 3)$ (or equivalent).

[3 marks available — 1 mark for finding y = 4ln 3, 1 mark for correct substitution of (1, 4ln3) and gradient from (a), and 1 mark for correct final answer.]

6 First, rearrange the equation to get it in terms of x^2:

$y = \frac{1}{x^2} \Rightarrow x^2 = \frac{1}{y}$. Putting this into the formula:

$V = \pi\int_1^3 \frac{1}{y}\,dy = \pi[\ln y]_1^3$

$= \pi[(\ln 3) - (\ln 1)] = \pi\ln 3$.

[5 marks available — 1 mark for rearranging equation, 1 mark for correct formula for volume, 1 mark for correct integration, 1 mark for substituting in limits, 1 mark for final answer (in terms of π and ln)]

7 To find the volume of the solid formed when R is rotated, find the volume for each curve separately then subtract. First, find the volume when the area under the curve $y = e^{1.5x}$ is rotated about the x-axis:

$y^2 = (e^{1.5x})^2 = e^{3x}$ ***[1 mark]***.

$V = \pi\int_1^2 e^{3x}\,dx = \pi\left[\frac{1}{3}e^{3x}\right]_1^2$ ***[1 mark]***

$= \pi\left(\frac{1}{3}e^6 - \frac{1}{3}e^3\right) = 401.436...$ ***[1 mark]***.

Now find the volume for $y = \sqrt{x}$:

As $y = \sqrt{x}$, $y^2 = x$.

$V = \pi\int_1^2 x\,dx = \pi\left[\frac{1}{2}x^2\right]_1^2$ ***[1 mark]***

$= \pi\left(\frac{1}{2}(2^2) - \frac{1}{2}(1^2)\right) = \frac{3\pi}{2} = 4.7123...$ ***[1 mark]***.

[1 mark for using correct formula for the volume of revolution for both curves]

To find the volume you want, you need to subtract 4.7123... from 401.436...:

401.436... – 4.7123... = 396.7 (4 s.f.) ***[1 mark]***.

8 a) Start by finding the missing side length of the triangular faces. Call the missing length s:

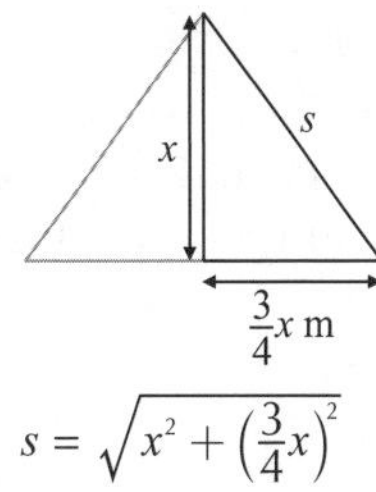

$s = \sqrt{x^2 + \left(\frac{3}{4}x\right)^2}$

$= \sqrt{x^2 + \frac{9}{16}x^2}$

$= \sqrt{\frac{25}{16}x^2}$

$= \frac{5}{4}x$ ***[1 mark]***

Now find A by adding up the area of each of the faces:

$A = 2(\frac{1}{2} \times \frac{3}{2}x \times x) + (\frac{3}{2}x \times 4x) + 2(\frac{5}{4}x \times 4x)$ ***[1 mark]***

$= \frac{3}{2}x^2 + 6x^2 + 10x^2$

$= \frac{35}{2}x^2$ ***[1 mark]***

Answers

b) $\frac{dA}{dt} = 0.07$

$A = \frac{35}{2}x^2 \Rightarrow \frac{dA}{dx} = 35x$ ***[1 mark]***

Using chain rule, $\frac{dx}{dt} = \frac{dx}{dA} \times \frac{dA}{dt}$ ***[1 mark]***

$= \frac{1}{\left(\frac{dA}{dx}\right)} \times \frac{dA}{dt} = \frac{1}{35x} \times 0.07$

$= \frac{0.07}{35 \times 0.5} = 0.004 \text{ m s}^{-1}$ ***[1 mark]***

c) First you need to figure out what the question is asking for. 'Find the rate of change of V' means we're looking for $\frac{dV}{dt}$.
Start by finding an expression for V:

$V = (\frac{1}{2} \times \frac{3}{2}x \times x) \times 4x = 3x^3$ ***[1 mark]***

So $\frac{dV}{dx} = 9x^2$ ***[1 mark]***

Using chain rule, $\frac{dV}{dt} = \frac{dV}{dx} \times \frac{dx}{dt}$ ***[1 mark]***

$= 9x^2 \times \frac{0.07}{35x} = \frac{9(1.2)^2 \times 0.07}{35 \times 1.2} = 0.0216 \text{ m}^3 \text{ s}^{-1}$ ***[1 mark]***

C3 Section 5 — Numerical Methods

Warm-up Questions

1) There are 2 roots (graph crosses the x-axis twice in this interval).

2) a) Sin $(2 \times 3) = -0.2794...$ and $\sin(2 \times 4) = 0.9893...$
Since $\sin(2x)$ is a continuous function, the change of sign means there is a root between 3 and 4.

b) $\ln(2.1 - 2) + 2 = -0.3025...$
and $\ln(2.2 - 2) + 2 = 0.3905...$
Since the function is continuous for $x > 2$, the change of sign means there is a root between 2.1 and 2.2.

c) Rearrange first to give $x^3 - 4x^2 - 7 = 0$, then:
$4.3^3 - 4 \times (4.3^2) - 7 = -1.453$ and
$4.5^3 - 4 \times (4.5^2) - 7 = 3.125$.
The function is continuous, so the change of sign means there is a root between 4.3 and 4.5.

3) If 1.2 is a root to 1 d.p. then there should be a sign change for f(x) between the upper and lower bounds:
$f(1.15) = 1.15^3 + 1.15 - 3 = -0.3291...$
$f(1.25) = 1.25^3 + 1.25 - 3 = 0.2031...$
There is a change of sign, and the function is continuous, so the root must lie between 1.15 and 1.25, so to 1 d.p. the root is at $x = 1.2$.

4) $x_1 = -\frac{1}{2}\cos(-1) = -0.2701...$
$x_2 = -\frac{1}{2}\cos(-0.2701...) = -0.4818...$
$x_3 = -\frac{1}{2}\cos(-0.4818...) = -0.4430...$
$x_4 = -\frac{1}{2}\cos(-0.4430...) = -0.4517...$
$x_5 = -\frac{1}{2}\cos(-0.4517...) = -0.4498...$
$x_6 = -\frac{1}{2}\cos(-0.4498...) = -0.4502...$
x_4, x_5 and x_6 all round to -0.45, so to 2 d.p. $x = -0.45$.

5) $x_1 = \sqrt{\ln 2 + 4} = 2.1663...$
$x_2 = \sqrt{\ln 2.1663... + 4} = 2.1847...$
$x_3 = \sqrt{\ln 2.1847... + 4} = 2.1866...$
$x_4 = \sqrt{\ln 2.1866... + 4} = 2.1868...$
$x_5 = \sqrt{\ln 2.1868... + 4} = 2.1868...$
x_3, x_4 and x_5 all round to 2.187, so to 3 d.p. $x = 2.187$.

6) a) i) $2x^2 - x^3 + 1 = 0 \Rightarrow 2x^2 - x^3 = -1$
$\Rightarrow x^2(2 - x) = -1 \Rightarrow x^2 = \frac{-1}{2-x} \Rightarrow x = \sqrt{\frac{-1}{2-x}}$.

ii) $2x^2 - x^3 + 1 = 0 \Rightarrow x^3 = 2x^2 + 1$
$\Rightarrow x = \sqrt[3]{2x^2 + 1}$.

iii) $2x^2 - x^3 + 1 = 0 \Rightarrow 2x^2 = x^3 - 1$
$\Rightarrow x^2 = \frac{x^3 - 1}{2} \Rightarrow x = \sqrt{\frac{x^3 - 1}{2}}$.

b) Using $x_{n+1} = \sqrt{\frac{-1}{2 - x_n}}$ with $x_0 = 2.3$ gives:
$x_1 = \sqrt{\frac{-1}{2 - 2.3}} = 1.8257...$
$x_2 = \sqrt{\frac{-1}{2 - 1.8257...}}$ has no real solution
so this formula does not converge to a root.

Using $x_{n+1} = \sqrt[3]{2x_n^2 + 1}$ with $x_0 = 2.3$ gives:
$x_1 = \sqrt[3]{2 \times (2.3)^2 + 1} = 2.2624...$
$x_2 = \sqrt[3]{2 \times (2.2624...)^2 + 1} = 2.2398...$
$x_3 = \sqrt[3]{2 \times (2.2398...)^2 + 1} = 2.2262...$
$x_4 = \sqrt[3]{2 \times (2.2262...)^2 + 1} = 2.2180...$
$x_5 = \sqrt[3]{2 \times (2.2180...)^2 + 1} = 2.2131...$
$x_6 = \sqrt[3]{2 \times (2.2131...)^2 + 1} = 2.2101...$
$x_7 = \sqrt[3]{2 \times (2.2101...)^2 + 1} = 2.2083...$
x_5, x_6 and x_7 all round to 2.21,
so to 2 d.p. $x = 2.21$ is a root.

Using $x_{n+1} = \sqrt{\frac{x_n^3 - 1}{2}}$ with $x_0 = 2.3$ gives:
$x_1 = \sqrt{\frac{2.3^3 - 1}{2}} = 2.3629...$
$x_2 = \sqrt{\frac{2.3629...^3 - 1}{2}} = 2.4691...$
$x_3 = \sqrt{\frac{2.4691...^3 - 1}{2}} = 2.6508...$
$x_4 = \sqrt{\frac{2.6508...^3 - 1}{2}} = 2.9687...$
This sequence is diverging so does not converge to a root.
The only formula that converges to a root is
$x_{n+1} = \sqrt[3]{2x_n^2 + 1}$.

7) a) The width of each strip is $\frac{4-1}{6} = 0.5$, so you need y-values for $x = 1, 1.5, 2, 2.5, 3, 3.5$ and 4:
$x_0 = 1, y_0 = 1.0986, x_1 = 1.5, y_1 = 1.1709, x_2 = 2, y_2 = 1.2279,$
$x_3 = 2.5, y_3 = 1.2757, x_4 = 3, y_4 = 1.3170,$
$x_5 = 3.5, y_5 = 1.3535, x_6 = 4, y_6 = 1.3863.$
Putting these values into the formula gives:
$A \approx \frac{1}{3}0.5[(1.0986 + 1.3863) + 4(1.1709 + 1.2757 + 1.3535) + 2(1.2279 + 1.3170)] = 3.7959$ (4 d.p.).

b) Simpson's Rule only works with an even number of strips, so 5 strips won't work.

Exam Questions

1 a) There will be a change of sign between f(0.7) and f(0.8) if p lies between 0.7 and 0.8.
$f(0.7) = (2 \times 0.7 \times e^{0.7}) - 3 = -0.1807...$ ***[1 mark]***
$f(0.8) = (2 \times 0.8 \times e^{0.8}) - 3 = 0.5608...$ ***[1 mark]***

Answers

f(x) is continuous, and there is a change of sign, so $0.7 < p < 0.8$ ***[1 mark]***.

b) If $2xe^x - 3 = 0$, then $2xe^x = 3 \Rightarrow xe^x = \frac{3}{2}$
$\Rightarrow x = \frac{3}{2e^x} \Rightarrow x = \frac{3}{2}e^{-x}$.
[2 marks available — 1 mark for partial rearrangement, 1 mark for correct final answer.]

c) $x_{n+1} = \frac{3}{2}e^{-x_n}$ and $x_0 = 0.7$, so:
$x_1 = \frac{3}{2}e^{-0.7} = 0.74487... = 0.7449$ to 4 d.p.
$x_2 = \frac{3}{2}e^{-0.74487...} = 0.71218... = 0.7122$ to 4 d.p.
$x_3 = \frac{3}{2}e^{-0.71218...} = 0.73585... = 0.7359$ to 4 d.p.
$x_4 = \frac{3}{2}e^{-0.73585...} = 0.71864... = 0.7186$ to 4 d.p.
[3 marks available — 1 mark for x_1 correct, 1 mark for x_2 correct, 1 mark for all 4 correct.]

d) If the root of f(x) = 0, p, is 0.726 to 3 d.p. then there must be a change of sign in f(x) between the upper and lower bounds of p.
Lower bound = 0.7255.
f(0.7255) = (2 × 0.7255 × $e^{0.7255}$) – 3 = –0.0025...
Upper bound = 0.7265.
f(0.7265) = (2 × 0.7265 × $e^{0.7265}$) – 3 = 0.0045...
f(x) is continuous, and there's a change of sign, so p = 0.726 to 3 d.p.

[3 marks available — 1 mark for identifying upper and lower bounds, 1 mark for finding value of the function at both bounds, 1 mark for indicating that the change in sign and the fact that it's a continuous function shows the root is correct to the given accuracy.]

2 a) Where $y = \sin 3x + 3x$ and $y = 1$ meet,
$\sin 3x + 3x = 1 \Rightarrow \sin 3x + 3x - 1 = 0$ ***[1 mark]***.

$x = a$ is a root of this equation, so if $x = 0.1$ and $x = 0.2$ produce different signs, then a lies between them. So for the continuous function f(x) = $\sin 3x + 3x - 1$:
f(0.1) = sin (3 × 0.1) + (3 × 0.1) – 1 = –0.4044... ***[1 mark]***
f(0.2) = sin (3 × 0.2) + (3 × 0.2) – 1 = 0.1646... ***[1 mark]***
There is a change of sign, so $0.1 < a < 0.2$ ***[1 mark]***.

b) $\sin 3x + 3x = 1 \Rightarrow 3x = 1 - \sin 3x \Rightarrow x = \frac{1}{3}(1 - \sin 3x)$.
[2 marks available — 1 mark for partial rearrangement, 1 mark for correct final answer.]

c) $x_{n+1} = \frac{1}{3}(1 - \sin 3x_n)$ and $x_0 = 0.2$:
$x_1 = \frac{1}{3}(1 - \sin(3 \times 0.2)) = 0.1451...$ ***[1 mark]***
$x_2 = \frac{1}{3}(1 - \sin(3 \times 0.1451...)) = 0.1927...$
$x_3 = \frac{1}{3}(1 - \sin(3 \times 0.1927...)) = 0.1511...$
$x_4 = \frac{1}{3}(1 - \sin(3 \times 0.1511...)) = 0.1873...$
So $x_4 = 0.187$ to 3 d.p. ***[1 mark]***.

3 a) $x_{n+1} = \sqrt[3]{x_n^2 - 4}$, $x_0 = -1$:
$x_1 = \sqrt[3]{(-1)^2 - 4} = -1.44224... = -1.4422$ to 4 d.p.
$x_2 = \sqrt[3]{(-1.4422...)^2 - 4} = -1.24287... = -1.2429$ to 4 d.p.
$x_3 = \sqrt[3]{(-1.2428...)^2 - 4} = -1.34906... = -1.3491$ to 4 d.p.
$x_4 = \sqrt[3]{(-1.3490...)^2 - 4} = -1.29664... = -1.2966$ to 4 d.p.
[3 marks available — 1 mark for x_1 correct, 1 mark for x_2 correct, 1 mark for all 4 correct.]

b) If b is a root of $x^3 - x^2 + 4 = 0$, then $x^3 - x^2 + 4 = 0$ will rearrange to form $x = \sqrt[3]{x^2 - 4}$, the iteration formula used in (a).

(This is like finding the iteration formula in reverse...)

$x^3 - x^2 + 4 = 0 \Rightarrow x^3 = x^2 - 4 \Rightarrow x = \sqrt[3]{x^2 - 4}$, and so b must be a root of $x^3 - x^2 + 4 = 0$.

[2 marks available — 1 mark for stating that b is a root if one equation can be rearranged into the other, 1 mark for correct demonstration of rearrangement.]

c) If the root of f(x) = $x^3 - x^2 + 4 = 0$, b, is –1.315 to 3 d.p. then there must be a change of sign in f(x) between the upper and lower bounds of b, which are –1.3145 and –1.3155.
f(–1.3145) = $(-1.3145)^3 - (-1.3145)^2 + 4$ = 0.00075...
f(–1.3155) = $(-1.3155)^3 - (-1.3155)^2 + 4$ = –0.00706...
f(x) is continuous, and there's a change of sign, so b = –1.315 to 3 d.p.

[3 marks available — 1 mark for identifying upper and lower bounds, 1 mark for finding value of the function at both bounds, 1 mark for indicating that the change in sign and the fact that it's a continuous function shows the root is correct to the given accuracy.]

4 a) For f(x) = ln(x + 3) – x + 2, there will be a change in sign between f(3) and f(4) if the root lies between those values.

f(3) = ln (3 + 3) – 3 + 2 = 0.7917... ***[1 mark]***
f(4) = ln (4 + 3) – 4 + 2 = –0.0540... ***[1 mark]***

There is a change of sign, and the function is continuous for $x > -3$, so the root, m, must lie between 3 and 4 ***[1 mark]***.

b) $x_{n+1} = \ln(x_n + 3) + 2$, and $x_0 = 3$, so:
$x_1 = \ln(3 + 3) + 2 = 3.7917...$
$x_2 = \ln(3.7917... + 3) + 2 = 3.9157...$
$x_3 = \ln(3.9157... + 3) + 2 = 3.9337...$
$x_4 = \ln(3.9337... + 3) + 2 = 3.9364...$
$x_5 = \ln(3.9364... + 3) + 2 = 3.9367...$
So m = 3.94 to 2 d.p.

[3 marks available — 1 mark for correct substitution of x_0 to find x_1, 1 mark for evidence of correct iterations up to x_5, 1 mark for correct final answer to correct accuracy.]

c) From b), m = 3.94 to 2 d.p. If this is correct then there will be a change of sign in f(x) between the upper and lower bounds of m, which are 3.935 and 3.945.
f(3.935) = ln (3.935 + 3) – 3.935 + 2 = 0.00158...
f(3.945) = ln (3.945 + 3) – 3.945 + 2 = –0.00697...

f(x) is continuous for $x > -3$, and there's a change of sign, so m = 3.94 is correct to 2 d.p.

[3 marks available — 1 mark for identifying upper and lower bounds, 1 mark for finding value of the function at both bounds, 1 mark for indicating that the change in sign and the fact that it's a continuous function shows the root is correct to the given accuracy.]

Answers

5 The width of each strip is $\frac{5-1}{4} = 1$, so you need y-values for $x = 1, 2, 3, 4$ and 5:
$x_0 = 1, y_0 = 0.25, x_1 = 2, y_1 = 0.1, x_2 = 3, y_2 = 0.0556,$
$x_3 = 4, y_3 = 0.0357, x_4 = 5, y_4 = 0.025.$
Putting these values into the formula gives:
$A \approx \frac{1}{3}1[(0.25 + 0.025) + 4(0.1 + 0.0357) + 2(0.0556)]$
$= 0.310$ (3 s.f.).

[4 marks available — 1 mark for correct x-values, 1 mark for correct y-values, 1 mark for correct use of formula, 1 mark for final answer]

C3 — Practice Exam One

1 a) For $3\ln x - \ln 3x = 0$, use the log laws to simplify to:
$\ln x^3 - \ln 3x = 0 \Rightarrow \ln \frac{x^3}{3x} = 0 \Rightarrow \ln \frac{x^2}{3} = 0$ ***[1 mark]***.
Taking e to the power of both sides gives:
$\frac{x^2}{3} = e^0 = 1 \Rightarrow x^2 = 3 \Rightarrow x = \sqrt{3}$ (ignore the negative solution as $x > 0$) ***[1 mark]***.

b) Let $y = f(x)$. Now, to find the inverse of $y = 3\ln x - \ln 3x$, make x the subject then swap x and y:
$y = \ln \frac{x^2}{3}$ (from (a)) $\Rightarrow e^y = \frac{x^2}{3} \Rightarrow x^2 = 3e^y$
$\Rightarrow x = \sqrt{3e^y}$ ***[1 mark]***.

So $f^{-1}(x) = \sqrt{3e^x}$ ***[1 mark]***.

c) When $\sqrt{3e^x} = 1$, squaring both sides gives:
$3e^x = 1 \Rightarrow e^x = \frac{1}{3}$ ***[1 mark]***.
Taking ln of both sides gives:
$x = \ln \frac{1}{3}$ ***[1 mark]***.

d) $f(x) = 3\ln x - \ln 3x$, so differentiating gives:
$f'(x) = \frac{3}{x} - \frac{3}{3x} = \frac{3}{x} - \frac{1}{x} = \frac{2}{x}$ ***[1 mark]***.
So when $x = 1$, $f'(x) = \frac{2}{1} = 2$ ***[1 mark]***.

2 a) (i)

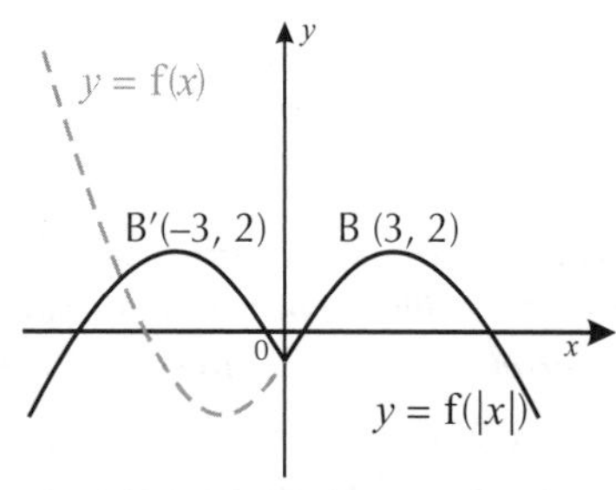

[3 marks available — 1 mark for reflection in the y-axis, 1 mark for each coordinate of B′ after transformation]

(ii)

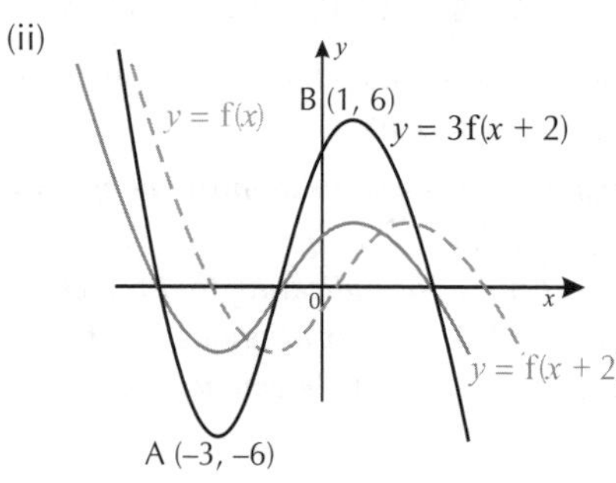

[3 marks available — 1 mark for shape (stretch and translation), 1 mark each for coordinates of A and B after transformation]

The solid grey line shows the graph of y = f(x + 2) — it's easier to do the transformation in two stages, instead of doing it all at once.

b) (i) $gh(4) = g(h(4)) = g\left(\frac{6}{4^2-4}\right) = g(0.5)$ ***[1 mark]***
$= \sqrt{(2 \cdot 0.5) + 3} = \sqrt{1+3} = \sqrt{4} = 2.$ ***[1 mark]***

(ii) $hg(3) = h(g(3)) = h(\sqrt{(2 \cdot 3) + 3}) = h(3)$ ***[1 mark]***
$= \frac{6}{3^2-4} = \frac{6}{9-4} = \frac{6}{5} = 1.2$ ***[1 mark]***.

(iii) $hg(x) = h(g(x)) = h(\sqrt{2x+3})$
$\frac{6}{(\sqrt{2x+3})^2 - 4} = \frac{6}{2x+3-4} = \frac{6}{2x-1}.$

[3 marks available — 1 mark for functions in the correct order, 1 mark for substituting g(x) into formula for h, 1 mark for simplifying].

3 a) When $x = 1.5$, $y = \frac{3\ln 1.5}{(1.5)^2} = 0.54062$ ***[1 mark]***, and when $x = 3$, $y = \frac{3\ln 3}{3^2} = 0.36620$ ***[1 mark]***.

b) $h = 0.5$. Putting h and the values from the table into the formula for Simpson's Rule:
$$A \approx \frac{0.5}{3}[0 + 0.36620 + 4(0.54062 + 0.43982) + 2(0.51986)]$$
$$= \frac{1}{6}[0.33620 + 3.92176 + 1.03972] = 0.88295\,(5\text{ d.p.}).$$

[4 marks available — 1 mark for correct value of h, 1 mark for putting the correct numbers into the formula for Simpson's Rule, 1 mark for correct working and 1 mark for correct answer].

4 a)

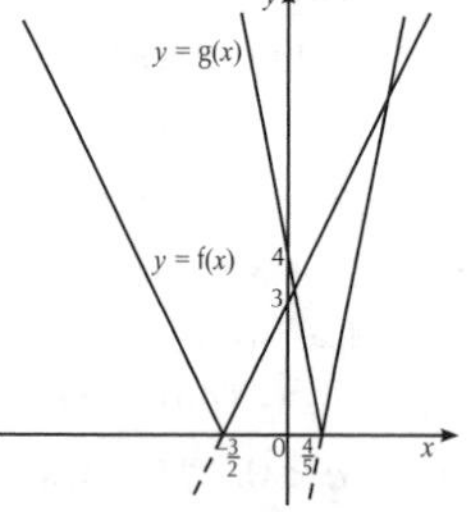

[3 marks available — 1 mark for y = |2x + 3| (with reflection in the x-axis and y-intercept at 3), 1 mark for y = |5x – 4| (with reflection in the x-axis and y-intercept at 4), 1 mark for showing graphs cross twice]

Make sure you draw enough of the graph to show where the lines cross — you'll need it for the next bit of the question.

b) From the graph, it is clear that there are two points where the graphs intersect. One is in the range $-\frac{3}{2} < x < \frac{4}{5}$, where $(2x + 3) > 0$ but $(5x - 4) < 0$. This gives $2x + 3 = -(5x - 4)$ ***[1 mark]***.
The other one is in the range $x > \frac{4}{5}$, where $(2x + 3) > 0$ and $(5x - 4) > 0$, so $2x + 3 = 5x - 4$ ***[1 mark]***. Solving the first equation gives: $2x + 3 = -5x + 4 \Rightarrow 7x = 1$, so $x = \frac{1}{7}$ ***[1 mark]***. Solving the second equation gives:
$2x + 3 = 5x - 4 \Rightarrow 7 = 3x$, so $x = \frac{7}{3}$ ***[1 mark]***.

Answers

You could also have solved this one by squaring both sides of the equation — you'd have ended up with the equation $21x^2 - 52x + 7$ which factorises to give $(3x - 7)(7x - 1)$ so you'd have got the same solutions as above.

c) For $|2x + 3| \geq |5x - 4|$, you need the region where the graph of $|2x + 3|$ is above the graph of $|5x - 4|$ ***[1 mark]***. From the sketch from part a) and the values of x from part b), this occurs when $\frac{1}{7} \leq x \leq \frac{7}{3}$ ***[1 mark]***.

5 a) $\text{cosec}\,\theta = \frac{5}{3} \Rightarrow \sin\theta = \frac{3}{5}$. Solving for θ gives $\theta = 0.644$, $\pi - 0.644 = 2.50$ (3 s.f.) ***[1 mark for each correct answer]***.

Sketch the graph of $y = \sin x$ to help you find the second solution.

b) (i) The identity $\text{cosec}^2\theta \equiv 1 + \cot^2\theta$ rearranges to give $\text{cosec}^2\theta - 1 \equiv \cot^2\theta$. Putting this into the equation:

$$3\,\text{cosec}\,\theta = (\text{cosec}^2\theta - 1) - 17$$
$$17 + 3\,\text{cosec}\,\theta - (\text{cosec}^2\theta - 1) = 0$$
$$18 + 3\,\text{cosec}\,\theta - \text{cosec}^2\theta = 0$$

as required.

[2 marks available — 1 mark for using correct identity, 1 mark for rearranging into required form]

(ii) To factorise the expression above, let $x = \text{cosec}\,\theta$. Then $18 + 3x - x^2 = 0$, so $(6 - x)(3 + x) = 0$ ***[1 mark]***. The roots of this quadratic occur at $x = 6$ and $x = -3$, so $\text{cosec}\,\theta = 6$ and $\text{cosec}\,\theta = -3$ ***[1 mark]***.

$\text{cosec}\,\theta = 1/\sin\theta$, so $\sin\theta = \frac{1}{6}$ and $\sin\theta = -\frac{1}{3}$.

Solving these equations for θ gives $\theta = 0.167, 2.97$ ***[1 mark]*** and $\theta = 3.48, 5.94$ ***[1 mark]***.

You don't have to use $x = \text{cosec}\,\theta$ — it's just a little easier to factorise without all those pesky cosecs flying around. Have a look back at Section 3 for stuff on cosec etc.

6 a) For $6^x = x + 2$, take ln of both sides:

$\ln 6^x = \ln(x + 2)$ ***[1 mark]***, and using log laws,

$x\ln 6 = \ln(x + 2) \Rightarrow x = \frac{\ln(x+2)}{\ln 6}$ ***[1 mark]***.

b) Using $x_{n+1} = \frac{\ln(x_n + 2)}{\ln 6}$ and $x_0 = 0.5$ gives:

$x_1 = \frac{\ln(0.5 + 2)}{\ln 6} = 0.51139... = 0.5114$ to 4 d.p. ***[1 mark]***

$x_2 = \frac{\ln(0.51139... + 2)}{\ln 6} = 0.51392... = 0.5139$ to 4 d.p. ***[1 mark]***

$x_3 = \frac{\ln(0.51392... + 2)}{\ln 6} = 0.51449... = 0.5145$ to 4 d.p. ***[1 mark]***

c) If $x = 0.515$ to 3 d.p., the upper and lower bounds are 0.5155 and 0.5145 ***[1 mark]*** — any value in this range would be rounded to 0.515. $f(x) = 6^x - x - 2$, and at point P, $f(x) = 0$. $f(0.5145) = -0.000537$ and $f(0.5155) = 0.00297$ ***[1 mark for both f(0.5145) negative and f(0.5155) positive]***. There is a change of sign, and since $f(x)$ is continuous there must be a root in this interval ***[1 mark]***.

7 $\sin 2\theta \equiv 2\sin\theta\cos\theta$, so $3\sin 2\theta\tan\theta \equiv 6\sin\theta\cos\theta\tan\theta$ ***[1 mark]***. As $\tan\theta \equiv \frac{\sin\theta}{\cos\theta}$,

$6\sin\theta\cos\theta\tan\theta \equiv 6\sin\theta\cos\theta\frac{\sin\theta}{\cos\theta} \equiv 6\sin^2\theta$ ***[1 mark]***,

so $3\sin 2\theta\tan\theta = 5 \Rightarrow 6\sin^2\theta = 5$ ***[1 mark]***.

Then $\sin^2\theta = \frac{5}{6} \Rightarrow \sin\theta = \pm\sqrt{\frac{5}{6}} = \pm 0.9129$ ***[1 mark]***.

Solving this for θ gives $\theta = 1.15, 1.99, 4.29, 5.13$ ***[2 marks for all 4 correct answers, 1 mark for 2 correct answers]***.

Don't forget the solutions for the negative square root as well — they're easy to miss. Drawing a sketch here is really useful — you can see that there are 4 solutions you need to find:

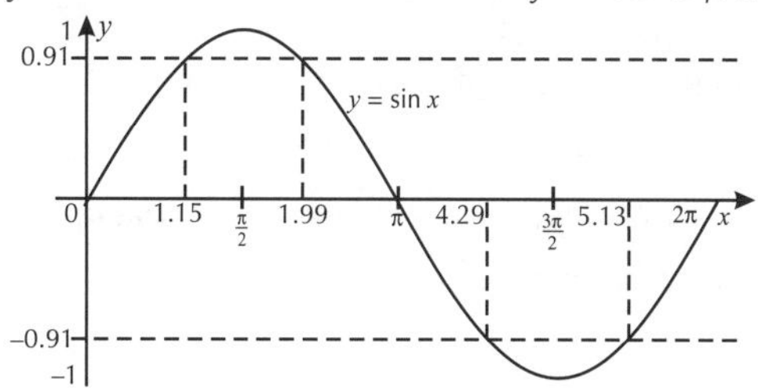

8 a) For $x = \frac{e^y + 2y}{e^y - 2y}$, use the quotient rule to find $\frac{dx}{dy}$:

$u = e^y + 2y \Rightarrow \frac{du}{dy} = e^y + 2$

$v = e^y - 2y \Rightarrow \frac{dv}{dy} = e^y - 2$

$$\frac{dx}{dy} = \frac{v\frac{du}{dy} - u\frac{dv}{dy}}{v^2} = \frac{(e^y - 2y)(e^y + 2) - (e^y + 2y)(e^y - 2)}{(e^y - 2y)^2}$$
$$= \frac{(e^{2y} + 2e^y - 2ye^y - 4y) - (e^{2y} - 2e^y + 2ye^y - 4y)}{(e^y - 2y)^2}$$
$$= \frac{4e^y - 4ye^y}{(e^y - 2y)^2} = \frac{4e^y(1 - y)}{(e^y - 2y)^2}.$$
$$\frac{dy}{dx} = \frac{1}{\frac{dx}{dy}} = \frac{(e^y - 2y)^2}{4e^y(1 - y)}.$$

[3 marks available — 1 mark for correct expressions for du/dy and dv/dy, 1 mark for finding expression for dx/dy using the quotient rule, and 1 mark for correct (or equivalent) expression for dy/dx]

b) At the point (1, 0), $y = 0$ and so $e^y = e^0 = 1$.

So the gradient of the tangent at that point is:

$$\frac{dy}{dx} = \frac{(1 - 0)^2}{4(1 - 0)} = \frac{1}{4}.$$

The gradient of the normal at that point is $-1 \div \frac{1}{4} = -4$.

Equation of a straight line is $y - y_1 = m(x - x_1)$, so at (1, 0) with $m = -4$, the equation of the normal is:

$y - 0 = -4(x - 1) \Rightarrow y = -4x + 4$.

[3 marks available — 1 mark for finding gradient of the normal, 1 mark for correct substitution of –4 and (1, 0) into equation, and 1 mark for rearrangement into the correct form.]

9 a) As $y = e^{2x+1}$, $y^2 = e^{4x+2}$. Putting this into the formula for a volume of revolution gives:

$$V = \pi\int_0^w e^{4x+2}dx = \pi\left[\frac{1}{4}e^{4x+2}\right]_0^w$$
$$= \frac{\pi}{4}[e^{4w+2} - e^2]$$
$$= \frac{\pi}{4}e^2(e^{4w} - 1).$$

Answers

[4 marks available — 1 mark for correct expression for y^2, 1 mark for correct volume of revolution formula, 1 mark for correct integration, 1 mark for rearranging to obtain solution in correct form.]

b) First, work out $\frac{dV}{dw}$: $\frac{dV}{dw} = \frac{\pi}{4}e^2 4e^{4w} = \pi e^{4w+2}$ ***[1 mark]***.
Then, by the chain rule,
$\frac{dV}{dt} = \frac{dV}{dw} \cdot \frac{dw}{dt}$ ***[1 mark]***
$= (\pi e^{4w+2})(2w + 3)$ ***[1 mark]***
$(= 2\pi w e^{4w+2} + 3\pi e^{4w+2})$
Substituting in $w = -0.5$ gives:
$\frac{dV}{dt} = 2\pi(-0.5)e^{4(-0.5)+2} + 3\pi e^{4(-0.5)+2}$
$= -\pi e^0 + 3\pi e^0 = -\pi + 3\pi = 2\pi$ ***[1 mark]***.
You're asked for an exact answer, so leave it in terms of π.

C3 — Practice Exam Two

1 a) $\sqrt{2}\cos\theta - 3\sin\theta \equiv R\cos(\theta + \alpha)$. Using the cos addition rule, $R\cos(\theta + \alpha) \equiv R\cos\theta\cos\alpha - R\sin\theta\sin\alpha$, so $R\cos\alpha = \sqrt{2}$ and $R\sin\alpha = 3$ ***[1 mark]***.
$\frac{R\sin\alpha}{R\cos\alpha} = \tan\alpha$, so $\tan\alpha = \frac{3}{\sqrt{2}}$
Solving this gives $\alpha = 1.13$ (3 s.f.) ***[1 mark]***.
$R = \sqrt{(\sqrt{2})^2 + 3^2} = \sqrt{2+9} = \sqrt{11}$ ***[1 mark]***,
$\sqrt{2}\cos\theta - 3\sin\theta = \sqrt{11}\cos(\theta + 1.13)$.

b) If $\sqrt{2}\cos\theta - 3\sin\theta = 3$, then $\sqrt{11}\cos(\theta + 1.13) = 3$.
So $\cos(\theta + 1.13) = \frac{3}{\sqrt{11}}$. Solving this gives $\theta + 1.13 = 0.441$ (3 s.f.) ***[1 mark]***. The range of solutions becomes $1.13 \le \theta + 1.13 \le 7.41$ $(2\pi + 1.13)$. To find the other values of θ within the new range, $2\pi - 0.441 = 5.84$, $2\pi + 0.441 = 6.72$ ***[1 mark]***. Subtracting 1.13 gives $\theta = 4.71, 5.59$ ***[1 mark for each correct value]***.
You can sketch the graph to help you find all the values of θ.

c) $(\sqrt{2}\cos\theta - 3\sin\theta)^4 = (\sqrt{11}\cos(\theta + 1.13))^4$. The maximum values occur when $\cos(\theta + 1.13) = \pm1$. This value is $(\sqrt{11})^4 = 121$ ***[1 mark]***. Solving $\cos(\theta + 1.13) = 1$ gives the location of the maximum as $2\pi - 1.13 = 5.15$. Solving $\cos(\theta + 1.13) = -1$ gives the location of the other maximum as $2\pi - 1.13 = 2.01$. So the maximum values occur at $\theta = 2.01$ and $\theta = 5.15$ ***[1 mark]***.
Since $(\sqrt{11}\cos(\theta + 1.13))^4 \ge 0$, the minimum value is 0 ***[1 mark]*** and it occurs when $\cos(\theta + 1.13) = 0$. Solving this gives the locations of the minimums at $\frac{\pi}{2} - 1.13 = 0.44$ and $\frac{3\pi}{2} - 1.13 = 3.58$ ***[1 mark]***.
This one was a bit nasty — if you didn't realise that $(\sqrt{11}\cos(\theta + 1.13))^4$ is never negative, you'd have got the minimum values wrong.

2 a) g has range $g(x) \ge -9$ ***[1 mark]***, as the minimum value of g is -9.

b) Neither f nor g are one-to-one functions, so they don't have inverses ***[1 mark]***.
f and g are many-to-one not one-to-one, as more than one value of x is mapped to the same f(x) or g(x) value, e.g. x = 1 and x = –1 are both mapped to f(x) = 1 and g(x)= –8.

c) (i) $fg(4) = f(4^2 - 9) = f(7)$ ***[1 mark]*** $= \frac{1}{7^2} = \frac{1}{49}$ ***[1 mark]***.
(ii) $gf(1) = g(1/1^2) = g(1)$ ***[1 mark]*** $= 1^2 - 9 = -8$ ***[1 mark]***.

d) (i) $fg(x) = f(x^2 - 9) = \frac{1}{(x^2-9)^2}$ ***[1 mark]***.
The domain of fg is $x \in \mathbb{R}$, $x \ne \pm 3$ ***[1 mark]***, as the denominator of the function can't be 0.
(ii) From part (i), you know that $fg(x) = \frac{1}{(x^2-9)^2}$, so
$\frac{1}{(x^2-9)^2} = \frac{1}{256} \Rightarrow (x^2-9)^2 = 256$ ***[1 mark]***
$x^2 - 9 = \pm\sqrt{256} = \pm 16$
$x^2 = 9 \pm 16 = 25, -7$ ***[1 mark]***
$x = \sqrt{25} = \pm 5$ ***[1 mark]***
You can ignore $x^2 = -7$, as this has no solutions in $x \in \mathbb{R}$.

3 First, rearrange the equation to get x^2 on its own:
$e^y = x^2 - 1$, so $x^2 = e^y + 1$. Now put this into the formula for a volume of revolution:
$V = \pi\int_1^3 e^y + 1\,dy = \pi[e^y + y]_1^3$
$= \pi[(e^3 + 3) - (e^1 + 1)] = 60.84$ (4 s.f.)
[5 marks available — 1 mark for taking exponentials of both sides of the equation, 1 mark for getting x^2 on its own, 1 mark for using the correct formula for the volume of revolution, 1 mark for correct integration and 1 mark for substituting the values to get the final answer]

4 a) $f(x) = (\sqrt{x+2})\ln(x+2)$,
so $f(7) = (\sqrt{7+2})\ln(7+2) = (\sqrt{9})\ln 9 = 3\ln 9$ ***[1 mark]***.
Using the log laws:
$f(7) = 3\ln(3^2) = 2 \times 3\ln 3 = 6\ln 3$ ***[1 mark]***.

b) For $y = (\sqrt{x+2})\ln(x+2)$, use the product rule:
$u = \sqrt{x+2} = (x+2)^{\frac{1}{2}} \Rightarrow \frac{du}{dx} = \frac{1}{2}(x+2)^{-\frac{1}{2}} = \frac{1}{2\sqrt{x+2}}$
$v = \ln(x+2) \Rightarrow \frac{dv}{dx} = \frac{1}{x+2}$.
$f'(x) = \frac{dy}{dx} = u\frac{dv}{dx} + v\frac{du}{dx} = \frac{\sqrt{x+2}}{x+2} + \frac{\ln(x+2)}{2\sqrt{x+2}}$.
So $f'(7) = \frac{\sqrt{7+2}}{7+2} + \frac{\ln(7+2)}{2\sqrt{7+2}} = \frac{3}{9} + \frac{\ln 9}{2 \times 3}$.
Since, using log laws, $\ln 9 = \ln 3^2 = 2\ln 3$,
$f'(7) = \frac{1}{3} + \frac{2\ln 3}{2 \times 3} = \frac{1}{3} + \frac{\ln 3}{3} = \frac{1}{3}(1 + \ln 3)$.
[4 marks available — 1 mark for correct expressions for du/dx and dv/dx, 1 mark for correct use of product rule formula, 1 mark for correct substitution of x = 7, and 1 mark for correct rearrangement using the log laws]

c) Equation of a straight line is $y - y_1 = m(x - x_1)$. For the tangent at $x = 7$, $y = 6\ln 3$ (from (a)) and $m = \frac{1}{3}(1 + \ln 3)$ (from (b)), so the equation of the tangent is:
$y - 6\ln 3 = \frac{1}{3}(1 + \ln 3)(x - 7)$
$\Rightarrow y = \frac{1}{3}(1 + \ln 3)(x - 7) + 6\ln 3$
$\Rightarrow 3y = (1 + \ln 3)(x - 7) + 18\ln 3$
$\Rightarrow 3y = x + x\ln 3 - 7 - 7\ln 3 + 18\ln 3$
$\Rightarrow 3y = x + x\ln 3 + 11\ln 3 - 7$.

Answers

[2 marks available — 1 mark for correct substitution of m, y_1 and x_1 into equation, 1 mark for correct rearrangement to give final answer]

5 a) $\frac{1+\cos x}{2} = \frac{1}{2}\left(1 + \cos 2\left(\frac{x}{2}\right)\right)$ ***[1 mark]***

$= \frac{1}{2}\left(1 + \left(2\cos^2\frac{x}{2} - 1\right)\right)$ ***[1 mark]***

$= \frac{1}{2}\left(2\cos^2\frac{x}{2}\right) = \cos^2\frac{x}{2}$ ***[1 mark]***

b) As $\cos^2\frac{x}{2} = 0.75$, then $\frac{1+\cos x}{2} = 0.75$.
So $1 + \cos x = 1.5$

$\cos x = 0.5 \Rightarrow x = \frac{\pi}{3}, \frac{5\pi}{3}$.

[4 marks available — 2 marks for rearranging equation to get in terms of cos x, 1 mark for each correct answer]

You should know the solutions to cos x = 0.5 from the trig triangles from Section 3.

6 a) $y = e^{2x} - 5e^x + 3x$, so, using chain rule:

$\frac{dy}{dx} = 2e^{2x} - 5e^x + 3$.

[2 marks available — 1 mark for $2e^{2x}$, 1 mark for rest of answer.]

b) Differentiating again gives: $\frac{d^2y}{dx^2} = 4e^{2x} - 5e^x$.

[2 marks available — 1 mark for $4e^{2x}$, 1 mark for $-5e^x$]

c) Stationary points occur when $\frac{dy}{dx} = 0$, so:
$2e^{2x} - 5e^x + 3 = 0$ ***[1 mark]***.

(This looks like a quadratic, so substitute y = e^x and factorise...)

$2y^2 - 5y + 3 = 0 \Rightarrow (2y - 3)(y - 1) = 0$ ***[1 mark]***.

So the solutions are:

$2y - 3 = 0 \Rightarrow y = \frac{3}{2} \Rightarrow e^x = \frac{3}{2} \Rightarrow x = \ln\frac{3}{2}$ ***[1 mark]***, and
$y - 1 = 0 \Rightarrow y = 1 \Rightarrow e^x = 1 \Rightarrow x = \ln 1 = 0$ ***[1 mark]***.

d) To determine the nature of the stationary points, find $\frac{d^2y}{dx^2}$ at $x = 0$ and $x = \ln\frac{3}{2}$:

$\frac{d^2y}{dx^2} = 4e^{2x} - 5e^x$ (from (b)), so when $x = 0$:

$\frac{d^2y}{dx^2} = 4e^0 - 5e^0 = 4 - 5 = -1$ ***[1 mark]***,

so $\frac{d^2y}{dx^2} < 0$, which means the point is a maximum ***[1 mark]***.

When $x = \ln\frac{3}{2}$:

$\frac{d^2y}{dx^2} = 4e^{2\ln\frac{3}{2}} - 5e^{\ln\frac{3}{2}} = 4\left(\frac{3}{2}\right)^2 - 5\left(\frac{3}{2}\right) = \frac{3}{2}$ ***[1 mark]***,

so $\frac{d^2y}{dx^2} > 0$, which means the point is a minimum ***[1 mark]***.

7 a) $P = 5700e^{-0.15t}$, so when $t = 0$, $P = 5700e^0 = 5700$ ***[1 mark]***.

b) At the start of 2020, $t = 10$,
so $P = 5700e^{-0.15 \times 10} = 1271.8419...$
$= 1271$

[2 marks available — 1 mark for correct substitution of t = 10, 1 mark for correct final answer]

Remember — round down as there are only 1271 whole birds.

c) When $P = 1000$: $1000 = 5700e^{-0.15t} \Rightarrow 1000 = \frac{5700}{e^{0.15t}}$

$\Rightarrow e^{0.15t} = \frac{5700}{1000} = 5.7$ ***[1 mark]***. Take ln of both sides:

$0.15t = \ln 5.7 \Rightarrow t = \frac{\ln 5.7}{0.15} = 11.6031...$ years.

So the population will drop below 1000 in the year 2021 ***[1 mark]***.

d)

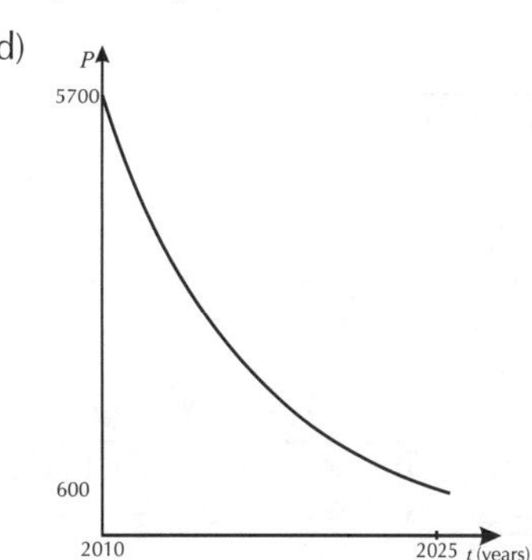

[3 marks available — 1 mark for correct shape of graph, 1 mark for (0, 5700) labelled, 1 mark for calculating P when t = 15 (the population ≈ 600 in 2025)]

8 a) To find the inverse, let $y = f(x)$, so $y = 4(x^2 - 1)$. Now make x the subject: $y = 4(x^2 - 1) \Rightarrow \frac{y}{4} = x^2 - 1 \Rightarrow \frac{y}{4} + 1 = x^2$

so $x = \sqrt{\frac{y}{4} + 1}$ ***[1 mark]*** (you can ignore the negative square root, as the domain of f(x) is $x \geq 0$). Finally, replace y with x and x with $f^{-1}(x)$: $f^{-1}(x) = \sqrt{\frac{x}{4} + 1}$ ***[1 mark]***.

$f^{-1}(x)$ is a reflection of f(x) in the line $y = x$ ***[1 mark]***, so the point at which the lines f(x) and $f^{-1}(x)$ meet is also the point where $f^{-1}(x)$ meets the line $y = x$. At this point, $x = \sqrt{\frac{x}{4} + 1}$ ***[1 mark]***.

b) Let $g(x) = \sqrt{\frac{x}{4} + 1} - x$ ***[1 mark]***.

If there is a root in the interval $1 < x < 2$ then there will be a change of sign for g(x) between 1 and 2:

$g(1) = \sqrt{\frac{1}{4} + 1} - 1 = 0.1180...$

$g(2) = \sqrt{\frac{2}{4} + 1} - 2 = -0.7752...$ ***[1 mark for both]***

There is a change of sign, so there is a root in the interval $1 < x < 2$ ***[1 mark]***.

c) $x_{n+1} = \sqrt{\frac{x_n}{4} + 1}$, and $x_0 = 1$, so:

$x_1 = \sqrt{\frac{1}{4} + 1} = 1.1180...$ ***[1 mark]***

$x_2 = \sqrt{\frac{1.1180...}{4} + 1} = 1.1311...$

$x_3 = \sqrt{\frac{1.1311...}{4} + 1} = 1.1326...$ ***[1 mark]***

So $x = 1.13$ to 3 s.f. ***[1 mark]***.

Answers

C4 Section 1 — Algebra and Functions

Warm-up Questions

1) a) $\frac{4x^2-25}{6x-15}=\frac{(2x+5)(2x-5)}{3(2x-5)}=\frac{2x+5}{3}$

b) $\frac{2x+3}{x-2}\times\frac{4x-8}{2x^2-3x-9}$

$=\frac{2x+3}{x-2}\times\frac{4(x-2)}{(2x+3)(x-3)}$

$=\frac{4}{x-3}$

c) $\frac{x^2-3x}{x+1}\div\frac{x}{2}=\frac{x(x-3)}{x+1}\times\frac{2}{x}$

$=\frac{x-3}{x+1}\times 2=\frac{2(x-3)}{x+1}$

2) a) $\frac{x}{2x+1}+\frac{3}{x^2}+\frac{1}{x}=\frac{x\cdot x^2}{x^2(2x+1)}+\frac{3(2x+1)}{x^2(2x+1)}+\frac{x(2x+1)}{x^2(2x+1)}$

$=\frac{x^3+6x+3+2x^2+x}{x^2(2x+1)}=\frac{x^3+2x^2+7x+3}{x^2(2x+1)}$

b) $\frac{2}{x^2-1}-\frac{3x}{x-1}+\frac{x}{x+1}$

$=\frac{2}{(x+1)(x-1)}-\frac{3x(x+1)}{(x+1)(x-1)}+\frac{x(x-1)}{(x+1)(x-1)}$

$=\frac{2-3x^2-3x+x^2-x}{(x+1)(x-1)}=\frac{2-2x^2-4x}{(x+1)(x-1)}$

$=\frac{2(1-x^2-2x)}{(x+1)(x-1)}$

3)
$$\begin{array}{r l}
 & x^2-2x+7\ \text{r}-9 \\
x+4 & \overline{)\,x^3+2x^2-x+19} \\
- & \underline{x^3+4x^2} \\
 & -2x^2-x \\
- & \underline{-2x^2-8x} \\
 & 7x+19 \\
- & \underline{7x+28} \\
 & -9
\end{array}$$

so $(x^3+2x^2-x+19)\div(x+4)=x^2-2x+7$ remainder -9.

4) $2x^3+8x^2+7x+8\equiv(Ax^2+Bx+C)(x+3)+D$.

Set $x=-3$: $2(-3)^3+8(-3)^2+7(-3)+8=0+D\Rightarrow D=5$.

Set $x=0$: $0+8=C(0+3)+D\Rightarrow C=1$.

Equating the coefficients of x^3 gives $2=A$.

Finally, equating the coefficients of x^2 gives $8=3A+B$

$\Rightarrow 8=(3\times 2)+B$, so $B=2$.

So $2x^3+8x^2+7x+8=(2x^2+2x+1)(x+3)+5$. The result when $2x^3+8x^2+7x+8$ is divided by $(x+3)$ is $2x^2+2x+1$ remainder 5.

For questions 5-7, you can use the substitution method or the equating coefficients method. I've just shown one method for each.

5) a) $\frac{4x+5}{(x+4)(2x-3)}\equiv\frac{A}{(x+4)}+\frac{B}{(2x-3)}$

$4x+5\equiv A(2x-3)+B(x+4)$

Using substitution method:

substitute $x=-4$: $-11=-11A\Rightarrow A=1$

substitute $x=1.5$: $11=5.5B\Rightarrow B=2$

$\frac{4x+5}{(x+4)(2x-3)}\equiv\frac{1}{(x+4)}+\frac{2}{(2x-3)}$

b) $\frac{-7x-7}{(3x+1)(x-2)}\equiv\frac{A}{(3x+1)}+\frac{B}{(x-2)}$

$-7x-7\equiv A(x-2)+B(3x+1)$

Using equating coefficients method:

coefficients of x: $-7=A+3B$

constants: $-7=-2A+B$

Solving simultaneously: $A=2$, $B=-3$

$\frac{-7x-7}{(3x+1)(x-2)}\equiv\frac{2}{(3x+1)}-\frac{3}{(x-2)}$

c) $\frac{x-18}{(x+4)(3x-4)}\equiv\frac{A}{(x+4)}+\frac{B}{(3x-4)}$

$x-18\equiv A(3x-4)+B(x+4)$

Using substitution method:

substitute $x=-4$: $-22=-16A\Rightarrow A=\frac{11}{8}$.

And using equating coefficients method:

coefficients of x: $1=3A+B$

Substituting $A=\frac{11}{8}$: $1=3A+B\Rightarrow B=1-\frac{33}{8}=-\frac{25}{8}$.

$\frac{x-18}{(x+4)(3x-4)}\equiv\frac{11}{8(x+4)}-\frac{25}{8(3x-4)}$

Don't worry if you get fractions for your coefficients — just put the numerator on the top and the denominator on the bottom.

d) Factorise the denominator:

$\frac{5x}{x^2+x-6}\equiv\frac{5x}{(x+3)(x-2)}\equiv\frac{A}{(x+3)}+\frac{B}{(x-2)}$

$5x\equiv A(x-2)+B(x+3)$

Using substitution method:

substitute $x=-3$: $-15=-5A\Rightarrow A=3$

substitute $x=2$: $10=5B\Rightarrow B=2$

$\frac{5x}{x^2+x-6}\equiv\frac{3}{(x+3)}+\frac{2}{(x-2)}$

e) Factorise the denominator:

$\frac{6+4y}{9-y^2}\equiv\frac{6+4y}{(3-y)(3+y)}\equiv\frac{A}{(3-y)}+\frac{B}{(3+y)}$

$6+4y\equiv A(3+y)+B(3-y)$

Using substitution method:

substitute $y=3$: $18=6A\Rightarrow A=3$

substitute $y=-3$: $-6=6B\Rightarrow B=-1$

$\frac{6+4y}{9-y^2}\equiv\frac{3}{(3-y)}-\frac{1}{(3+y)}$

f) $\frac{10x^2+32x+16}{(x+3)(2x+4)(x-2)}\equiv\frac{A}{(x+3)}+\frac{B}{(2x+4)}+\frac{C}{(x-2)}$

$10x^2+32x+16$

$\equiv A(2x+4)(x-2)+B(x+3)(x-2)+C(x+3)(2x+4)$

Using substitution method:

substitute $x=2$: $120=40C\Rightarrow C=3$

substitute $x=-3$: $10=10A\Rightarrow A=1$

substitute $x=-2$: $-8=-4B\Rightarrow B=2$

$\frac{10x^2+32x+16}{(x+3)(2x+4)(x-2)}\equiv\frac{1}{(x+3)}+\frac{2}{(2x+4)}+\frac{3}{(x-2)}$

Answers

g) Factorise the denominator:

$$\frac{4x^2+12x+6}{x^3+3x^2+2x} \equiv \frac{4x^2+12x+6}{x(x^2+3x+2)} \equiv \frac{4x^2+12x+6}{x(x+1)(x+2)}$$

$$\equiv \frac{A}{x} + \frac{B}{(x+1)} + \frac{C}{(x+2)}$$

$4x^2 + 12x + 6 \equiv A(x+1)(x+2) + Bx(x+2) + Cx(x+1)$

Using substitution method:

substitute $x = -1$: $-2 = -B \Rightarrow B = 2$

substitute $x = 0$: $6 = 2A \Rightarrow A = 3$

substitute $x = -2$: $-2 = 2C \Rightarrow C = -1$

$$\frac{4x^2+12x+6}{x^3+3x^2+2x} \equiv \frac{3}{x} + \frac{2}{(x+1)} - \frac{1}{(x+2)}$$

h) $$\frac{-11x^2+6x+11}{(2x+1)(3-x)(x+2)} \equiv \frac{A}{(2x+1)} + \frac{B}{(3-x)} + \frac{C}{(x+2)}$$

$-11x^2 + 6x + 11$

$\equiv A(3-x)(x+2) + B(2x+1)(x+2) + C(2x+1)(3-x)$

Using substitution method:

substitute $x = 3$: $-70 = 35B \Rightarrow B = -2$

substitute $x = -2$: $-45 = -15C \Rightarrow C = 3$

substitute $x = -0.5$: $5.25 = 5.25A \Rightarrow A = 1$

$$\frac{-11x^2+6x+11}{(2x+1)(3-x)(x+2)} \equiv \frac{1}{(2x+1)} - \frac{2}{(3-x)} + \frac{3}{(x+2)}$$

6) a) $$\frac{2x+2}{(x+3)^2} \equiv \frac{A}{(x+3)} + \frac{B}{(x+3)^2}$$

$2x + 2 \equiv A(x+3) + B$

Using substitution method:

substitute $x = -3$: $-4 = B$

substitute $x = 0$: $2 = 3A - 4 \Rightarrow A = 2$

$$\frac{2x+2}{(x+3)^2} \equiv \frac{2}{(x+3)} - \frac{4}{(x+3)^2}$$

b) $$\frac{6x^2+17x+5}{x(x+2)^2} \equiv \frac{A}{x} + \frac{B}{(x+2)} + \frac{C}{(x+2)^2}$$

$6x^2 + 17x + 5 \equiv A(x+2)^2 + Bx(x+2) + Cx$

substitute $x = -2$: $-5 = -2C \Rightarrow C = \frac{5}{2}$

substitute $x = 0$: $5 = 4A \Rightarrow A = \frac{5}{4}$

coefficients of x^2: $6 = A + B$

substitute $A = \frac{5}{4}$: $6 = \frac{5}{4} + B \Rightarrow B = \frac{19}{4}$

$$\frac{6x^2+17x+5}{x(x+2)^2} \equiv \frac{5}{4x} + \frac{19}{4(x+2)} + \frac{5}{2(x+2)^2}$$

c) $$\frac{-18x+14}{(2x-1)^2(x+2)} \equiv \frac{A}{(2x-1)} + \frac{B}{(2x-1)^2} + \frac{C}{(x+2)}$$

$-18x + 14 \equiv A(2x-1)(x+2) + B(x+2) + C(2x-1)^2$

substitute $x = -2$: $50 = 25C \Rightarrow C = 2$

substitute $x = 0.5$: $5 = 2.5B \Rightarrow B = 2$

coefficients of x^2: $0 = 2A + 4C$

substitute $C = 2$: $0 = 2A + 8 \Rightarrow A = -4$

$$\frac{-18x+14}{(2x-1)^2(x+2)} \equiv \frac{-4}{(2x-1)} + \frac{2}{(2x-1)^2} + \frac{2}{(x+2)}$$

d) Factorise the denominator:

$$\frac{8x^2-x-5}{x^3-x^2} \equiv \frac{8x^2-x-5}{x^2(x-1)} \equiv \frac{A}{x} + \frac{B}{x^2} + \frac{C}{(x-1)}$$

$8x^2 - x - 5 \equiv Ax(x-1) + B(x-1) + Cx^2$

coefficients of x^2: $8 = A + C$ (eq. 1)

coefficients of x: $-1 = -A + B$ (eq. 2)

constants: $-5 = -B \Rightarrow B = 5$

substitute $B = 5$ in eq. 2: $-1 = -A + 5 \Rightarrow A = 6$

substitute $A = 6$ in eq. 1: $8 = 6 + C \Rightarrow C = 2$

$$\frac{8x^2-x-5}{x^3-x^2} \equiv \frac{6}{x} + \frac{5}{x^2} + \frac{2}{(x-1)}$$

7) a) Expand the denominator:

$$\frac{2x^2+18x+26}{(x+2)(x+4)} \equiv \frac{2x^2+18x+26}{x^2+6x+8}$$

Divide the fraction:

$$\begin{array}{r} 2 \\ x^2+6x+8\overline{)2x^2+18x+26} \\ \underline{2x^2+12x+16} \\ 6x+10 \end{array}$$

$$\frac{2x^2+18x+26}{(x+2)(x+4)} \equiv 2 + \frac{6x+10}{(x+2)(x+4)}$$

Now express $\frac{6x+10}{(x+2)(x+4)}$ as partial fractions:

$$\frac{6x+10}{(x+2)(x+4)} \equiv \frac{A}{(x+2)} + \frac{B}{(x+4)}$$

$6x + 10 \equiv A(x+4) + B(x+2)$

substitute $x = -4$: $-14 = -2B \Rightarrow B = 7$

substitute $x = -2$: $-2 = 2A \Rightarrow A = -1$

So overall $\frac{2x^2+18x+26}{(x+2)(x+4)} \equiv 2 - \frac{1}{(x+2)} + \frac{7}{(x+4)}$

b) Expand the denominator:

$$\frac{3x^2+9x+2}{x(x+1)} \equiv \frac{3x^2+9x+2}{x^2+x}$$

Divide the fraction:

$$\begin{array}{r} 3 \\ x^2+x\overline{)3x^2+9x+2} \\ \underline{3x^2+3x} \\ 6x+2 \end{array}$$

$$\frac{3x^2+9x+2}{x(x+1)} \equiv 3 + \frac{6x+2}{x(x+1)}$$

Now express $\frac{6x+2}{x(x+1)}$ as partial fractions:

$$\frac{6x+2}{x(x+1)} \equiv \frac{A}{x} + \frac{B}{(x+1)}$$

$6x + 2 \equiv A(x+1) + Bx$

substitute $x = -1$: $-4 = -B \Rightarrow B = 4$

substitute $x = 0$: $2 = A$

So overall $\frac{3x^2+9x+2}{x(x+1)} \equiv 3 + \frac{2}{x} + \frac{4}{(x+1)}$

c) Expand the denominator:

$$\frac{24x^2-70x+53}{(2x-3)^2} \equiv \frac{24x^2-70x+53}{4x^2-12x+9}$$

Divide the fraction:

$$\begin{array}{r} 6 \\ 4x^2-12x+9\overline{)24x^2-70x+53} \\ \underline{24x^2-72x+54} \\ 2x-1 \end{array}$$

$$\frac{24x^2-70x+53}{(2x-3)^2} \equiv 6 + \frac{2x-1}{(2x-3)^2}$$

Answers

Now express $\frac{2x-1}{(2x-3)^2}$ as partial fractions:

$$\frac{2x-1}{(2x-3)^2} \equiv \frac{A}{(2x-3)} + \frac{B}{(2x-3)^2}$$

$2x - 1 \equiv A(2x - 3) + B$

substitute $x = 1.5$: $2 = B$

substitute $x = 0$, and $B = 2$: $-1 = -3A + 2 \Rightarrow A = 1$

So overall $\frac{24x^2 - 70x + 53}{(2x-3)^2} \equiv 6 + \frac{1}{(2x-3)} + \frac{2}{(2x-3)^2}$

d) Expand the denominator:

$$\frac{3x^3 - 2x^2 - 2x - 3}{(x+1)(x-2)} \equiv \frac{3x^3 - 2x^2 - 2x - 3}{x^2 - x - 2}$$

Divide the fraction using $f(x) = q(x)d(x) + r(x)$:

$3x^3 - 2x^2 - 2x - 3 = (Ax + B)(x^2 - x - 2) + Cx + D$

coefficients of x^3: $3 = A$

coefficients of x^2: $-2 = -A + B$

substitute $A = 3$: $-2 = -3 + B \Rightarrow B = 1$

coefficients of x: $-2 = -2A - B + C$

substitute $A = 3$ and $B = 1$: $-2 = -6 - 1 + C \Rightarrow C = 5$

constants: $-3 = -2B + D$

substitute $B = 1$: $-3 = -2 + D \Rightarrow D = -1$

$$\frac{3x^3 - 2x^2 - 2x - 3}{(x+1)(x-2)} \equiv 3x + 1 + \frac{5x-1}{(x+1)(x-2)}$$

Now express $\frac{5x-1}{(x+1)(x-2)}$ as partial fractions:

$$\frac{5x-1}{(x+1)(x-2)} \equiv \frac{M}{(x+1)} + \frac{N}{(x-2)}$$

$5x - 1 \equiv M(x - 2) + N(x + 1)$

substitute $x = 2$: $9 = 3N \Rightarrow N = 3$

substitute $x = -1$: $-6 = -3M \Rightarrow M = 2$

So overall $\frac{3x^3 - 2x^2 - 2x - 3}{(x+1)(x-2)} \equiv 3x + 1 + \frac{2}{(x+1)} + \frac{3}{(x-2)}$

I used the remainder theorem to divide this fraction, because it's a bit trickier than the rest have been. You could have used the remainder theorem in 7)a)-c) too, but I reckon they were easier to do with long division.

Exam Questions

1 Add the partial fractions and equate the numerators:

$5 + 9x \equiv A + B(1 + 3x)$ ***[1 mark]***

Using substitution method:

substitute $x = -\frac{1}{3}$: $2 = A \Rightarrow A = 2$ ***[1 mark]***

substitute $x = 0$: $5 = 2 + B \Rightarrow B = 3$ ***[1 mark]***

2 $$\frac{2x^2 - 9x - 35}{x^2 - 49} = \frac{(2x+5)(x-7)}{(x+7)(x-7)} = \frac{2x+5}{x+7}$$

[3 marks available — 1 mark for factorising the numerator, 1 mark for factorising the denominator and 1 mark for correct answer (after cancelling)]

3 Expand the denominator:

$$\frac{18x^2 - 15x - 62}{(3x+4)(x-2)} \equiv \frac{18x^2 - 15x - 62}{3x^2 - 2x - 8}$$

Divide the fraction:

$$\begin{array}{r} 6 \\ 3x^2 - 2x - 8 \overline{)\,18x^2 - 15x - 62} \\ \underline{18x^2 - 12x - 48} \\ -3x - 14 \end{array}$$

Watch out for the negative signs here. You're subtracting the bottom line from the top, so be sure to get it right.

You could use alternative methods — e.g. the remainder theorem for the division. You'll still get the marks, so use the one you're happiest with unless they tell you otherwise.

$$\frac{18x^2 - 15x - 62}{(3x+4)(x-2)} \equiv 6 + \frac{-3x - 14}{(3x+4)(x-2)}$$

$A = 6$ ***[1 mark]***

$$\frac{-3x - 14}{(3x+4)(x-2)} \equiv \frac{B}{(3x+4)} + \frac{C}{(x-2)}$$

$-3x - 14 \equiv B(x - 2) + C(3x + 4)$ ***[1 mark]***

substitute $x = 2$: $-20 = 10C \Rightarrow C = -2$ ***[1 mark]***

coefficients of x: $-3 = B + 3C$

$-3 = B - 6 \Rightarrow B = 3$ ***[1 mark]***

I used the equating coefficients method for the last bit, because I realised that I'd need to substitute $-\frac{4}{3}$ in for x, and I really couldn't be bothered.

4 $5x^2 + 3x + 6 \equiv A(2x - 1)^2 + B(3 - x) + C(2x - 1)(3 - x)$

[1 mark]

Using substitution method:

substitute $x = 3$: $60 = 25A \Rightarrow A = \frac{12}{5}$ ***[1 mark]***

substitute $x = \frac{1}{2}$: $\frac{35}{4} = \frac{5}{2}B \Rightarrow B = \frac{7}{2}$ ***[1 mark]***

coefficients of x^2: $5 = 4A - 2C$

substitute $A = \frac{12}{5}$: $5 = \frac{48}{5} - 2C$

$-\frac{23}{5} = -2C \Rightarrow C = \frac{23}{10}$ ***[1 mark]***

5 First put $x = -6$ into both sides of the identity $x^3 + 15x^2 + 43x - 30 \equiv (Ax^2 + Bx + C)(x + 6) + D$:
$(-6)^3 + 15(-6)^2 + 43(-6) - 30 = D \Rightarrow 36 = D$ ***[1 mark]***.
Now set $x = 0$ to get $-30 = 6C + D$, so $C = -11$ ***[1 mark]***.
Equating the coefficients of x^3 gives $1 = A$. Equating the coefficients of x^2 gives $15 = 6A + B$, so $B = 9$ ***[1 mark]***.
So $x^3 + 15x^2 + 43x - 30 = (x^2 + 9x - 11)(x + 6) + 36$.

You could also do this question by algebraic long division — you just have to use your answer to work out A, B, C and D.

6 Expand the denominator:

$$\frac{-80x^2 + 49x - 9}{(5x-1)(2-4x)} \equiv \frac{-80x^2 + 49x - 9}{-20x^2 + 14x - 2}$$

Divide the fraction:

$$\begin{array}{r} 4 \\ -20x^2 + 14x - 2 \overline{)\,-80x^2 + 49x - 9} \\ \underline{-80x^2 + 56x - 8} \\ -7x - 1 \end{array}$$

$$\frac{-80x^2 + 49x - 9}{(5x-1)(2-4x)} \equiv 4 + \frac{-7x - 1}{(5x-1)(2-4x)}$$ ***[1 mark]***

$$\frac{-7x - 1}{(5x-1)(2-4x)} \equiv \frac{A}{(5x-1)} + \frac{B}{(2-4x)}$$

$-7x - 1 \equiv A(2 - 4x) + B(5x - 1)$ ***[1 mark]***

Answers

substitute $x = 0.5$: $-4.5 = 1.5B \Rightarrow B = -3$ ***[1 mark]***

coefficients of x: $-7 = -4A + 5B$

substitute $B = -3$: $-7 = -4A - 15$

$8 = -4A \Rightarrow A = -2$ ***[1 mark]***

7 a) Expand the denominator:

$$\frac{3x^2 + 12x - 11}{(x+3)(x-1)} \equiv \frac{3x^2 + 12x - 11}{x^2 + 2x - 3}$$

Divide the fraction:

$$x^2 + 2x - 3\overline{)3x^2 + 12x - 11}$$ with quotient 3

$3x^2 + 6x - 9$

$6x - 2 \Rightarrow -2 + 6x$ ***[1 mark]***

$$\frac{3x^2 + 12x - 11}{(x+3)(x-1)} \equiv 3 + \frac{-2 + 6x}{(x+3)(x-1)}$$

$A = 3$ ***[1 mark]***, $B = -2$ ***[1 mark]***, $C = 6$ ***[1 mark]***

b) $$\frac{3x^2 + 12x - 11}{(x+3)(x-1)} \equiv 3 + \frac{-2 + 6x}{(x+3)(x-1)} \equiv 3 + \frac{M}{(x+3)} + \frac{N}{(x-1)}$$

$-2 + 6x \equiv M(x-1) + N(x+3)$

substitute $x = 1$: $4 = 4N \Rightarrow N = 1$ ***[1 mark]***

substitute $x = -3$: $-20 = -4M \Rightarrow M = 5$ ***[1 mark]***

So overall $\frac{3x^2 + 12x - 11}{(x+3)(x-1)} \equiv 3 + \frac{5}{(x+3)} + \frac{1}{(x-1)}$ ***[1 mark]***

C4 Section 2 — Parametric Equations Warm-up Questions

1) a) Substitute the values of t into the parametric equations to find the corresponding values of x and y:

$t = 0 \Rightarrow x = \frac{6-0}{2} = 3,\ y = 2(0)^2 + 0 + 4 = 4$

$t = 1 \Rightarrow x = \frac{6-1}{2} = 2.5,\ y = 2(1)^2 + 1 + 4 = 7$

$t = 2 \Rightarrow x = \frac{6-2}{2} = 2,\ y = 2(2)^2 + 2 + 4 = 14$

$t = 3 \Rightarrow x = \frac{6-3}{2} = 1.5,\ y = 2(3)^2 + 3 + 4 = 25$

b) Use the given values in the parametric equations and solve for t:

(i) $\frac{6-t}{2} = -7 \Rightarrow t = 20$

(ii) $2t^2 + t + 4 = 19$

$\Rightarrow 2t^2 + t - 15 = 0$

$\Rightarrow (2t - 5)(t + 3) = 0$

$\Rightarrow t = 2.5,\ t = -3$

c) Rearrange the parametric equation for x to make t the subject:

$x = \frac{6-t}{2} \Rightarrow 2x = 6 - t \Rightarrow t = 6 - 2x$

Now substitute this into the parametric equation for y:

$y = 2t^2 + t + 4$

$= 2(6 - 2x)^2 + (6 - 2x) + 4$

$= 2(36 - 24x + 4x^2) + 10 - 2x$

$y = 8x^2 - 50x + 82.$

2) a) Substitute the values of θ into the parametric equations to find the corresponding values of x and y:

(i) $x = 2\sin\frac{\pi}{4} = \frac{2}{\sqrt{2}} = \sqrt{2}$

$y = \cos^2\frac{\pi}{4} + 4 = \left(\cos\frac{\pi}{4}\right)^2 + 4 = \left(\frac{1}{\sqrt{2}}\right)^2 + 4 = \frac{1}{2} + 4 = \frac{9}{2}$

So the coordinates are $\left(\sqrt{2}, \frac{9}{2}\right)$.

(ii) $x = 2\sin\frac{\pi}{6} = 2 \times \frac{1}{2} = 1$

$y = \cos^2\frac{\pi}{6} + 4 = \left(\cos\frac{\pi}{6}\right)^2 + 4 = \left(\frac{\sqrt{3}}{2}\right)^2 + 4 = \frac{3}{4} + 4 = \frac{19}{4}$

So the coordinates are $\left(1, \frac{19}{4}\right)$.

b) Use the identity $\cos^2\theta = 1 - \sin^2\theta$ in the equation for y so both equations are in terms of $\sin\theta$:

$y = \cos^2\theta + 4$

$= 1 - \sin^2\theta + 4$

$= 5 - \sin^2\theta$

Rearrange the equation for x to get $\sin^2\theta$ in terms of x:

$x = 2\sin\theta \Rightarrow \frac{x}{2} = \sin\theta \Rightarrow \sin^2\theta = \frac{x^2}{4}$

So $y = 5 - \sin^2\theta \Rightarrow y = 5 - \frac{x^2}{4}$

c) $x = 2\sin\theta$, and $-1 \le \sin\theta \le 1$ so $-2 \le x \le 2$.

I know what you're thinking — this answer section would be brightened up immensely by a cheery song-and-dance number. Sorry, no such luck I'm afraid. Here's the next answer instead...

3) Use the identity $\cos 2\theta = 1 - 2\sin^2\theta$ in the equation for y:

$y = 3 + 2\cos 2\theta$

$= 3 + 2(1 - 2\sin^2\theta)$

$= 5 - 4\sin^2\theta$

Rearrange the equation for x to get $\sin^2\theta$ in terms of x:

$x = \frac{\sin\theta}{3} \Rightarrow 3x = \sin\theta \Rightarrow \sin^2\theta = 9x^2$

So $y = 5 - 4\sin^2\theta$

$\Rightarrow y = 5 - 4(9x^2)$

$\Rightarrow y = 5 - 36x^2$

4) a) On the y-axis:

$x = 0 \Rightarrow t^2 - 1 = 0 \Rightarrow t = \pm 1$

If $t = 1$, $y = 4 + \frac{3}{1} = 7$

If $t = -1$, $y = 4 + \frac{3}{-1} = 1$

So the curve crosses the y-axis at (0, 1) and (0, 7).

b) Substitute the parametric equations into the equation of the line:

$x + 2y = 14$

$\Rightarrow (t^2 - 1) + 2(4 + \frac{3}{t}) = 14$

$\Rightarrow t^2 - 1 + 8 + \frac{6}{t} = 14$

$\Rightarrow t^2 - 7 + \frac{6}{t} = 0$

$\Rightarrow t^3 - 7t + 6 = 0$

$\Rightarrow (t - 1)(t^2 + t - 6) = 0$

$\Rightarrow (t - 1)(t - 2)(t + 3) = 0$

$\Rightarrow t = 1,\ t = 2,\ t = -3$

When $t = 1$, $x = 0$, $y = 7$ (from part (i))

When $t = 2$, $x = 2^2 - 1 = 3$, $y = 4 + \frac{3}{2} = 5.5$

When $t = -3$, $x = (-3)^2 - 1 = 8$, $y = 4 + \frac{3}{-3} = 3$

So the curve crosses the line $x + 2y = 14$ at (0, 7), (3, 5.5) and (8, 3).

Answers

Exam Questions

1 a) Substitute the given value of θ into the parametric equations:

$\theta = \frac{\pi}{3} \Rightarrow x = 1 - \tan\frac{\pi}{3} = 1 - \sqrt{3}$

$y = \frac{1}{2}\sin\left(\frac{2\pi}{3}\right) = \frac{1}{2}\left(\frac{\sqrt{3}}{2}\right) = \frac{\sqrt{3}}{4}$

So $P = \left(1 - \sqrt{3}, \frac{\sqrt{3}}{4}\right)$

[2 marks available — 1 mark for substituting $\theta = \frac{\pi}{3}$ into the parametric equations, 1 mark for both coordinates of P correct.]

b) Use $y = -\frac{1}{2}$ to find the value of θ:

$-\frac{1}{2} = \frac{1}{2}\sin 2\theta \Rightarrow \sin 2\theta = -1$

$\Rightarrow 2\theta = -\frac{\pi}{2}$

$\Rightarrow \theta = -\frac{\pi}{4}$

You can also find θ using the parametric equation for x, with x = 2.

[2 marks available — 1 mark for substituting given x- or y-value into the correct parametric equation, 1 mark for finding the correct value of θ.]

c) $x = 1 - \tan\theta \quad \Rightarrow \tan\theta = 1 - x$

$y = \frac{1}{2}\sin 2\theta$

$= \frac{1}{2}\left(\frac{2\tan\theta}{1 + \tan^2\theta}\right)$

$= \frac{\tan\theta}{1 + \tan^2\theta}$

$= \frac{(1 - x)}{1 + (1 - x)^2}$

$= \frac{1 - x}{1 + 1 - 2x + x^2}$

$= \frac{1 - x}{x^2 - 2x + 2}$

[3 marks available — 1 mark for using the given identity to rearrange one of the parametric equations, 1 mark for eliminating θ from the parametric equation for y, 1 mark for correctly expanding to give the Cartesian equation given in the question.]

Just think, if you lived in the Bahamas, you could be doing this revision on the beach. (Please ignore that comment if you actually do live in the Bahamas. Or anywhere else where you can revise on the beach.)

2 a) Substitute $y = 1$ into the parametric equation for y:

$t^2 - 2t + 2 = 1$

$\Rightarrow t^2 - 2t + 1 = 0$

$\Rightarrow (t - 1)^2 = 0$

$\Rightarrow t = 1$ ***[1 mark]***

So a is the value of x when $t = 1$.

$a = t^3 + t = 1^3 + 1 = 2$ ***[1 mark]***

b) Substitute the parametric equations for x and y into the equation of the line:

$8y = x + 6$

$\Rightarrow 8(t^2 - 2t + 2) = (t^3 + t) + 6$ ***[1 mark]***

$\Rightarrow 8t^2 - 16t + 16 = t^3 + t + 6$

$\Rightarrow t^3 - 8t^2 + 17t - 10 = 0$

We know that this line passes through K, and from a) we know that $t = 1$ at K, so $t = 1$ is a solution of this equation, and $(t - 1)$ is a factor:

$\Rightarrow (t - 1)(t^2 - 7t + 10) = 0$ ***[1 mark]***

$\Rightarrow (t - 1)(t - 2)(t - 5) = 0$

So $t = 2$ at L and $t = 5$ at M. ***[1 mark]***

If you got stuck on this bit, go back and look up 'factorising cubics' in your AS notes.

Substitute $t = 2$ and $t = 5$ back into the parametric equations: ***[1 mark]***

If $t = 2$, then $x = 2^3 + 2 = 10$

and $y = 2^2 - 2(2) + 2 = 2$

If $t = 5$, then $x = 5^3 + 5 = 130$

and $y = 5^2 - 2(5) + 2 = 17$

So $L = (10, 2)$ ***[1 mark]***

and $M = (130, 17)$ ***[1 mark]***

3 a) Substitute $t = 0.5$ into the parametric equations for x and y:

$x = t^3 = 0.5^3 = 0.125$ ***[1 mark]***

$y = t^2 - 4 = 0.5^2 - 4 = -3.75$ ***[1 mark]***.

So the coordinates of F are (0.125, –3.75).

b) First, put the parametric equations into the equation of the line and rearrange: $3(t^2 - 4) = 2(t^3) - 11$

$\Rightarrow 3t^2 - 12 = 2t^3 - 11 \Rightarrow 2t^3 - 3t^2 + 1 = 0$ ***[1 mark]***.

Now solve for t: Putting $t = 1$ into the equation gives 0, so 1 is a root. This means that $(t - 1)$ is a factor ***[1 mark]***.

$(t - 1)(2t^2 - t - 1) = 0 \Rightarrow (t - 1)(2t + 1)(t - 1) = 0$.

So $t = 1$ ***[1 mark]*** and $t = -\frac{1}{2}$ ***[1 mark]*** (ignore the repeated root). Putting these values of t back into the parametric equations gives the coordinates (1, –3) ***[1 mark]*** and (–0.125, –3.75) ***[1 mark]***.

4 a) Use the x- or y-coordinate of H in the relevant parametric equation to find θ:

At H, $3 + 4\sin\theta = 5$

$\Rightarrow 4\sin\theta = 2$

$\Rightarrow \sin\theta = \frac{1}{2}$

$\Rightarrow \theta = \frac{\pi}{6}$

OR

At H, $\frac{1 + \cos 2\theta}{3} = \frac{1}{2}$

$\Rightarrow 1 + \cos 2\theta = \frac{3}{2}$

$\Rightarrow \cos 2\theta = \frac{1}{2}$

$\Rightarrow 2\theta = \frac{\pi}{3}$

$\Rightarrow \theta = \frac{\pi}{6}$

[2 marks available — 1 mark for substituting one coordinate of H into the correct parametric equation, 1 mark finding the correct value of θ.]

b) Rearrange the parametric equation for x to make $\sin\theta$ the subject:

$x = 3 + 4\sin\theta \Rightarrow \sin\theta = \frac{x - 3}{4}$ ***[1 mark]***

Use the identity $\cos 2\theta = 1 - 2\sin^2\theta$ to rewrite the parametric equation for y in terms of $\sin\theta$:

Answers

$$y = \frac{1+\cos 2\theta}{3}$$
$$= \frac{1+(1-2\sin^2\theta)}{3}$$ ***[1 mark]***
$$= \frac{2-2\sin^2\theta}{3}$$
$$= \tfrac{2}{3}(1-\sin^2\theta)$$
$$= \tfrac{2}{3}\left(1-\left(\tfrac{x-3}{4}\right)^2\right)$$ ***[1 mark]***
$$= \tfrac{2}{3}\left(1-\frac{(x-3)^2}{16}\right)$$
$$= \tfrac{2}{3}\left(\frac{16-(x^2-6x+9)}{16}\right)$$
$$= \tfrac{2}{3}\left(\frac{-x^2+6x+7}{16}\right)$$
$$= \frac{-x^2+6x+7}{24}$$ ***[1 mark]***

c) $-\frac{\pi}{2} \le \theta \le \frac{\pi}{2} \Rightarrow -1 \le \sin\theta \le 1$

$\Rightarrow -4 \le 4\sin\theta \le 4$

$\Rightarrow -1 \le 3 + 4\sin\theta \le 7$

$\Rightarrow -1 \le x \le 7$ ***[1 mark]***

As Shakespeare himself might have put it "That section was a ruddy pain in the backside, but at least it's finished."*
**Arnold Shakespeare (1948–)*

C4 Section 3 — Binomial Expansions

Warm-up Questions

1) a) $(1+2x)^3 = 1 + 3(2x) + \frac{3\times 2}{1\times 2}(2x)^2 + \frac{3\times 2\times 1}{1\times 2\times 3}(2x)^3$

$= 1 + 6x + 12x^2 + 8x^3$

You could have used Pascal's Triangle to get the coefficients here. I've done it the long way because I like to show off.

b) $(1-x)^4 = 1 + 4(-x) + \frac{4\times 3}{1\times 2}(-x)^2 + \frac{4\times 3\times 2}{1\times 2\times 3}(-x)^3 + \frac{4\times 3\times 2\times 1}{1\times 2\times 3\times 4}(-x)^4$

$= 1 - 4x + 6x^2 - 4x^3 + x^4$

c) $(1-4x)^4 = 1 + 4(-4x) + \frac{4\times 3}{1\times 2}(-4x)^2 + \frac{4\times 3\times 2}{1\times 2\times 3}(-4x)^3 + \frac{4\times 3\times 2\times 1}{1\times 2\times 3\times 4}(-4x)^4$

$= 1 - 16x + 96x^2 - 256x^3 + 256x^4$

Be extra careful with terms like $(-4x)^2$... remember to square everything in the brackets — the x, the 4 and the minus.

2) Positive integer values (and zero).

3) a) $(1+x)^{-4}$

$\approx 1 + (-4)x + \frac{-4\times -5}{1\times 2}x^2 + \frac{-4\times -5\times -6}{1\times 2\times 3}x^3$

$= 1 - 4x + 10x^2 - 20x^3$

b) $(1-3x)^{-3} \approx 1 + (-3)(-3x) + \frac{-3\times -4}{1\times 2}(-3x)^2 + \frac{-3\times -4\times -5}{1\times 2\times 3}(-3x)^3$

$= 1 + 9x + 54x^2 + 270x^3$

c) $(1-5x)^{\frac{1}{2}}$

$\approx 1 + \frac{1}{2}(-5x) + \frac{\frac{1}{2}\times -\frac{1}{2}}{1\times 2}(-5x)^2 + \frac{\frac{1}{2}\times -\frac{1}{2}\times -\frac{3}{2}}{1\times 2\times 3}(-5x)^3$

$= 1 - \frac{5}{2}x - \frac{25}{8}x^2 - \frac{125}{16}x^3$

4) a) $\left|\frac{dx}{c}\right| < 1$ (or $|x| < |\frac{c}{d}|$)

b) 3) a): expansion valid for $|x| < 1$

3) b): expansion valid for $|-3x| < 1 \Rightarrow |-3||x| < 1 \Rightarrow |x| < \frac{1}{3}$

3) c): expansion valid for $|-5x| < 1 \Rightarrow |-5||x| < 1 \Rightarrow |x| < \frac{1}{5}$

5) a) $(3+2x)^{-2} = \left(3\left(1+\frac{2}{3}x\right)\right)^{-2} = \frac{1}{9}\left(1+\frac{2}{3}x\right)^{-2}$

$\approx \frac{1}{9}\left(1 + (-2)\left(\frac{2}{3}x\right) + \frac{-2\times -3}{1\times 2}\left(\frac{2}{3}x\right)^2\right)$

$= \frac{1}{9}\left(1 - \frac{4}{3}x + \frac{4}{3}x^2\right)$

$= \frac{1}{9} - \frac{4}{27}x + \frac{4}{27}x^2$

This expansion is valid for $\left|\frac{2x}{3}\right| < 1 \Rightarrow \frac{2}{3}|x| < 1 \Rightarrow |x| < \frac{3}{2}$.

b) $(8-x)^{\frac{1}{3}} = \left(8\left(1-\frac{1}{8}x\right)\right)^{\frac{1}{3}} = 2\left(1-\frac{1}{8}x\right)^{\frac{1}{3}}$

$\approx 2\left(1 + \frac{1}{3}\left(-\frac{1}{8}x\right) + \frac{\frac{1}{3}\times -\frac{2}{3}}{1\times 2}\left(-\frac{1}{8}x\right)^2\right)$

$= 2\left(1 - \frac{1}{24}x - \frac{1}{576}x^2\right)$

$= 2 - \frac{1}{12}x - \frac{1}{288}x^2$

This expansion is valid for $\left|\frac{-x}{8}\right| < 1 \Rightarrow \frac{|-1||x|}{8} < 1$
$\Rightarrow |x| < 8$.

Exam Questions

1 a) $f(x) = (9-4x)^{-\frac{1}{2}} = (9)^{-\frac{1}{2}}\left(1-\frac{4}{9}x\right)^{-\frac{1}{2}} = \frac{1}{3}\left(1-\frac{4}{9}x\right)^{-\frac{1}{2}}$

$= \frac{1}{3}\left(1 + \left(-\frac{1}{2}\right)\left(-\frac{4}{9}x\right) + \frac{(-\frac{1}{2})\times(-\frac{3}{2})}{1\times 2}\left(-\frac{4}{9}x\right)^2 + \frac{(-\frac{1}{2})\times(-\frac{3}{2})\times(-\frac{5}{2})}{1\times 2\times 3}\left(-\frac{4}{9}x\right)^3 + \ldots\right)$

$= \frac{1}{3}\left(1 + \left(-\frac{1}{2}\right)\left(-\frac{4}{9}x\right) + \frac{(\frac{3}{4})}{2}\left(-\frac{4}{9}x\right)^2 + \frac{(-\frac{15}{8})}{6}\left(-\frac{4}{9}x\right)^3 + \ldots\right)$

$= \frac{1}{3}\left(1 + \left(-\frac{1}{2}\right)\left(-\frac{4}{9}x\right) + \frac{3}{8}\left(-\frac{4}{9}x\right)^2 + \left(-\frac{5}{16}\right)\left(-\frac{4}{9}x\right)^3 + \ldots\right)$

$= \frac{1}{3}\left(1 + \frac{2}{9}x + \frac{2}{27}x^2 + \frac{20}{729}x^3 + \ldots\right)$

$= \frac{1}{3} + \frac{2}{27}x + \frac{2}{81}x^2 + \frac{20}{2187}x^3 + \ldots$

[5 marks available in total:
- ***1 mark for factorising out $(9)^{-\frac{1}{2}}$ or $\frac{1}{3}$***
- ***1 mark for expansion of an expression of the form $(1+ax)^{-\frac{1}{2}}$***
- ***2 marks for the penultimate line of working — 1 for the first two terms in brackets correct, 1 for the 3rd and 4th terms in brackets correct.***
- ***1 mark for the final answer correct]***

Multiplying out those coefficients can be pretty tricky. Don't try to do things all in one go — you won't be penalised for writing an extra line of working, but you probably will lose marks if your final answer's wrong.

Answers

b) $(2-x)\left(\frac{1}{3}+\frac{2}{27}x+\frac{2}{81}x^2+\frac{20}{2187}x^3+...\right)$

You only need the first three terms of the expansion, so just write the terms up to x^2 when you multiply out the brackets:

$$=\frac{2}{3}+\frac{4}{27}x+\frac{4}{81}x^2+...$$
$$-\frac{1}{3}x-\frac{2}{27}x^2+...$$
$$=\frac{2}{3}-\frac{5}{27}x-\frac{2}{81}x^2+...$$

[4 marks available in total:
- ***1 mark for multiplying your answer to part (a) by (2 – x)***
- ***1 mark for multiplying out brackets to find constant term, two x-terms and two x^2-terms.***
- ***1 mark for correct constant and x-terms in final answer***
- ***1 mark for correct x^2-term in final answer]***

2 a) Expand each term separately:

$$2(4+3x)^{-1}=2\left(4\left(1+\frac{3}{4}x\right)\right)^{-1}=\frac{1}{2}\left(1+\frac{3}{4}x\right)^{-1}$$
$$=\frac{1}{2}\left(1+(-1)\left(\frac{3}{4}x\right)+\frac{(-1)\times(-2)}{1\times 2}\left(\frac{3}{4}x\right)^2+...\right)$$
$$=\frac{1}{2}\left(1-\frac{3}{4}x+\frac{9}{16}x^2+...\right)=\frac{1}{2}-\frac{3}{8}x+\frac{9}{32}x^2+...$$

Now the second term: $-2(1-3x)^{-1}=$

$$-2\left(1+(-1)(-3x)+\frac{(-1)\times(-2)}{1\times 2}(-3x)^2+...\right)$$
$$=-2(1+3x+9x^2+...)=-2-6x-18x^2+...$$

And the final term: $-(1-3x)^{-2}=$

$$-\left(1+(-2)(-3x)+\frac{(-2)\times(-3)}{1\times 2}(-3x)^2+...\right)$$
$$=-(1+6x+27x^2+...)=-1-6x-27x^2+...$$

Putting it all together gives

$$\frac{1}{2}-\frac{3}{8}x+\frac{9}{32}x^2-2-6x-18x^2-1-6x-27x^2$$
$$=-\frac{5}{2}-\frac{99}{8}x-\frac{1431}{32}x^2+...$$

[6 marks available in total:
- ***1 mark for rewriting f(x) in the form $2(4+3x)^{-1}-2(1-3x)^{-1}-(1-3x)^{-2}$***
- ***1 mark for correct binomial expansion of $(4+3x)^{-1}$***
- ***1 mark for correct binomial expansion of $(1-3x)^{-1}$***
- ***1 mark for correct binomial expansion of $(1-3x)^{-2}$***
- ***1 mark for correct constant and x-terms in final answer***
- ***1 mark for correct x^2-term in final answer]***

You know what, I can't think of anything else remotely useful, witty or interesting to say about binomials... Seriously, I'm going to have to resort to slightly weird jokes in a minute... You've been warned...

b) Expansion of $(4+3x)^{-1}$ is valid for $\left|\frac{3x}{4}\right|<1\Rightarrow\frac{3|x|}{4}<1$
$\Rightarrow |x|<\frac{4}{3}$

Expansions of $(1-3x)^{-1}$ and $(1-3x)^{-2}$ are valid for
$\left|\frac{-3x}{1}\right|<1\Rightarrow\frac{|-3||x|}{1}<1\Rightarrow|x|<\frac{1}{3}$

The combined expansion is valid for the narrower of these two ranges. So the expansion of f(x) is valid for $|x|<\frac{1}{3}$.

[2 marks available in total:
- ***1 mark for identifying the valid range of the expansion of f(x) as being the narrower of the two valid ranges shown***
- ***1 mark for correct answer]***

3 a) $(16+3x)^{\frac{1}{4}}=16^{\frac{1}{4}}\left(1+\frac{3}{16}x\right)^{\frac{1}{4}}=2\left(1+\frac{3}{16}x\right)^{\frac{1}{4}}$

$$\approx 2\left(1+\left(\frac{1}{4}\right)\left(\frac{3}{16}x\right)+\frac{\frac{1}{4}\times-\frac{3}{4}}{1\times 2}\left(\frac{3}{16}x\right)^2\right)$$
$$=2\left(1+\left(\frac{1}{4}\right)\left(\frac{3}{16}x\right)+\left(-\frac{3}{32}\right)\left(\frac{9}{256}x^2\right)\right)$$
$$=2\left(1+\frac{3}{64}x-\frac{27}{8192}x^2\right)$$
$$=2+\frac{3}{32}x-\frac{27}{4096}x^2$$

[5 marks available in total:
- ***1 mark for factorising out $16^{\frac{1}{4}}$ or 2***
- ***1 mark for expansion of an expression of the form $(1+ax)^{\frac{1}{4}}$***
- ***2 marks for the penultimate line of working — 1 for the first two terms in brackets correct, 1 for the 3rd term in brackets correct.***
- ***1 mark for the final answer correct]***

b) (i) $16+3x=12.4\Rightarrow x=-1.2$

So $(12.4)^{\frac{1}{4}}\approx 2+\frac{3}{32}(-1.2)-\frac{27}{4096}(-1.2)^2$
$=2-0.1125-0.0094921875$
$=1.878008$ (to 6 d.p.)

[2 marks available in total:
- ***1 mark for substituting x = –1.2 into the expansion from part (a)***
- ***1 mark for correct answer]***

(ii) Percentage error

$=\left|\frac{\text{real value}-\text{estimate}}{\text{real value}}\right|\times 100$ ***[1 mark]***

$=\left|\frac{\sqrt[4]{12.4}-1.878008}{\sqrt[4]{12.4}}\right|\times 100$

$=\frac{|1.876529...-1.878008|}{1.876529...}\times 100$

$=0.0788\%$ (to 3 s.f.) ***[1 mark]***

Why did the binomial expansion cross the road? Don't be silly, binomial expansions can't move independently... ...can they?

4 a) $\left(1-\frac{4}{3}x\right)^{-\frac{1}{2}}$

$$\approx 1+\left(-\frac{1}{2}\right)\left(-\frac{4}{3}x\right)+\frac{(-\frac{1}{2})\times(-\frac{3}{2})}{1\times 2}\left(-\frac{4}{3}x\right)^2+\frac{(-\frac{1}{2})\times(-\frac{3}{2})\times(-\frac{5}{2})}{1\times 2\times 3}\left(-\frac{4}{3}x\right)^3$$
$$=1+\left(-\frac{1}{2}\right)\left(-\frac{4}{3}x\right)+\frac{(\frac{3}{4})}{2}\left(-\frac{4}{3}x\right)^2+\frac{(-\frac{15}{8})}{6}\left(-\frac{4}{3}x\right)^3$$
$$=1+\left(-\frac{1}{2}\right)\left(-\frac{4}{3}x\right)+\frac{3}{8}\left(\frac{16}{9}x^2\right)+\left(-\frac{15}{48}\right)\left(-\frac{64}{27}x^3\right)$$
$$=1+\frac{2}{3}x+\frac{2}{3}x^2+\frac{20}{27}x^3$$

[4 marks available in total:
- ***1 mark for writing out binomial expansion formula with $n=-\frac{1}{2}$***
- ***1 mark for writing out binomial expansion formula substituting $-\frac{4}{3}x$ for x***
- ***1 mark for correct constant and x-terms in final answer***
- ***1 mark for correct x^2- and x^3-terms in final answer]***

Answers

b) $\sqrt{\frac{27}{(3-4x)}} = \sqrt{\frac{27}{3\left(1-\frac{4}{3}x\right)}} = \sqrt{\frac{9}{\left(1-\frac{4}{3}x\right)}} = \frac{3}{\sqrt{\left(1-\frac{4}{3}x\right)}}$

$= 3\left(1-\frac{4}{3}x\right)^{-\frac{1}{2}}$

$\approx 3\left(1+\frac{2}{3}x+\frac{2}{3}x^2\right)$

$= 3+2x+2x^2$

So $a = 3$, $b = 2$, $c = 2$.

Expansion is valid for $\left|-\frac{4}{3}x\right| < 1 \Rightarrow \left|-\frac{4}{3}\right||x| < 1 \Rightarrow |x| < \frac{3}{4}$

[3 marks available in total:
- ***1 mark for showing expression is equal to $3\left(1-\frac{4}{3}x\right)^{-\frac{1}{2}}$***
- ***1 mark for using expansion from part a) to find the correct values of a, b and c.***
- ***1 mark for correct valid range]***

Doctor, doctor, I keep thinking I'm a binomial expansion...
I'm sorry, I don't think I can help you, I'm a cardiologist.

5 a) (i) $\sqrt{\frac{1+2x}{1-3x}} = \frac{\sqrt{1+2x}}{\sqrt{1-3x}} = (1+2x)^{\frac{1}{2}}(1-3x)^{-\frac{1}{2}}$ ***[1 mark]***

$(1+2x)^{\frac{1}{2}} \approx 1+\frac{1}{2}(2x)+\frac{\left(\frac{1}{2}\right)\times\left(-\frac{1}{2}\right)}{1\times 2}(2x)^2$

$= 1+x-\frac{1}{2}x^2$ ***[1 mark]***

$(1-3x)^{-\frac{1}{2}} \approx 1+\left(-\frac{1}{2}\right)(-3x)+\frac{\left(-\frac{1}{2}\right)\times\left(-\frac{3}{2}\right)}{1\times 2}(-3x)^2$

$= 1+\frac{3}{2}x+\frac{27}{8}x^2$ ***[1 mark]***

$\sqrt{\frac{1+2x}{1-3x}} \approx \left(1+x-\frac{1}{2}x^2\right)\left(1+\frac{3}{2}x+\frac{27}{8}x^2\right)$ ***[1 mark]***

$\approx 1+\frac{3}{2}x+\frac{27}{8}x^2+x+\frac{3}{2}x^2-\frac{1}{2}x^2$

(ignoring any terms in x^3 or above)

$= 1+\frac{5}{2}x+\frac{35}{8}x^2$ ***[1 mark]***

(ii) Expansion of $(1+2x)^{\frac{1}{2}}$ is valid for $|2x| < 1 \Rightarrow |x| < \frac{1}{2}$

Expansion of $(1-3x)^{-\frac{1}{2}}$ is valid for $|-3x| < 1$

$\Rightarrow |-3||x| < 1 \Rightarrow |x| < \frac{1}{3}$

The combined expansion is valid for the narrower of these two ranges.

So the expansion of $\sqrt{\frac{1+2x}{1-3x}}$ is valid for $|x| < \frac{1}{3}$.

[2 marks available in total:
- ***1 mark for identifying the valid range of the expansion as being the narrower of the two valid ranges shown***
- ***1 mark for correct answer]***

b) $x = \frac{2}{15} \Rightarrow \sqrt{\frac{1+2x}{1-3x}} = \sqrt{\frac{1+\frac{4}{15}}{1-\frac{6}{15}}} = \sqrt{\frac{\frac{19}{15}}{\frac{9}{15}}} = \sqrt{\frac{19}{9}} = \frac{1}{3}\sqrt{19}$

[1 mark]

$\Rightarrow \sqrt{19} \approx 3\left(1+\frac{5}{2}\left(\frac{2}{15}\right)+\frac{35}{8}\left(\frac{2}{15}\right)^2\right)$

$= 3\left(1+\frac{1}{3}+\frac{7}{90}\right)$

$= 3\left(\frac{127}{90}\right)$

$= \frac{127}{30}$ ***[1 mark]***

The binomial expansion walks into a bar and asks for a pint. The barman says, "I'm sorry, I can't serve alcohol in a joke that may be read by under-18s."

6 a) (i) $(2x-1)^{-1} = -(1-2x)^{-1}$ ***[1 mark]***

$\approx -\left(1+(-1)(-2x)+\frac{(-1)\times(-2)}{1\times 2}(-2x)^2\right)$

$= -(1+2x+4x^2)$

$= -1-2x-4x^2$ ***[1 mark]***

(ii) $(5-3x)^{-1} = 5^{-1}\left(1-\frac{3}{5}x\right)^{-1} = \frac{1}{5}\left(1-\frac{3}{5}x\right)^{-1}$

$\approx \frac{1}{5}\left(1+(-1)\left(-\frac{3}{5}x\right)+\frac{(-1)\times(-2)}{1\times 2}\left(-\frac{3}{5}x\right)^2\right)$

$= \frac{1}{5}\left(1+\frac{3}{5}x+\frac{9}{25}x^2\right)$

$= \frac{1}{5}+\frac{3}{25}x+\frac{9}{125}x^2$

[5 marks available in total:
- ***1 mark for factorising out 5^{-1} or $\frac{1}{5}$***
- ***1 mark for expansion of an expression of the form $(1 + ax)^{-1}$***
- ***2 marks for the penultimate line of working — 1 mark for the first two terms in brackets correct, 1 mark for the 3rd term in brackets correct.***
- ***1 mark for the final answer correct]***

b) $\frac{13x-17}{(5-3x)(2x-1)} = \frac{2}{(5-3x)} - \frac{3}{(2x-1)}$

$= 2(5-3x)^{-1} - 3(2x-1)^{-1}$ ***[1 mark]***

$\approx 2\left(\frac{1}{5}+\frac{3}{25}x+\frac{9}{125}x^2\right)-3(-1-2x-4x^2)$

$= \frac{2}{5}+\frac{6}{25}x+\frac{18}{125}x^2+3+6x+12x^2$

$= \frac{17}{5}+\frac{156}{25}x+\frac{1518}{125}x^2$

[1 mark]

C4 Section 4 — Differentiation

Warm-up Questions

1) a) For $f(x) = y = \sin^2(x+2)$, use the chain rule twice:

$y = u^2$, where $u = \sin(x+2)$

$\frac{dy}{du} = 2u = 2\sin(x+2)$ and $\frac{du}{dx} = \cos(x+2)\cdot 1$ (by chain rule)

$\Rightarrow \frac{dy}{dx} = f'(x) = 2\sin(x+2)\cos(x+2)$ [$= \sin(2x+4)$].

b) $f(x) = y = 2\cos 3x$:

$y = 2\cos u$, where $u = 3x$

$\frac{dy}{du} = -2\sin u = -2\sin 3x$ and $\frac{du}{dx} = 3$

$\Rightarrow \frac{dy}{dx} = f'(x) = -6\sin 3x$.

c) $f(x) = y = \sqrt{\tan x} = (\tan x)^{\frac{1}{2}}$:

$y = u^{\frac{1}{2}}$, where $u = \tan x$

$\frac{dy}{du} = \frac{1}{2}u^{-\frac{1}{2}} = \frac{1}{2\sqrt{u}} = \frac{1}{2\sqrt{\tan x}}$ and $\frac{du}{dx} = \sec^2 x$

$\Rightarrow \frac{dy}{dx} = f'(x) = \frac{\sec^2 x}{2\sqrt{\tan x}}$.

Answers

2) $y = \text{cosec}\,(3x - 2)$, so use chain rule:
$y = \text{cosec}\,u$ where $u = 3x - 2$
$\frac{dy}{du} = -\text{cosec}\,u \cot u = -\text{cosec}\,(3x-2)\cot(3x-2)$
and $\frac{du}{dx} = 3$,
$\Rightarrow \frac{dy}{dx} = -3\,\text{cosec}\,(3x-2)\cot(3x-2)$
$= \frac{-3}{\sin(3x-2)\tan(3x-2)}$.
When $x = 0$, $\frac{dy}{dx} = \frac{-3}{\sin(-2)\tan(-2)} = 1.51$ (to 3 s.f.).

3) a) $\frac{dx}{dt} = 2t$, $\frac{dy}{dt} = 9t^2 - 4$, so $\frac{dy}{dx} = \frac{dy}{dt} \div \frac{dx}{dt} = \frac{9t^2-4}{2t}$

b) The stationary points are when $\frac{9t^2-4}{2t} = 0$
$\Rightarrow 9t^2 = 4 \Rightarrow t = \pm\frac{2}{3}$
$t = \frac{2}{3} \Rightarrow x = \left(\frac{2}{3}\right)^2 = \frac{4}{9}$, $y = 3\left(\frac{2}{3}\right)^3 - 4\left(\frac{2}{3}\right) = \frac{8}{9} - \frac{8}{3} = -\frac{16}{9}$
$t = -\frac{2}{3} \Rightarrow x = \left(-\frac{2}{3}\right)^2 = \frac{4}{9}$,
$y = 3\left(-\frac{2}{3}\right)^3 - 4\left(-\frac{2}{3}\right) = -\frac{8}{9} + \frac{8}{3} = \frac{16}{9}$
So the stationary points are $\left(\frac{4}{9}, -\frac{16}{9}\right)$ and $\left(\frac{4}{9}, \frac{16}{9}\right)$.

4) a) Differentiate each term separately with respect to x:
$\frac{d}{dx}4x^2 - \frac{d}{dx}2y^2 = \frac{d}{dx}7x^2y$
Differentiate $4x^2$ first:
$\Rightarrow 8x - \frac{d}{dx}2y^2 = \frac{d}{dx}7x^2y$
Differentiate $2y^2$ using chain rule:
$\Rightarrow 8x - \frac{d}{dy}2y^2\frac{dy}{dx} = \frac{d}{dx}7x^2y$
$\Rightarrow 8x - 4y\frac{dy}{dx} = \frac{d}{dx}7x^2y$
Differentiate $7x^2y$ using product rule:
$\Rightarrow 8x - 4y\frac{dy}{dx} = 7x^2\frac{d}{dx}y + y\frac{d}{dx}7x^2$
$\Rightarrow 8x - 4y\frac{dy}{dx} = 7x^2\frac{dy}{dx} + 14xy$
Rearrange to make $\frac{dy}{dx}$ the subject:
$\Rightarrow (4y + 7x^2)\frac{dy}{dx} = 8x - 14xy$
$\Rightarrow \frac{dy}{dx} = \frac{8x - 14xy}{4y + 7x^2}$
For implicit differentiation questions, you need to know what you're doing with the chain rule and product rule. If you're struggling to keep up with what's going on here, go back to C3 and refresh your memory.

b) Differentiate each term separately with respect to x:
$\frac{d}{dx}3x^4 - \frac{d}{dx}2xy^2 = \frac{d}{dx}y$
Differentiate $3x^4$ first:
$\Rightarrow 12x^3 - \frac{d}{dx}2xy^2 = \frac{dy}{dx}$
Differentiate $2xy^2$ using product rule:
$\Rightarrow 12x^3 - \left(y^2\frac{d}{dx}2x + 2x\frac{d}{dy}y^2\frac{dy}{dx}\right) = \frac{dy}{dx}$
$\Rightarrow 12x^3 - 2y^2 - 4xy\frac{dy}{dx} = \frac{dy}{dx}$
Rearrange to make $\frac{dy}{dx}$ the subject:
$\Rightarrow (1 + 4xy)\frac{dy}{dx} = 12x^3 - 2y^2$
$\Rightarrow \frac{dy}{dx} = \frac{12x^3 - 2y^2}{1 + 4xy}$

c) Use the product rule to differentiate each term separately with respect to x:
$\frac{d}{dx}\cos x \sin y = \frac{d}{dx}xy$
$\Rightarrow \cos x\frac{d}{dx}(\sin y) + \sin y\frac{d}{dx}(\cos x) = x\frac{d}{dx}y + y\frac{d}{dx}x$
Use the chain rule on $\frac{d}{dx}(\sin y)$:
$\Rightarrow \cos x\frac{d}{dy}(\sin y)\frac{dy}{dx} + \sin y\frac{d}{dx}(\cos x) = x\frac{d}{dx}y + y\frac{d}{dx}x$
$\Rightarrow (\cos x \cos y)\frac{dy}{dx} - \sin y \sin x = x\frac{dy}{dx} + y$
Rearrange to make $\frac{dy}{dx}$ the subject:
$\Rightarrow (\cos x \cos y - x)\frac{dy}{dx} = y + \sin x \sin y$
$\Rightarrow \frac{dy}{dx} = \frac{\sin x \sin y + y}{\cos x \cos y - x}$
Make sure you're happy with how to differentiate trig functions. Chances are they'll come up in your C4 exam. And even if they don't, that sort of skill will make you a hit at parties. Trust me.

5) a) At $(1, -4)$, $\frac{dy}{dx} = \frac{8x - 14xy}{4y + 7x^2}$
$= \frac{8(1) - 14(1)(-4)}{4(-4) + 7(1)^2} = \frac{8 + 56}{-16 + 7} = -\frac{64}{9}$

b) At $(1, 1)$, $\frac{dy}{dx} = \frac{12x^3 - 2y^2}{1 + 4xy}$
$= \frac{12(1)^3 - 2(1)^2}{1 + 4(1)(1)} = \frac{12 - 2}{1 + 4} = \frac{10}{5} = 2$
So the gradient of the normal is $-\frac{1}{2}$.

Exam Questions

1 a) Start by differentiating x and y with respect to θ:
$\frac{dy}{d\theta} = 2\cos\theta$ ***[1 mark]***
$\frac{dx}{d\theta} = 3 + 3\sin 3\theta$ ***[1 mark]***
$\frac{dy}{dx} = \frac{dy}{d\theta} \div \frac{dx}{d\theta} = \frac{2\cos\theta}{3 + 3\sin 3\theta}$ ***[1 mark]***

b) (i) We need the value of θ at $(\pi + 1, \sqrt{3})$:
$y = 2\sin\theta = \sqrt{3}$, for $-\pi \leq \theta \leq \pi \Rightarrow \theta = \frac{\pi}{3}$ or $\frac{2\pi}{3}$
[1 mark]
If $\theta = \frac{\pi}{3}$, then $x = 3\theta - \cos 3\theta = \pi - \cos\pi = \pi + 1$.
If $\theta = \frac{2\pi}{3}$, then $x = 3\theta - \cos 3\theta = 2\pi - \cos 2\pi = 2\pi - 1$.
So at $(\pi + 1, \sqrt{3})$, $\theta = \frac{\pi}{3}$ ***[1 mark]***
$\theta = \frac{\pi}{3} \Rightarrow \frac{dy}{dx} = \frac{2\cos\frac{\pi}{3}}{3 + 3\sin\pi} = \frac{2\left(\frac{1}{2}\right)}{3 + 0} = \frac{1}{3}$ ***[1 mark]***

(ii) $\theta = \frac{\pi}{6} \Rightarrow x = \frac{\pi}{2} - \cos\frac{\pi}{2} = \frac{\pi}{2} - 0 = \frac{\pi}{2}$
$\theta = \frac{\pi}{6} \Rightarrow y = 2\sin\frac{\pi}{6} = 2 \times \frac{1}{2} = 1$
So $\theta = \frac{\pi}{6}$ at the point $(\frac{\pi}{2}, 1)$ ***[1 mark]***

Answers

$\theta = \frac{\pi}{6} \Rightarrow \frac{dy}{dx} = \frac{2\cos\frac{\pi}{6}}{3 + 3\sin\frac{\pi}{2}} = \frac{2\left(\frac{\sqrt{3}}{2}\right)}{3 + 3(1)} = \frac{\sqrt{3}}{6}$ ***[1 mark]***

Gradient of normal $= -\frac{1}{\left(\frac{dy}{dx}\right)} = -\frac{6}{\sqrt{3}} = -\frac{6\sqrt{3}}{3}$

$= -2\sqrt{3}$ ***[1 mark]***

So the normal is $y = -2\sqrt{3}x + c$ for some c.

$\Rightarrow 1 = -2\sqrt{3} \times \frac{\pi}{2} + c = -\pi\sqrt{3} + c$

$\Rightarrow c = 1 + \pi\sqrt{3}$

The equation of the normal is $y = -2\sqrt{3}x + 1 + \pi\sqrt{3}$ ***[1 mark]***

2 a) c is the value of y when $x = 2$. If $x = 2$, then

$6x^2y - 7 = 5x - 4y^2 - x^2 \Rightarrow 6(2)^2y - 7 = 5(2) - 4y^2 - (2)^2$

$\Rightarrow 24y - 7 = 6 - 4y^2$

$\Rightarrow 4y^2 + 24y - 13 = 0$

$\Rightarrow (2y + 13)(2y - 1) = 0$

$\Rightarrow y = -6.5$ or $y = 0.5$ ***[1 mark]***

$c > 0$, so $c = 0.5$ ***[1 mark]***

b) (i) Q is another point on C where $y = 0.5$.

If $y = 0.5$, then $6x^2y - 7 = 5x - 4y^2 - x^2$

$\Rightarrow 6x^2(0.5) - 7 = 5x - 4(0.5)^2 - x^2$ ***[1 mark]***

$\Rightarrow 3x^2 - 7 = 5x - 1 - x^2$

$\Rightarrow 4x^2 - 5x - 6 = 0$

$\Rightarrow (x - 2)(4x + 3)$

$\Rightarrow x = 2$ or $x = -0.75$

$x \neq 2$, as $x = 2$ at the other point where T crosses C.

So the coordinates of Q are $(-0.75, 0.5)$. ***[1 mark]***

(ii) To find the gradient of C, use implicit differentiation.

Differentiate each term separately with respect to x:

$\frac{d}{dx}6x^2y - \frac{d}{dx}7 = \frac{d}{dx}5x - \frac{d}{dx}4y^2 - \frac{d}{dx}x^2$ ***[1 mark]***

Differentiate x-terms and constant terms:

$\Rightarrow \frac{d}{dx}6x^2y - 0 = 5 - \frac{d}{dx}4y^2 - 2x$ ***[1 mark]***

Differentiate y-terms using chain rule:

$\Rightarrow \frac{d}{dx}6x^2y = 5 - \frac{d}{dy}4y^2\frac{dy}{dx} - 2x$

$\Rightarrow \frac{d}{dx}6x^2y = 5 - 8y\frac{dy}{dx} - 2x$ ***[1 mark]***

Differentiate xy-terms using product rule:

$\Rightarrow 6x^2\frac{dy}{dx} + y\frac{d}{dx}6x^2 = 5 - 8y\frac{dy}{dx} - 2x$

$\Rightarrow 6x^2\frac{dy}{dx} + 12xy = 5 - 8y\frac{dy}{dx} - 2x$ ***[1 mark]***

Rearrange to make $\frac{dy}{dx}$ the subject:

$\Rightarrow 6x^2\frac{dy}{dx} + 8y\frac{dy}{dx} = 5 - 2x - 12xy$

$\Rightarrow \frac{dy}{dx} = \frac{5 - 2x - 12xy}{6x^2 + 8y}$ ***[1 mark]***

So at $Q = (-0.75, 0.5)$,

$\frac{dy}{dx} = \frac{5 - 2\left(-\frac{3}{4}\right) - 12\left(-\frac{3}{4}\right)\left(\frac{1}{2}\right)}{6\left(-\frac{3}{4}\right)^2 + 8\left(\frac{1}{2}\right)} = \frac{5 + \frac{3}{2} + \frac{9}{2}}{\frac{27}{8} + 4}$

$= \frac{11}{\left(\frac{59}{8}\right)} = 11 \times \frac{8}{59} = \frac{88}{59}$ ***[1 mark]***

3 a) (i) Using implicit differentiation:

$3e^x + 6y = 2x^2y \Rightarrow \frac{d}{dx}3e^x + \frac{d}{dx}6y = \frac{d}{dx}2x^2y$ ***[1 mark]***

$\Rightarrow 3e^x + 6\frac{dy}{dx} = 2x^2\frac{dy}{dx} + y\frac{d}{dx}2x^2$

$\Rightarrow 3e^x + 6\frac{dy}{dx} = 2x^2\frac{dy}{dx} + 4xy$ ***[1 mark]***

$\Rightarrow 2x^2\frac{dy}{dx} - 6\frac{dy}{dx} = 3e^x - 4xy$

$\Rightarrow \frac{dy}{dx} = \frac{3e^x - 4xy}{2x^2 - 6}$ ***[1 mark]***

(ii) At the stationary points of C, $\frac{dy}{dx} = 0$

$\Rightarrow \frac{3e^x - 4xy}{2x^2 - 6} = 0$ ***[1 mark]***

$\Rightarrow 3e^x - 4xy = 0$

$\Rightarrow y = \frac{3e^x}{4x}$ ***[1 mark]***

b) Substitute $y = \frac{3e^x}{4x}$ into the original equation of curve C:

$3e^x + 6y = 2x^2y \Rightarrow 3e^x + 6\frac{3e^x}{4x} = 2x^2\frac{3e^x}{4x}$ ***[1 mark]***

$\Rightarrow 3e^x(1 + \frac{3}{2x} - \frac{x}{2}) = 0$

$3e^x = 0$ has no solutions, so $(1 + \frac{3}{2x} - \frac{x}{2}) = 0$ ***[1 mark]***

$\Rightarrow x^2 - 2x - 3 = 0$

$\Rightarrow (x + 1)(x - 3) = 0$

$\Rightarrow x = -1$ or $x = 3$

$x = -1 \Rightarrow y = \frac{3e^{-1}}{4(-1)} = -\frac{3}{4e}$

$x = 3 \Rightarrow y = \frac{3e^3}{4(3)} = \frac{1}{4}e^3$

So the stationary points of C are $(-1, -\frac{3}{4e})$ and $(3, \frac{1}{4}e^3)$

[2 marks — 1 mark for each correct pair of coordinates]

Don't forget — if the question asks you for an exact answer, that usually means leaving it in terms of something like π or ln or, in this case, e.

4 a) First find the value of t when $y = -6$:

$y = 2 - t^3 = -6 \Rightarrow t^3 = 8 \Rightarrow t = 2$ ***[1 mark]***

$\Rightarrow x = 2^2 + 2(2) - 3 = 5$

Now find the gradient of the curve:

$\frac{dy}{dt} = -3t^2$, $\frac{dx}{dt} = 2t + 2$

So $\frac{dy}{dx} = \frac{dy}{dt} \div \frac{dx}{dt} = \frac{-3t^2}{2t + 2}$ ***[1 mark]***

So when $t = 2$, $\frac{dy}{dx} = \frac{-3(2)^2}{2(2) + 2} = \frac{-12}{6} = -2$ ***[1 mark]***

So the tangent at $y = -6$ is

$y = -2x + c \Rightarrow -6 = -2(5) + c \Rightarrow c = 4$

The equation of L is $y = -2x + 4$ ***[1 mark]***

b) (i) Sub $y = 2 - t^3$ and $x = t^2 + 2t - 3$ into the equation of L:

$y = -2x + 4$

$\Rightarrow 2 - t^3 = -2(t^2 + 2t - 3) + 4$ ***[1 mark]***

$\Rightarrow 2 - t^3 = -2t^2 - 4t + 10$

$\Rightarrow t^3 - 2t^2 - 4t + 8 = 0$

We know from part (a) that $t = 2$ is a root, so take out $(t - 2)$ as a factor:

$\Rightarrow (t - 2)(t^2 - 4) = 0$ ***[1 mark]***

$\Rightarrow (t - 2)(t + 2)(t - 2) = 0$

$\Rightarrow t = 2$ or $t = -2$ ***[1 mark]***

So t must be -2 at P.

Answers

$t = -2 \Rightarrow x = (-2)^2 + 2(-2) - 3 = -3, y = 2 - (-2)^3 = 10.$
The coordinates of P are $(-3, 10)$. ***[1 mark]***

(ii) At P, $t = -2$, so $\frac{dy}{dx} = \frac{-3(-2)^2}{2(-2)+2} = \frac{-12}{-2} = 6$. ***[1 mark]***

So the gradient of the normal at P is

$-\frac{1}{\left(\frac{dy}{dx}\right)} = -\frac{1}{6}$ ***[1 mark]***

The equation of the normal at P is

$y = -\frac{1}{6}x + c \Rightarrow 10 = -\frac{(-3)}{6} + c \Rightarrow c = \frac{19}{2}$

So the normal to the curve at point P is

$y = -\frac{1}{6}x + \frac{19}{2}$ ***[1 mark]***

5 $f(x) = \sec x = \frac{1}{\cos x}$, so using the quotient rule:
$u = 1 \Rightarrow \frac{du}{dx} = 0$ and $v = \cos x \Rightarrow \frac{dv}{dx} = -\sin x$.

$$\frac{dy}{dx} = \frac{v\frac{du}{dx} - u\frac{dv}{dx}}{v^2} = \frac{(\cos x \cdot 0) - (1 \cdot - \sin x)}{\cos^2 x} = \frac{\sin x}{\cos^2 x}.$$

Since $\tan x = \frac{\sin x}{\cos x}$, and $\sec x = \frac{1}{\cos x}$,

$f'(x) = \frac{dy}{dx} = \frac{\sin x}{\cos x} \times \frac{1}{\cos x} = \sec x \tan x.$

[4 marks available — 1 mark for correct identity for sec x, 1 mark for correct entry into quotient rule, 1 mark for correct answer from quotient rule, and 1 mark for correct rearrangement to sec x tan x.]

6 For $y = \sin^2 x - 2\cos 2x$, use the chain rule on each part:
For $y = \sin^2 x$, $y = u^2$ where $u = \sin x$, so $\frac{dy}{du} = 2u = 2\sin x$
and $\frac{du}{dx} = \cos x$, so $\frac{dy}{dx} = 2\sin x \cos x$ ***[1 mark]***.

For $y = 2\cos 2x$, $y = 2\cos u$ where $u = 2x$, so $\frac{dy}{du} = -2\sin u$
$= -2\sin 2x$ and $\frac{du}{dx} = 2$, so $\frac{dy}{dx} = -4\sin 2x$ ***[1 mark]***.

Overall $\frac{dy}{dx} = 2\sin x \cos x + 4\sin 2x$.

(Think 'double angle formula' for the sin x cos x...)

$\sin 2x \equiv 2\sin x \cos x$, so:

$\frac{dy}{dx} = \sin 2x + 4\sin 2x = 5\sin 2x$ ***[1 mark]***.

(For gradient of the tangent, put the x value into dy/dx...)

Gradient of the tangent when $x = \frac{\pi}{12}$ is:

$5 \times \sin\frac{\pi}{6} = 2.5$ ***[1 mark]***.

7 For $x = \sin 4y$, $\frac{dx}{dy} = 4\cos 4y$ ***[1 mark]*** (using chain rule),
and so $\frac{dy}{dx} = \frac{1}{4\cos 4y}$ ***[1 mark]***.

At $(0, \frac{\pi}{4})$, $y = \frac{\pi}{4}$ and so $\frac{dy}{dx} = \frac{1}{4\cos\pi} = -\frac{1}{4}$ ***[1 mark]***.

(This is the gradient of the tangent at that point, so to find the gradient of the normal do −1 ÷ gradient of tangent...)

Gradient of normal at $(0, \frac{\pi}{4}) = -1 \div -\frac{1}{4} = 4$ ***[1 mark]***.

Equation of a straight line is:
$y - y_1 = m(x - x_1)$, where m is the gradient.

For the normal at $(0, \frac{\pi}{4})$, $x_1 = 0$, $y_1 = \frac{\pi}{4}$, and $m = 4$.

So the equation is:

$y - \frac{\pi}{4} = 4(x - 0)$ ***[1 mark]*** $\Rightarrow y = 4x + \frac{\pi}{4}$ (or equivalent) ***[1 mark]***.

C4 Section 5 — Integration

Warm-up Questions

1) a) Just integrate each term separately: $\int \cos 4x\,dx = \frac{1}{4}\sin 4x$, $\int \sec^2 7x = \frac{1}{7}\tan 7x\,dx$. Putting these bits together gives: $\frac{1}{4}\sin 4x - \frac{1}{7}\tan 7x + C$.

b) Again, just integrate each term separately:
$\int 6\sec 3x \tan 3x\,dx = 2\sec 3x$, $\int -\operatorname{cosec}^2\frac{x}{5}\,dx = 5\cot\frac{x}{5}$.
Putting these bits together gives: $2\sec 3x + 5\cot\frac{x}{5} + C$.

2) $\ln|\sin x| + C$

3) $e^{x^3} + C$

4) $4\ln|x^5 + x^3 - 3x| + C$

5) Use the double angle formula for tan 2x to write $\frac{2\tan 3x}{1 - \tan^2 3x}$ as $\tan 6x$. The integral becomes
$\int \tan 6x\,dx = \int \frac{\sin 6x}{\cos 6x}\,dx = -\frac{1}{6}\ln|\cos 6x| + C$.

Don't forget to double the coefficient of x when you use the double angle formula.

6) From the identity $\sec^2 x \equiv 1 + \tan^2 x$, write $2\tan^2 3x$ as $2\sec^2 3x - 2$. The integral becomes:
$\int 2\sec^2 3x - 2 + 2\,dx$
$= \int 2\sec^2 3x\,dx = \frac{2}{3}\tan 3x + C$.

7) If $u = e^x - 1$, then $\frac{du}{dx} = e^x$ (so $\frac{du}{e^x} = dx$) and $e^x + 1 = u + 2$.
Substituting this into the integral gives:

$$\int e^x(u+2)u^2\frac{du}{e^x} = \int (u+2)u^2\,du$$
$$= \int u^3 + 2u^2\,du = \frac{1}{4}u^4 + \frac{2}{3}u^3 + C$$
$$= \frac{1}{4}(e^x - 1)^4 + \frac{2}{3}(e^x - 1)^3 + C$$

Make sure you put u = eˣ back into your final answer.

8) If $u = \sec x$, then $\frac{du}{dx} = \sec x \tan x$ (so $\frac{du}{\sec x \tan x} = dx$).
Change the limits: when $x = \frac{\pi}{4}$, $u = \sec\frac{\pi}{4} = \sqrt{2}$ and when $x = \frac{\pi}{3}$, $u = \sec\frac{\pi}{3} = 2$. Substituting into the integral gives:

$$\int_{\sqrt{2}}^{2} \sec x \tan x\, u^3 \frac{du}{\sec x \tan x} = \int_{\sqrt{2}}^{2} u^3\,du = [\tfrac{1}{4}u^4]_{\sqrt{2}}^{2}$$
$$= [\tfrac{1}{4}(2)^4] - [\tfrac{1}{4}(\sqrt{2})^4]$$
$$= \tfrac{1}{4}(16) - \tfrac{1}{4}(4) = 4 - 1 = 3.$$

9) Let $u = \ln x$ and let $\frac{dv}{dx} = 3x^2$. So $\frac{du}{dx} = \frac{1}{x}$ and $v = x^3$.
Putting these into the formula gives:

$$\int 3x^2 \ln x\,dx = x^3\ln x - \int \frac{x^3}{x}dx = [x^3 \ln x] - \int x^2 dx$$
$$= x^3\ln x - \tfrac{1}{3}x^3 + C = x^3(\ln x - \tfrac{1}{3}) + C$$

10) Let $u = 4x$, and let $\frac{dv}{dx} = \cos 4x$. So $\frac{du}{dx} = 4$ and $v = \frac{1}{4}\sin 4x$.
Putting these into the formula gives:

$$\int 4x\cos 4x\,dx = 4x(\tfrac{1}{4}\sin 4x) - \int 4(\tfrac{1}{4}\sin 4x)dx$$
$$= x\sin 4x + \tfrac{1}{4}\cos 4x + C$$

11) First, find the partial fractions: If
$\frac{3x + 10}{(2x+3)(x-4)} \equiv \frac{A}{2x+3} + \frac{B}{x-4}$,
then $3x + 10 \equiv A(x - 4) + B(2x + 3)$.
From this, you get the simultaneous equations $3 = A + 2B$ and $10 = -4A + 3B$. Solving these gives $A = -1$ and $B = 2$:

Answers

$$\frac{3x+10}{(2x+3)(x-4)} = \frac{-1}{2x+3} + \frac{2}{x-4}.$$

Now putting this into the integral gives:

$$\int \frac{-1}{2x+3} + \frac{2}{x-4}\,dx = -\frac{1}{2}\ln|2x+3| + 2\ln|x-4| + C$$

12) $\frac{dy}{dx} = \frac{1}{y}\cos x \Rightarrow y\,dy = \cos x\,dx$

so $\int y\,dy = \int \cos x\,dx \Rightarrow \frac{y^2}{2} = \sin x + C_0$

$\Rightarrow y^2 = 2\sin x + C_1$ (where $C_1 = 2C_0$)

13) a) $\frac{dS}{dt} = kS$

b) Solving the differential equation above gives:

$\frac{dS}{dt} = kS \Rightarrow \int \frac{1}{S}\,dS = \int k\,dt$

$\ln|S| = kt + C$

$S = Ae^{kt}$ where $A = e^C$

For the initial population, $t = 0$. Put $S = 30$ and $t = 0$ into the equation to find the value of A: $30 = Ae^0 \Rightarrow A = 30$.

Now, use $S = 150$, $k = 0.2$ and $A = 30$ to find t:

$150 = 30e^{0.2t} \Rightarrow 5 = e^{0.2t} \Rightarrow \ln 5 = 0.2t$, so $t = 8.047$.

It will take the squirrels 8 weeks before they can take over the forest.

Go squirrels go!

Exam Questions

1 Use the identity $\text{cosec}^2 x \equiv 1 + \cot^2 x$ to write $2\cot^2 x$ as $2\text{cosec}^2 x - 2$ ***[1 mark]***. The integral becomes:

$\int 2\text{cosec}^2 x - 2\,dx = -2\cot x - 2x + C$

[1 mark for −2cot x, 1 mark for −2x + C].

2 $-\ln|\cot x + 2x| + C$

[1 mark for answer in the form k ln |f(x)|, 1 mark for correct value of k and 1 mark for correct function f(x). Lose 1 mark if C is missed off]

3 Let $u = x$, so $\frac{du}{dx} = 1$. Let $\frac{dv}{dx} = \sin x$, so $v = -\cos x$ ***[1 mark for both parts correct]***. Using integration by parts,

$\int_0^\pi x\sin x\,dx = [-x\cos x]_0^\pi - \int_0^\pi -\cos x\,dx$ ***[1 mark]***

$= [-x\cos x]_0^\pi + [\sin x]_0^\pi$ ***[1 mark]***

$= (\pi - 0) + (0) = \pi$ ***[1 mark]***

If you'd tried to use u = sin x, you'd have ended up with a more complicated function to integrate ($x^2\cos x$).

4 a) $\frac{dy}{dx} = \frac{\cos x\cos^2 y}{\sin x} \Rightarrow \frac{1}{\cos^2 y}\,dy = \frac{\cos x}{\sin x}\,dx$

$\Rightarrow \int \sec^2 y\,dy = \int \frac{\cos x}{\sin x}\,dx$

$\Rightarrow \tan y = \ln|\sin x| + C$

[4 marks available — 1 mark for separating the variables into functions of x and y, 1 mark for correct integration of RHS, 1 mark for correct integration of LHS, 1 mark for general solution]

b) If $y = \pi$ when $x = \frac{\pi}{6}$, that means that

$\tan\pi = \ln|\sin\frac{\pi}{6}| + C$

$0 = \ln|\frac{1}{2}| + C$ ***[1 mark]***

As $\ln \frac{1}{2} = \ln 1 - \ln 2 = -\ln 2$ (as $\ln 1 = 0$), it follows that $C = \ln 2$.

So $\tan y = \ln|\sin x| + \ln 2$ or $\tan y = \ln|2\sin x|$ ***[1 mark]***.

This is the particular solution — you found the general solution in part a).

5 If $u = \ln x$, then $\frac{du}{dx} = \frac{1}{x}$, so $x\,du = dx$. Changing the limits: when $x = 1$, $u = \ln 1 = 0$. When $x = 2$, $u = \ln 2$.

Substituting all this into the integral gives:

$$\int_1^2 \frac{8}{x}(\ln x + 2)^3\,dx = \int_0^{\ln 2} \frac{8}{x}(u+2)^3 x\,du = \int_0^{\ln 2} 8(u+2)^3\,du$$

$$= [2(u+2)^4]_0^{\ln 2}$$

$$= [2(\ln 2 + 2)^4] - [2(0+2)^4]$$

$$= 105.21 - 32 = 73.21 \text{ (4 s.f.)}.$$

[6 marks available — 1 mark for finding substitution for dx, 1 mark for finding correct limits, 1 mark for correct integral in terms of u, 2 marks for correct integration (1 for an answer in the form k(u + 2)ⁿ, 1 mark for correct values of k and n), 1 mark for final answer (to 4 s.f.)]

6 a) $\frac{dm}{dt} = k\sqrt{m}$, $k > 0$ ***[1 mark for RHS, 1 mark for LHS]***

b) First solve the differential equation to find m:

$\frac{dm}{dt} = k\sqrt{m} \Rightarrow \frac{1}{\sqrt{m}}\,dm = k\,dt$

$\Rightarrow \int m^{-\frac{1}{2}}\,dm = \int k\,dt$ ***[1 mark]***

$\Rightarrow 2m^{\frac{1}{2}} = kt + C$

$\Rightarrow m = \left(\frac{1}{2}(kt + C)\right)^2 = \frac{1}{4}(kt + C)^2$ ***[1 mark]***

At the start of the campaign, $t = 0$. Putting $t = 0$ and $m = 900$ into the equation gives: $900 = \frac{1}{4}(0 + C)^2 \Rightarrow 3600 = C^2 \Rightarrow C = 60$ (C must be positive, otherwise the sales would be decreasing). ***[1 mark]***. This gives the equation $m = \frac{1}{4}(kt + 60)^2$ ***[1 mark]***.

c) Substituting $t = 5$ and $k = 2$ into the equation gives:

$m = \frac{1}{4}((2 \times 5) + 60)^2 = 1225$ tubs sold.

[3 marks available — 2 marks for substituting correct values of t and k, 1 mark for answer]

C4 Section 6 — Vectors

Warm-up Questions

1) Any multiples of the vectors will do:

a) e.g. **a** and 4**a**

b) e.g. 6**i** + 8**j** – 4**k** and 9**i** + 12**j** – 6**k**

c) e.g. $\begin{pmatrix}2\\4\\-2\end{pmatrix}$ and $\begin{pmatrix}4\\8\\-4\end{pmatrix}$

2) a) **b** – **a** b) **a** – **b** c) **b** – **c** d) **c** – **a**

3) 2**i** – 4**j** + 5**k**

4) a) $\sqrt{3^2 + 4^2 + (-2)^2} = \sqrt{29}$

b) $\sqrt{1^2 + 2^2 + (-1)^2} = \sqrt{6}$

5) a) $\sqrt{(3-1)^2 + (-1-2)^2 + (-2-3)^2} = \sqrt{38}$

b) $\sqrt{1^2 + 2^2 + 3^2} = \sqrt{14}$

Answers

c) $\sqrt{3^2 + (-1)^2 + (-2)^2} = \sqrt{14}$

6) a) $\mathbf{r} = (4\mathbf{i} + \mathbf{j} + 2\mathbf{k}) + t(3\mathbf{i} + \mathbf{j} - \mathbf{k})$ or $\mathbf{r} = \begin{pmatrix}4\\1\\2\end{pmatrix} + t\begin{pmatrix}3\\1\\-1\end{pmatrix}$

b) $\mathbf{r} = (2\mathbf{i} - \mathbf{j} + \mathbf{k}) + t((2\mathbf{j} + 3\mathbf{k}) - (2\mathbf{i} - \mathbf{j} + \mathbf{k}))$

$\Rightarrow \mathbf{r} = (2\mathbf{i} - \mathbf{j} + \mathbf{k}) + t(-2\mathbf{i} + 3\mathbf{j} + 2\mathbf{k})$

or $\mathbf{r} = \begin{pmatrix}2\\-1\\1\end{pmatrix} + t\begin{pmatrix}-2\\3\\2\end{pmatrix}$

7) E.g. If $t = 1$, $((3 + 1(-1)), (2 + 1(3)), (4 + 1(0))) = (2, 5, 4)$

If $t = 2$, $((3 + 2(-1)), (2 + 2(3)), (4 + 2(0))) = (1, 8, 4)$

If $t = -1$, $((3 + -1(-1)), (2 + -1(3)), (4 + -1(0))) = (4, -1, 4)$

8) a) $(3\mathbf{i} + 4\mathbf{j}).(\mathbf{i} - 2\mathbf{j} + 3\mathbf{k}) = 3 - 8 + 0 = -5$

b) $\begin{pmatrix}4\\2\\1\end{pmatrix} \cdot \begin{pmatrix}3\\-4\\-3\end{pmatrix} = (4 \times 3) + (2 \times -4) + (1 \times -3) = 1$

9) a) $\begin{pmatrix}2\\-1\\2\end{pmatrix} + t\begin{pmatrix}-4\\6\\-2\end{pmatrix} = \begin{pmatrix}3\\2\\4\end{pmatrix} + u\begin{pmatrix}-1\\3\\0\end{pmatrix}$

Where the lines intersect, these 3 equations are true:

$2 - 4t = 3 - u$

$-1 + 6t = 2 + 3u$

$2 - 2t = 4$

Solve the third equation to give $t = -1$.

Substituting $t = -1$ in either of the other equations gives $u = -3$.

Substituting $t = -1$ and $u = -3$ in the remaining equation gives a true result, so the lines intersect.

Substituting $t = -1$ in the first vector equation gives the position vector of the intersection point:

$\begin{pmatrix}6\\-7\\4\end{pmatrix}$

You'll often have to solve a pair of equations simultaneously (both variables will usually be in all three equations).

b) To find the angle between the lines, only consider the direction components of the vector equations:

$\begin{pmatrix}-4\\6\\-2\end{pmatrix} \cdot \begin{pmatrix}-1\\3\\0\end{pmatrix} = 4 + 18 + 0 = 22$

magnitude of 1st vector: $\sqrt{(-4)^2 + 6^2 + (-2)^2} = \sqrt{56}$

magnitude of 2nd vector: $\sqrt{(-1)^2 + 3^2 + (0)^2} = \sqrt{10}$

$\cos\theta = \frac{22}{\sqrt{56}\sqrt{10}} = \Rightarrow \theta = 21.6°$

10) Find values for a, b and c that give a scalar product of 0 when the two vectors are multiplied together.

$(3\mathbf{i} + 4\mathbf{j} - 2\mathbf{k}).(a\mathbf{i} + b\mathbf{j} + c\mathbf{k}) = 3a + 4b - 2c = 0$

E.g. $a = 2$, $b = 1$, $c = 5$

Perpendicular vector = $(2\mathbf{i} + \mathbf{j} + 5\mathbf{k})$

Just pick values for a and b, then see what value of c is needed to make the scalar product zero.

Exam Questions

1 a) $\overrightarrow{AB} = \mathbf{b} - \mathbf{a} = \begin{pmatrix}3\\2\\1\end{pmatrix} - \begin{pmatrix}1\\5\\9\end{pmatrix} = \begin{pmatrix}2\\-3\\-8\end{pmatrix}$

[2 marks available — 1 mark for attempting to subtract position vector a from position vector b, 1 mark for correct answer.]

b) l_1: $\mathbf{r} = \mathbf{c} + \mu(\mathbf{d} - \mathbf{c}) = \begin{pmatrix}-2\\4\\3\end{pmatrix} + \mu\left(\begin{pmatrix}5\\-1\\-7\end{pmatrix} - \begin{pmatrix}-2\\4\\3\end{pmatrix}\right)$ ***[1 mark]***

$\mathbf{r} = \begin{pmatrix}-2\\4\\3\end{pmatrix} + \mu\begin{pmatrix}7\\-5\\-10\end{pmatrix}$ ***[1 mark]***

c) Equation of line through AB:

$\overrightarrow{AB}$: $\mathbf{r} = \mathbf{a} + t(\mathbf{b} - \mathbf{a}) = \begin{pmatrix}1\\5\\9\end{pmatrix} + t\begin{pmatrix}2\\-3\\-8\end{pmatrix}$ ***[1 mark]***

At intersection of lines:

$\begin{pmatrix}1\\5\\9\end{pmatrix} + t\begin{pmatrix}2\\-3\\-8\end{pmatrix} = \begin{pmatrix}-2\\4\\3\end{pmatrix} + \mu\begin{pmatrix}7\\-5\\-10\end{pmatrix}$ ***[1 mark]***

Any two of: $1 + 2t = -2 + 7\mu$

$5 - 3t = 4 - 5\mu$

$9 - 8t = 3 - 10\mu$ ***[1 mark]***

Solving any two equations simultaneously gives

$t = 2$ or $\mu = 1$ ***[1 mark]***

Substituting $t = 2$ in the equation of the line through AB (or $\mu = 1$ in the equation for l_1) gives: $(5, -1, -7)$ ***[1 mark]***

d) (i) Vectors needed are $\begin{pmatrix}2\\-3\\-8\end{pmatrix}$ and $\begin{pmatrix}7\\-5\\-10\end{pmatrix}$ (direction vector of l_1).

$\begin{pmatrix}2\\-3\\-8\end{pmatrix} \cdot \begin{pmatrix}7\\-5\\-10\end{pmatrix} = 14 + 15 + 80 = 109$ ***[1 mark]***

magnitude of 1st vector: $\sqrt{2^2 + (-3)^2 + (-8)^2} = \sqrt{77}$

magnitude of 2nd vector:

$\sqrt{7^2 + (-5)^2 + (-10)^2} = \sqrt{174}$ ***[1 mark]***

$\cos\theta = \frac{109}{\sqrt{77}\sqrt{174}}$ ***[1 mark]***

$\Rightarrow \theta = 19.7°$ ***[1 mark]***

(ii) Draw a diagram:

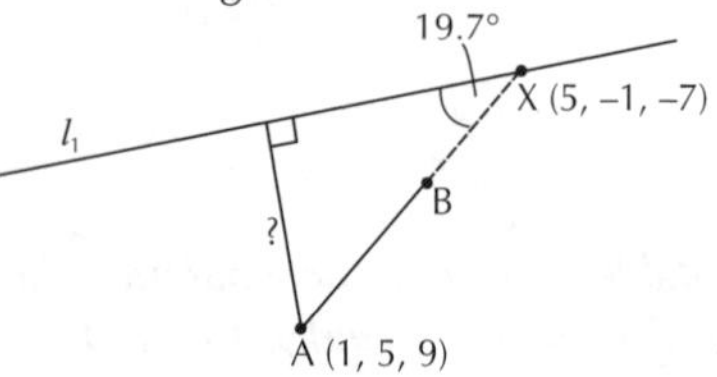

[1 mark for showing that the shortest distance is perpendicular to l_1]

X is the intersection point found in part c) — (5, –1, –7)

Answers

Distance from A to X =

$\sqrt{(5-1)^2+(-1-5)^2+(-7-9)^2} = \sqrt{308}$

[1 mark]

Now you've got a right-angled triangle, so just use trig to find the side you want:

Shortest distance from A to l_1

$= \sqrt{308} \times \sin 19.7°$ ***[1 mark]*** = 5.9 units ***[1 mark]***

The tricky thing here is figuring out how to go about it. Drawing a diagram definitely helps you see what you know and what you need to work out. Often, you'll be meant to use something you worked out in a previous part of the question.

2 a) $-3(\mathbf{i} - 4\mathbf{j} + 2\mathbf{k}) = -3\mathbf{i} + 12\mathbf{j} - 6\mathbf{k}$ ***[1 mark]***

b) **i** component: $3 + (\mu \times 1) = 2$ gives $\mu = -1$ ***[1 mark]***

So $\mathbf{r} = (3\mathbf{i} - 3\mathbf{j} - 2\mathbf{k}) - 1(\mathbf{i} - 4\mathbf{j} + 2\mathbf{k}) = 2\mathbf{i} + \mathbf{j} - 4\mathbf{k}$ ***[1 mark]***

This is the position vector of the point A(2, 1, –4)

c) B lies on l_2 so it has position vector

$\mathbf{b} = (10\mathbf{i} - 21\mathbf{j} + 11\mathbf{k}) + \lambda(-3\mathbf{i} + 12\mathbf{j} - 6\mathbf{k})$ ***[1 mark]***

So $\overrightarrow{AB} = \mathbf{b} - \mathbf{a}$

$= ((10\mathbf{i} - 21\mathbf{j} + 11\mathbf{k}) + \lambda(-3\mathbf{i} + 12\mathbf{j} - 6\mathbf{k})) - (2\mathbf{i} + \mathbf{j} - 4\mathbf{k})$

$= (8 - 3\lambda)\mathbf{i} + (-22 + 12\lambda)\mathbf{j} + (15 - 6\lambda)\mathbf{k}$ ***[1 mark]***

You know the scalar product of the direction vector of l_1 and $\overrightarrow{AB}$ must equal zero as they're perpendicular:

$(\mathbf{i} - 4\mathbf{j} + 2\mathbf{k}).((8 - 3\lambda)\mathbf{i} + (-22 + 12\lambda)\mathbf{j} + (15 - 6\lambda)\mathbf{k})$ ***[1 mark]***

$= (8 - 3\lambda) + (88 - 48\lambda) + (30 - 12\lambda)$

$= 126 - 63\lambda = 0$

$\Rightarrow \lambda = 2$ ***[1 mark]***

Substitute in $\lambda = 2$ to find the position vector **b**:

$\mathbf{b} = (10\mathbf{i} - 21\mathbf{j} + 11\mathbf{k}) + 2(-3\mathbf{i} + 12\mathbf{j} - 6\mathbf{k})$ ***[1 mark]***

$= 4\mathbf{i} + 3\mathbf{j} - \mathbf{k}$

Position vector of B = $4\mathbf{i} + 3\mathbf{j} - \mathbf{k}$ ***[1 mark]***

You could have multiplied $\overrightarrow{AB}$ by the direction bit of the l_2 vector equation, as $\overrightarrow{AB}$ is perpendicular to both l_1 and l_2. But the numbers for the l_1 vector are smaller, making your calculations easier.

d) $\overrightarrow{AB} = \mathbf{b} - \mathbf{a}$

$= (4\mathbf{i} + 3\mathbf{j} - \mathbf{k}) - (2\mathbf{i} + \mathbf{j} - 4\mathbf{k}) = 2\mathbf{i} + 2\mathbf{j} + 3\mathbf{k}$ ***[1 mark]***

$|\overrightarrow{AB}| = \sqrt{2^2 + 2^2 + 3^2} = \sqrt{17} = 4.1$ ***[1 mark]***

3 a) At an intersection point: $\begin{pmatrix}3\\0\\-2\end{pmatrix} + \lambda\begin{pmatrix}1\\3\\-2\end{pmatrix} = \begin{pmatrix}0\\2\\1\end{pmatrix} + \mu\begin{pmatrix}2\\-5\\-3\end{pmatrix}$

[1 mark]

This gives equations: $3 + \lambda = 2\mu$

$3\lambda = 2 - 5\mu$

$-2 - 2\lambda = 1 - 3\mu$ ***[1 mark]***

Solving the first two equations simultaneously gives:

$\lambda = -1,\ \mu = 1$ ***[1 mark]***

Substituting these values in the third equation gives:

$-2 - 2(-1) = 1 - 3(1) \Rightarrow 0 \neq -2$ ***[1 mark]***

So the lines are skew (they don't intersect).

You could have solved any two of the equations simultaneously, then substituted the results in the remaining equation to show that they don't work and there's no intersection point.

b) (i) At the intersection point of PQ and l_1:

$\begin{pmatrix}3\\0\\-2\end{pmatrix} + \lambda\begin{pmatrix}1\\3\\-2\end{pmatrix} = \begin{pmatrix}5\\4\\-9\end{pmatrix} + t\begin{pmatrix}0\\2\\3\end{pmatrix}$ ***[1 mark]***

This gives equations: $3 + \lambda = 5$

$3\lambda = 4 + 2t$

$-2 - 2\lambda = -9 + 3t$

[1 mark for any two equations]

Solving two of these equations gives: $\lambda = 2$, $t = 1$

[1 mark]

Intersection point = $\begin{pmatrix}5\\4\\-9\end{pmatrix} + 1\begin{pmatrix}0\\2\\3\end{pmatrix} = \begin{pmatrix}5\\6\\-6\end{pmatrix}$ = (5, 6, –6)

[1 mark]

(ii) If perpendicular, the scalar product of direction vectors of lines will equal 0:

$\begin{pmatrix}0\\2\\3\end{pmatrix} \cdot \begin{pmatrix}1\\3\\-2\end{pmatrix}$ ***[1 mark]***

$= (0 \times 1) + (2 \times 3) + (3 \times -2) = 0$ ***[1 mark]***

(iii) Call intersection point X.

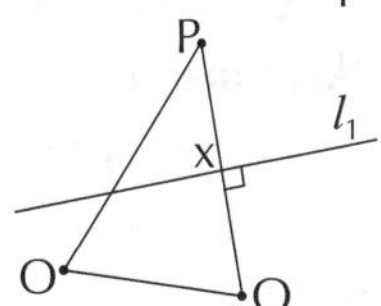

$\overrightarrow{PX} = \mathbf{x} - \mathbf{p}$

$= \begin{pmatrix}5\\6\\-6\end{pmatrix} - \begin{pmatrix}5\\8\\-3\end{pmatrix} = \begin{pmatrix}0\\-2\\-3\end{pmatrix}$ ***[1 mark]***

$\overrightarrow{OQ} = \overrightarrow{OP} + 2\overrightarrow{PX} = \begin{pmatrix}5\\8\\-3\end{pmatrix} + 2\begin{pmatrix}0\\-2\\-3\end{pmatrix}$ ***[1 mark]***

$= \begin{pmatrix}5\\4\\-9\end{pmatrix}$ ***[1 mark]***

The trick with this one is to realise that point Q lies the same distance from the intersection point as P does — drawing a quick sketch will definitely help.

4 a) $(\overrightarrow{OA}).(\overrightarrow{OB})$ ***[1 mark]***

$= (3\mathbf{i} + 2\mathbf{j} + \mathbf{k}).(3\mathbf{i} - 4\mathbf{j} - \mathbf{k}) = 9 - 8 - 1 = 0$ ***[1 mark]***

Therefore, side OA is perpendicular to side OB, and the triangle has a right angle. ***[1 mark]***

You could also have found the lengths $|OA|$, $|OB|$ and $|AB|$ and shown by Pythagoras that AOB is a right-angled triangle ($|AB|^2 = |OA|^2 + |OB|^2$).

b) $\overrightarrow{BA} = \mathbf{a} - \mathbf{b} = (3\mathbf{i} + 2\mathbf{j} + \mathbf{k}) - (3\mathbf{i} - 4\mathbf{j} - \mathbf{k}) = (6\mathbf{j} + 2\mathbf{k})$ ***[1 mark]***

$\overrightarrow{BO} = -3\mathbf{i} + 4\mathbf{j} + \mathbf{k}$

$\overrightarrow{BA}.\overrightarrow{BO} = 24 + 2 = 26$ ***[1 mark]***

$|\overrightarrow{BA}| = \sqrt{6^2 + 2^2} = \sqrt{40}$

$|\overrightarrow{BO}| = \sqrt{(-3)^2 + 4^2 + 1^2} = \sqrt{26}$ ***[1 mark]***

$\cos\angle ABO = \dfrac{\overrightarrow{BA} \cdot \overrightarrow{BO}}{|\overrightarrow{BA}| \cdot |\overrightarrow{BO}|} = \dfrac{26}{\sqrt{40}\sqrt{26}}$ ***[1 mark]***

$\angle ABO = 36.3°$ ***[1 mark]***

Answers

c) (i) $\overrightarrow{AC} = \mathbf{c} - \mathbf{a} = (3\mathbf{i} - \mathbf{j}) - (3\mathbf{i} + 2\mathbf{j} + \mathbf{k}) = (-3\mathbf{j} - \mathbf{k})$ ***[1 mark]***

$|\overrightarrow{AC}| = \sqrt{(-3)^2 + (-1)^2} = \sqrt{10}$

$|\overrightarrow{OC}| = \sqrt{3^2 + (-1)^2} = \sqrt{10}$ ***[1 mark]***

Sides AC and OC are the same length, so the triangle is isosceles. ***[1 mark]***

(ii) You know side lengths AC and OC from part c)(i). Calculate length of OA:

$|\overrightarrow{OA}| = \sqrt{3^2 + 2^2 + 1^2} = \sqrt{14}$ ***[1 mark]***

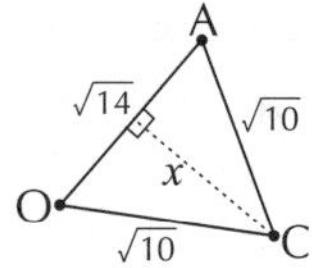

Now find the height of the triangle, x, using Pythagoras:

$$x = \sqrt{(\sqrt{10})^2 - \left(\frac{\sqrt{14}}{2}\right)^2} = \sqrt{6.5} \quad \textbf{[1 mark]}$$

Area $= \frac{1}{2}(\text{base} \times \text{height})$
$= \frac{1}{2}(\sqrt{14} \times \sqrt{6.5})$ ***[1 mark]***
$= 4.77$ square units ***[1 mark]***

d) (i) $\mathbf{r} = \mathbf{a} + t(\mathbf{b} - \mathbf{a})$

$\mathbf{r} = (3\mathbf{i} + 2\mathbf{j} + \mathbf{k}) + t((3\mathbf{i} - 4\mathbf{j} - \mathbf{k}) - (3\mathbf{i} + 2\mathbf{j} + \mathbf{k}))$ ***[1 mark]***

$\mathbf{r} = (3\mathbf{i} + 2\mathbf{j} + \mathbf{k}) + t(-6\mathbf{j} - 2\mathbf{k})$ ***[1 mark]***

(ii) $\mathbf{k}$ component: $1 - 2t = 1,\ t = 0$ ***[1 mark]***

$\mathbf{r} = (3\mathbf{i} + 2\mathbf{j} + \mathbf{k}) + 0(6\mathbf{j} + 2\mathbf{k}) = 3\mathbf{i} + 2\mathbf{j} + \mathbf{k}$

$a = 3$ ***[1 mark]***, $b = 2$ ***[1 mark]***

C4 — Practice Exam One

1 a) $$\frac{(x^2-9)(3x^2-10x-8)}{(6x+4)(x^2-7x+12)} = \frac{(x+3)(x-3)(3x+2)(x-4)}{2(3x+2)(x-3)(x-4)} = \frac{x+3}{2}$$

[2 marks available — 1 mark for correctly factorising numerator <u>or</u> denominator, 1 mark for correct final answer]

b)
$$\begin{array}{r} 2x + 5 \qquad \text{r}\ x + 8 \\ x^2 - 3x - 1\overline{)2x^3 - x^2 - 16x + 3} \\ -\ \underline{2x^3 - 6x^2 - 2x} \\ 5x^2 - 14x + 3 \\ -\ \underline{5x^2 - 15x - 5} \\ x + 8 \end{array}$$

so the quotient is $(2x + 5)$ and the remainder is $(x + 8)$.

[4 marks available — up to 2 marks for correct working, 1 mark for quotient and 1 mark for remainder]

If you'd tried to use the remainder theorem formula for this question, you'd have found it a bit tricky as the divisor doesn't factorise easily. Instead, you'd need to equate coefficients of x^3, x^2 and x, as well as putting in $x = 0$.

2 Let $u = \ln x$, so $\frac{du}{dx} = \frac{1}{x}$. Let $\frac{dv}{dx} = \frac{3}{x^2}$, so $v = -\frac{3}{x}$.

Putting this into the formula for integration by parts gives:

$$3\int_1^3 \frac{\ln x}{x^2}\,dx = 3\Big[-\frac{\ln x}{x}\Big]_1^3 - 3\int_1^3 -\frac{1}{x}\frac{1}{x}\,dx$$
$$= 3\Big[-\frac{\ln x}{x}\Big]_1^3 + 3\int_1^3 \frac{1}{x^2}\,dx = 3\Big[-\frac{\ln x}{x}\Big]_1^3 + 3\Big[-\frac{1}{x}\Big]_1^3$$
$$= \frac{-3\ln 3}{3} + \frac{3\ln 1}{1} - \frac{3}{3} + \frac{3}{1}$$
$$= -\ln 3 - 1 + 3 = 2 - \ln 3 = 0.90139$$

[5 marks available — 1 mark for correct expression for du/dx, 1 mark for correct expression for v, 1 mark for correct formula for integration by parts, 1 mark for correct working and 1 mark for correct answer]

If the question asked for the exact value, you'd leave your answer as 2 – ln 3.

3 If $x = \sin\theta$, then $\frac{dx}{d\theta} = \cos\theta$, so $dx = d\theta\cos\theta$ ***[1 mark]***.

Change the limits: as $x = \sin\theta$, $\theta = \sin^{-1}x$,

so when $x = 0$, $\theta = 0$ and when $x = 0.5$, $\theta = \frac{\pi}{6}$ ***[1 mark]***.

Putting all this into the integral gives:

$$\int_0^{\frac{1}{2}} \frac{x}{1-x^2}\,dx = \int_0^{\frac{\pi}{6}} \frac{\sin\theta}{1-\sin^2\theta}\cos\theta\,d\theta \quad \textbf{[1 mark]}$$

Using the identity $\sin^2\theta + \cos^2\theta = 1$, replace $1 - \sin^2\theta$:

$$\int_0^{\frac{\pi}{6}} \frac{\sin\theta\cos\theta}{\cos^2\theta}\,d\theta = \int_0^{\frac{\pi}{6}} \frac{\sin\theta}{\cos\theta}\,d\theta = \int_0^{\frac{\pi}{6}} \tan\theta\,d\theta \quad \textbf{[1 mark]}$$
$$= [-\ln|\cos\theta|]_0^{\frac{\pi}{6}} \quad \textbf{[1 mark]}$$
$$= -\ln|\cos\tfrac{\pi}{6}| + \ln|\cos 0| = -\ln\frac{\sqrt{3}}{2} + \ln 1$$
$$= -\ln\sqrt{3} + \ln 2$$
$$= \ln 2 - \ln\sqrt{3}\ \left(= \ln\frac{2}{\sqrt{3}}\right) \quad \textbf{[1 mark]}$$

Be careful when the substitution is of the form $x = f(\theta)$ rather than $\theta = f(x)$ — when you change the limits, you need to find the inverse of $f(\theta)$ then put in the given values of x.

4 a) (i) $\frac{dx}{d\theta} = \frac{\cos\theta}{2}$, $\frac{dy}{d\theta} = 2\sin 2\theta$ ***[1 mark]***

So $\frac{dy}{dx} = \frac{dy}{d\theta} \times \frac{d\theta}{dx} = \frac{dy}{d\theta} \div \frac{dx}{d\theta}$ ***[1 mark]***

$= 2\sin 2\theta \div \frac{\cos\theta}{2} = \frac{4\sin 2\theta}{\cos\theta}$ ***[1 mark]***

Use the double angle formula for sin to simplify this: $\sin 2\theta \equiv 2\sin\theta\cos\theta$, so

$\frac{4\sin 2\theta}{\cos\theta} = \frac{4(2\sin\theta\cos\theta)}{\cos\theta} = 8\sin\theta$ ***[1 mark]***.

(ii) $\theta = \frac{\pi}{6} \Rightarrow \frac{dy}{dx} = 8\sin\frac{\pi}{6} = 8 \times 0.5 = 4$ ***[1 mark]***

$x = \frac{1}{2}\sin\frac{\pi}{6} - 3 = \frac{1}{2} \times \frac{1}{2} - 3 = \frac{1}{4} - 3 = -\frac{11}{4}$

$y = 5 - \cos\frac{\pi}{3} = 5 - \frac{1}{2} = \frac{9}{2}$

[1 mark for x and y values both correct]

So $y = mx + c$

$\Rightarrow \frac{9}{2} = 4 \times -\frac{11}{4} + c = -11 + c$

$\Rightarrow c = 11 + \frac{9}{2} = \frac{31}{2}$

The equation of the tangent when $\theta = \frac{\pi}{6}$ is $y = 4x + \frac{31}{2}$ ***[1 mark]***

(iii) At the stationary points, $\frac{dy}{dx} = 0$, so $8\sin\theta = 0$.

Solving this gives $\theta = 0, \pi, 2\pi$, so $\theta = \pi$ in the given range. Substituting π into the parametric equations gives: $x = \frac{\sin\pi}{2} - 3 = -3$,

$y = 5 - \cos 2(\pi) = 5 - 1 = 4$.

So the coordinates of the stationary point are $(-3, 4)$ ***[1 mark for x-coordinate, 1 mark for y-coordinate]***.

Answers

b) Rewrite the equation for y using the identity $\cos 2\theta \equiv 1 - 2\sin^2\theta$:
$y = 5 - \cos 2\theta = 5 - (1 - 2\sin^2\theta) = 4 + 2\sin^2\theta$ ***[1 mark]***
Now rearrange the equation for x to make $\sin\theta$ the subject:
$x = \frac{\sin\theta}{2} - 3 \Rightarrow 2x + 6 = \sin\theta$ ***[1 mark]***
Sub this into the equation for y:
$y = 4 + 2\sin^2\theta = 4 + 2(2x + 6)^2$
$\Rightarrow y = 4 + 2(4x^2 + 24x + 36)$
$\Rightarrow y = 8x^2 + 48x + 76$ ***[1 mark]***

5 a) (i) $(p + x)^{-3} = p^{-3}\left(1 + \frac{1}{p}x\right)^{-3}$

$$= p^{-3}\left[1 + (-3)\frac{1}{p}x + \frac{(-3)(-4)\left(\frac{1}{p}x\right)^2}{1 \times 2} + \frac{(-3)(-4)(-5)\left(\frac{1}{p}x\right)^3}{1 \times 2 \times 3} + \ldots\right]$$

$$= p^{-3}\left[1 - \frac{3}{p}x + \frac{6}{p^2}x^2 - \frac{10}{p^3}x^3 + \ldots\right]$$

$$= \frac{1}{p^3} - \frac{3}{p^4}x + \frac{6}{p^5}x^2 - \frac{10}{p^6}x^3 + \ldots$$

[4 marks available — 1 mark for taking p^{-3} outside the brackets, 1 mark for correct expansion, 1 mark for each 2 correct coefficients in final solution.]

(ii) The coefficient of x^2 is $\frac{6}{p^5}$, so $\frac{6}{p^5} = \frac{3}{16} \Rightarrow (6 \times 16) = 3p^5$
$\Rightarrow p = 2$ ***[1 mark]***.

b) As $p = 2$, $(p + x)^{-3} = \frac{1}{8} - \frac{3}{16}x + \frac{3}{16}x^2 - \frac{5}{32}x^3 + \ldots$ ***[1 mark]***
So $\frac{2 + x^2}{(p + x)^3} = (2 + x^2)(2 + x)^{-3}$ ***[1 mark]***
$= (2 + x^2)(\frac{1}{8} - \frac{3}{16}x + \frac{3}{16}x^2 - \frac{5}{32}x^3 + \ldots)$ ***[1 mark]***
$= \frac{1}{4} - \frac{3}{8}x + \frac{3}{8}x^2 - \frac{5}{16}x^3 + \frac{1}{8}x^2 - \frac{3}{16}x^3 + \frac{3}{16}x^4 - \frac{5}{32}x^5 + \ldots$
[1 mark]
$= \frac{1}{4} - \frac{3}{8}x + \frac{1}{2}x^2 - \frac{1}{2}x^3 + \ldots$ ***[1 mark]***

6 a) Differentiate each term with respect to x:
$x^3 + x^2y = y^2 - 1$
$\Rightarrow \frac{d}{dx}x^3 + \frac{d}{dx}x^2y = \frac{d}{dx}y^2 - \frac{d}{dx}1$
Differentiate x^3 and 1 first:
$\Rightarrow 3x^2 + \frac{d}{dx}x^2y = \frac{d}{dx}y^2 - 0$ ***[1 mark]***
Differentiate y^2 using the chain rule:
$\Rightarrow 3x^2 + \frac{d}{dx}x^2y = \frac{d}{dy}y^2\frac{dy}{dx}$ ***[1 mark]***
$\Rightarrow 3x^2 + \frac{d}{dx}x^2y = 2y\frac{dy}{dx}$
Differentiate x^2y using the product rule:
$\Rightarrow 3x^2 + x^2\frac{d}{dx}y + y\frac{d}{dx}x^2 = 2y\frac{dy}{dx}$
$\Rightarrow 3x^2 + x^2\frac{dy}{dx} + 2xy = 2y\frac{dy}{dx}$ ***[1 mark]***
Rearrange to make $\frac{dy}{dx}$ the subject:
$\Rightarrow (2y - x^2)\frac{dy}{dx} = 3x^2 + 2xy$
$\Rightarrow \frac{dy}{dx} = \frac{3x^2 + 2xy}{2y - x^2}$ ***[1 mark]***

b) (i) Substitute $x = 1$ into the original equation:
$x = 1 \Rightarrow (1)^3 + (1)^2y = y^2 - 1$ ***[1 mark]***
$\Rightarrow y^2 - y - 2 = 0$
$\Rightarrow (y - 2)(y + 1) = 0$
$\Rightarrow y = 2$ or $y = -1$
$a > b$, so $a = 2$, $b = -1$ ***[1 mark]***

(ii) At $Q = (1, -1)$,
$\frac{dy}{dx} = \frac{3(1)^2 + 2(1)(-1)}{2(-1) - (1)^2} = \frac{3 - 2}{-2 - 1} = -\frac{1}{3}$ ***[1 mark]***
So the gradient of the normal at $Q = 3$. ***[1 mark]***
$(y - y_1) = m(x - x_1)$
$\Rightarrow (y + 1) = 3(x - 1)$
$\Rightarrow y = 3x - 4$ ***[1 mark]***

7 a) Vector equation of line through P and Q:

$$\mathbf{r} = \begin{pmatrix}-2\\-2\\-1\end{pmatrix} + \mu\left(\begin{pmatrix}-5\\-4\\1\end{pmatrix} - \begin{pmatrix}-2\\-2\\-1\end{pmatrix}\right)$$

$$\mathbf{r} = \begin{pmatrix}-2\\-2\\-1\end{pmatrix} + \mu\begin{pmatrix}-3\\-2\\2\end{pmatrix}$$ ***[1 mark]***

Where lines intersect:
$-1 + 2\lambda = -2 - 3\mu$
$2\lambda = -2 - 2\mu$
$3 + \lambda = -1 + 2\mu$ ***[1 mark]***
Solving any pair of equations simultaneously gives $\lambda = -2$ and $\mu = 1$. ***[1 mark]***
Substitute these values into the remaining equation to show that the lines intersect. E.g. $3 + \lambda = -1 + 2\mu$
$\Rightarrow 3 + -2 = -1 + 2(1) \Rightarrow 1 = 1$ ***[1 mark]***
Intersection point:

$$\mathbf{r} = \begin{pmatrix}-2\\-2\\-1\end{pmatrix} + \mu\begin{pmatrix}-3\\-2\\2\end{pmatrix} \Rightarrow \mathbf{r} = \begin{pmatrix}-2\\-2\\-1\end{pmatrix} + 1\begin{pmatrix}-3\\-2\\2\end{pmatrix} = \begin{pmatrix}-5\\-4\\1\end{pmatrix}$$

$\Rightarrow (-5, -4, 1)$ ***[1 mark]***

b) $\overrightarrow{OT} = 3\begin{pmatrix}-2\\-2\\-1\end{pmatrix} = \begin{pmatrix}-6\\-6\\-3\end{pmatrix}$ ***[1 mark]***

$\overrightarrow{QT} = \begin{pmatrix}-6\\-6\\-3\end{pmatrix} - \begin{pmatrix}-5\\-4\\1\end{pmatrix} = \begin{pmatrix}-1\\-2\\-4\end{pmatrix}$ ***[1 mark]***

$|\overrightarrow{QT}| = \sqrt{(-1)^2 + (-2)^2 + (-4)^2} = \sqrt{21}$ ***[1 mark]***

c) $\overrightarrow{PV} = \begin{pmatrix}0\\f\\g\end{pmatrix} - \begin{pmatrix}-2\\-2\\-1\end{pmatrix} = \begin{pmatrix}2\\f+2\\g+1\end{pmatrix}$ ***[1 mark]***

The scalar product of $\overrightarrow{PV}$ and the direction vector of L_1 must be zero as they're perpendicular.
$(2 \times 2) + (2 \times (f + 2)) + (1 \times (g + 1)) = 0$ ***[1 mark]***
$4 + 2f + 4 + g + 1 = 0 \Rightarrow 2f + g = -9$ ***[1 mark]***

d) $\cos\alpha = \frac{(2 \times 1) + (2 \times 1) + (1 \times 1)}{(\sqrt{2^2 + 2^2 + 1^2}) \times (\sqrt{1^2 + 1^2 + 1^2})}$ ***[1 mark]***
$\cos\alpha = \frac{5}{(\sqrt{9}) \times (\sqrt{3})} = 0.962$ ***[1 mark]***
$\alpha = 15.8°$ (3 s.f.) ***[1 mark]***

8 a) $\frac{dN}{dt} = k\sqrt{N}$, $k > 0$ ***[1 mark for LHS, 1 mark for RHS]***
When $N = 36$, $\frac{dN}{dt} = 0.36$. Putting these values into the equation gives $0.36 = k\sqrt{36} = 6k \Rightarrow k = 0.06$ ***[1 mark]*** (the population is increasing so ignore the negative square root).
So the differential equation is $\frac{dN}{dt} = 0.06\sqrt{N}$ ***[1 mark]***.

Answers

b) (i) $\frac{dN}{dt} = \frac{kN}{\sqrt{t}} \Rightarrow \int \frac{1}{N}\,dN = \int \frac{k}{\sqrt{t}}\,dt$

$\ln|N| = 2k\sqrt{t} + C$ ***[1 mark]***

$\Rightarrow N = e^{2k\sqrt{t}+C} = Ae^{2k\sqrt{t}}$, where $A = e^C$ ***[1 mark]***

For the initial population, $t = 0$, so $N = 25$ when $t = 0$. Putting these values into the equation:

$25 = Ae^0 \Rightarrow 25 = A$, so the equation for N is:

$N = 25e^{2k\sqrt{t}}$ ***[1 mark]***.

(ii) When initial population has doubled, $N = 50$ ***[1 mark]***. Put this value and the value for k into the equation and solve for t:

$50 = 25e^{2(0.05)\sqrt{t}} \Rightarrow 2 = e^{0.1\sqrt{t}} \Rightarrow \ln 2 = 0.1\sqrt{t}$ ***[1 mark]***

$10\ln 2 = \sqrt{t} \Rightarrow (10\ln 2)^2 = t \Rightarrow t = 48.045$

So it will take 48 weeks ***[1 mark]*** (to the nearest week) for the population to double.

C4 — Practice Exam Two

1 a) $5x^2 + 10x - 13 \equiv A(2 - x)(1 + 4x) + B(1 + 4x) + C(2 - x)^2$ ***[1 mark]***

Substitute values of x to make the brackets on the RHS equal to zero: ***[1 mark]***

Let $x = 2$, then $5(2)^2 + 10(2) - 13 = B(1 + 4(2))$

$\Rightarrow 27 = 9B \Rightarrow B = 3$ ***[1 mark]***

Let $x = -\frac{1}{4}$, then $5\left(-\frac{1}{4}\right)^2 + 10\left(-\frac{1}{4}\right) - 13 = C\left(2 - \left(-\frac{1}{4}\right)\right)^2$

$\Rightarrow \frac{5}{16} - \frac{5}{2} - 13 = C\frac{81}{16} \Rightarrow -\frac{243}{16} = \frac{81}{16}C \Rightarrow C = -3$ ***[1 mark]***

Equate the terms in x^2:

$5 = -4A + C = -4A - 3 \Rightarrow 8 = -4A \Rightarrow A = -2$ ***[1 mark]***

so $\frac{5x^2 + 10x - 13}{(2 - x)^2(1 + 4x)} = \frac{-2}{2 - x} + \frac{3}{(2 - x)^2} - \frac{3}{1 + 4x}$.

b) $\int \frac{5x^2 + 10x - 13}{(2 - x)^2(1 + 4x)}\,dx \equiv \int \frac{-2}{2 - x} + \frac{3}{(2 - x)^2} - \frac{3}{1 + 4x}\,dx$

$= 2\ln|2 - x| + \frac{3}{2 - x} - \frac{3}{4}\ln|1 + 4x| + C$

[4 marks available — 1 mark for using partial fractions from part a), 1 mark for each correct term of the answer (not including C)]

2 a) $(1 - x)^{-\frac{1}{2}} \approx 1 + \left(-\frac{1}{2}\right)(-x) + \frac{\left(-\frac{1}{2}\right) \times \left(-\frac{3}{2}\right)}{1 \times 2}(-x)^2 + \frac{\left(-\frac{1}{2}\right) \times \left(-\frac{3}{2}\right) \times \left(-\frac{5}{2}\right)}{1 \times 2 \times 3}(-x)^3$ ***[1 mark]***

$= 1 + \frac{x}{2} + \frac{3}{8}x^2 + \frac{5}{16}x^3$

[2 marks for all 4 terms correct, or 1 mark for 2 or 3 terms correct]

b) (i) $(25 - 4x)^{-\frac{1}{2}}$

$= (25)^{-\frac{1}{2}}\left(1 - \frac{4}{25}x\right)^{-\frac{1}{2}} = \frac{1}{5}\left(1 - \frac{4}{25}x\right)^{-\frac{1}{2}}$ ***[1 mark]***

$= \frac{1}{5}\left(1 + \frac{1}{2}\left(\frac{4}{25}x\right) + \frac{3}{8}\left(\frac{4}{25}x\right)^2 + \frac{5}{16}\left(\frac{4}{25}x\right)^3\right)$ ***[1 mark]***

$= \frac{1}{5}\left(1 + \frac{1}{2}\left(\frac{4}{25}x\right) + \frac{3}{8}\left(\frac{16}{625}x^2\right) + \frac{5}{16}\left(\frac{64}{15625}x^3\right)\right)$

$= \frac{1}{5}\left(1 + \frac{2}{25}x + \frac{6}{625}x^2 + \frac{4}{3125}x^3\right)$

$= \frac{1}{5} + \frac{2}{125}x$ ***[1 mark]*** $+ \frac{6}{3125}x^2 + \frac{4}{15625}x^3$ ***[1 mark]***

(ii) The expansion is valid for $\left|\frac{-4x}{25}\right| < 1 \Rightarrow \frac{|-4||x|}{25} < 1$

$\Rightarrow |x| < \frac{25}{4}$ ***[1 mark]***

c) $25 - 4x = 20 \Rightarrow x = \frac{5}{4}$ ***[1 mark]***

So $\frac{1}{\sqrt{20}} = \left(25 - 4\left(\frac{5}{4}\right)\right)^{-\frac{1}{2}}$

$\approx \frac{1}{5} + \frac{2}{125}\left(\frac{5}{4}\right) + \frac{6}{3125}\left(\frac{5}{4}\right)^2 + \frac{4}{15625}\left(\frac{5}{4}\right)^3$ ***[1 mark]***

$= \frac{1}{5} + \frac{2}{125}\left(\frac{5}{4}\right) + \frac{6}{3125}\left(\frac{25}{16}\right) + \frac{4}{15625}\left(\frac{125}{64}\right)$

$= \frac{1}{5} + \frac{1}{50} + \frac{3}{1000} + \frac{1}{2000}$

$= \frac{447}{2000}$ ***[1 mark]***

3 a) Let $u = 4x$, so $\frac{du}{dx} = 4$. Let $\frac{dv}{dx} = e^{-2x}$, so $v = -½e^{-2x}$.

Putting this into the integral gives:

$\int 4xe^{-2x}dx = [4x(-\frac{1}{2}e^{-2x})] - \int 4(-\frac{1}{2}e^{-2x})\,dx$

$= -2xe^{-2x} + \int 2e^{-2x}dx$

$= -2xe^{-2x} - e^{-2x} + C\ (= -e^{-2x}(2x + 1) + C)$

[5 marks available — 1 mark for correct choice of u and dv/dx, 1 mark for correct differentiation and integration to obtain du/dx and v, 1 mark for correct integration by parts method, 1 mark for integrating, 1 mark for answer]

b) As $u = \ln x$, $\frac{du}{dx} = \frac{1}{x}$, so $x\,du = dx$ ***[1 mark]***. The limits $x = 1$ and $x = 2$ become $u = \ln 1 = 0$ and $u = \ln 2$ ***[1 mark]***.

$\left(\frac{\ln x}{\sqrt{x}}\right)^2 = \frac{(\ln x)^2}{x}$ ***[1 mark]***. So the integral is:

$\int_0^{\ln 2} \frac{u^2}{x}x\,du = \int_0^{\ln 2} u^2\,du$ ***[1 mark]***

$= \left[\frac{u^3}{3}\right]_0^{\ln 2} = \frac{(\ln 2)^3}{3} = 0.111$ (3 s.f.) ***[1 mark]***.

4 a) As $x = \tan\theta$, $\frac{dx}{d\theta} = \sec^2\theta$ ***[1 mark]***.

As $y = \sin\theta$, $\frac{dy}{d\theta} = \cos\theta$ ***[1 mark]***.

So $\frac{dy}{dx} = \frac{dy}{d\theta} \div \frac{dx}{d\theta} = \frac{\cos\theta}{\sec^2\theta} = \cos^3\theta$. ***[1 mark]***

At P, $\tan\theta = 1$ and $\sin\theta = \frac{1}{\sqrt{2}}$. The value of θ in the given range that satisfies both these equations is $\theta = \frac{\pi}{4}$ ***[1 mark]***.

Putting this value into the expression for $\frac{dy}{dx}$:

$\frac{dy}{dx} = (\cos\frac{\pi}{4})^3 = (\frac{1}{\sqrt{2}})^3 = \frac{1}{2\sqrt{2}}$ ***[1 mark]***.

b) At P, the gradient of the tangent is $\frac{1}{2\sqrt{2}}$, so the gradient of the normal is $-1 \div \frac{1}{2\sqrt{2}} = -2\sqrt{2}$ ***[1 mark]***.

The coordinates of P are $(1, \frac{1}{\sqrt{2}})$. Putting all this into the equation of a line gives:

$y = mx + c \Rightarrow \frac{1}{\sqrt{2}} = (-2\sqrt{2} \times 1) + c$ ***[1 mark]***

$\Rightarrow c = \frac{1}{\sqrt{2}} + 2\sqrt{2} = \frac{5}{\sqrt{2}} = \frac{5\sqrt{2}}{2}$.

So the equation of the normal at P is $y = -2\sqrt{2}x + \frac{5\sqrt{2}}{2}$ ***[1 mark]***.

5 a) $\frac{x^2 + 5x - 14}{2x^2 - 4x} = \frac{(x + 7)(x - 2)}{2x(x - 2)} = \frac{x + 7}{2x}$

[3 marks available — 1 mark for factorising the numerator, 1 mark for factorising the denominator and 1 mark for cancelling to obtain correct answer]

Answers

b) $\frac{x^2+5x-14}{2x^2-4x}+\frac{14}{x(x-4)}=\frac{x+7}{2x}+\frac{14}{x(x-4)}$

$=\frac{(x+7)(x-4)}{2x(x-4)}+\frac{2\cdot 14}{2x(x-4)}$

$=\frac{x^2+3x-28+28}{2x(x-4)}=\frac{x^2+3x}{2x(x-4)}$

$=\frac{x(x+3)}{2x(x-4)}=\frac{x+3}{2(x-4)}$

[3 marks available — 1 mark for putting fractions over a common denominator, 1 mark for multiplying out and simplifying the numerator and 1 mark for cancelling to obtain correct answer]

6 a) First, rearrange the equation into the form $\frac{dy}{dx}=f(x)g(y)$:

$\frac{dy}{dx}=2y\frac{e^{2x}+x}{e^{2x}+x^2}$.

Then separate out the variables and integrate:

$\frac{1}{y}dy=\frac{2(e^{2x}+x)}{e^{2x}+x^2}dx \Rightarrow \int\frac{1}{y}dy=\int\frac{2(e^{2x}+x)}{e^{2x}+x^2}dx$

$\Rightarrow \ln|y|=\ln|e^{2x}+x^2|+C$

$\Rightarrow y=A(e^{2x}+x^2)$.

[7 marks available — 1 mark for separating variables, 1 mark for integrating LHS correctly, 1 mark for spotting that RHS is of the form f′(x)/f(x), 1 mark for integrating this correctly, 1 mark for adding C, 1 mark for simplifying to remove ln, 1 mark for rearranging to get in terms of y]

For this one, you need to spot that $2(e^{2x}+x)$ is the derivative of $e^{2x}+x^2$. A is just a constant (= e^C). You don't need the modulus signs around y as you're told that $y \geq 0$.

b) (i) Substitute $y = 3$ and $x = 0$ ***[1 mark]*** into the equation above to find the value of A:

$3=A(e^0+0^2) \Rightarrow 3=A\cdot 1 \Rightarrow A=3$.

So the particular solution is $y=3(e^{2x}+x^2)$. ***[1 mark]***

(ii) When $x = 3$, $y=3(e^{2\cdot 3}+3^2)=3e^6+27$. ***[1 mark]***

So $y = 3e^6 + 27$ ***[1 mark]***.

You have to leave the e^6 in your answer because you're asked for the exact value.

7 a) Differentiate each term with respect to x:

$\sin \pi x - \cos\frac{\pi y}{2}=0.5$

$\Rightarrow \frac{d}{dx}(\sin \pi x)-\frac{d}{dx}\left(\cos\frac{\pi y}{2}\right)=\frac{d}{dx}(0.5)$

Differentiate $\sin \pi x$ and 0.5 first:

$\Rightarrow \pi\cos\pi x-\frac{d}{dx}\left(\cos\frac{\pi y}{2}\right)=0$

Differentiate $\cos\frac{\pi y}{2}$ using the chain rule:

$\Rightarrow \pi\cos\pi x-\frac{d}{dy}\left(\cos\frac{\pi y}{2}\right)\frac{dy}{dx}=0$ ***[1 mark]***

$\Rightarrow \pi\cos\pi x+\left(\frac{\pi}{2}\sin\frac{\pi y}{2}\right)\frac{dy}{dx}=0$

Rearrange to make $\frac{dy}{dx}$ the subject:

$\Rightarrow \frac{dy}{dx}=-\frac{\pi\cos\pi x}{\frac{\pi}{2}\sin\frac{\pi y}{2}}=-\frac{2\cos\pi x}{\sin\frac{\pi y}{2}}$ ***[1 mark]***

b) (i) The stationary point is where the gradient is zero.

$\frac{dy}{dx}=0 \Rightarrow -\frac{2\cos\pi x}{\sin\frac{\pi y}{2}}=0 \Rightarrow \cos\pi x=0$ ***[1 mark]***

$\Rightarrow x=\frac{1}{2}$ or $x=\frac{3}{2}$ ***[1 mark]***

$x=\frac{3}{2} \Rightarrow \sin\frac{3\pi}{2}-\cos\frac{\pi y}{2}=0.5$

$\Rightarrow -1-\cos\frac{\pi y}{2}=0.5$

$\Rightarrow \cos\frac{\pi y}{2}=-1.5$

So y has no solutions when $x=\frac{3}{2}$ ***[1 mark]***

$x=\frac{1}{2} \Rightarrow \sin\frac{\pi}{2}-\cos\frac{\pi y}{2}=0.5$

$\Rightarrow 1-\cos\frac{\pi y}{2}=0.5$

$\Rightarrow \cos\frac{\pi y}{2}=0.5$

$\Rightarrow \frac{\pi y}{2}=\frac{\pi}{3}$

$\Rightarrow y=\frac{2}{3}$

So the only stationary point of the graph of $\sin\pi x-\cos\frac{\pi y}{2}=0.5$ for the given ranges of x and y is at $\left(\frac{1}{2},\frac{2}{3}\right)$. ***[1 mark]***

(ii) $x=\frac{1}{6} \Rightarrow \sin\frac{\pi}{6}-\cos\frac{\pi y}{2}=0.5$ ***[1 mark]***

$\Rightarrow 0.5-\cos\frac{\pi y}{2}=0.5$

$\Rightarrow \cos\frac{\pi y}{2}=0$

$\Rightarrow \frac{\pi y}{2}=\frac{\pi}{2}$

$\Rightarrow y=1$ ***[1 mark]***

At $\left(\frac{1}{6},1\right)$, $\frac{dy}{dx}=-\frac{2\cos\frac{\pi}{6}}{\sin\frac{\pi}{2}}=\frac{-2\left(\frac{\sqrt{3}}{2}\right)}{1}=-\sqrt{3}$ ***[1 mark]***

8 a) (i) The scalar product of perpendicular vectors is 0.

So **x.y** $= 15p - 12 + 3q = 0$

So **x.z** $=\frac{3}{2}p-\frac{6}{5}+4q=0$ ***[1 mark]***

Solving simultaneously gives $p=\frac{4}{5}$ ***[1 mark]***, $q = 0$ ***[1 mark]***

(ii) $|\mathbf{y}|=\sqrt{15^2+(-20)^2+3^2}=\sqrt{634}$ ***[1 mark]***

Unit vector in the direction of **y**

$=\frac{1}{\sqrt{634}}(15\mathbf{i}-20\mathbf{j}+3\mathbf{k})$ ***[1 mark]***

Unit vectors have a magnitude of 1 — that's all there is to it.

b) $\cos\alpha=\frac{\mathbf{y.z}}{|\mathbf{y}||\mathbf{z}|}=\frac{74.5}{(\sqrt{634})\times\left(\sqrt{\left(\frac{3}{2}\right)^2+(-2)^2+4^2}\right)}$ ***[1 mark]***

$=\frac{74.5}{118.77}=0.627$ ***[1 mark]*** $\Rightarrow \alpha=51°$ ***[1 mark]***

Answers

S2 Section 1 — The Poisson Distribution

Warm-up Questions

1) a) $P(X = 2) = \frac{e^{-3.1} \times 3.1^2}{2!} = 0.2165$ (to 4 d.p.).

b) $P(X = 1) = \frac{e^{-3.1} \times 3.1}{1!} = 0.1397$ (to 4 d.p.).

c) $P(X = 0) = \frac{e^{-3.1} \times 3.1^0}{0!} = 0.0450$ (to 4 d.p.).

d) $P(X < 3) = P(X = 0) + P(X = 1) + P(X = 2)$
$= 0.0450 + 0.1397 + 0.2165 = 0.4012$

e) $P(X \geq 3) = 1 - P(X < 3)$
$= 1 - 0.4012 = 0.5988$ (to 4 d.p.).

2) a) $P(X = 2) = \frac{e^{-8.7} \times 8.7^2}{2!} = 0.0063$ (to 4 d.p.).

b) $P(X = 1) = \frac{e^{-8.7} \times 8.7}{1!} = 0.0014$ (to 4 d.p.).

c) $P(X = 0) = \frac{e^{-8.7} \times 8.7^0}{0!} = 0.0002$ (to 4 d.p.).

d) $P(X < 3) = P(X = 0) + P(X = 1) + P(X = 2)$
$= 0.0002 + 0.0014 + 0.0063 = 0.0079$

e) $P(X \geq 3) = 1 - P(X < 3)$
$= 1 - 0.0079 = 0.9921$ (to 4 d.p.).

3) a) $E(X) = Var(X) = 8$
standard deviation $= \sigma = \sqrt{8} = 2.828$ (to 3 d.p.).

b) $E(X) = Var(X) = 12.11$
standard deviation $= \sigma = \sqrt{12.11} = 3.480$ (to 3 d.p.).

c) $E(X) = Var(X) = 84.2227$
standard deviation $= \sigma = \sqrt{84.2227} = 9.177$ (to 3 d.p.).

4) Using tables:

a) $P(X \leq \mu) = P(X \leq 9) = 0.5874$, $P(X \leq \mu - \sigma) = P(X \leq 6) = 0.2068$

b) $P(X \leq \mu) = P(X \leq 4) = 0.6288$, $P(X \leq \mu - \sigma) = P(X \leq 2) = 0.2381$

5) a) The defective products occur randomly, singly and (on average) at a constant rate, and the random variable represents the number of 'events' (i.e. defective products) within a fixed period, so this would follow a Poisson distribution.

b) There is a fixed number of trials in this situation, and so this situation would be modelled by a binomial distribution. (Or you could say it won't follow a Poisson distribution, as the events don't occur at a constant rate over the 25 trials.)

c) If the random variable represents the number of people joining the queue within a fixed period, and assuming that the people join the queue randomly, singly and (on average) at a constant rate, then this would follow a Poisson distribution.

You do need to make a couple of assumptions here — the Poisson model wouldn't work if you had, say, big groups of factory workers all coming in together a couple of minutes after the lunchtime hooter sounds.

d) The mistakes occur randomly, singly and (on average) at a constant rate, and the random variable represents the number of mistakes within a fixed 'period' (i.e. the number of pages in the document), so this would follow a Poisson distribution.

6) a) The number of atoms decaying in an hour would follow the Poisson distribution Po(2000). So the number decaying in a minute would follow Po(2000 ÷ 60) = Po(33.3).

b) The number of atoms decaying in a day would follow Po(2000 × 24) = Po(48 000).

7) a) If X represents the number of atoms from the first sample decaying per minute, then $X \sim Po(60)$. And if Y represents the number of atoms from the second sample decaying per minute, then $Y \sim Po(90)$. So $X + Y$ (the total number of atoms decaying per minute) ~ Po(60 + 90) = Po(150).

b) The total number of atoms decaying per hour would be distributed as Po(150 × 60) = Po(9000).

8) a) $P(X \leq 2) = 0.0138$

b) $P(X \leq 7) = 0.4530$

c) $P(X \leq 5) = 0.1912$

d) $P(X < 9) = P(X \leq 8) = 0.5925$

e) $P(X \geq 8) = 1 - P(X < 8) = 1 - P(X \leq 7)$
$= 1 - 0.4530 = 0.5470$

f) $P(X > 1) = 1 - P(X \leq 1) = 1 - 0.0030 = 0.9970$

g) $P(X > 7) = 1 - P(X \leq 7) = 1 - 0.4530 = 0.5470$

h) $P(X = 6) = P(X \leq 6) - P(X \leq 5) = 0.3134 - 0.1912 = 0.1222$

i) $P(X = 4) = P(X \leq 4) - P(X \leq 3) = 0.0996 - 0.0424 = 0.0572$

j) $P(X = 3) = P(X \leq 3) - P(X \leq 2) = 0.0424 - 0.0138 = 0.0286$

9) If X represents the number of geese in a random square metre of field, then $X \sim Po(1)$ — since the 'rate' at which geese occur is constant, they're randomly scattered, and geese only occur singly.

a) $P(X = 0) = \frac{e^{-1} \times 1^0}{0!} = 0.3679$

b) $P(X = 1) = \frac{e^{-1} \times 1^1}{1!} = 0.3679$

c) $P(X = 2) = \frac{e^{-1} \times 1^2}{2!} = 0.1839$

d) $P(X > 2) = 1 - P(X \leq 2) = 1 - (0.3679 + 0.3679 + 0.1839)$
$= 1 - 0.9197 = 0.0803$

This is one of those questions where you could use either your Poisson tables or the probability function.

10) a) No — $n < 50$ (and p is not very small).

b) Yes — $n > 50$ and $np < 5$, so approximate with Po(0.7).

c) No — $np > 5$.

d) No — n is too small (and you don't need to approximate it anyway).

e) Yes — $n > 50$ and $np < 5$. It should follow Po(2.5) very closely.

f) If Y represents the number of 'successes' in 80 trials, then define a new random variable X representing the number of 'failures' in those 80 trials. Then $X \sim B(80, 0.05)$.
Since $n > 50$, and $np < 5$, you could approximate X with Po(80 × 0.05) = Po(4). Then $Y = 80 - X$.

Answers

Exam Questions

1 a) Events need to happen at a constant average rate ***[1 mark]*** and singly ("one at a time") ***[1 mark]***.

You could also have had "events occur randomly" or "independently".

b) (i) If X represents the number of chaffinches visiting the observation spot, then $X \sim \text{Po}(7)$ ***[1 mark]***.
Using tables, $P(X < 4) = P(X \leq 3) = 0.0818$ ***[1 mark]***.

(ii) $P(X \geq 7) = 1 - P(X < 7) = 1 - P(X \leq 6)$ ***[1 mark]***
$= 1 - 0.4497 = 0.5503$ ***[1 mark]***

(iii) $P(X = 9) = P(X \leq 9) - P(X \leq 8)$ ***[1 mark]***
$= 0.8305 - 0.7291 = 0.1014$ ***[1 mark]***

Or you could work this last one out using the formula:
$P(X = 9) = \frac{e^{-7}7^9}{9!} = 0.1014$
— you get the same answer either way, obviously.

c) If X is the number of visiting chaffinches in x hours, then $X \sim \text{Po}(7x)$.

$P(X = 0) = \frac{e^{-\lambda} \times \lambda^x}{x!} = \frac{e^{-\lambda} \times \lambda^0}{0!} = e^{-\lambda}$

So, $e^{-\lambda} = 0.24$ ***[1 mark]***, for some value of λ.
You can find λ by taking logs:
$\ln e^{-\lambda} = \ln 0.24$ ***[1 mark]***
$\Rightarrow -\lambda \ln e = \ln 0.24$
$\Rightarrow \lambda = -\ln 0.24 = 1.427$ ***[1 mark]***
But you want to find x, where $7x = \lambda$.
So $x = \lambda \div 7 = 1.427 \div 7 = 0.203...$ hours
$= 12$ minutes (to nearest min) ***[1 mark]***

2 a) (i) If the mean is 20, then the number of calls per hour follows Po(20). So the number of calls in a random 30-minute period follows $\text{Po}(20 \div 2) = \text{Po}(10)$ ***[1 mark]***.
Using tables for $\lambda = 10$:
$P(X = 8) = P(X \leq 8) - P(X \leq 7)$ ***[1 mark]***
$= 0.3328 - 0.2202 = 0.1126$ ***[1 mark]***

Or you could work this out using the formula:
$P(X = 8) = \frac{e^{-10}10^8}{8!} = 0.1126.$

(ii) $P(X > 8) = 1 - P(X \leq 8)$ ***[1 mark]***
$= 1 - 0.3328 = 0.6672$ ***[1 mark]***

b) In this context, independently means that receiving a phone call at one particular instant does not affect whether or not a call will be received at a different instant. ***[1 mark]***.

3 a) The number of trials here is fixed (= 200) and the probability of the engineer being unable to fix a fault is constant (= 0.02). This means X (the total number of unsuccessful call-outs) will follow a binomial distribution ***[1 mark]***. In fact, $X \sim B(200, 0.02)$ ***[1 mark]***.

b) (i) To approximate a binomial distribution $B(n, p)$ with a Poisson distribution, n should be large / > 50 ***[1 mark]*** and p should be small / $np < 5$ ***[1 mark]***.

(ii) $\text{Po}(200 \times 0.02) = \text{Po}(4)$ ***[1 mark]***.

(iii) Mean = 4 and variance = 4 ***[1 mark]***.

(iv) P(engineer unable to fix fewer than 5 faults)
$= P(X < 5) = P(X \leq 4)$ ***[1 mark]***.
Using Poisson tables for $\lambda = 4$:
$P(X \leq 4) = 0.6288$ ***[1 mark]***.

S2 Section 2 — Continuous Random Variables

Warm-up Questions

1) a) Sketch the p.d.f.:

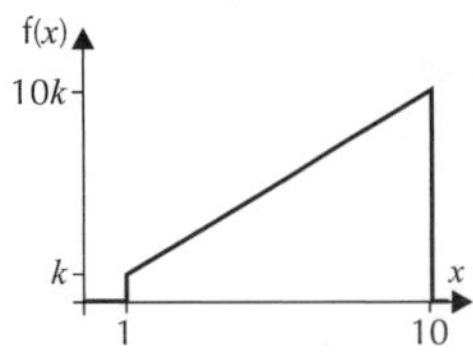

Area under p.d.f. $= \frac{10k + k}{2} \times (10 - 1) = \frac{99k}{2} = 1.$

So $k = \frac{2}{99}$.

b) Sketch the p.d.f.:

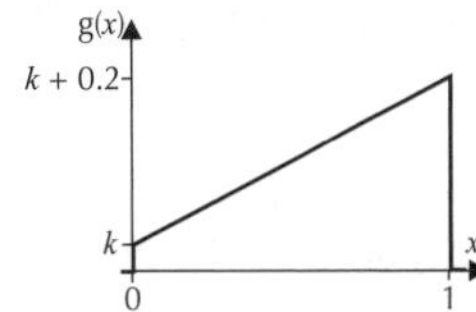

Area under p.d.f. $= \frac{2k + 0.2}{2} \times 1 = k + 0.1 = 1.$

So $k = 0.9$.

2 a) Sketch the p.d.f.:

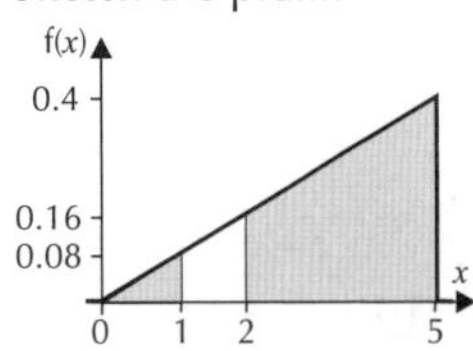

(i) Area under p.d.f. between $x = 0$ and $x = 1$ is:
$1 \times 0.08 \div 2 = 0.04$, so $P(X < 1) = 0.04$.

(ii) Area under p.d.f. between $x = 2$ and $x = 5$ is:
$\frac{0.16 + 0.4}{2} \times 3 = 0.84$, so $P(2 \leq X \leq 5) = 0.84$.

(iii) Area under p.d.f. at the point $x = 4$ is 0.
So $P(X = 4) = 0$.

b) Sketch the p.d.f.:

(i) Area under p.d.f. between $x = 0$ and $x = 1$ is:
$\frac{0.2 + 0.18}{2} \times 1 = 0.19$, so $P(X < 1) = 0.19$.

(ii) Area under p.d.f. between $x = 2$ and $x = 5$ is:
$\frac{0.16 + 0.1}{2} \times 3 = 0.39$, so $P(2 \leq X \leq 5) = 0.39$.

(iii) Area under p.d.f. at the point $x = 4$ is 0.
So $P(X = 4) = 0$.

Answers

3 a) $\int_{-\infty}^{\infty} f(x)dx = k\int_0^5 x^2 dx = k\left[\frac{x^3}{3}\right]_0^5 = \frac{125k}{3} = 1$, so $k = \frac{3}{125}$.

$P(X < 1) = \int_0^1 \frac{3}{125}x^2 dx = \frac{3}{125}\left[\frac{x^3}{3}\right]_0^1 = \frac{1}{125}$.

b) $\int_{-\infty}^{\infty} g(x)dx = \int_0^2 (0.1x^2 + kx)dx$

$= \left[\frac{0.1x^3}{3} + \frac{kx^2}{2}\right]_0^2 = \frac{0.8}{3} + 2k = 1.$

So $k = \frac{1}{2} - \frac{0.4}{3} = \frac{15-4}{30} = \frac{11}{30}$

$P(X < 1) = \int_0^1 \left(0.1x^2 + \frac{11}{30}x\right)dx = \left[\frac{0.1x^3}{3} + \frac{11x^2}{60}\right]_0^1$

$= \frac{0.1}{3} + \frac{11}{60} = \frac{13}{60}$

4 a) $\int_{-\infty}^{\infty} f(x)dx = \int_0^2 (0.1x^2 + 0.2)dx$

$= \left[\frac{0.1x^3}{3} + 0.2x\right]_0^2 = \frac{0.8}{3} + 0.4 \neq 1$

So f(x) is not a p.d.f.

b) $g(x) < 0$ for $-1 \leq x < 0$, so g(x) is not a p.d.f.

5 a) $E(X) = \int_{-\infty}^{\infty} xf(x)dx = \int_0^5 0.08x^2 dx = 0.08\left[\frac{x^3}{3}\right]_0^5$

$= \frac{125 \times 0.08}{3} = \frac{10}{3}$

$E(Y) = \int_{-\infty}^{\infty} yg(y)dy = \int_0^{10} 0.02y(10 - y)dy$

$= 0.02\left[5y^2 - \frac{y^3}{3}\right]_0^{10}$

$= 0.02\left(500 - \frac{1000}{3}\right) = 10 - \frac{20}{3} = \frac{10}{3}$

b) $Var(X) = \int_{-\infty}^{\infty} x^2 f(x)dx - \mu^2 = \int_0^5 0.08x^3 dx - \left(\frac{10}{3}\right)^2$

$= 0.08\left[\frac{x^4}{4}\right]_0^5 - \left(\frac{10}{3}\right)^2 = \frac{625 \times 0.08}{4} - \left(\frac{10}{3}\right)^2$

$= \frac{25}{2} - \left(\frac{10}{3}\right)^2 = \frac{25}{18} = 1.39$ (to 2 d.p.).

$Var(Y) = \int_{-\infty}^{\infty} y^2 g(y)dy - \mu^2$

$= \int_0^{10} 0.02y^2(10 - y)dy - \left(\frac{10}{3}\right)^2$

$= 0.02\left[\frac{10y^3}{3} - \frac{y^4}{4}\right]_0^{10} - \left(\frac{10}{3}\right)^2$

$= 0.02 \times \left(\frac{10\,000}{3} - \frac{10\,000}{4}\right) - \left(\frac{10}{3}\right)^2$

$= \frac{50}{3} - \left(\frac{10}{3}\right)^2 = \frac{50}{9} = 5.56$ (to 2 d.p.).

c) Sketch the p.d.f.:

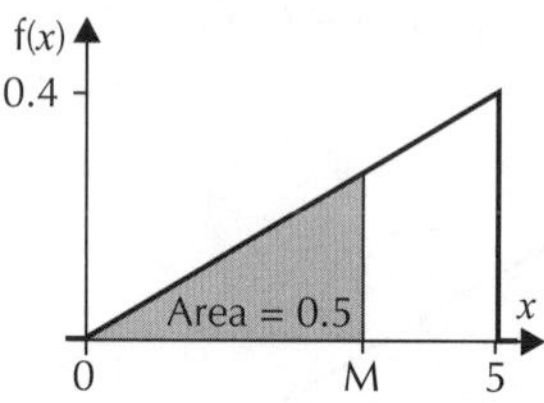

The median is M, where:

$\int_0^M 0.08x dx = 0.08\left[\frac{x^2}{2}\right]_0^M = 0.04M^2 = 0.5$

So the median = $\sqrt{12.5}$ = 3.54 (to 2 d.p.).

6 The shape of g(x) shows that the distribution of Y is more spread out than the distribution of X, so the variance of Y is greater than the variance of X.

Exam Questions

1 a) $\int_{-\infty}^{\infty} f(x)dx = \frac{1}{k}\int_0^2 (x + 4)dx = \frac{1}{k}\left[\frac{x^2}{2} + 4x\right]_0^2 = \frac{10}{k}$ ***[1 mark]***

This must be equal to 1 ***[1 mark]***.
So k = 10 ***[1 mark]***.

b) (i) $E(X) = \int_{-\infty}^{\infty} xf(x)dx = \int_0^2 0.1(x^2 + 4x)dx$ ***[1 mark]***

$= 0.1\left[\frac{x^3}{3} + 2x^2\right]_0^2$ ***[1 mark]***

$= 0.1\left(\frac{8}{3} + 8\right) = \frac{32}{30} = \frac{16}{15}$

$= 1.07$ (to 3 sig. fig.) ***[1 mark]***

(ii) $Var(X) = \int_{-\infty}^{\infty} x^2 f(x)dx - \mu^2$

$= 0.1\int_0^2 (x^3 + 4x^2)dx - \left(\frac{16}{15}\right)^2$ ***[1 mark]***

$= 0.1\left[\frac{x^4}{4} + \frac{4x^3}{3}\right]_0^2 - \left(\frac{16}{15}\right)^2$ ***[1 mark]***

$= 0.1\left(4 + \frac{32}{3}\right) - \left(\frac{16}{15}\right)^2$

$= \frac{44}{30} - \left(\frac{16}{15}\right)^2 = \frac{74}{225}$

= 0.329 (to 3 sig. fig.) ***[1 mark]***

If you worked out the integral but forgot to subtract the square of the mean, then you've just thrown a couple of marks away — at least, you would have done if that had been a real exam.

c) $P(0 < X < 1.5) = \frac{1}{10}\int_0^{1.5} (x + 4)dx$ ***[1 mark]*** $= \frac{1}{10}\left[\frac{x^2}{2} + 4x\right]_0^{1.5}$

$= \frac{1}{10}[(1.125 + 6) - 0] = \frac{7.125}{10} = 0.7125$ ***[1 mark]***

d) The median, M, is given by:

$\frac{1}{10}\int_0^M (x + 4)\,dx = 0.5$ ***[1 mark]***

$\Rightarrow \frac{1}{10}\left[\frac{x^2}{2} + 4x\right]_0^M = 0.5$ ***[1 mark]***

$\Rightarrow \frac{1}{10}\left(\frac{M^2}{2} + 4M\right) = 0.5 \Rightarrow \frac{M^2}{20} + \frac{4M}{10} = 0.5$

$\Rightarrow M^2 + 8M - 10 = 0$ ***[1 mark]***

Using the quadratic formula (and choosing the positive answer ***[1 mark]***) gives

$M = \frac{-8 + \sqrt{104}}{2} = 1.099$ (to 3 d.p.) ***[1 mark]***.

2 a)

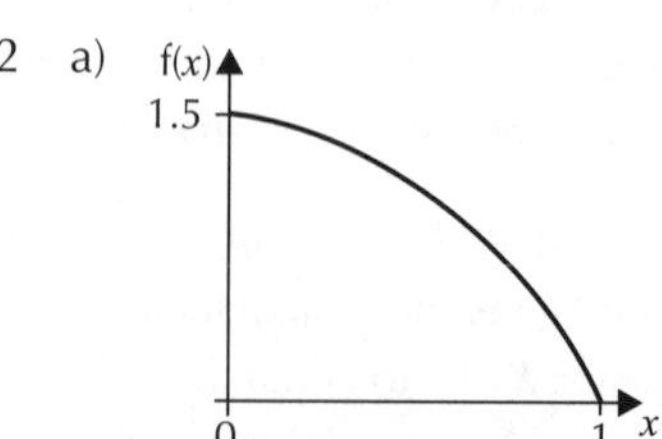

[1 mark for correct shape]

I always draw a graph of the p.d.f. whether the question asks me to or not. You should too. It not only makes questions easier, but you'll often get marks for doing something that you were going to do anyway. It's like free marks.

Answers

b) Mean $= \int_{-\infty}^{\infty} xf(x)dx$

$= 1.5\int_0^1 (x - x^3)dx$ ***[1 mark]***

$= 1.5\left[\frac{x^2}{2} - \frac{x^4}{4}\right]_0^1$ ***[1 mark]***

$= 1.5\left(\frac{1}{2} - \frac{1}{4}\right) = 1.5 \times 0.25 = 0.375$ ***[1 mark]***

c) Variance $= \int_{-\infty}^{\infty} x^2 f(x)dx - \mu^2$

$= 1.5\int_0^1 (x^2 - x^4)dx - 0.375^2$ ***[1 mark]***

$= 1.5\left[\frac{x^3}{3} - \frac{x^5}{5}\right]_0^1 - 0.375^2$ ***[1 mark]***

$= 1.5\left(\frac{1}{3} - \frac{1}{5}\right) - 0.375^2 = 0.2 - 0.375^2$

$= 0.059$ (to 3 d.p.) ***[1 mark]***

I hope you remembered to subtract the square of the mean.

d) $P(X < 0.2) = 1.5\int_0^{0.2} (1 - x^2)\,dx$

$= 1.5\left[x - \frac{x^3}{3}\right]_0^{0.2}$ ***[1 mark]***

$= 1.5\left(0.2 - \frac{0.2^3}{3}\right) = 0.296$ ***[1 mark]***

e) Let Y represent the number of observations that are less than 0.2. Then, $Y \sim B(20, 0.296)$ ***[1 mark for specifying a binomial distribution and 1 mark for both parameters correct]***.

$P(Y = 5) = \binom{20}{5} \times 0.296^5 \times 0.704^{15}$ ***[1 mark]***

$= 15\,504 \times 0.296^5 \times 0.704^{15}$

$= 0.182$ (to 3 sig. fig.) ***[1 mark]***

Look what's happened here — they've gone and sneaked in the binomial distribution, that's what. Well, that reminds me to say that they'll expect you to be able to use what you learnt in S1 in your S2 exam, so make sure you're prepared.

S2 Section 3 — The Normal Distribution Warm-up Questions

1) Use the Z-tables:

a) $P(Z < 0.84) = 0.7995$

b) $P(Z < 2.95) = 0.9984$

c) $P(Z > 0.68) = 1 - P(Z \leq 0.68) = 1 - 0.7517 = 0.2483$

d) $P(Z \geq 1.55) = 1 - P(Z < 1.55) = 1 - 0.9394 = 0.0606$

e) $P(Z < -2.10) = P(Z > 2.10) = 1 - P(Z \leq 2.10)$
$= 1 - 0.9821 = 0.0179$

f) $P(Z \leq -0.01) = P(Z \geq 0.01)$
$= 1 - P(Z < 0.01) = 1 - 0.5040 = 0.4960$

g) $P(Z > 0.10) = 1 - P(Z \leq 0.10) = 1 - 0.5398 = 0.4602$

h) $P(Z \leq 0.647) = 0.7412$

i) $P(Z > 0.234) = 1 - P(Z \leq 0.234) = 1 - 0.5925 = 0.4075$

j) $P(0.10 < Z \leq 0.50) = P(Z \leq 0.50) - P(Z \leq 0.10)$
$= 0.6915 - 0.5398 = 0.1517$

k) $P(-0.62 \leq Z < 1.10) = P(Z < 1.10) - P(Z < -0.62)$
$= P(Z < 1.10) - P(Z > 0.62) = P(Z < 1.10) - (1 - P(Z \leq 0.62))$
$= 0.8643 - (1 - 0.7324) = 0.5967$

l) $P(-0.99 < Z \leq -0.74) = P(Z \leq -0.74) - P(Z \leq -0.99)$
$= P(Z \geq 0.74) - P(Z \geq 0.99)$
$= (1 - P(Z < 0.74)) - (1 - P(Z < 0.99))$
$= (1 - 0.7704) - (1 - 0.8389) = 0.0685$

I know... these all get a bit fiddly. As always — take it nice and slow, and double-check each step as you do it.

2) a) If $P(Z < z) = 0.9131$, then from the Z-table, $z = 1.360$.

b) If $P(Z < z) = 0.5871$, then from the Z-table, $z = 0.220$.

c) If $P(Z > z) = 0.0359$, then $P(Z \leq z) = 0.9641$.
From the Z-table, $z = 1.800$.

d) If $P(Z > z) = 0.01$, then $P(Z \leq z) = 0.99$. From the critical values table, $z = 2.326$.

e) If $P(Z \leq z) = 0.4013$, then z must be negative (and so won't be in the Z-table).
But this means $P(Z < -z) = 1 - 0.4013 = 0.5987$.
Using the Z-table, $-z = 0.250$, so $z = -0.250$.
It's getting a bit trickier here, with all the z and −z business. If you need to draw a graph here to make it a bit clearer what's going on, then draw one.

f) If $P(Z \geq z) = 0.995$, then $P(Z \leq -z) = 0.995$.
From the critical values table, $-z = 2.576$.
So $z = -2.576$.
*When you've answered a question like this, always ask yourself whether your answer looks 'about right'. Here, you need a number that Z is very very likely to be greater than... so your answer is going to be negative, and it's going to be pretty big.
So z = −2.576 looks about right.*

3) a) $P(X < 55) = P\left(Z < \frac{55 - 50}{\sqrt{16}}\right) = P(Z < 1.25) = 0.8944$

b) $P(X < 42) = P\left(Z < \frac{42 - 50}{\sqrt{16}}\right) = P(Z < -2)$
$= P(Z > 2) = 1 - P(Z \leq 2) = 1 - 0.9772 = 0.0228$

c) $P(X > 56) = P\left(Z > \frac{56 - 50}{\sqrt{16}}\right) = P(Z > 1.5)$
$= 1 - P(Z \leq 1.5) = 1 - 0.9332 = 0.0668$

d) $P(47 < X < 57) = P(X < 57) - P(X \leq 47)$
$= P(Z < 1.75) - P(Z \leq -0.75)$
$= 0.9599 - P(Z \geq 0.75)$
$= 0.9599 - (1 - P(Z < 0.75))$
$= 0.9599 - (1 - 0.7734) = 0.7333$

4) $P(X < 8) = 0.8925$ means $P\left(Z < \frac{8 - \mu}{\sqrt{10}}\right) = 0.8925$.

From tables, $\frac{8 - \mu}{\sqrt{10}} = 1.240$.

So $\mu = 8 - 1.240 \times \sqrt{10} = 4.08$ (to 3 sig. fig.).

5) $P(X > 26) = 0.05$ means $P\left(Z > \frac{26 - 11}{\sigma}\right) = 0.05$,

or $P\left(Z \leq \frac{26 - 11}{\sigma}\right) = 1 - 0.05 = 0.95$.

From the critical values table, $\frac{26 - 11}{\sigma} = 1.645$.

So $\sigma = \frac{26 - 11}{1.645} = 9.12$ (to 3 sig. fig.).

Answers

6) If X represents the mass of an item, then:

a) $P(X < 55) = P\left(Z < \frac{55-55}{4.4}\right) = P(Z < 0) = 0.5.$

b) $P(X < 50) = P\left(Z < \frac{50-55}{4.4}\right) = P(Z < -1.136)$
$= P(Z > 1.136) = 1 - P(Z \leq 1.136)$
$= 1 - 0.8720 = 0.1280$

c) $P(X > 60) = P\left(Z > \frac{60-55}{4.4}\right) = P(Z > 1.136)$
$= 1 - P(Z \leq 1.136) = 1 - 0.8720 = 0.1280$

7) If X represents the mass of an egg in kg, then:

a) $P(X < 1) = P\left(Z < \frac{1-1.4}{0.3}\right) = P(Z < -1.333)$
$= P(Z > 1.333) = 1 - P(Z \leq 1.333)$
$= 1 - 0.9087 = 0.0913$

b) $P(X > 1.5) = P\left(Z > \frac{1.5-1.4}{0.3}\right) = P(Z > 0.333)$
$= 1 - P(Z \leq 0.333)$
$= 1 - 0.6304 = 0.3696$

c) $P(1.3 < X < 1.6) = P(X < 1.6) - P(X \leq 1.3)$
$= P\left(Z < \frac{1.6-1.4}{0.3}\right) - P\left(Z \leq \frac{1.3-1.4}{0.3}\right)$
$= P(Z < 0.667) - P(Z \leq -0.333)$
$= 0.7477 - (1 - P(Z < 0.333))$
$= 0.7477 - (1 - 0.6304) = 0.3781$

8) Use the normal approximation $X \sim N(45, 24.75)$.

a) $P(X > 50) \approx P(X > 50.5) = P\left(Z > \frac{50.5-45}{\sqrt{24.75}}\right)$
$= P(Z > 1.106)$
$= 1 - P(Z \leq 1.106)$
$= 1 - 0.8655 = 0.1345$

b) $P(X \leq 45) \approx P(X < 45.5) = P\left(Z < \frac{45.5-45}{\sqrt{24.75}}\right)$
$= P(Z < 0.101)$
$= 0.5402$

c) $P(40 < X \leq 47) \approx P(X \leq 47.5) - P(X \leq 40.5)$
$= P\left(Z \leq \frac{47.5-45}{\sqrt{24.75}}\right) - P\left(Z \leq \frac{40.5-45}{\sqrt{24.75}}\right)$
$= P(Z \leq 0.503) - P(Z \leq -0.905)$
$= P(Z \leq 0.503) - (1 - P(Z < 0.905))$
$= 0.6925 - 1 + 0.8172 = 0.5097$

9) Use the normal approximation $X \sim N(25, 25)$.

a) $P(X \leq 20) \approx P(X \leq 20.5) = P\left(Z \leq \frac{20.5-25}{5}\right)$
$= P(Z \leq -0.9)$
$= 1 - P(Z < 0.9)$
$= 1 - 0.8159 = 0.1841$

b) $P(X > 15) \approx P(X > 15.5) = P\left(Z > \frac{15.5-25}{5}\right)$
$= P(Z > -1.90)$
$= P(Z < 1.90) = 0.9713$

c) $P(20 \leq X < 30) \approx P(X \leq 29.5) - P(X \leq 19.5)$
$= P\left(Z \leq \frac{29.5-25}{5}\right) - P\left(Z \leq \frac{19.5-25}{5}\right)$
$= P(Z \leq 0.90) - P(Z \leq -1.10)$
$= P(Z \leq 0.90) - (1 - P(Z < 1.10))$
$= 0.8159 - 1 + 0.8643 = 0.6802$

10) People join the queue (on average) at a constant rate. Assuming they join the queue randomly and singly, the total number of people joining the queue in a 15-minute period follows a Poisson distribution, Po(7).

a) If X represents the number of people joining the queue in a 7-hour day, then $X \sim Po(7 \times 28) = Po(196)$. $\lambda > 15$, so use the normal approximation $X \sim N(196, 196)$.
$P(X > 200) \approx P(X > 200.5) = P\left(Z > \frac{200.5-196}{14}\right)$
$= P(Z > 0.321)$
$= 1 - P(Z \leq 0.321)$
$= 1 - 0.6259 = 0.3741$

b) Let C represent the number of people out of the 200 customers who are seen within 1 minute.
Then $C \sim B(200, 0.7)$.
$np = 200 \times 0.7 = 140$ and $nq = 200 \times 0.3 = 60$ are both greater than 5, so use the normal approximation, i.e. $C \sim N(140, 42)$.
You need to find $P(C < 70\%$ of $200)$, i.e. $P(C < 140)$.
$P(C < 140) \approx P(C < 139.5) = P\left(Z < \frac{139.5-140}{\sqrt{42}}\right)$
$= P(Z < -0.077)$
$= 1 - P(Z \leq 0.077)$
$= 1 - 0.5307 = 0.4693$

Exam Questions

1 Assume that the lives of the batteries are distributed as: $N(\mu, \sigma^2)$. Then $P(X < 20) = 0.25$ and $P(X < 30) = 0.9$. ***[1 mark]***

Transform these 2 equations to get:
$P\left[Z < \frac{20-\mu}{\sigma}\right] = 0.25$ and $P\left[Z < \frac{30-\mu}{\sigma}\right] = 0.9$ ***[1 mark]***
Since $P(Z < z) = 0.25$, then $P(Z > -z) = 0.25$
which means $P(Z \leq -z) = 0.75$.
So you can use your critical values table to get:
$\frac{20-\mu}{\sigma} = -0.674$ ***[1 mark]*** and $\frac{30-\mu}{\sigma} = 1.282$ ***[1 mark]***

Now rewrite these as:

$20 - \mu = -0.674\sigma$ and $30 - \mu = 1.282\sigma$. ***[1 mark]***

Subtract these two equations to get:
$10 = (1.282 + 0.674)\sigma$
i.e. $\sigma = \frac{10}{1.282 + 0.674} = 5.112$ ***[1 mark]***

Now use this value of σ in one of the equations above:
$\mu = 20 + 0.674 \times 5.112 = 23.45$ ***[1 mark]***
So $X \sim N(23.45, 5.11^2)$ i.e. $X \sim N(23.45, 26.1)$

Answers

2 a) (i) $np > 5$ ***[1 mark]*** and $nq > 5$ ***[1 mark]***
OR n large ***[1 mark]*** and p close to 0.5 ***[1 mark]***.

Engrave upon your heart all the conditions required for the various approximations to work. Well... actually, that might be considered to be cheating, so don't do that. But make sure you know them.

(ii) A binomial distribution is discrete ***[1 mark]***, whereas a normal distribution is continuous. The continuity correction means probabilities can be calculated for the continuous normal distribution that correspond approximately to the discrete binomial probabilities ***[1 mark]***.

b) (i) $np = 60 > 5$ and $nq = 40 > 5$, so use the normal approximation N(60, 24) ***[1 mark]***.

$$P(X \geq 65) \approx P(X > 64.5)$$
$$= P\left(Z > \frac{64.5 - 60}{\sqrt{24}}\right) \textbf{ [1 mark]}$$
$$= P(Z > 0.919)$$
$$= 1 - P(Z \leq 0.919) \textbf{ [1 mark]}$$
$$= 1 - 0.8209 = 0.1791 \textbf{ [1 mark]}$$

(ii) $P(50 < X < 62)$

$$\approx P(X < 61.5) - P(X < 50.5) \textbf{ [1 mark]}$$
$$= P\left(Z < \frac{61.5 - 60}{\sqrt{24}}\right) - P\left(Z < \frac{50.5 - 60}{\sqrt{24}}\right)$$
$$= P(Z < 0.306) - P(Z < -1.939) \textbf{ [1 mark]}$$
$$= P(Z < 0.306) - (1 - P(Z \leq 1.939))$$
$$= 0.6201 - (1 - 0.9737) = 0.5938 \textbf{ [1 mark]}$$

All the usual tricks involved there... normal approximation, continuity correction, subtracting values of $\Phi(z)$ (the function in your big 'normal distribution table'). They'll all be there on exam day too.

3 a) The normal approximation is: $Y \sim N(\mu, \sigma^2)$.

$P(X \leq 151) \approx P(Y < 151.5)$ ***[1 mark]***

$$= P\left(Z < \frac{151.5 - \mu}{\sigma}\right) = 0.8944 \textbf{ [1 mark]}.$$

From tables, $\frac{151.5 - \mu}{\sigma} = 1.25$.

So $\underline{\mu + 1.25\sigma = 151.5}$ ***[1 mark]***.

$P(X > 127) \approx P(Y > 127.5)$ ***[1 mark]***

$$= P\left(Z > \frac{127.5 - \mu}{\sigma}\right) = 0.9970 \textbf{ [1 mark]}.$$

This means $P\left(Z \leq \frac{127.5 - \mu}{\sigma}\right) = 0.0030$.

But this probability is less than 0.5, so $\frac{127.5 - \mu}{\sigma} < 0$.

So find $1 - 0.0030 = 0.9970$.

$P(Z \leq z) = 0.9970$ means $z = 2.75$.

This tells you that $\frac{127.5 - \mu}{\sigma} = -2.75$,

or $\underline{\mu - 2.75\sigma = 127.5}$ ***[1 mark]***.

Now you can subtract the underlined equations to give $4\sigma = 24$, or $\sigma = 6$ ***[1 mark]***.
This then gives $\mu = 144$ ***[1 mark]***.

I call this question "The Beast" — there's loads to do here. But as always in maths, when something looks hard, the best thing to do is take a deep breath, look at the information you have (here, some probabilities from a normal approximation), and write down some formulas containing that information. Then you can start piecing things together, and try to find out things you don't yet know. The worst thing you can do is panic and start thinking it's too hard. That's what Luke Skywalker did in that film before Yoda told him to chill out a bit. Something like that anyway.

b) You know $\mu = \underline{np = 144}$ ***[1 mark]***
and $\sigma^2 = \underline{np(1 - p) = 36}$ ***[1 mark]***.
Divide the second underlined equation by the first to give $1 - p = 36 \div 144 = 0.25$, or $p = 0.75$ ***[1 mark]***.
Then $n = 144 \div 0.75 = 192$ ***[1 mark]***.

Phew... made it.

4 a) Let X represent the number of items that the new customer could order per week. Then X follows a Poisson distribution with an average of 40, and so $X \sim Po(40)$ ***[1 mark]***.

b) Here, λ is quite large (i.e. $\lambda > 15$), and so X will approximately follow the normal distribution N(40, 40) ***[1 mark]***.

$$P(X > 50) \approx P(X > 50.5) = P\left(Z > \frac{50.5 - 40}{\sqrt{40}}\right) \textbf{ [1 mark]}$$
$$= P(Z > 1.660)$$
$$= 1 - P(Z \leq 1.660)$$
$$= 1 - 0.9515 = 0.0485 \textbf{ [1 mark]}$$

c) The probability that the factory will not be able to meet the new customer's order in two consecutive weeks will be $0.0485^2 = 0.00235...$, which is less than 0.01.
So the manager should sign the contract ***[1 mark for 'yes', with a clear explanation]***.

This question looks quite tough because there are so many words. But it's a pussycat really.

S2 Section 4 — Sampling and Hypothesis Tests

Warm-up Questions

1) Simple random sampling means the sample will not be affected by sampling bias.

2) a) Yes

b) No — it contains unknown parameter σ.

c) No — it contains unknown parameter μ.

d) Yes

There's no excuse for getting these ones wrong. You've just got to look for any unknown parameters — if you find one, it's not a statistic.

3) $X \sim N(8, 2) \Rightarrow \overline{X} \sim N\left(8, \frac{2}{10}\right) = N(8, 0.2)$

$$P(\overline{X} < 7) = P\left(Z < \frac{7 - 8}{\sqrt{0.2}}\right) = P(Z < -2.236)$$
$$= P(Z > 2.236) = 1 - P(Z < 2.236)$$
$$= 1 - 0.9873 = 0.0127$$

Answers

4) The sample mean is an unbiased estimate of the population mean — this is: $\frac{\sum x}{n} = \frac{80.5}{10} = 8.05$
An unbiased estimate of the population variance is:
$$\frac{n}{n-1}\left[\frac{\sum x^2}{n} - \left(\frac{\sum x}{n}\right)^2\right] = \frac{10}{9}\left[\frac{653.13}{10} - \left(\frac{80.5}{10}\right)^2\right]$$
$$= 0.567 \text{ (to 3 d.p.)}.$$

5) a) i) One-tailed — Salma is only interested in whether the average height is greater than 160 cm.
ii) Two-tailed — Joy is interested in either an increase or a decrease in the mean diameter.
iii) Two-tailed test — Henry doesn't know if the coin is biased towards heads or tails.
iv) One-tailed test — the typist is only interested in a decrease in the rate of errors.

b) i) $H_0: \mu = 160$ and $H_1: \mu > 160$
ii) $H_0: \mu = 2.2$ and $H_1: \mu \neq 2.2$
iii) $H_0: p = 0.5$, $H_1: p \neq 0.5$
iv) $H_0: \lambda = 20$, $H_1: \lambda < 20$

6) A type I error — he rejects H_0 when it's actually true.

7) $H_0: \mu = 45$, $H_1: \mu < 45$, $\alpha = 0.05$ and $\sigma^2 = 9$.
Under H_0, $\overline{X} \sim N\left(45, \frac{9}{16}\right)$ and $z = \frac{42 - 45}{3/4} = -4$
Critical region is $Z < -1.645$.
$-4 < -1.645$, so there is evidence to reject H_0 at the 5% level.

8) $H_0: p = 0.2$, $H_1: p < 0.2$, $\alpha = 0.05$ and $x = 2$:
Under H_0, $X \sim B(20, 0.2)$
$P(X \leq 2) = 0.2061$
$0.2061 > 0.05$, so there is insufficient evidence at the 5% level of significance to reject H_0.

9) $H_0: \lambda = 2.5$, $H_1: \lambda > 2.5$, $\alpha = 0.1$ and $x = 4$:
Under H_0, $X \sim Po(2.5)$
$P(X \geq 4) = 1 - P(X \leq 3) = 1 - 0.7576 = 0.2424$
$0.2424 > 0.1$, so there is insufficient evidence at the 10% level of significance to reject H_0.

10) a) $H_0: p = 0.3$, $H_1: p < 0.3$, $\alpha = 0.05$
Under H_0, $X \sim B(10, 0.3)$
Critical region = biggest possible set of 'low' values of X with a total probability of ≤ 0.05.
$P(X \leq 0) = 0.0282$, $P(X \leq 1) = 0.1493$,
so CR is $X = 0$.

b) $H_0: \lambda = 6$, $H_1: \lambda < 6$, $\alpha = 0.1$
Under H_0, $X \sim Po(6)$
Critical region = biggest possible set of 'low' values of X with a total probability of ≤ 0.1.
$P(X \leq 2) = 0.0620$, $P(X \leq 3) = 0.1512$,
so CR is $X \leq 2$.

These might be getting a bit tedious, but a significant amount of practice is critical when it comes to hypothesis testing.

Exam Questions

1 a) $\bar{x} = \frac{\sum x}{n} = \frac{490}{100} = 4.9$ m ***[1 mark]***
$$s^2 = \frac{n}{n-1}\left[\frac{\sum x^2}{n} - \left(\frac{\sum x}{n}\right)^2\right]$$
$$= \frac{100}{99}\left[\frac{2421}{100} - 4.9^2\right] \textbf{\textit{[1 mark]}}$$
$$= \frac{20}{99} = 0.202 \text{ (to 3 d.p.)} \textbf{\textit{[1 mark]}}$$

b) Let μ = mean height of trees in 2nd area.
$H_0: \mu = 5.0$ and $H_1: \mu \neq 5.0$ ***[1 mark]***
Under H_0, $\overline{X} \sim N\left(5.0, \frac{20/99}{100}\right)$ ***[1 mark]*** $= N\left(5.0, \frac{1}{495}\right)$
$Z = \frac{4.9 - 5.0}{\sqrt{1/495}}$ ***[1 mark]*** $= -2.225$ ***[1 mark]***
This is a two-tailed test at the 1% level, so the critical values you need are z such that $P(Z < z) = 0.005$ and $P(Z > z) = 0.005$. Looking these up in the normal tables you get critical values of –2.576 and 2.576 ***[1 mark]***. Since $-2.225 > -2.576$, the result isn't significant. There is insufficient evidence at the 1% level to reject H_0 that the trees have the same mean height ***[1 mark]***.

c) When the sample mean is 4.95:
$$Z = \frac{4.95 - 5.0}{\sqrt{\frac{20/99}{n}}}$$
P(Type I error) < 0.01 means that $|Z| > 2.576$.
$$\left|\frac{4.95 - 5.0}{\sqrt{\frac{20/99}{n}}}\right| > 2.576 \Rightarrow \frac{0.05}{\sqrt{\frac{20/99}{n}}} > 2.576 \textbf{\textit{ [1 mark]}}$$
$$\Rightarrow 0.05 > 2.576 \times \frac{\sqrt{20/99}}{\sqrt{n}} \Rightarrow \sqrt{n} > \frac{2.576 \times \sqrt{20/99}}{0.05} \textbf{\textit{ [1 mark]}}$$
$$\Rightarrow n > 536.224...$$
So n should be at least 537 ***[1 mark]***.

2 a) First-serve faults must occur randomly (or independently of each other) and at a constant average rate per service game.
[1 mark for saying first-serve faults must occur randomly or independently, and 1 mark for saying first-serve faults must occur at a constant average rate per service game.]

b) $H_0: \lambda = 3$ and $H_1: \lambda < 3$ ***[1 mark]***, where λ is the rate of first-serve faults per service game.
X = number of first-serve faults in 4 service games.
Under H_0, $X \sim Po(12)$ ***[1 mark]***
$\alpha = 0.05$
$P(X \leq 6) = 0.0458$ ***[1 mark]***
$0.0458 < 0.05$, so the result is significant. ***[1 mark]***
There is evidence at the 5% level of significance to reject H_0 and to say that the rate of first-serve faults has decreased. ***[1 mark]***

3 a) E.g. a random sample will ensure that the observations are independent. The correct population is being sampled from.
[2 marks for two correct statements.]

Answers

b) H_0: $p = 0.2$ and H_0: $p \neq 0.2$
X = number of sampled residents against the plan
Under H_0, $X \sim B(30, 0.2)$ ***[1 mark]***
It's a two-tailed test, so the critical region is split into two.
For the lower end: $P(X \le 3) = 0.1227$, $P(X \le 2) = 0.0442$ ***[1 mark]***, which is the greatest probability less than 0.05.
For the upper end: $P(X \ge 10) = 1 - 0.9389 = 0.0611$,
$P(X \ge 11) = 1 - 0.9744 = 0.0256$ ***[1 mark]***, which is the greatest probability less than 0.05.
So CR is $X \le 2$ ***[1 mark]*** and $X \ge 11$ ***[1 mark]***

c) P(Type I error) is the same as the actual significance level.
So, it's $P(X \le 2) + P(X \ge 11)$ ***[1 mark]***
$= 0.0442 + 0.0256$
$= 0.0698$ ***[1 mark]***

d) The value 5 doesn't lie in the critical region ***[1 mark]***, so there is insufficient evidence at the 10% level to reject the claim that the proportion of residents against the plan is 20% ***[1 mark]***. ***(Allow follow-through for a correct conclusion drawn from an incorrectly calculated critical region in part b).)***

S2 — Practice Exam One

1 Between the two students, there are 80 independent events with a 0.05 probability each time of 'success'.
So if X represents the number of golden tickets they find, then $X \sim B(80, 0.05)$ ***[1 mark]***.
Since $n = 80 > 50$ and $np = 4 < 5$ ***[1 mark]***, the Poisson approximation Po(4) ***[1 mark]*** is suitable.
You've got to write all this down to get the marks for the 'justifying' part of the question. And you may as well (seeing as you'll have calculated it anyway).
So $P(X \ge 3) = 1 - P(X < 3) = 1 - P(X \le 2)$
$= 1 - 0.2381 = 0.7619$ ***[1 mark]***.

2 $P(X < 60) = 0.1587 \Rightarrow P\left(Z < \frac{60-\mu}{\sigma}\right) = 0.1587$.
If $P(Z < z) = 0.1587$, then $P(Z < -z) = 0.8413$ ***[1 mark]***.
Using tables, $-z = 1$ and $z = -1$,
and so $\frac{60-\mu}{\sigma} = -1$ ***[1 mark]***
$P(X < 97.5) = 0.9332 \Rightarrow P\left(Z < \frac{97.5-\mu}{\sigma}\right) = 0.9332$.
Using tables, $z = 1.5$, and so $\frac{97.5-\mu}{\sigma} = 1.5$ ***[1 mark]***
Now you need to solve the simultaneous equations $60 - \mu = -\sigma$ and $97.5 - \mu = 1.5\sigma$:
Rearranging the first equation gives you $\sigma = \mu - 60$, and substituting this in the second equation gives:
$97.5 - \mu = 1.5(\mu - 60)$, so $2.5\mu = 187.5$, and $\mu = 75$.
σ is then $75 - 60 = 15$.
[1 mark for attempting to solve the two equations simultaneously, 1 mark for μ and 1 mark for σ.]

3 a) (i) Since the average number of houses sold per week is 2, $X \sim Po(2)$ ***[1 mark]***.
$P(X = 1) = \frac{e^{-2}2^1}{1!} = \frac{2}{e^2} = 0.271$ (to 3 s.f.) ***[1 mark]***
You can do this with tables, but here it's quicker just to use the formula.
(ii) $P(2 \le X \le 4) = P(X \le 4) - P(X < 2)$
$= P(X \le 4) - P(X \le 1)$ ***[1 mark]***
$= 0.9473 - 0.4060$ ***[1 mark]***
$= 0.5413$ ***[1 mark]***.
And you could do this one by working out P(X = 2), P(X = 3) and P(X = 4) using the formula, and then adding the results. Do it the way that seems to involve less work, that's my (obvious) advice.

b) Let Y represent the total number of houses sold over the next 26 weeks. Y will follow the Poisson distribution $Po(26 \times 2) = Po(52)$ ***[1 mark]***.
Since $\lambda > 15$, this can be approximated by a normal distribution, i.e. $Y \sim N(52, 52)$ ***[1 mark]***.
$P(Y < 52) = P(Y < 51.5)$ ***[1 mark]***
$= P\left(Z < \frac{51.5-52}{\sqrt{52}}\right)$
$= P(Z < -0.069)$ ***[1 mark]***
$= 1 - P(Z < 0.069)$ ***[1 mark]***
$= 1 - 0.5275 = 0.4725$ ***[1 mark]***

4 This is one of those where you have to 'standardise' the normal variable (i.e. subtract the mean and divide by the standard deviation) and use tables for the standard normal variable Z.

a) $P(X < 7.5) = P\left(\frac{X-8}{\sqrt{1.2}} < \frac{7.5-8}{\sqrt{1.2}}\right)$
$= P(Z < -0.456)$ ***[1 mark]***
$= 1 - P(Z \le 0.456)$ ***[1 mark]***
$= 1 - 0.6758 = 0.3242$ ***[1 mark]***

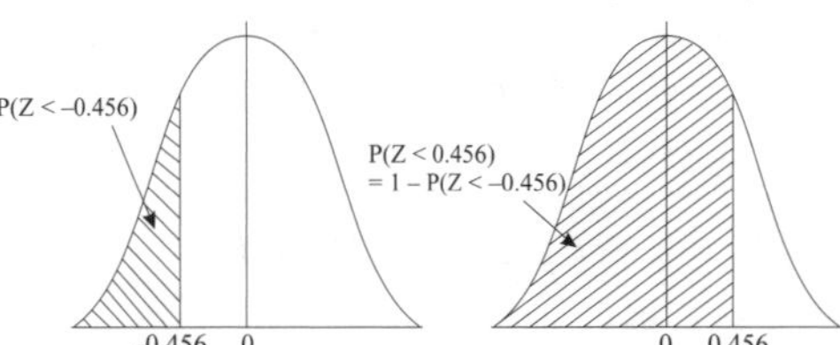

A quick sketch always helps.

b) You need to find d where: $P(X > d) = 0.01$.
$P(X > d) = 0.01$, so $P\left(Z > \frac{d-8}{\sqrt{1.2}}\right) = 0.01$ ***[1 mark]***,
and so $P\left(Z < \frac{d-8}{\sqrt{1.2}}\right) = 0.99$.
Using the critical values table: $\frac{d-8}{\sqrt{1.2}} = 2.326$ ***[1 mark]***.
So $d = \sqrt{1.2} \times 2.326 + 8$ ***[1 mark]***,
i.e. $d = 10.5$ minutes (to 3 sig. fig.) ***[1 mark]***

c) (i) $X \sim N(8, 1.2)$, so $\overline{X} \sim N\left(8, \frac{1.2}{20}\right) = N(8, 0.06)$.
[1 mark for saying a normal distribution and 1 mark for both the mean and variance correct.]
(ii) $P(\overline{X} > 8.5) = P\left(Z > \frac{8.5-8}{\sqrt{0.06}}\right) = P(Z > 2.041)$ ***[1 mark]***
$= 1 - P(Z < 2.041) = 1 - 0.9793 = 0.0207$ ***[1 mark]***

Answers

These 'standardise the normal variable' questions get everywhere. They look hard, but you soon get used to them. And once you get your head round the basic idea, you'll be able to do pretty much anything they ask you.

5 a) X = number of people in sample of 15 who use the pool.
$X \sim B(15, p)$
$H_0: p = 0.45$ and $H_1: p < 0.45$ ***[2 marks for both correct, or 1 mark for one correct]***
So under H_0, $X \sim B(15, 0.45)$ ***[1 mark]***
$\alpha = 0.05$
The binomial tables don't give values for $n = 15$, so you need to use the binomial formula.
$P(X \leq 3) = P(X = 0) + P(X = 1) + P(X = 2) + P(X = 3)$
$= 0.55^{15} + 15 \times 0.45 \times 0.55^{14} + 105 \times 0.45^2 \times 0.55^{13}$
$+ 455 \times 0.45^3 \times 0.55^{12}$ ***[1 mark]***
$= 0.0424$ (to 3 sig. fig.) ***[1 mark]***
Since $0.0424 < 0.05$, the result is significant. ***[1 mark]***
So there is evidence at the 5% level of significance to suggest that the popularity of the pool has decreased. ***[1 mark]***

b) For the 2nd test:
Let X be the number of people in a sample of 30 who use the pool. Then $X \sim B(30, p)$.
$H_0: p = 0.45$ and $H_1: p < 0.45$ and $\alpha = 0.05$.
So under H_0, $X \sim B(30, 0.45)$ ***[1 mark]***
The result of the test is that the manager rejects H_0, so you're looking for the biggest possible value x such that $P(X \leq x) \leq 0.05$.
Using the binomial tables, $P(X \leq 8) = 0.0312$ ***[1 mark]*** and $P(X \leq 9) = 0.0694$ ***[1 mark]***.
So the maximum possible number in the sample who use the pool is 8 ***[1 mark]***.

Part b) is a bit trickier, but you just need to go through the usual steps to work out how to use the information you're given to get the answer.

6 a) $\int_{-\infty}^{\infty} f(x)\,dx = 1 \Rightarrow k\int_0^4 \frac{x}{2}\,dx = 1$ ***[1 mark]***

$\Rightarrow k\left[\frac{x^2}{4}\right]_0^4 = 1$ ***[1 mark]*** $\Rightarrow k\left(\frac{16}{4} - 0\right) = 1$

$\Rightarrow 4k = 1 \Rightarrow k = \frac{1}{4} = 0.25$ ***[1 mark]***

b) $E(X) = \int_{-\infty}^{\infty} xf(x)\,dx = \int_0^4 \frac{x^2}{8}\,dx$ ***[1 mark]***

$= \left[\frac{x^3}{24}\right]_0^4$ ***[1 mark]*** $= \left(\frac{64}{24} - 0\right) = \frac{8}{3}$ ***[1 mark]***

c) The median, M, is given by:
$\int_{-\infty}^{M} f(x)\,dx = 0.5 \Rightarrow \int_0^M \frac{x}{8}\,dx = 0.5$ ***[1 mark]***

$\Rightarrow \left[\frac{x^2}{16}\right]_0^M = 0.5$ ***[1 mark]*** $\Rightarrow \left(\frac{M^2}{16} - 0\right) = 0.5$

$\Rightarrow M^2 = 8 \Rightarrow M = \sqrt{8} = 2.83$ (to 3 sig. fig.) ***[1 mark]***

7 a) $\bar{x} = \frac{\sum x}{n} = \frac{3400}{40} = 85$ mph ***[1 mark]***

$s^2 = \frac{\sum(x - \bar{x})^2}{n - 1} = \frac{120}{39} = 3.08$ (to 3 sig. fig.) ***[1 mark]***

b) The estimated distribution of X is $X \sim N(85, 3.08)$ ***[1 mark]***.
So $P(X < 90) = P\left(Z < \frac{90 - 85}{\sqrt{3.08}}\right)$
$= P(Z < 2.849) = 0.9978$ ***[1 mark]***

c) No. Since X has a normal distribution, you know that $\bar{X}$ has a normal distribution ***[1 mark]***, with the same mean as X and variance $\frac{\sigma^2}{n}$, where $\sigma^2 = Var(X)$ ***[1 mark]***.

8 a) $H_0: \mu = 150$ ***[1 mark]*** and $H_1: \mu \neq 150$ ***[1 mark]***. $\alpha = 0.05$.
Under H_0, $\bar{X} \sim N\left(150, \frac{22}{10}\right) = N(150, 2.2)$ ***[1 mark]***

So $z = \frac{\bar{x} - 150}{\sqrt{2.2}} = \frac{146 - 150}{\sqrt{2.2}} = -2.697$ ***[1 mark]***

It's a two-tailed test at the 5% level, so the critical values are ± 1.960 ***[1 mark]*** and the critical region is $Z < -1.960$ and $Z > 1.960$.
Since $-2.697 < -1.960$, the result is significant and you can reject H_0 ***[1 mark]***. There is evidence at the 5% level to suggest that the average height is different. ***[1 mark]***

b) $H_0: \mu = 150$ and $H_1: \mu < 150$. $\alpha = 0.05$.
Under H_0, $\bar{Y} \sim N\left(150, \frac{22}{10}\right) = N(150, 2.2)$ ***[1 mark]***

So $Z = \frac{\bar{Y} - 150}{\sqrt{2.2}} \sim N(0, 1)$ ***[1 mark]***

It's a one-tailed test at the 5% level, so the critical value is -1.645, and so the critical region is $Z < -1.645$ ***[1 mark]***.

$Z < -1.645 \Rightarrow \frac{\bar{Y} - 150}{\sqrt{2.2}} < -1.645$ ***[1 mark]***

$\Rightarrow \bar{Y} < -1.645 \times \sqrt{2.2} + 150 \Rightarrow \bar{Y} < 147.56...$

$\Rightarrow \bar{Y} < 147.6$ (to nearest 0.1 cm) ***[1 mark]***

c) This suggests that the distribution of heights isn't symmetrical ***[1 mark]***, so a normal distribution isn't a suitable model to use ***[1 mark]***.

S2 — Practice Exam Two

1 Let R be the number of cars in the sample that rattle. Then $R \sim B(200, 0.65)$ ***[1 mark]***. Since $np = 130 > 5$ and $nq = 70 > 5$ ***[1 mark]***, the normal approximation $N(130, 45.5)$ ***[1 mark]*** is suitable.

$P(R = 140) = P(139.5 \leq R \leq 140.5)$ ***[1 mark]***

$= P\left(Z \leq \frac{140.5 - 130}{\sqrt{45.5}}\right) - P\left(Z \leq \frac{139.5 - 130}{\sqrt{45.5}}\right)$ ***[1 mark]***

$= P(Z \leq 1.557) - P(Z \leq 1.408)$

$= 0.9402 - 0.9203$ ***[1 mark]***

$= 0.0199$ ***[1 mark]***

This question is slightly autobiographical because I used to have a rattly car. I kept taking it to the garage to get it fixed, but they could never find the fault. Turned out there was a rattlesnake under the passenger seat. Was quite a common problem in that model, apparently.

Answers

2 $A \sim \text{Po}(40)$. Since $\lambda > 15$ ***[1 mark]***, the normal approximation N(40, 40) ***[1 mark]*** is appropriate.
Applying the continuity correction, $P(A > 35)$ becomes:
$P(A > 35.5)$ ***[1 mark]*** $= P\left(Z > \frac{35.5 - 40}{\sqrt{40}}\right)$ ***[1 mark]***
$= P(Z > -0.712) = P(Z < 0.712)$ ***[1 mark]***
$= 0.7617$ ***[1 mark]***

3 a) Let X represent the number of customers per hour.
Then, $X \sim \text{Po}(2)$
[1 mark for 'Poisson' and 1 mark for $\lambda = 2$].

b) (i) $P(X < 3) = P(X \leq 2) = 0.6767$ ***[1 mark]***

(ii) $P(X = 1) = P(X \leq 1) - P(X \leq 0)$ ***[1 mark]***
$= 0.4060 - 0.1353 = 0.2707$ ***[1 mark]***

c) Y = number of customers on a Saturday and $Y \sim \text{Po}(6\lambda)$.
H_0: $\lambda = 2$ ***[1 mark]*** and H_1: $\lambda > 2$ ***[1 mark]***
Under H_0, $Y \sim \text{Po}(12)$ ***[1 mark]***
$\alpha = 0.01$
$P(Y \geq 25) = 1 - P(Y \leq 24) = 1 - 0.9993 = 0.0007$ ***[1 mark]***
Since $0.0007 < 0.01$, the result is significant. ***[1 mark]***
There is evidence at the 1% level of significance to suggest that there are more customers per hour on a Saturday.
[1 mark]

Don't let yourself be distracted by imagining Daisy, Derrick and co. plodding up and down the beach 25 times. There are 6 marks for part c) — go through your answer and check you've written down every step in the working.

4 a) (i) $T \sim N(132, 40^2)$. So
$P(T > 160) = P\left(Z > \frac{160 - 132}{40}\right) = P(Z > 0.7)$ ***[1 mark]***
$= 1 - P(Z \leq 0.7)$ ***[1 mark]***
$= 1 - 0.7580$
$= 0.2420$ ***[1 mark]***

(ii) $P(60 \leq T \leq 90) = P(T \leq 90) - P(T < 60)$ ***[1 mark]***
$= P\left(Z \leq \frac{90 - 132}{40}\right) - P\left(Z \leq \frac{60 - 132}{40}\right)$
$= P(Z \leq -1.05) - P(Z \leq -1.8)$ ***[1 mark]***
$= (1 - P(Z \leq 1.05))$
$- (1 - P(Z \leq 1.8))$ ***[1 mark]***
$= (1 - 0.8531) - (1 - 0.9641)$
$= 0.1110$ ***[1 mark]***

b) $\overline{T} \sim N\left(132, \frac{40^2}{n}\right)$ and $P(\overline{T} > 135) = 0.2266$.
So $P\left(Z > \frac{135 - 132}{40/\sqrt{n}}\right) = 0.2266$ ***[1 mark]***
$\Rightarrow P\left(Z < \frac{3}{40/\sqrt{n}}\right) = 0.7734$ ***[1 mark]***

Looking up 0.7734 in the normal distribution table, you find that $P(Z < 0.75) = 0.7734$, so:
$\frac{3}{40/\sqrt{n}} = 0.75$ ***[1 mark]*** $\Rightarrow \frac{40}{\sqrt{n}} = \frac{3}{0.75} \Rightarrow \sqrt{n} = \frac{40 \times 0.75}{3}$
$\Rightarrow n = 100$ ***[1 mark]***

You should have got lots of practice with the normal distribution by now, so hopefully it feels like a good friend.

5 a) (i) E.g. he is selecting people randomly / each selection is independent / all members of the population are equally likely to be chosen / the correct population is being sampled from.
[2 marks for two correct statements]

(ii) E.g. all the members who aren't in this particular class would be excluded from selection ***[1 mark]***. It's likely that the sample would be biased — a 'basic' class would be more likely to contain a higher proportion of beginners, and an 'advanced' class would be more likely to contain a higher proportion of people who have done judo for a long time ***[1 mark]***.

b) X = number of people in the sample of 20 who have done judo for at least two years. Then $X \sim B(20, p)$.
H_0: $p = 0.2$ ***[1 mark]*** and H_1: $p \neq 0.2$ ***[1 mark]***
So under H_0, $X \sim B(20, 0.2)$ ***[1 mark]***
It's a two-tailed test, so the critical region is split into two, with a probability of ≤ 0.025 in each tail.
For the lower tail:
$P(X \leq 0) = 0.0115$ and $P(X \leq 1) = 0.0692$.
For the upper tail:
$P(X \geq 9) = 1 - 0.9900 = 0.0100$ and
$P(X \geq 8) = 1 - 0.9679 = 0.0321$.
So CR is $X = 0$ ***[1 mark]*** and $X \geq 9$ ***[1 mark]***

c) P(Type I error) $= P(X = 0) + P(X \geq 9)$ ***[1 mark]***
$= 0.0115 + 0.0100 = 0.0215$ or 2.15% ***[1 mark]***

d) 7 does not lie in the critical region, so do not reject H_0 ***[1 mark]***. There is no evidence at the 5% level to suggest that the proportion who have done judo for at least two years isn't 0.2 ***[1 mark]***.

6 a) $E(X) = \int_{-\infty}^{\infty} x f(x)\,dx = \int_0^1 3x^3\,dx$ ***[1 mark]***
$= \left[\frac{3x^4}{4}\right]_0^1$ ***[1 mark]*** $= \left(\frac{3}{4} - 0\right) = \frac{3}{4}$ ***[1 mark]***

b) $\text{Var}(X) = \int_{-\infty}^{\infty} x^2 f(x)\,dx - \mu^2 = \int_0^1 3x^4\,dx - \left(\frac{3}{4}\right)^2$ ***[1 mark]***
$= \left[\frac{3x^5}{5}\right]_0^1 - \frac{9}{16}$ ***[1 mark]*** $= \frac{3}{5} - \frac{9}{16} = \frac{3}{80} = 0.0375$ ***[1 mark]***

c) $P(0 \leq X \leq 0.5) = \int_0^{0.5} 3x^2\,dx = \left[\frac{3x^3}{3}\right]_0^{0.5}$ ***[1 mark]***
$= 0.125 - 0 = 0.125$ ***[1 mark]***

d) $Y \sim B(50, 0.125)$ ***[1 mark for 'binomial' and 1 mark for both parameters correct]***

7 a) $\bar{x} = \frac{\sum x}{n} = \frac{24\,500}{50} = 490$ cm ***[1 mark]***
$s^2 = \frac{n}{n-1}\left[\frac{\sum x^2}{n} - \left(\frac{\sum x}{n}\right)^2\right]$
$= \frac{50}{49} \times \left(\frac{12\,011\,500}{50} - 490^2\right)$ ***[1 mark]***
$= \frac{50}{49} \times 130 = \frac{6500}{49}$ ***[1 mark]***

Answers

b) H_0: $\mu = 500$ ***[1 mark]*** and H_1: $\mu < 500$ ***[1 mark]***. $\alpha = 0.05$.
n is large enough to apply the Central Limit Theorem, so:

$$\overline{X} \sim N\left(\mu, \frac{S^2}{n}\right)$$

Under H_0, $\overline{X} \sim N\left(500, \frac{6500/49}{50}\right) = N\left(500, \frac{130}{49}\right)$

So $Z = \frac{\overline{X} - 500}{\sqrt{130/49}} \sim N(0, 1)$ ***[1 mark]***

It's a one-tailed test at the 5% level, so the critical value is -1.645, and so the critical region is $Z < -1.645$.

$Z < -1.645 \Rightarrow \frac{\overline{X} - 500}{\sqrt{130/49}} < -1.645$ ***[1 mark]***

$\Rightarrow \overline{X} < -1.645 \times \sqrt{130/49} + 500 \Rightarrow \overline{X} < 497.3$ ***[1 mark]***

c) Since $490 < 497.3$, there is evidence to reject H_0 ***[1 mark]***.
There is evidence to support the manager's claim at the 5% level. ***[1 mark]***

d) P(Type II error | $\mu = 496$)

$= P(\overline{X} \geq 497.3 \mid \mu = 496) = P\left(Z \geq \frac{497.3 - 496}{\sqrt{130/49}}\right)$ ***[1 mark]***

$= P(Z \geq 0.798)$ ***[1 mark]*** $= 1 - P(Z < 0.798)$ ***[1 mark]***

$= 1 - 0.7876 = 0.2124$

(or you'd get 0.2087 if you use the unrounded critical value from part b))

[1 mark]

Answers

M2 Section 1 — Centres of Mass

Warm-up Questions

1) a) Particles in a horizontal line so use $\Sigma mx = \bar{x}\Sigma m$

$m_1x_1 + m_2x_2 + m_3x_3 = \bar{x}(m_1 + m_2 + m_3)$

$\Rightarrow (1 \times 1) + (2 \times 2) + (3 \times 3) = \bar{x}(1 + 2 + 3)$

$\Rightarrow 14 = 6\bar{x} \Rightarrow \bar{x} = 14 \div 6 = 2\frac{1}{3}$.

So coordinates are $(2\frac{1}{3}, 0)$.

b) Particles in a vertical line so use $\Sigma my = \bar{y}\Sigma m$

$m_1y_1 + m_2y_2 + m_3y_3 = \bar{y}(m_1 + m_2 + m_3)$

$\Rightarrow (1 \times 3) + (2 \times 2) + (3 \times 1) = \bar{y}(1 + 2 + 3)$

$\Rightarrow 10 = 6\bar{y} \Rightarrow \bar{y} = 10 \div 6 = 1\frac{2}{3}$.

So coordinates are $(0, 1\frac{2}{3})$.

c) Particles in 2D so consider x and y coordinates separately.

$m_1x_1 + m_2x_2 + m_3x_3 = \bar{x}(m_1 + m_2 + m_3)$

$\Rightarrow (1 \times 3) + (2 \times 3) + (3 \times 1) = \bar{x}(1 + 2 + 3)$

$\Rightarrow 12 = 6\bar{x} \Rightarrow \bar{x} = 12 \div 6 = 2$

$m_1y_1 + m_2y_2 + m_3y_3 = \bar{y}(m_1 + m_2 + m_3)$

$\Rightarrow (1 \times 4) + (2 \times 1) + (3 \times 0) = \bar{y}(1 + 2 + 3)$

$\Rightarrow 6 = 6\bar{y} \Rightarrow \bar{y} = 6 \div 6 = 1$

So coordinates are (2, 1).

2) Particles in 2D so consider x and y coordinates separately.

Using $\Sigma mx = \bar{x}\Sigma m$:

$(m \times 0) + (2m \times 0) + (3m \times 5) + (12 \times 5)$

$= 3.5 \times (m + 2m + 3m + 12)$

$\Rightarrow 15m + 60 = 21m + 42$

$\Rightarrow 6m = 18 \Rightarrow m = 3$ kg.

So you don't even need to consider the y-coordinates. Get in.

3) a) Triangle (1) has area $\frac{1}{2} \times 4 \times 3 = 6$, so $m_1 = 6$.

$x_1 = 2$ (symmetry) and $y_1 = 5 - (\frac{2}{3} \times 3) = 3$ ($\frac{2}{3}$ down the median from the top vertex).

Rectangle (2) has area $1 \times 2 = 2$, so $m_2 = 2$.

$x_2 = 2$ and $y_2 = 1.5$ (symmetry).

Combined shape has $\bar{x} = 2$ (symmetry) and:

$m_1y_1 + m_2y_2 = \bar{y}(m_1 + m_2)$

$\Rightarrow (6 \times 3) + (2 \times 1.5) = (6 + 2)\bar{y}$

$\Rightarrow 21 = 8\bar{y} \Rightarrow \bar{y} = 21 \div 8 = 2.625$.

So coordinates are (2, 2.625).

b) Semicircle (1) has area $\frac{1}{2} \times \pi \times 3^2 = 4.5\pi$, so $m_1 = 4.5\pi$.

$x_1 = 8$ (symmetry) and $y_1 = 1 + \dfrac{2 \times 3 \times \sin\frac{\pi}{2}}{\frac{3\pi}{2}} = \dfrac{4 + \pi}{\pi}$

(COM is $\frac{2r\sin\alpha}{3\alpha}$ up from the centre of the circle, where $2\alpha = \pi$).

Don't forget — the arc angle is 2α not α...

Triangle (2) has area $\frac{1}{2} \times 2 \times 1 = 1$, so $m_2 = 1$.

$x_2 = 8$ (symmetry) and $y_2 = \frac{2}{3} \times 1 = \frac{2}{3}$ ($\frac{2}{3}$ up the median from the bottom vertex).

Combined shape has $\bar{x} = 8$ (symmetry) and:

$m_1y_1 + m_2y_2 = \bar{y}(m_1 + m_2)$

$\Rightarrow (4.5\pi \times \frac{4 + \pi}{\pi}) + (1 \times \frac{2}{3}) = (4.5\pi + 1)\bar{y}$

$\Rightarrow 18\frac{2}{3} + 4.5\pi = (4.5\pi + 1)\bar{y}$

$\Rightarrow \bar{y} = (18\frac{2}{3} + 4.5\pi) \div (4.5\pi + 1) = 2.167$ (to 3 d.p.).

So coordinates are (8, 2.167).

c) Circle (1) has area $\pi \times 2^2 = 4\pi$, so $m_1 = 4\pi$.

$x_1 = 14$ and $y_1 = 2$ (symmetry).

Square (2) has area $1 \times 1 = 1$, so $m_2 = 1$.

$x_2 = 14.5$ and $y_2 = 2.5$ (symmetry).

Using the removal method, find the x-coordinate of COM:

$m_1x_1 - m_2x_2 = \bar{x}(m_1 - m_2)$

$\Rightarrow (4\pi \times 14) - 14.5 = (4\pi - 1)\bar{x}$

$\Rightarrow 56\pi - 14.5 = (4\pi - 1)\bar{x}$

$\Rightarrow \bar{x} = (56\pi - 14.5) \div (4\pi - 1) = 13.957$ (to 3 d.p.).

Now find the y-coordinate using the same method:

$m_1y_1 - m_2y_2 = \bar{y}(m_1 - m_2)$

$\Rightarrow (4\pi \times 2) - 2.5 = (4\pi - 1)\bar{y}$

$\Rightarrow 8\pi - 2.5 = (4\pi - 1)\bar{y}$

$\Rightarrow \bar{y} = (8\pi - 2.5) \div (4\pi - 1) = 1.957$ (to 3 d.p.).

So coordinates are (13.957, 1.957).

4)

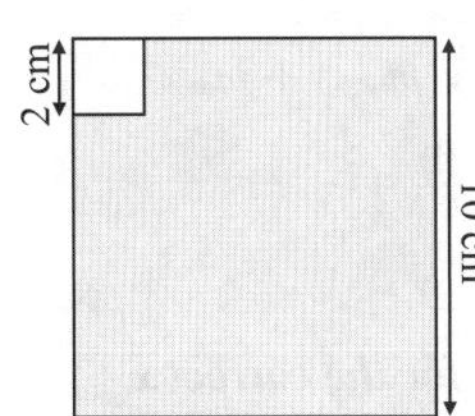

Large square (1) has area $10 \times 10 = 100$, so $m_1 = 100$.

$y_1 = 5$ cm from top edge (symmetry).

Small square (2) has area $2 \times 2 = 4$, so $m_2 = 4$.

$y_2 = 1$ cm from top edge (symmetry).

Using the removal method:

$m_1y_1 - m_2y_2 = \bar{y}(m_1 - m_2)$

$\Rightarrow (100 \times 5) - (4 \times 1) = (100 - 4)\bar{y}$

$\Rightarrow 496 = 96\bar{y} \Rightarrow \bar{y} = 496 \div 96 = 5.167$ cm from the top edge (to 3 d.p.).

You can pick any place to be the origin, but the top edge makes most sense here.

5) P is a uniform cylinder, so the COM will be directly in the middle: on the axis of symmetry, 3 cm up from the base. When P is on the point of toppling, its COM is directly above the 'bottom edge', as shown:

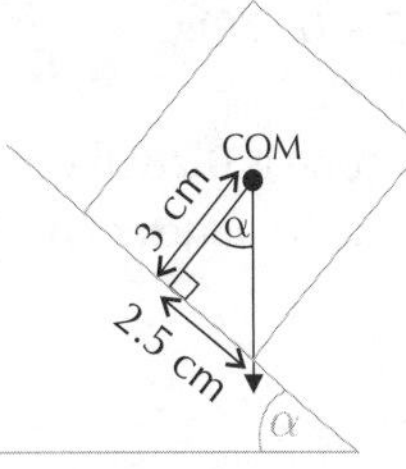

Now using trig on the right-angled triangle:

$\alpha = \tan^{-1}\left(\frac{2.5}{3}\right) = 40°$ to the nearest degree.

Answers

Exam Questions

1 a) Using the formula $\Sigma my = \bar{y}\Sigma m$

$m_1y_1 + m_2y_2 + m_3y_3 = \bar{y}(m_1 + m_2 + m_3)$

$\Rightarrow (4 \times 3) + (3 \times 1) + (2 \times y) = 2 \times (4 + 3 + 2)$ ***[1 mark]***

$\Rightarrow 15 + 2y = 18$ ***[1 mark]***

$\Rightarrow y = (18 - 15) \div 2 = 1.5$ ***[1 mark]***.

b) Using the formula $\Sigma mx = \bar{x}\Sigma m$

$m_1x_1 + m_2x_2 + m_3x_3 = \bar{x}(m_1 + m_2 + m_3)$

$\Rightarrow (4 \times 1) + (3 \times 5) + (2 \times 4) = \bar{x}(4 + 3 + 2)$ ***[1 mark]***

$\Rightarrow 27 = 9\bar{x}$ ***[1 mark]***

$\Rightarrow \bar{x} = 27 \div 9 = 3$ ***[1 mark]***.

c) Centre of mass of the lamina is at (3.5, 2.5), due to the symmetry of the shape, and $m_{lamina} = 6$ kg.
Centre of mass of the group of particles is (3, 2) (from (b)) and $m_{particles} = 4 + 3 + 2 = 9$ kg.

Using $\Sigma mx = \bar{x}\Sigma m$:

$m_{lamina}x_{lamina} + m_{particles}x_{particles} = \bar{x}(m_{lamina} + m_{particles})$

$(6 \times 3.5) + (9 \times 3) = \bar{x} \times (6 + 9)$

$\Rightarrow \bar{x} = 48 \div 15 = 3.2$

Now using $\Sigma my = \bar{y}\Sigma m$:

$m_{lamina}y_{lamina} + m_{particles}y_{particles} = \bar{y}(m_{lamina} + m_{particles})$

$(6 \times 2.5) + (9 \times 2) = \bar{x} \times (6 + 9)$

$\Rightarrow \bar{y} = 33 \div 15 = 2.2$

So the coordinates are (3.2, 2.2).

[6 marks available — 1 mark for the correct x_{lamina}, 1 mark for the correct y_{lamina}, 1 mark for correct use of formula for $\bar{x}$, 1 mark for correct use of formula for $\bar{y}$, 1 mark for x coordinate of 3.2, 1 mark for y coordinate of 2.2.]

2 As the traffic cone is made from uniform material, the masses of the parts are proportional to their areas.
So $m_B = 0.25$. ***[1 mark]***

Find the sloped length of A using Pythagoras:

$l = \sqrt{0.15^2 + 1.2^2} = 1.209\,\text{m}$ (4 s.f.).

So $m_A = \pi \times 0.15 \times 1.209 = 0.570$ (3 s.f.). ***[1 mark]***

As B is a uniform square lamina, its centre of mass is at its centre, O, i.e. $y_B = 0$ m from O. ***[1 mark]***

Using the formula for COM of conical shell:

$y_A = \frac{1}{3}(1.2) = 0.4$ m from O. ***[1 mark]***

Now use $\Sigma my = \bar{y}\Sigma m$ to find the COM of C: ***[1 mark]***

$m_By_B + m_Ay_A = m_Cy_C$

$\Rightarrow 0.25(0) + 0.570(0.4) = (0.25 + 0.570)y_C$

$\Rightarrow y_C = 0.28$ m (2 s.f.)

So, centre of mass of the traffic cone is 0.28 m vertically above O, on a line through O and the vertex of A. ***[1 mark]***

3 a) Splitting up the shape into a triangle (1), large square (2) and small square (3), where the mass of each shape is proportional to the area, gives the following masses:

$m_1 = \frac{1}{2} \times 70 \times 30 = 1050.$

$m_2 = 50 \times 50 = 2500.$

$m_3 = 10 \times 10 = 100.$ ***[1 mark for all three masses]***

Taking the point A as the origin, the position vectors of the centres of mass of each shape are as follows:

Triangle:

$x_1 = 25$ (due to the symmetry of the shape) and

$y_1 = 50 + (\frac{1}{3} \times 30) = 60$ (since the COM of a triangle is $\frac{2}{3}$ down the median from the vertex, and so $\frac{1}{3}$ up from the edge). So $(x_1, y_1) = (25, 60)$ ***[1 mark]***

Large Square:

$x_2 = 25$ and $y_2 = 25$ (due to the symmetry of the shape). So $(x_2, y_2) = (25, 25)$. ***[1 mark]***

Small Square:

$x_3 = 50 + 5 = 55$ and $y_3 = 5$ (due to the symmetry of the shape). So $(x_3, y_3) = (55, 5)$. ***[1 mark]***

Using the formula $\Sigma mx = \bar{x}\Sigma m$:

$m_1x_1 + m_2x_2 + m_3x_3 = \bar{x}(m_1 + m_2 + m_3)$

$\Rightarrow (1050 \times 25) + (2500 \times 25) + (100 \times 55)$ ***[1 mark]***

$= \bar{x}(1050 + 2500 + 100)$

$\Rightarrow \bar{x} = 94\,250 \div 3650 = 25.8219...$

And now using the formula $\Sigma my = \bar{y}\Sigma m$:

$m_1y_1 + m_2y_2 + m_3y_3 = \bar{y}(m_1 + m_2 + m_3)$ ***[1 mark]***

$\Rightarrow (1050 \times 60) + (2500 \times 25) + (100 \times 5)$

$= \bar{y}(1050 + 2500 + 100)$

$\Rightarrow \bar{y} = 126\,000 \div 3650 = 34.5205...$

So, to 3 s.f., the centre of mass of the sign is 25.8 cm from AB ***[1 mark]*** and 34.5 cm from AI ***[1 mark]***.

b) For the sign to hang with AI horizontal, the centre of mass of the whole system (sign + particle) must be vertically below D, i.e. $\bar{x}$ must be 25 (taking A as the origin again).

Given that $m_{sign} = 1$ kg and $x_{sign} = 25.8219...$ (from (a)), and $x_{particle} = 0$ (since it's attached at the origin):

$m_{sign}x_{sign} + m_{particle}x_{particle} = \bar{x}(m_{sign} + m_{particle})$

$(1 \times 25.8219...) + 0 = 25(1 + m_{particle})$

$\Rightarrow 25.8219... \div 25 = 1 + m_{particle}$

$\Rightarrow 1.03287... - 1 = m_{particle}$

$\Rightarrow m_{particle} = 0.0329$ kg, to 3 s.f.

[3 marks available — 1 mark for stating the correct required value of $\bar{x}$, 1 mark for correct entry of values into the formula, 1 mark for correct final answer.]

Answers

4 a) The stencil is a rectangle (1) with a quarter circle (2) of radius (10 – 2) = 8 cm removed. The lamina is uniform so mass is proportional to area, so $m_1 = 12 \times 10 = 120$, and $m_2 = \frac{1}{4} \times \pi \times 8^2 = 16\pi$.

Taking O as the origin, the position of the centre of mass of the rectangle, $(x_1, y_1) = (6, 5)$ (from the symmetry of the shape).

The sector angle $2\alpha = \frac{\pi}{2}$, so $\alpha = \frac{\pi}{4}$, and the centre of mass of the sector is $\frac{2r\sin\alpha}{3\alpha}$ from O along the axis of symmetry

$= \dfrac{2 \times 8 \times \sin\frac{\pi}{4}}{\frac{3\pi}{4}} = \dfrac{64}{3\pi\sqrt{2}}$ cm.

This is on the formula sheet — you just have to know how to use it. And you'll have to use trig to find the position vector... In the right-angled triangle below, cos α = x/hyp, and sin α = y/hyp, so with a bit of rearranging you can find x and y for the position vector...

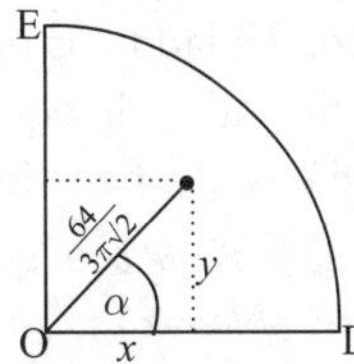

The coordinates of the COM of the sector can be found:

$x_2 = \dfrac{64}{3\pi\sqrt{2}} \times \cos\frac{\pi}{4} = \dfrac{32}{3\pi}$

$y_2 = \dfrac{64}{3\pi\sqrt{2}} \times \sin\frac{\pi}{4} = \dfrac{32}{3\pi}$

So $(x_2, y_2) = \left(\dfrac{32}{3\pi}, \dfrac{32}{3\pi}\right)$

Using the removal method:

$m_1x_1 - m_2x_2 = \bar{x}(m_1 - m_2)$

$\Rightarrow (120 \times 6) - \left(16\pi \times \dfrac{32}{3\pi}\right) = \bar{x}(120 - 16\pi)$

$\Rightarrow \bar{x} = 7.8774...$

And:

$m_1y_1 - m_2y_2 = \bar{y}(m_1 - m_2)$

$\Rightarrow (120 \times 5) - \left(16\pi \times \dfrac{32}{3\pi}\right) = \bar{y}(120 - 16\pi)$

$\Rightarrow \bar{y} = 6.1566...$

So, to 3 s.f., the coordinates of the centre of mass of the stencil are (7.88, 6.16).

[7 marks available — 1 mark for the correct total mass, 1 mark for correct (x_1, y_1), 1 mark for correct (x_2, y_2), 1 mark for correct entry of x-coordinates in the formula, 1 mark for correct entry of y-coordinates in the formula, 1 mark for final x-coordinate of 7.88, 1 mark for final y-coordinate of 6.16.]

b) At the point of toppling, the centre of mass will be vertically above the point D, as shown:

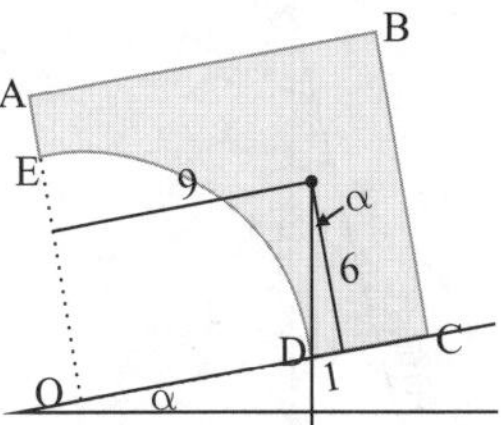

Horizontal distance from D to the centre of mass = 9 – 8 = 1 cm ***[1 mark]***.

Using trig, $\alpha = \tan^{-1}\left(\frac{1}{6}\right)$ ***[1 mark]*** = 0.165 rads to 3 s.f. ***[1 mark]***.

5 a) Find the centre of mass using the removal method, by subtracting the triangle (2) from the circle (1).

Since both the circle and the triangle that's removed from it are made from the same uniform material, their masses are in proportion to their areas:

Circle $m_1 = \pi r^2 = \pi \times 2^2 = 4\pi$.

Triangle $m_2 = \frac{1}{2} \times 1.5 \times 1.5 = 1.125$.

Taking the point P as the origin, the centre of mass of the circle, $(x_1, y_1) = (0, 0)$, since P is the centre of the circle.

The centre of mass of the triangle is at the mean of the coordinates of $P(0,0)$, $Q(0, 1.5)$ and $R(1.5, 0)$, so:

$x_2 = (0 + 0 + 1.5) \div 3 = 0.5$

$y_2 = (0 + 1.5 + 0) \div 3 = 0.5$

So $(x_2, y_2) = (0.5, 0.5)$

Using the removal method:

$m_1x_1 - m_2x_2 = \bar{x}(m_1 - m_2)$

$\Rightarrow (4\pi \times 0) - (1.125 \times 0.5) = \bar{x}(4\pi - 1.125)$

$\Rightarrow \bar{x} = -0.5625 \div 11.4413... = -0.04916...$

Similarly for y:

$m_1y_1 - m_2y_2 = \bar{y}(m_1 - m_2)$

$\Rightarrow (4\pi \times 0) - (1.125 \times 0.5) = \bar{y}(4\pi - 1.125)$

$\Rightarrow \bar{y} = -0.5625 \div 11.4413... = -0.04916...$

So $(\bar{x}, \bar{y}) = (-0.04916..., -0.04916...)$

The distance of the COM from P can now be found using Pythagoras:

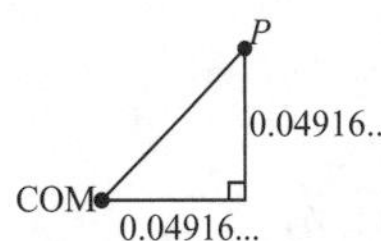

Distance = $\sqrt{0.04916...^2 + 0.04916...^2} = 0.06952...$ = 0.070 cm to 3 d.p.

There are other ways to find the centre of mass of this shape, because you can think of it in a different orientation, or take another point as the origin, but this way's as easy as any.

[5 marks available — 1 mark for correct masses of both shapes, 1 mark for individual centre of mass for both shapes, 1 mark for correct use of removal method formula, 1 mark for correct coordinates of centre of mass, 1 mark for correct distance from P.]

Answers

b) The shape is being hung from Q. Drawing a sketch will make it easier to see what's going on:

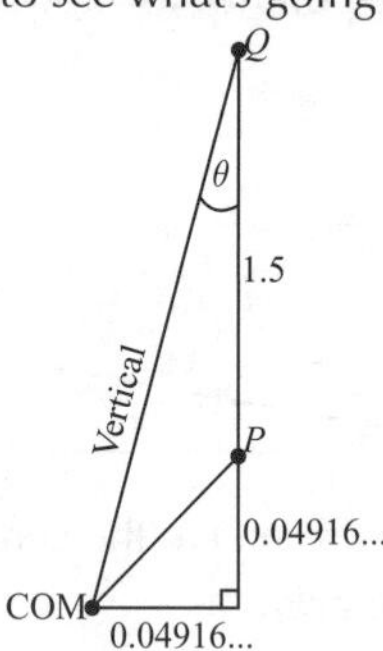

θ is the angle that PQ makes with the vertical. Using basic trigonometry:

$\theta = \tan^{-1}(\frac{0.04916...}{1.5 + 0.04916...}) = 1.8177... = 1.8°$ to 1 d.p.

[3 marks available — 1 mark for correct sides of the right-angled triangle, 1 mark for correct working, 1 mark for correct final answer.]

M2 Section 2 — Statics of Rigid Bodies
Warm-up Questions

1) Moments about B: $60g \times 3 = T_2 \times 8$

So $T_2 = \frac{180g}{8} = 220.5$ N

Vertically balanced forces, so $T_1 + T_2 = 60g$

$T_1 = 367.5$ N

2) a)

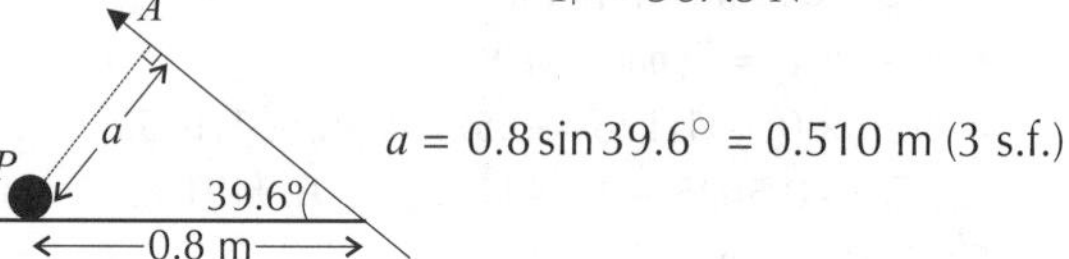

$a = 0.8 \sin 39.6° = 0.510$ m (3 s.f.)

b)

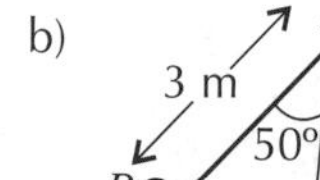

$b = 3 \sin 50° = 2.30$ m (3 s.f.)

c)

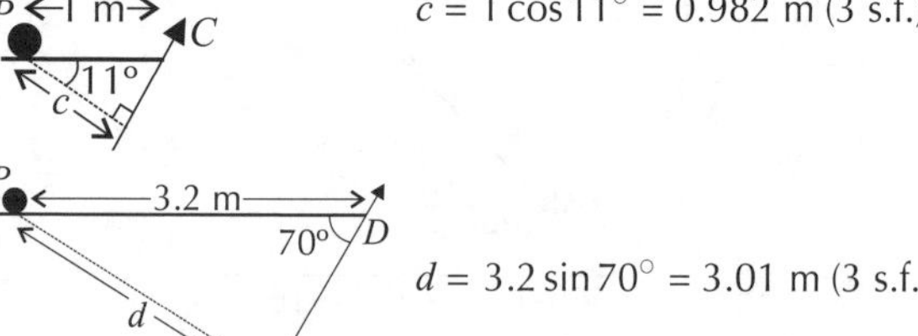

$c = 1 \cos 11° = 0.982$ m (3 s.f.)

$d = 3.2 \sin 70° = 3.01$ m (3 s.f.)

The perpendicular distance is always the shortest distance between a point and a force's line of action. Simple.

3) A rod (a long, thin, inextensible object) where the centre of mass is not at the central point of the rod.

M2 statics is pretty rod-heavy. Think of them as a really simple stick. They don't bend, don't stretch or compress, and have no width.

4) a) Resolving the forces vertically:

$42 = 28\cos 30° + T\cos 38.3°$

so $T = \frac{42 - 14\sqrt{3}}{\cos 38.3°} = 22.6$ N (3 s.f.)

b) Taking moments about the left-end:

$42xy = 28\cos30°(xy + y)$

$42xy - (28\cos30°)(xy) = (28\cos30°)y$

$17.75xy = 24.25y$

$x = 1.37$ (3 s.f.)

5) P (or N), $\frac{1}{2}l$, 20°, mg, R, F

Where:
mg = weight of the ladder
F = friction between ground and ladder
R = normal reaction of the ground
P / N = normal reaction of the wall

As the rod is uniform the weight of the ladder acts at the centre of the rod (i.e. at half of l).

Assumptions: e.g. the ladder can be modelled as a rod, the ladder is rigid, friction is sufficient to keep the ladder in equilibrium, the ladder is perpendicular to the wall when viewed from above.

'Perpendicular' and 'normal' are both used in M2 (as are 'P' and 'N' to label the forces). No need to panic — they mean the same thing in all you'll do here.

Exam Questions

1

T, x m, 12 N, 3 m, A, 18 N

Taking moments about end string:

$12 \times 3 = 18 \times \frac{x}{2}$ so, $36 = 9x$

$x = 4$ m

[3 marks available in total]:
- ***1 mark for diagram***
- ***1 mark for correct workings***
- ***1 mark for showing that x = 4 m***

2

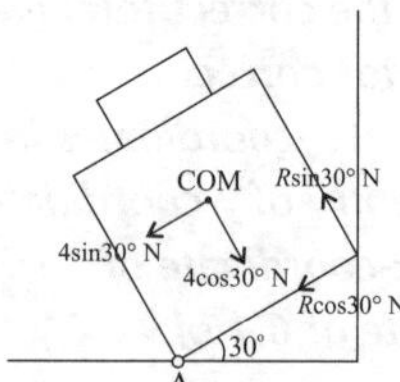

Resolve all forces into components parallel and perpendicular to the base of the shape, as shown above.

Taking moments about A:

$4\sin30° \times 2.28 + R\cos30° \times 0 + R\sin30° \times 4 = 4\cos30° \times 2$

$2 \times 2.28 + 2R = 8\cos30°$

$\Rightarrow R = (8\cos30° \div 2) - 2.28 = 1.18$ N (3 s.f.)

[4 marks available in total — 1 mark for resolving, 1 mark for attempting to take moments, 1 mark for using correct values when taking moments, 1 mark for correct answer]

Answers

3 a) Resolve horizontally:

$T\cos\theta = 72.5$ N

$\tan\theta = \dfrac{0.8}{1.7}$

$\Rightarrow \theta = 25.2°$

so $T = \dfrac{72.5}{0.9048} = 80.126...$

$= 80.1$ N (3s.f.)

[4 marks available in total]:
- ***1 mark for resolving horizontally***
- ***1 mark for calculating θ or cosθ***
- ***1 mark for correct workings***
- ***1 mark for correct value of T***

b) Taking moments about A:

$(1.2 \times 3g) + (2.4 \times mg) = 1.7 \times 80.126... \times \sin 25.2°$

so $23.52m = 58.00 - 35.28 = 22.72$

and $m = 0.96598... = 0.966$ kg (3 s.f)

[3 marks available in total]:
- ***1 mark for taking moments about A***
- ***1 mark for correct workings***
- ***1 mark for correct value of m***

c) Resolving vertically:

$F + 80.13\sin 25.2° = 3g + 0.96598... \times g$

so $F = 38.87 - 34.12 = 4.75$ N (3 s.f)

[3 marks available in total]:
- ***1 mark for resolving vertically***
- ***1 mark for correct workings***
- ***1 mark for correct value of F***

4 a) Taking moments about A:

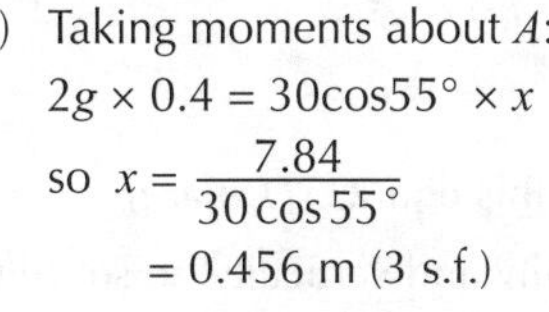

$2g \times 0.4 = 30\cos 55° \times x$

so $x = \dfrac{7.84}{30\cos 55°}$

$= 0.456$ m (3 s.f.)

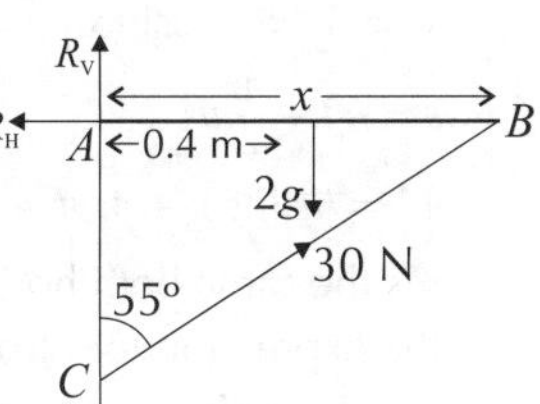

[3 marks available in total]:
- ***1 mark for taking moments about A***
- ***1 mark for correct workings***
- ***1 mark for correct value of x***

I've made an educated guess in the diagram above at which directions R_V and R_H act in. If I work out their values and they turn out to be negative then I just need to reverse their direction.

b) Resolving vertically:

$R_V = 2g - 30\cos 55° = 2.393$ N (4 s.f.)

Resolving horizontally:

$R_H = 30\sin 55° = 24.57$ N (4 s.f.)

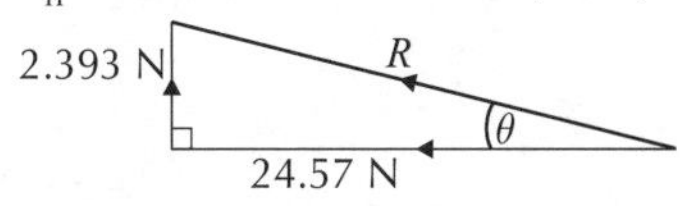

$|R| = \sqrt{2.393^2 + 24.57^2} = 24.7$ N (3 s.f.)

$\tan\theta = \dfrac{2.393}{24.57}$

so $\theta = 5.56°$ (3 s.f.) to the horizontal

[5 marks available in total]:
- ***1 mark for resolving vertically***
- ***1 mark for resolving horizontally***
- ***1 mark for correct workings***
- ***1 mark for correct magnitude of R***
- ***1 mark for correct direction***

5 a) Taking moments about B:

$(mg\cos\theta \times 1.4) + (180\cos\theta \times 2.1)$

$= (490\sin\theta \times 4.2)$

Dividing by $\cos\theta$ gives:

$1.4mg + 378 = 2058\tan\theta = 2058 \times \dfrac{8}{11}$

so, $1.4mg = 2058 \times \dfrac{8}{11} - 378$

so $m = 81.539... = 82$ kg (nearest kg)

[4 marks available in total]:
- ***1 mark for taking moments about B***
- ***1 mark for both sides of moments equation correct***
- ***1 mark for correct workings***
- ***1 mark for the correct value of m***

b) Resolving horizontally:

$F = 490$ N

Resolving vertically:

$R = 180 + 81.54g = 979.1$ N

As equilibrium is limiting, $F = \mu R$

so $979.1\mu = 490$ N and $\mu = 0.500$ (3 s.f.)

[5 marks available in total]:
- ***1 mark for resolving horizontally***
- ***1 mark for resolving vertically***
- ***1 mark for using F = μR***
- ***1 mark for correct workings***
- ***1 mark for correct value of μ***

6 a)

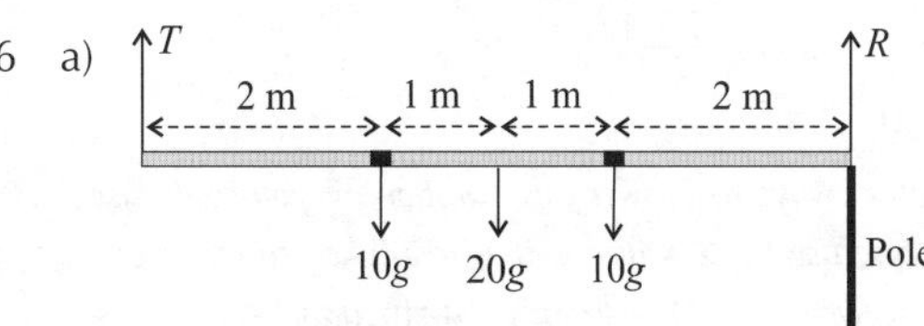

[2 marks available in total]:
- ***1 mark for diagram***
- ***1 mark for correct labelling***

b) Take moments about the pole:

$6T = (2 \times 10g) + (3 \times 20g) + (4 \times 10g)$

$6T = 20g + 60g + 40g = 120g$

So, $T = 20g$

[3 marks available in total]:
- ***1 mark for taking moments about the pole***
- ***1 mark for correct workings***
- ***1 mark for correct value of T***

Why work around the pole? Because we have no idea what the magnitude of R is and working there allows us to ignore it.

c) Resolve vertically:

$T + R = 10g + 20g + 10g$

$20g + R = 40g$

So, $R = 20g$

[2 marks available in total]:
- ***1 mark for resolving vertically***
- ***1 mark for correct value of R***

I suppose we could have found R first and then T, but that's not the order the questions are in, so it's best just to run with it...

Answers

M2 Section 3 — Projectiles

Warm-up Questions

1)

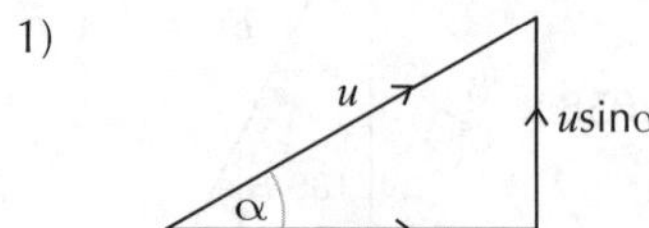

So, parallel to the horizontal, the initial velocity is $u\cos\alpha$.

2) Resolving horizontally (taking right as +ve):
$u = 120;\ s = 60;\ a = 0;\ t = ?$
$s = ut + \frac{1}{2}at^2$
$60 = 120t + \frac{1}{2} \times 0 \times t^2$
$t = 0.5$ s
Resolving vertically (taking down as +ve):
$u = 0;\ s = ?;\ a = 9.8;\ t = 0.5$
$s = ut + \frac{1}{2}at^2$
$= (0 \times 0.5) + (0.5 \times 9.8 \times 0.5^2)$
$= 1.23$ m (to 3 s.f.)

3) Resolving vertically (taking up as +ve):
$u = 22\sin\alpha;\ a = -9.8;\ t = 4;\ s = 0$
s = 0 because the ball lands at the same vertical level it started at.
$s = ut + \frac{1}{2}at^2$
$0 = 22\sin\alpha \times 4 + (0.5 \times -9.8 \times 4^2)$
Rearranging: $\sin\alpha = \frac{78.4}{88}$
$\Rightarrow \alpha = 63.0°$ (3 s.f.)
There are other ways to answer this question — you could use v = u + at and use t = 2, which is the time taken to reach the highest point, when v = 0. I like my way though.

Exam Questions

1 Resolving horizontally, taking right as +ve :
$u = 20\cos 30°;\ s = 30;\ a = 0;\ t = ?$

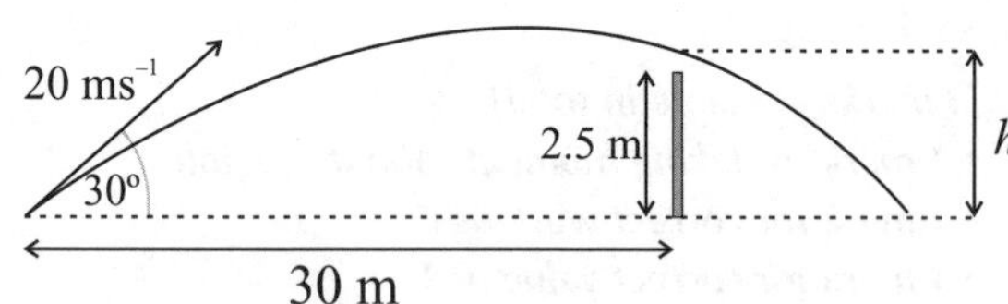

$s = ut + \frac{1}{2}at^2$ ***[1 mark]***
$30 = (20\cos 30° \times t)$
$t = 1.732$ s ***[1 mark]***
Resolving vertically, taking up as +ve:
$s = h;\ u = 20\sin 30°;\ t = 1.732;\ a = -9.8$
$s = ut + \frac{1}{2}at^2$ ***[1 mark]***
$h = (20\sin 30° \times 1.732) + (\frac{1}{2} \times -9.8 \times 1.732^2)$
$= 2.62$ m (to 3 s.f.) ***[1 mark]***
Therefore the ball goes over the crossbar. ***[1 mark]***
Assumptions: e.g. ball is a point mass/no air or wind resistance/no spin on the ball ***[1 mark]***
That was always my problem when I was taking free kicks — I didn't model the flight of the ball properly before kicking it, so no wonder I never scored.

2 a) $\tan\alpha = \frac{3}{4} \Rightarrow \cos\alpha = \frac{4}{5},\ \sin\alpha = \frac{3}{5}$ ***[1 mark]***
Resolving vertically, taking down as +ve:
$u = u_y = 15\sin\alpha = 9;$ ***[1 mark]***
$s = 11;\ a = 9.8;\ t = ?$
$s = ut + \frac{1}{2}at^2$ ***[1 mark]***
$11 = 9t + 4.9t^2$ ***[1 mark]***
Use the quadratic formula to find:
$t = 0.839$ s (3 s.f.) ***[1 mark]***

b) Resolving horizontally, taking right as +ve:
$u = u_x = 15\cos\alpha = 15 \times \frac{4}{5} = 12;$ ***[1 mark]***
$s = ?;\ t = 0.8390$ s
$a = 0$, so $s = ut \Rightarrow OB = 12 \times 0.8390$ ***[1 mark]***
So, $OB = 10.07$ m
So stone misses H by $10.07 - 9 = 1.07$ m (3 s.f.) ***[1 mark]***

c) Resolving horizontally, taking right as +ve:
$s = 9;\ u_x = u\cos\alpha;\ a = 0;\ t = ?$
$s = u_x t + \frac{1}{2}at^2$ ***[1 mark]***
$9 = (u\cos\alpha)t$
$\Rightarrow t = \frac{9}{u\cos\alpha}$ — call this **eqn 1**. ***[1 mark]***
Now resolve vertically, taking down as +ve:
$s = 11;\ u_y = u\sin\alpha;\ a = 9.8;\ t = ?$
$s = u_y t + \frac{1}{2}at^2$
$11 = (u\sin\alpha)t + 4.9t^2$ — call this **eqn 2**. ***[1 mark]***
t is the same both horizontally and vertically, so substitute the expression for t from **eqn 1** into **eqn 2** to eliminate t:
$11 = 9\left(\frac{u\sin\alpha}{u\cos\alpha}\right) + 4.9\left(\frac{9}{u\cos\alpha}\right)^2$ ***[1 mark]***
$11 = 9\tan\alpha + \frac{4.9 \times 81}{u^2\cos^2\alpha}$
$\tan\alpha = \frac{3}{4}$ and $\cos\alpha = \frac{4}{5}$, so substituting and simplifying:
$u^2 = 145.919$
so $u = 12.1$ ms^{-1} (3 s.f.) ***[1 mark]***
Wooo. What a beauty part c) is — I'd do that again just for kicks. But then I do love a bit of substituting and eliminating.
If you're confused by this question, then look back over the section — there's an example which is a bit more general, but it uses a lot of the same working.

Answers

M2 Section 4 — Uniform Circular Motion

Warm-up Questions

1) a) $\omega = \frac{\theta}{t} = \frac{2\pi}{1.5} = \frac{4\pi}{3}$ radians s^{-1}

$a = r\omega^2 = 3 \times \left(\frac{4\pi}{3}\right)^2 = \frac{16\pi^2}{3}$ ms^{-2}

Don't forget the units — it's radians per second for angular speed.

b) $\omega = \frac{\theta}{t} = \frac{15 \times 2\pi}{60} = \frac{\pi}{2}$ radians s^{-1}

$a = r\omega^2 = 3 \times \left(\frac{\pi}{2}\right)^2 = \frac{3\pi^2}{4}$ ms^{-2}

c) $\omega = \frac{\theta}{t} = \frac{\frac{160}{360} \times 2\pi}{1} = \frac{8}{9}\pi$ radians s^{-1}

$a = r\omega^2 = 3 \times \left(\frac{8}{9}\pi\right)^2 = \frac{64\pi^2}{27}$ ms^{-2}

d) $\omega = \frac{v}{r} = \frac{10}{3}$ radians s^{-1}

$a = \frac{v^2}{r} = \frac{10^2}{3} = \frac{100}{3}$ ms^{-2}

2 a) $F = mr\omega^2 = 2 \times 0.4 \times (10\pi)^2 = 80\pi^2$ N

b) $F = \frac{mv^2}{r} = \frac{2 \times 4^2}{0.4} = 80$ N

This formula is just the old F = ma in disguise. Just make sure you know the circular motion acceleration formulas.

3 a) Resolving vertically:

$T\cos 45° = 4g \Rightarrow T = 55.4$ N (3 s.f.)

b) Resolving horizontally:

$T\sin 45° = \frac{mv^2}{r} \Rightarrow 55.44\sin 45° = \frac{4v^2}{r}$

$r = 0.102v^2$ m (3 s.f.)

Exam Questions

1 At the greatest speed, the centripetal force will be greatest, and so friction will be at its greatest value, i.e. $F = \mu R$.

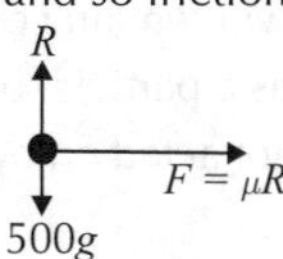

Resolving vertically: $R = 500g$ ***[1 mark]***

Resolving horizontally: $\mu R = \frac{mv^2}{r}$ ***[1 mark]***

$0.5 \times 500g = \frac{500v^2}{30}$ ***[1 mark]***

$0.5g = \frac{v^2}{30}$

$v^2 = 15g$ ***[1 mark]*** $\Rightarrow v = 12.1 ms^{-1}$ (3 s.f.) ***[1 mark]***

2 a)

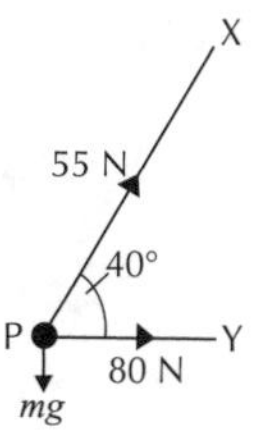

Resolving vertically: $mg = 55\sin 40°$ ***[1 mark]***

$\Rightarrow m = 3.6074... = 3.61$ kg (3 s.f.) ***[1 mark]***

b) Resolving horizontally:

$F = \frac{mv^2}{r}$ ***[1 mark]***

$55\cos 40° + 80 = \frac{3.607 \times 3^2}{r}$ ***[1 mark]***

$\Rightarrow r = \frac{3.607 \times 3^2}{55\cos 40° + 80} = 0.26580...$

$= 0.266$ m (3 s.f.) ***[1 mark]***

The radius is the same as the length of the horizontal string.

c) $\omega = \frac{v}{r} = \frac{3}{0.2658} = 11.29$ radians s^{-1} ***[1 mark]***

2π radians = 1 revolution

$\frac{11.29}{2\pi} = 1.796$ revolutions per second ***[1 mark]***

$1.796 \times 60 = 108$ revolutions per minute (3 s.f.) ***[1 mark]***

3 a) Here's a diagram of the forces acting on P:

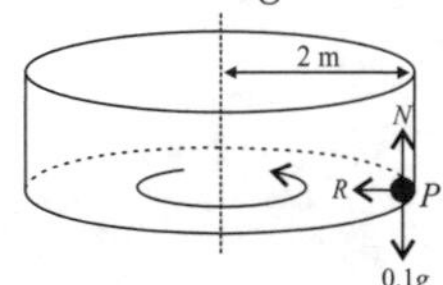

Here, N is the normal reaction of the base of the cylinder on P and R is the normal reaction of the curved surface of the cylinder on P.

P moves through π rads every second, so $\omega = \pi$.

Resolving horizontally and using $F = mr\omega^2$:

$R = mr\omega^2 = 0.1 \times 2 \times \pi^2$ ***[1 mark]***

$= 0.2\pi^2 = 1.97$ N (3 s.f.) ***[1 mark]***

b) Again, here's a diagram of forces:

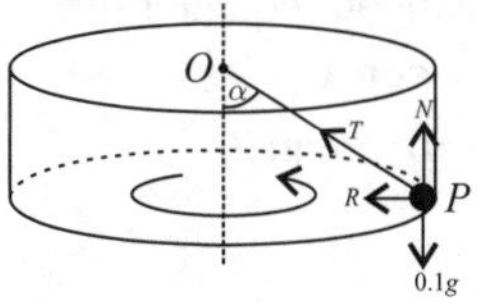

Here, T is the tension in the string and N and R are the reaction forces from the surfaces of the cylinder.

Resolving vertically:

$N + T\cos\alpha = mg$

You are given in the question that $N = 0.75$, so:

$0.75 + T\cos\alpha = 0.1g$

Resolving horizontally and using $F = mr\omega^2$:

$R + T\sin\alpha = mr\omega^2$

$R + T\sin\alpha = 0.2\pi^2$

You are given in the question that $R = 1.7$, so:

$1.7 + T\sin\alpha = 0.2\pi^2$

You can take the value of $mr\omega^2$ straight from part a), as P is moving with the same angular speed and radius now as it was then.

Answers

You now have a pair of simultaneous equations:

$T\cos\alpha = 0.1g - 0.75$ **eqn 1**

$T\sin\alpha = 0.2\pi^2 - 1.7$ **eqn 2**

Dividing **eqn 2** by **eqn 1**:

$$\tan\alpha = \frac{0.2\pi^2 - 1.7}{(0.1 \times 9.8) - 0.75}$$

$\Rightarrow \alpha = 49.981... = 50.0°$ (3 s.f.)

So, from **eqn 2**:

$$T = \frac{0.2\pi^2 - 1.7}{\sin(49.981...)°}$$

$= 0.358$ N (3 s.f.)

[7 marks available in total]:

- ***1 mark for resolving horizontally***
- ***1 mark for resolving vertically***
- ***1 mark for forming pair of simultaneous equations***
- ***1 mark for working to find α***
- ***1 mark for correct value of α***
- ***1 mark for working to find T***
- ***1 mark for correct value of T***

4 a) Here's the diagram of forces:

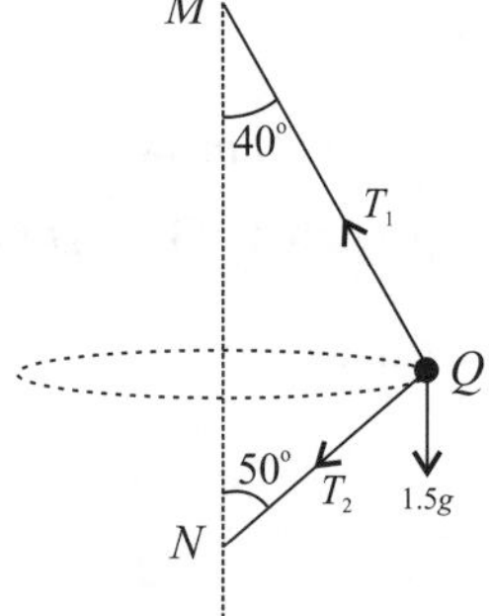

Resolving vertically:

$T_1\cos 40° = 1.5g + T_2\cos 50°$ ***[1 mark]***

Resolving horizontally and using $F = mr\omega^2$:

$T_1\sin 40° + T_2\sin 50° = 1.5 \times r \times (2\pi)^2$ ***[1 mark]***

You are told that MQ has length 0.5 m, so the radius of Q's motion is $r = 0.5\sin 40°$ ***[1 mark]***. So:

$T_1\sin 40° + T_2\sin 50° = 1.5 \times 0.5\sin 40° \times 4\pi^2$

$\Rightarrow T_1\sin 40° + T_2\sin 50° = 3\pi^2\sin 40°$ ***[1 mark]***

You now have a pair of simultaneous equations:

$T_1\cos 40° = 1.5g + T_2\cos 50°$ **eqn 1**

$T_1\sin 40° + T_2\sin 50° = 3\pi^2\sin 40°$ **eqn 2**

Eliminating T_1:

$$T_1 = \frac{1.5g + T_2\cos 50°}{\cos 40°}$$

$$\Rightarrow \frac{1.5g + T_2\cos 50°}{\cos 40°}\sin 40° + T_2\sin 50° = 3\pi^2\sin 40°$$

$\Rightarrow 1.5g\tan 40° + T_2\cos 50°\tan 40° + T_2\sin 50° = 3\pi^2\sin 40°$

$$\Rightarrow T_2 = \frac{3\pi^2\sin 40° - (1.5 \times 9.8 \times \tan 40°)}{(\cos 50° \times \tan 40°) + \sin 50°}$$ ***[1 mark]***

$= 5.1305... = 5.13$ N (3 s.f.) ***[1 mark]***

Plugging this back into **eqn 1**:

$$T_1 = \frac{1.5g + (5.1305...)\cos 50°}{\cos 40°}$$ ***[1 mark]***

$= 23.4945... = 23.5$ N (3 s.f.) ***[1 mark]***

b) When NQ is on the point of becoming slack, $T_2 = 0$.

Resolving vertically:

$T_1\cos 40° = 1.5g$ ***[1 mark]***

$$\Rightarrow T_1 = \frac{1.5g}{\cos 40°}$$

Resolving horizontally and using $F = mr\omega^2$:

$T_1\sin 40° = mr\omega^2$ ***[1 mark]***

The kinetic energy of Q is given by:

$\text{K.E.} = \frac{1}{2}mv^2 = \frac{1}{2}mr^2\omega^2 = \frac{1}{2}r(mr\omega^2)$

So $\text{K.E.} = \frac{1}{2} \times r \times T_1\sin 40$

$$= \frac{1}{2} \times 0.5\sin 40° \times \frac{1.5g}{\cos 40°} \times \sin 40°$$ ***[1 mark]***

$= 1.98$ J (3 s.f.) ***[1 mark]***

The important thing to realise in part b) is that the value of T_1 will change when T_2 becomes slack — so don't go using your value of T_1 from part a), or you'll get the wrong answer. You don't have to do that little bit of trickery at the end — you could always just find ω, and then use it in the kinetic energy formula. It's up to you.

If you've never come across kinetic energy before, then you'd best have a goosey at page 171 to see what it's all about.

M2 Section 5 — Energy, Work and Power Warm-up Questions

1) Work done $= F \times s$

$= 250 \times 3 = 750$ J

2) Work done against gravity $= mgh$

$34\,000 = m \times 9.8 \times 12$

$m = 289$ kg (3 s.f.)

3) Kinetic Energy $= \frac{1}{2}mv^2$

$= \frac{1}{2} \times 450 \times 13^2$

$= 38\,025$ J $= 38.0$ kJ (3 s.f.)

4) Work done = Change in Kinetic Energy

$800 = \frac{1}{2}m(v^2 - u^2)$

$u = 0$ and $m = 65$, so:

$v^2 = \frac{1600}{65} \Rightarrow v = 4.96$ ms^{-1} (3 s.f.)

5) Increase in Potential Energy = mg × increase in height

$= 0.5 \times 9.8 \times 150$

$= 735$ J

6) "If there are no external forces doing work on an object, the total mechanical energy of the object will remain constant." You usually need to model the object as a particle, because you have to assume that the object is not acted on by any external forces such as air resistance.

7) When the hat reaches its maximum height, its velocity will be zero. Using conservation of energy:

Change in potential energy = change in kinetic energy

$mgh = \frac{1}{2}m(u^2 - v^2)$

Cancel m from both sides, and substitute $u = 5$, $v = 0$ and $g = 9.8$:

$9.8h = \frac{1}{2} \times 25 \Rightarrow h = 1.28$ m (3 s.f.)

Answers

8) "The work done on an object by external forces is equal to the change in the total mechanical energy of that object." An external force is any force other than an object's weight.

9) Power of engine = driving force × velocity
$350\ 000 = F \times 22 \Rightarrow F = 15\ 900$ N (3 s.f.)

Exam Questions

1 a) Use the work rate to find the 'driving' force, F of the cyclist:
$250 = F \times 4$ ***[1 mark]***
$F = 62.5$ N
Resolve parallel to the slope: ***[1 mark]***
$62.5 - 35 - 88g\sin\alpha = 0$ ***[1 mark]***
$\alpha = \sin^{-1}\frac{27.5}{88g} = 1.83°$ (3 s.f.) ***[1 mark]***

b) Use the new work rate to find the new 'driving' force, F':
$370 = F' \times 4$ ***[1 mark]***
$F' = 92.5$ N
Resolve parallel to the slope to find a: ***[1 mark]***
$92.5 - 35 - 88g\sin\alpha = 88a$ ***[1 mark]***
$a = 0.341$ ms^{-2} (3 s.f.) ***[1 mark]***

2 a) Work done = Force × distance moved
$= 800\cos40° \times 320 = 196$ kJ (3 s.f.)

[3 marks available in total]:
- ***1 mark for using the horizontal component of the force***
- ***1 mark for correct use of formula for work done***
- ***1 mark for correct final answer.***

b)

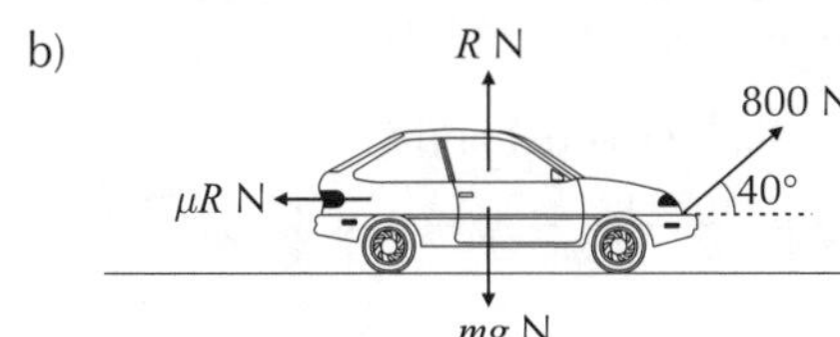

No acceleration vertically, so:
$R + 800\sin40° = mg$
$R = 1500g - 800\sin40° = 14\ 190$ N ***[1 mark]***
Car is moving only horizontally, so:
Work done = change in kinetic energy ***[1 mark]***
$(800\cos40° - \mu R) \times 320 = \frac{1}{2} \times 1500 \times (16^2 - 11^2)$ ***[1 mark]***
Rearrange to find μ:
$\mu = \frac{196\,107 - 101250}{4\,541000} = 0.0209$ (3 s.f.) ***[1 mark]***

3 a)

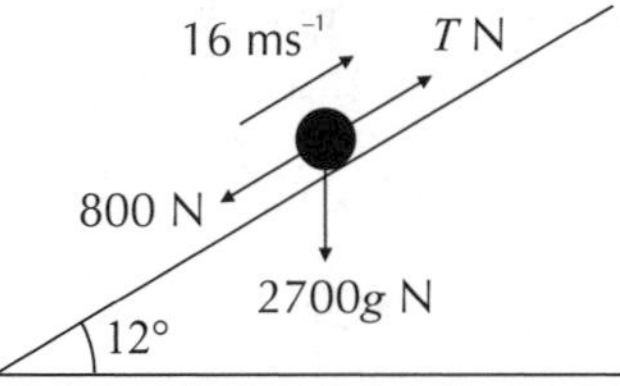

Resolving parallel to the slope using $F = ma$ with $a = 0$:
$T - 800 - 2700g\sin12° = 0$ ***[1 mark]***
So, $T = 6301$ N ***[1 mark]***
Power of engine = Driving Force × Velocity ***[1 mark]***
$= 6301 \times 16 = 101$ kW (3 s.f.) ***[1 mark]***

b) Work done by resistive force to stop van $= -800x$ ***[1 mark]***
Change in total energy = Change in P.E. + Change in K.E.
$= (2700 \times g \times x\sin12°) - \left(\frac{1}{2} \times 2700 \times 16^2\right)$ ***[1 mark]***
By work-energy principle,
$-800x = 2700gx\sin12° - 345\ 600$ ***[1 mark]***
Rearrange to find x:
$x = \frac{345\,600}{2700g\sin12° + 800} = 54.8$ m (3 s.f.) ***[1 mark]***

c) Resolve parallel to the slope using $F = ma$ to find a:
$-800 - 2700g\sin12° = 2700a$ ***[1 mark]***
$a = -2.334$ ms^{-2} ***[1 mark]***
Use $v = u + at$ to find the time taken to come to rest:
$0 = 16 - 2.334t$ ***[1 mark]***
$t = \frac{16}{2.334} = 6.86$ s (3 s.f.) ***[1 mark]***

4 a) K.E. $= \frac{1}{2}mv^2 = \frac{1}{2} \times 0.3 \times 20^2$ ***[1 mark]***
$= 60$ J ***[1 mark]***

b) Only force acting on the stone is its weight, so use conservation of mechanical energy:
Change in K.E. = Change in P.E. ***[1 mark]***
$60 - 0 = 0.3 \times 9.8 \times h$ ***[1 mark]***
$h = 20.4$ m (3 s.f.) ***[1 mark]***

c) Stone's change in K.E. after hitting the water:
$\frac{1}{2} \times 0.3 \times 1^2 - 60 = -59.85$ J ***[1 mark]***
Call the depth the stone has sunk x m.
Change in P.E. after hitting the water:
$-mgx = -2.94x$ ***[1 mark]***
Work done on the stone by resistive force
$= Fs = -23x$ ***[1 mark]***
By the work-energy principle:
Work done on the stone = Change in total energy ***[1 mark]***
$-23x = -59.85 - 2.94x$
Rearrange to find x:
$x = 2.98$ m (3 s.f) ***[1 mark]***

5 a) Find T, the driving force of the car, using Power $= Tv$:
$T = \text{Power} \div v = 20\ 000 \div 10 = 2000$ N. ***[1 mark]***
Resolve forces parallel to the slope:
$T - mg\sin\theta - kv = 0$ ***[1 mark]***.
$\Rightarrow 2000 - (1000 \times 9.8 \times 0.1) - 10k = 0$
$\Rightarrow 10k = 1020$
$\Rightarrow k = 102$ ***[1 mark]***

b) (i) Call the new driving force F. Using Power $= Fv$:
$F = \frac{50\ 000}{u}$ ***[1 mark]***
Resolve forces parallel to the slope:
$\frac{50\ 000}{u} - mg\sin\theta - 102u = 0.$ ***[1 mark]***
Rearranging and substituting known values gives:
$50\ 000 - (1000 \times 9.8 \times 0.1)u - 102u^2 = 0$ ***[1 mark]***.
This rearranges to:
$102u^2 + 980u - 50\ 000 = 0$ — as required ***[1 mark]***.

Answers

(ii) Solve for u using the quadratic formula:

$$u = \frac{-980 + \sqrt{980^2 - (4 \times 102 \times -50\,000)}}{2 \times 102}$$

$u = 17.9\ \text{ms}^{-1}$ (3 s.f.)

[2 marks available in total]:

- ***1 mark for correctly using quadratic formula***
- ***1 mark for correct value for u***

You don't need to worry about the negative part of ± in the formula, as you're after a speed — which is always positive.

c) Using $F = ma$ gives $T - 102v = ma$. ***[1 mark]***
This time, $T = P \div v = 21000 \div 12$, and so:
$(21000 \div 12) - (102 \times 12) = 1000a$ ***[1 mark]***
$\Rightarrow a = 0.526\ \text{ms}^{-2}$ ***[1 mark]***

6 a) Increase in Kinetic Energy $= \frac{1}{2}m(v^2 - u^2)$ ***[1 mark]***
$= \frac{1}{2} \times 90 \times (6^2 - 4^2) = 900$ J ***[1 mark]***
Increase in Gravitational Potential Energy $= mgh$ ***[1 mark]***
$= 90 \times 9.8 \times 28\sin30° = 12\,348$ J ***[1 mark]***

Increase in total Energy = Increase in K.E. + Increase in P.E.
$= 900 + 12\,348 = 13\,248$ J $= 13.2$ kJ (3 s.f.) ***[1 mark]***

b) Using the work-energy principle:
Work done on skier = Change in total energy ***[1 mark]***
$(L - 66) \times 28 = 13\,248$ ***[1 mark]***
$L = \frac{13\,248 + (66 \times 28)}{28} = 539$ N (3 s.f.) ***[1 mark]***

M2 Section 6 — Collisions
Warm-up Questions

1) Impulse acts against motion, so $I = -2$ Ns
$I = mv - mu$
$-2 = 0.3v - (0.3 \times 5)$
$v = -1\frac{2}{3}\ \text{ms}^{-1}$
Impulse has 2 different equations, I = mv – mu and I = Ft. Remember both.

2) You need to find the particle's velocities just before and just after impact. Falling (down = +ve):

$u = 0$, $s = 2$, $a = 9.8$, $v = ?$
$v^2 = u^2 + 2as$
$v = \sqrt{2 \times 9.8 \times 2}$
$v = 6.261\text{ms}^{-1}$

Rebound (this time, let up = +ve):

$v = 0$, $u = ?$, $a = -9.8$, $s = 1⅓$
$v^2 = u^2 + 2as$
$0 - u^2 = 2 \times -9.8 \times 1⅓$
$u = 5.112\text{ms}^{-1}$

Taking up = +ve:
Impulse $= mv - mu$
$= (0.45 \times 5.112) - (0.45 \times -6.261)$
$= 5.12$ Ns

3) Call the particles A and B. If $u_A = u$ then $u_B = -u$ (as it's going in the opposite direction at the same speed). After the collision, $v_A = 0$ and $v_B = \frac{u}{2}$ (as it's going in the opposite direction to its original motion at half the speed).

$$e = \frac{\text{speed of separation of particles}}{\text{speed of approach of particles}} = \frac{v_B - v_A}{u_A - u_B}$$

$$\Rightarrow e = \frac{\frac{u}{2} - 0}{u - (-u)} = \frac{\frac{u}{2}}{2u} = \frac{u}{4u} = \frac{1}{4}.$$

4) a) For collision with a plane surface, $e = \frac{v}{u}$, so rebound speed $v = eu \Rightarrow v = 0.4 \times 10 = 4\ \text{ms}^{-1}$.

b) Call the particles A and B, so

$$e = \frac{\text{speed of separation of particles}}{\text{speed of approach of particles}} = \frac{v_B - v_A}{u_A - u_B}$$

$\Rightarrow 0.4 = \frac{v_B - v_A}{10 - (-12)} \Rightarrow v_B - v_A = 0.4 \times 22$
$\Rightarrow v_B - v_A = 8.8$ ...*[1]*

Using the conservation of momentum:
$m_Au_A + m_Bu_B = m_Av_A + m_Bv_B$
$(1 \times 10) + (2 \times -12) = (1 \times v_A) + (2 \times v_B)$
$10 - 24 = v_A + 2v_B \Rightarrow v_A + 2v_B = -14$ ...*[2]*

Equation *[1]* + equation *[2]* gives:
$3v_B = -5.2 \Rightarrow v_B = -1.7333...\ \text{ms}^{-1}$.

Substituting in equation *[1]* gives:
$-1.7333... - v_A = 8.8$
$\Rightarrow v_A = -1.7333... - 8.8 = -10.5333...\ \text{ms}^{-1}$.
So, to 3 s.f., the original particle's rebound speed is $10.5\ \text{ms}^{-1}$.

5) For the first collision, between A and B:

$$e = \frac{v_B - v_A}{u_A - u_B} \Rightarrow \frac{1}{4} = \frac{v_B - v_A}{3u - 2u} \Rightarrow v_B - v_A = \frac{u}{4} \text{ ...[1]}$$

And:
$m_Au_A + m_Bu_B = m_Av_A + m_Bv_B$
$(1 \times 3u) + (4 \times 2u) = (1 \times v_A) + (4 \times v_B)$
$3u + 8u = v_A + 4v_B \Rightarrow v_A + 4v_B = 11u$ ...*[2]*

Equation *[1]* + equation *[2]* gives:
$5v_B = 11u + \frac{u}{4} \Rightarrow 5v_B = \frac{45u}{4} \Rightarrow v_B = \frac{9u}{4}$.
Substituting in equation *[2]* gives:
$v_A + 9u = 11u \Rightarrow v_A = 11u - 9u = 2u$.

For the second collision, between B and C:

$$e = \frac{v_C - v_B}{u_B - u_C} \Rightarrow \frac{1}{3} = \frac{v_C - v_B}{\frac{9u}{4} - u} \Rightarrow v_C - v_B = \frac{5u}{12} \text{ ...[3]}$$

And:
$m_Bu_B + m_Cu_C = m_Bv_B + m_Cv_C$

$(4 \times \frac{9u}{4}) + (5 \times u) = (4 \times v_B) + (5 \times v_C)$
$\Rightarrow 4v_B + 5v_C = 14u$ ...*[4]*

4 × Equation *[3]* + equation *[4]* gives:
$9v_C = \frac{5u}{3} + 14u \Rightarrow 9v_C = \frac{47u}{3} \Rightarrow v_C = \frac{47u}{27}$.
Substituting in equation *[3]* gives:
$\frac{47u}{27} - v_B = \frac{5u}{12} \Rightarrow v_B = \frac{47u}{27} - \frac{5u}{12} = \frac{143u}{108}$.

Answers

So after both collisions:

A is travelling at $2u = \frac{216u}{108}$,

and B is travelling at $\frac{143u}{108}$,

which means that A is travelling faster than B and so they should collide again.

6) $e = \frac{v_2 - v_1}{u_1 - u_2} \Rightarrow 0.3 = \frac{v_2 - v_1}{3 - 0} \Rightarrow v_2 - v_1 = 0.9$ ...*[1]*

And: $m_1u_1 + m_2u_2 = m_1v_1 + m_2v_2$

$\Rightarrow (2 \times 3) + (3 \times 0) = 2v_1 + 3v_2$

$\Rightarrow 6 = 2v_1 + 3v_2 \Rightarrow v_1 + 1.5v_2 = 3$ ...*[2]*

Equation *[1]* + equation *[2]* gives:

$2.5v_2 = 3.9 \Rightarrow v_2 = 1.56 \text{ ms}^{-1}$.

In equation *[1]*:

$1.56 - v_1 = 0.9 \Rightarrow v_1 = 1.56 - 0.9 = 0.66 \text{ ms}^{-1}$.

Loss of K.E. $= (\frac{1}{2}m_1u_1^2 + \frac{1}{2}m_2u_2^2) - (\frac{1}{2}m_1v_1^2 + \frac{1}{2}m_2v_2^2)$

$= [(\frac{1}{2} \times 2 \times 3^2) + 0] - [(\frac{1}{2} \times 2 \times 0.66^2) + (\frac{1}{2} \times 3 \times 1.56^2)]$

$= 9 - 4.086 = 4.914$ J.

Exam Questions

1 Using the principle of conservation of momentum for the collision:

$m_1u_1 + m_2u_2 = m_1v_1 + m_2v_2$

Since marble 2 is stationary before the impact:

$(0.02 \times 2) + (0.06 \times 0) = 0.02v_1 + 0.06v_2$ ***[1 mark]***

$\Rightarrow 0.02v_1 + 0.06v_2 = 0.04$

$\Rightarrow v_1 + 3v_2 = 2$ ...*[1]*

Since the collision is perfectly elastic, and so $e = 1$, the Law of Restitution gives a second equation:

$e = \frac{\text{speed of separation of particles}}{\text{speed of approach of particles}} = \frac{v_2 - v_1}{u_1 - u_2}$

$\Rightarrow 1 = \frac{v_2 - v_1}{2 - 0}$ ***[1 mark]*** $\Rightarrow v_2 - v_1 = 2$ ...*[2]*

Equation *[1]* + equation *[2]* gives:

$4v_2 = 4 \Rightarrow v_2 = 1 \text{ ms}^{-1}$ ***[1 mark]***.

Substituting in equation *[1]* gives:

$v_1 + (3 \times 1) = 2 \Rightarrow v_1 = -1 \text{ ms}^{-1}$ ***[1 mark]***.

So after the collision, both particles are travelling at a speed of 1 ms^{-1} (but the first particle is going in the opposite direction to its initial path).

2 a) Using the Law of Restitution for the collision between P and Q, where P is travelling at u and Q at $-u$ (i.e. in the opposite direction):

$e = \frac{v_Q - v_P}{u_P - u_Q} \Rightarrow \frac{3}{4} = \frac{v_Q - v_P}{u - (-u)}$ ***[1 mark]*** $\Rightarrow \frac{3}{4} = \frac{v_Q - v_P}{2u}$

$\Rightarrow v_Q - v_P = \frac{3u}{2}$ ...*[1]*

Using conservation of momentum:

$m_Pu_P + m_Qu_Q = m_Pv_P + m_Qv_Q$

$2mu - mu = 2mv_P + mv_Q$ ***[1 mark]***

$\Rightarrow 2v_P + v_Q = u$ ...*[2]*

Equation *[2]* – equation *[1]* gives:

$3v_P = -\frac{u}{2} \Rightarrow v_P = -\frac{u}{6}$ ***[1 mark]***.

Substituting in equation *[1]* gives:

$v_Q - (-\frac{u}{6}) = \frac{3u}{2} \Rightarrow v_Q = \frac{4u}{3}$ ***[1 mark]***.

Since P's velocity was initially positive, and is now negative, and Q's was initially negative but is now positive, the collision has reversed the directions of both particles ***[1 mark]***.

Sure about that? Yep, positive. I mean negative... erm...

$|v_Q| \div |v_P| = \frac{4u}{3} \div \frac{u}{6} = 8$,

so Q is now going 8 times faster than P ***[1 mark]***.

b) For the collision with the wall, $e_{wall} = \frac{\text{speed of rebound}}{\text{speed of approach}}$.

Q approaches the wall with a speed of $\frac{4u}{3}$ (from a)), so if v_{Qwall} is its rebound speed:

$e_{wall} = \frac{v_{Qwall}}{\frac{4u}{3}} \Rightarrow v_{Qwall} = \frac{4ue_{wall}}{3}$ ***[1 mark]***.

Since Q collides again with P, v_{Qwall} must be greater than v_P, which is $\frac{u}{6}$ (from a)), so:

$\frac{4ue_{wall}}{3} > \frac{u}{6}$ ***[1 mark]*** $\Rightarrow e_{wall} > \frac{3u}{6 \times 4u} \Rightarrow e_{wall} > \frac{1}{8}$ ***[1 mark]***.

c) If $e_{wall} = \frac{3}{5}$, then (from b)):

$v_{Qwall} = \frac{4ue_{wall}}{3} = \frac{4u \times 3}{3 \times 5} = \frac{4u}{5}$ ***[1 mark]***.

Q is now travelling in the same direction as P, which is still travelling at a speed of $\frac{u}{6}$ (from a)), and the particles have a coefficient of restitution of $\frac{3}{4}$, so using the Law of Restitution for the second collision between P and Q:

$e = \frac{v_P - v_Q}{u_Q - u_P} \Rightarrow \frac{3}{4} = \frac{v_P - v_Q}{\left(\frac{4u}{5}\right) - \frac{u}{6}}$ ***[1 mark]*** $\Rightarrow \frac{3}{4} = \frac{v_P - v_Q}{\frac{19u}{30}}$

$\Rightarrow v_P - v_Q = \frac{19u}{40}$ ...*[1]*

Using conservation of momentum:

$m_Qu_Q + m_Pu_P = m_Qv_Q + m_Pv_P$

$\frac{4um}{5} + \frac{2um}{6} = mv_Q + 2mv_P$ ***[1 mark]***

$\Rightarrow v_Q + 2v_P = \frac{17u}{15}$ ...*[2]*

Equation *[2]* – 2 × equation *[1]* gives:

$3v_Q = \frac{17u}{15} - \frac{19u}{20} = \frac{11u}{60}$ ***[1 mark]***

$\Rightarrow v_Q = \frac{11u}{180}$ ***[1 mark]***.

Since $v_Q = 0.22 \text{ ms}^{-1}$:

$\frac{11u}{180} = 0.22$ ***[1 mark]***

$\Rightarrow u = (0.22 \times 180) \div 11 = 3.6 \text{ ms}^{-1}$ ***[1 mark]***.

Answers

3 a) Using the Law of Restitution for the collision between particles 1 and 2 gives:

$e = \frac{v_2 - v_1}{u_1 - u_2} \Rightarrow \frac{1}{4} = \frac{v_2 - v_1}{3u - 2u}$ ***[1 mark]***

$\Rightarrow v_2 - v_1 = \frac{u}{4}$ ...*[1]*

Using conservation of momentum:

$m_1u_1 + m_2u_2 = m_1v_1 + m_2v_2$

$(2m \times 3u) + (3m \times 2u) = 2mv_1 + 3mv_2$ ***[1 mark]***

$\Rightarrow 2v_1 + 3v_2 = 12u$ ...*[2]*

Equation *[1]* × 2 gives:

$2v_2 - 2v_1 = \frac{u}{2}$ ...*[3]*

Equation *[2]* + equation *[3]* gives:

$5v_2 = 12u + \frac{u}{2} \Rightarrow v_2 = \frac{25u}{2 \times 5} = \frac{5u}{2}$ ***[1 mark]***.

Substituting in equation *[1]* gives:

$\frac{5u}{2} - v_1 = \frac{u}{4}$

$\Rightarrow v_1 = \frac{5u}{2} - \frac{u}{4} = \frac{9u}{4}$ ***[1 mark]***.

b) Loss of kinetic energy =

$(\frac{1}{2}m_1u_1^2 + \frac{1}{2}m_2u_2^2) - (\frac{1}{2}m_1v_1^2 + \frac{1}{2}m_2v_2^2)$

$= [(\frac{1}{2} \times 2m \times (3u)^2) + (\frac{1}{2} \times 3m \times (2u)^2)] -$

$[(\frac{1}{2} \times 2m \times (\frac{9u}{4})^2) + (\frac{1}{2} \times 3m \times (\frac{5u}{2})^2)]$

$= (9mu^2 + 6mu^2) - (\frac{81mu^2}{16} + \frac{150mu^2}{16})$

$= (15 - \frac{231}{16})mu^2 = \frac{9mu^2}{16}$.

[4 marks available — 1 mark for correct values in formula for initial kinetic energy, 1 mark for correct values in formula for final kinetic energy, 1 mark for correct calculation of initial and final energy and 1 mark for correct final answer as the difference between the two.]

4 a) For the collision between A and B, the Law of Restitution gives the following equation:

$e = \frac{v_B - v_A}{u_A - u_B} \Rightarrow e = \frac{v_B - v_A}{4u - 0}$ ***[1 mark]***

$\Rightarrow v_B - v_A = 4ue$ ...*[1]*

Using conservation of momentum:

$m_Au_A + m_Bu_B = m_Av_A + m_Bv_B$

$4mu + 0 = mv_A + 2mv_B$ ***[1 mark]***

$\Rightarrow v_A + 2v_B = 4u$ ...*[2]*

Equation *[1]* + equation *[2]* gives:

$3v_B = 4u(1 + e) \Rightarrow v_B = \frac{4u}{3}(1 + e)$ ***[1 mark]***.

Substituting in equation *[1]* gives:

$\frac{4u}{3}(1 + e) - v_A = 4ue$

$\Rightarrow v_A = \frac{4u}{3}(1 + e) - 4ue = \frac{4u}{3}(1 - 2e)$ ***[1 mark]***.

Since the coefficient of restitution must be between 0 and 1, and the coefficient of restitution between B and C is $2e$, then $0 \le 2e \le 1 \Rightarrow 1 - 2e \ge 0$ ***[1 mark]***.

i.e. $v_A = \frac{4u}{3}(1 - 2e)$, where $u > 0$ and $1 - 2e \ge 0$. So:

v_A cannot be negative ***[1 mark]***, so the collision does not reverse the direction of A's motion ***[1 mark]***.

b) After the collision, A is travelling at $\frac{4u}{3}(1 - 2e)$ and B is travelling at $\frac{4u}{3}(1 + e)$ (from a)). In the time it takes B to travel a distance d, A has travelled $\frac{d}{4}$. So the speed of A must be a quarter of the speed of B ***[1 mark]*** i.e.

$\frac{4u}{3}(1 - 2e) = \frac{u}{3}(1 + e)$ ***[1 mark]***

$\Rightarrow 4 - 8e = 1 + e$

$\Rightarrow 9e = 3 \Rightarrow e = \frac{1}{3}$ ***[1 mark]***

c) Since $e = \frac{1}{3}$ (from b)), the speed of B as it approaches C is:

$\frac{4u}{3}(1 + \frac{1}{3}) = \frac{16u}{9}$ ***[1 mark]***. The coefficient of restitution between B and C is $2e = \frac{2}{3}$ ***[1 mark]***. So, using the Law of Restitution: $e = \frac{v_C - v_B}{u_B - u_C} \Rightarrow \frac{2}{3} = \frac{v_C - v_B}{\frac{16u}{9} - 0}$ ***[1 mark]***

$\Rightarrow v_C - v_B = \frac{32u}{27}$ ...*[1]*

Using conservation of momentum:

$m_Bu_B + m_Cu_C = m_Bv_B + m_Cv_C$

$(2m \times \frac{16u}{9}) + 0 = 2mv_B + 4mv_C$ ***[1 mark]***

$\Rightarrow v_B + 2v_C = \frac{16u}{9}$ ...*[2]*

Equation *[1]* + equation *[2]* gives:

$3v_C = \frac{80u}{27} \Rightarrow v_C = \frac{80u}{81}$ ***[1 mark]***.

5 First find the speed of P before the collision:

$I = m_Pu_P - 0$ (as it is stationary before the impulse acts on it)

$8 = 4u_P$ ***[1 mark]***

$\Rightarrow u_P = 8 \div 4 = 2 \text{ ms}^{-1}$ ***[1 mark]***

Now using coefficient of restitution for the collision:

$e = \frac{v_Q - v_P}{u_P}$

$0.25 = \frac{v_Q - v_P}{2}$ ***[1 mark]***

$\Rightarrow v_Q - v_P = 0.5$ **eqn 1** ***[1 mark]***

And now using conservation of momentum:

$m_Pu_P = m_Pv_P + m_Qv_Q$

$8 = 4v_P + 6v_Q$ **eqn 2** ***[1 mark]***

Eliminate v_Q to solve the simultaneous equations:

From **eqn 1**: $v_Q = 0.5 + v_P$

Plugging this into **eqn 2**:

$8 = 4v_P + 6(0.5 + v_P)$

$8 = 4v_P + 3 + 6v_P$

$5 = 10v_P$

[1 mark for attempting to solve simultaneous equations]

$\Rightarrow v_P = 0.5 \text{ ms}^{-1}$ ***[1 mark]***

Subbing this back into **eqn 1**:

$v_Q = 0.5 + 0.5 = 1 \text{ ms}^{-1}$. ***[1 mark]***

Simultaneous equations, eh? Gotta love 'em.

6 Using conservation of momentum, taking the direction that B moves *after* the collision as positive:

$m_Au_A + m_Bu_B = m_Av_A + m_Bv_B$

$3u_A + 4u_B = (3 \times -1) + (4 \times 2)$ ***[1 mark]***

$3u_A + 4u_B = 5$ **eqn 1** ***[1 mark]***

Considering loss of kinetic energy:

$\left(\frac{1}{2}m_Au_A^2 + \frac{1}{2}m_Bu_B^2\right) - \left(\frac{1}{2}m_Av_A^2 + \frac{1}{2}m_Bv_B^2\right) = 96$

Answers

$\left(\frac{1}{2}(3)u_A^2 + \frac{1}{2}(4)u_B^2\right) - \left(\frac{1}{2}(3)(-1)^2 + \frac{1}{2}(4)(2)^2\right) = 96$

[1 mark]

$(3u_A^2 + 4u_B^2) - (3(-1)^2 + 4(2)^2) = 192$

$3u_A^2 + 4u_B^2 = 211$ **eqn 2** ***[1 mark]***

Eliminate u_A to solve the simultaneous equations:

From **eqn 1**: $u_A = \frac{5}{3} - \frac{4}{3}u_B$

Plugging this into **eqn 2**:

$3\left(\frac{5}{3} - \frac{4}{3}u_B\right)^2 + 4u_B^2 = 211$

$3\left(\frac{25}{9} - \frac{40}{9}u_B + \frac{16}{9}u_B^2\right) + 4u_B^2 = 211$

$25 - 40u_B + 16u_B^2 + 12u_B^2 = 633$

$28u_B^2 - 40u_B - 608 = 0$

$7u_B^2 - 10u_B - 152 = 0$

[1 mark for attempting to solve simultaneous equations, 1 mark for forming quadratic equation]

Using the quadratic formula to solve for u_B:

$u_B = \frac{10 \pm \sqrt{(-10)^2 - (4 \times 7 \times -152)}}{2 \times 7}$ ***[1 mark]***

$u_B = \frac{10 \pm 66}{14}$ ***[1 mark]***

So $u_B = -4$ ms^{-1} or $u_B = 5.428...$ ms^{-1}.

Subbing these back into **eqn 1**:

$u_B = -4 \Rightarrow 3u_A = 5 - (4 \times -4)$

$\Rightarrow u_A = 7$ ms^{-1} ***[1 mark]***

OR:

$u_B = 5.428... \Rightarrow 3u_A = 5 - (4 \times 5.428...)$

$\Rightarrow u_A = -5.571...$ ms^{-1} ***[1 mark]***

As is often the case, a diagram will help sort things out:

Consider the case where $u_B = 5.428...$ ms^{-1} and $u_A = -5.571...$ ms^{-1}:

Before: A ← 5.571... ms^{-1}, B → 5.428... ms^{-1} — After: A ← 1 ms^{-1}, B → 2 ms^{-1}

Clearly this won't work, as A and B will never collide.

Now consider the case where $u_B = -4$ ms^{-1} and $u_A = 7$ ms^{-1}:

Before: A → 7 ms^{-1}, B ← 4 ms^{-1} — After: A ← 1 ms^{-1}, B → 2 ms^{-1}

This will work quite nicely.

So, you can conclude that $u_B = -4$ ms^{-1} and $u_A = 7$ ms^{-1}, i.e. before the collision, A and B were moving towards each other with speeds 7 ms^{-1} and 4 ms^{-1} respectively.

[1 mark for correct values of u_A and u_B, 1 mark for explanation for why they are correct.]

That, right there, is the end of the last M2 section. Only exam papers await, and now would be a good time for a cup of tea.

M2 — Practice Exam One

1 a) Kinetic energy $= \frac{1}{2}mv^2$ ***[1 mark]***

$= \frac{1}{2} \times 80 \times 11^2 = 4840$ J ***[1 mark]***

b) The only force acting on the fireman is his weight, so, by conservation of mechanical energy:

G.P.E. lost = K.E. gained ***[1 mark]***

i.e. $mgh = 4840$ J ***[1 mark]***

$\Rightarrow h = 4840 \div (80 \times 9.8) = 6.17$ m (3 s.f.) ***[1 mark]***.

2 a) $\omega = \frac{\theta}{t} = \frac{2\pi \times 100}{60}$ ***[1 mark]***

$\omega = \frac{10\pi}{3}$ radians s^{-1} ***[1 mark]***

b) 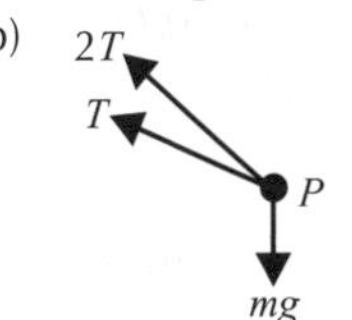

[1 mark]

c) Resolving vertically:

$2T\cos 50° + T\cos 70° = 2g$ ***[1 mark]***

$T \times (2\cos 50° + \cos 70°) = 2g$

$T \times 1.628 = 19.6$ ***[1 mark]***

$T = 12.0$ N (3 s.f.) — as required ***[1 mark]***

3 a) Call the driving force of the engine F.

Car will be travelling at maximum speed when engine is working at maximum power; i.e. acceleration will be zero.

So, resolving horizontally:

$F - 40v = 0 \Rightarrow F = 40v$ ***[1 mark]***

Find the maximum power of the engine using $P = Fv$:

$P = 40v \times v$ ***[1 mark]***

$= 40 \times 70 \times 70 = 196$ kW ***[1 mark]***.

b) Resolving forces parallel to the slope, and using $F_{net} = ma$:

$T - 40v - mg\sin\alpha = m \times 0$,

where T is the car's driving force.

So $T = 40v + mg\sin\alpha = 40v + (1300 \times 9.8 \times 0.4)$

$= 40v + 5096$ ***[1 mark]***

Now using $P = Tv$:

$40000 = Tv$ ***[1 mark]***

$40000 = v(40v + 5096)$

$\Rightarrow 40v^2 + 5096v - 40000 = 0$ ***[1 mark]***

$5v^2 + 637v - 5000 = 0$

Using the quadratic formula to solve for v:

$v = \frac{-637 + \sqrt{637^2 - (4 \times 5 \times -5000)}}{2 \times 5}$ ***[1 mark]***

$= 7.417...$ ***[1 mark]***

You can ignore the other solution that the formula gives, as it is negative, and we're looking for a (positive) speed.

So $T = \frac{40\,000}{v} = \frac{40\,000}{7.417...}$ ***[1 mark]***

$= 5390$ N (3 s.f.) ***[1 mark]***

Answers

4 a) Use the Law of Restitution for the collision between A and B, where A is travelling at $5u$ which changes to $-u$ ***[1 mark]*** after the collision. B has an initial velocity of 0:

$e = \frac{v_B - v_A}{u_A - u_B} \Rightarrow \frac{4}{5} = \frac{v_B - (-u)}{5u - 0}$ ***[1 mark]*** $\Rightarrow \frac{4}{5} = \frac{v_B + u}{5u}$

$\Rightarrow v_B = 4u - u = 3u$ ***[1 mark]***.

With collisions questions you're usually going to have to use either the Law of Restitution, or conservation of momentum, or both. So if you're stuck, plug the numbers you have into both formulas and see what you come up with.

b) Use conservation of momentum to find the mass of B:

$m_Au_A + m_Bu_B = m_Av_A + m_Bv_B$

$(1 \times 5u) + (M \times 0) = (1 \times -u) + (M \times 3u)$ ***[1 mark]***

$\Rightarrow 5u = (3M - 1)u \Rightarrow 3M - 1 = 5$ ***[1 mark]***

$\Rightarrow M = (5 + 1) \div 3 = 2$ kg ***[1 mark]***.

c) $I = Mv_B - Mu_B = 2(3u) - 2(0)$ ***[1 mark]*** $= 6u$ ***[1 mark]***.

d) Using the Law of Restitution for the collision between B and the wall: $e = \frac{v}{u}$, so rebound speed $v = 3eu$ ***[1 mark]***, since B is travelling towards the wall at $3u$ (from a)).

For B to collide again with A, its rebound speed v must be greater than A's speed, which is u. So:

$3eu > u$ ***[1 mark]***

$3e > 1$

$e > \frac{1}{3}$ ***[1 mark]***.

5 a) Taking moments about C:

$1.1 \times R_V = 0.9 \times 1.8g$

so, $1.1R_V = 15.876$

and $R_V = 14.432...$

$= 14.4$ N (to 3 s.f.)

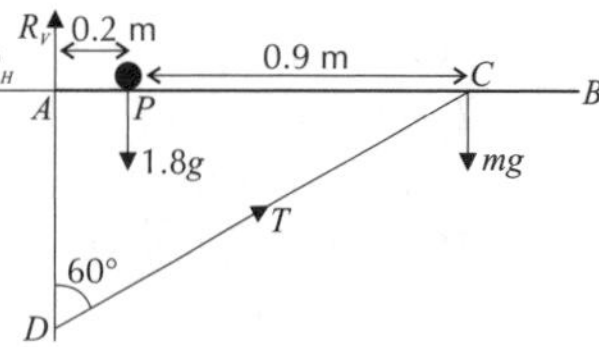

[3 marks available in total]:
- ***1 mark for taking moments about C***
- ***1 mark for correct workings***
- ***1 mark for correct value of R_V***

It's easy to get confused by which directions R_H and R_V act in. My suggestion — make an educated guess and if you're wrong they'll just turn out to be negative. No need to panic then.

b)

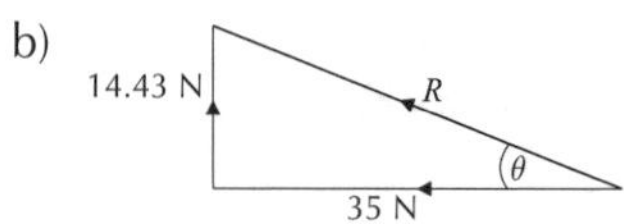

Magnitude: $|R| = \sqrt{14.43^2 + 35^2} = 37.9$ N (to 3 s.f.)

Direction: $\tan\theta = \frac{14.43}{35}$, so $\theta = 22.4°$ (to 3 s.f.) to the horizontal

[3 marks available in total]:
- ***1 mark for correct workings***
- ***1 mark for correct magnitude***
- ***1 mark for correct direction***

Pythagoras, a man of great, er, magnitude. His work is useful in pretty much any situation — try it next time you're out dancing.

c) Resolving horizontally:

$T\sin 60° = R_H = 35$

so, $T = \frac{35}{\sin 60°} = 40.414... = 40.4$ N (to 3 s.f.)

[3 marks available in total]:
- ***1 mark for resolving horizontally***
- ***1 mark for correct workings***
- ***1 mark for correct value of T***

d) Taking moments about A:

$(0.2 \times 1.8g) + (1.1 \times mg) = 1.1 \times T\cos 60°$

so, $10.78m = 22.227... - 3.528 = 18.699..$

and $m = 1.73$ kg (to 3 s.f.)

[3 marks available in total]:
- ***1 mark for taking moments about A***
- ***1 mark for correct workings***
- ***1 mark for correct value of m***

6 a) The ice cream has an axis of symmetry running through OA, so the COM must lie on this line.

First find the centres of mass of the sphere and conical shell separately.

By symmetry, the COM of the sphere is at A, i.e. 12 cm above O ***[1 mark]***.

The centre of mass of a conical shell is $\frac{1}{3}h$ above the 'base', on the line from the centre of the 'base' to the vertex, where h is the shell's height.

i.e. the COM of the conical shell in this example is:

$\frac{1}{3}(12)$ cm below A = 4 cm below A, or 8 cm above O ***[1 mark]***.

Now just use the method for finding the COM of composite shapes to find the COM of the whole ice cream:

Using $\Sigma my = \bar{y}\Sigma m$:

$(0.4 \times 12) + (0.02 \times 8) = \bar{y}(0.4 + 0.02)$ ***[1 mark]***

$\Rightarrow \bar{y} = 4.96 \div 0.42 = 11.809... = 11.8$ (3 s.f.) ***[1 mark]***

So the COM of the ice cream is 11.8 cm above O, correct to 3 significant figures.

b) Here's a diagram of the forces acting on the model:

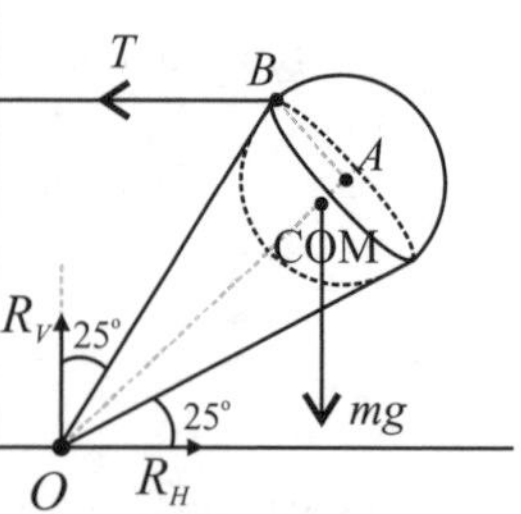

Resolving forces parallel and perpendicular to the ice cream would be a bit tricky, as it's a bit of a weird shape. Instead, the best idea is probably to find the perpendicular distances from O to the lines of action of the forces, i.e. the vertical distance from O to the wire and the horizontal distance from O to the COM. These can both be found using trig.

The components of the reaction force, R, can be ignored as moments are being taken about O.

Answers

First consider the vertical distance from O to the wire, marked y on the diagram:

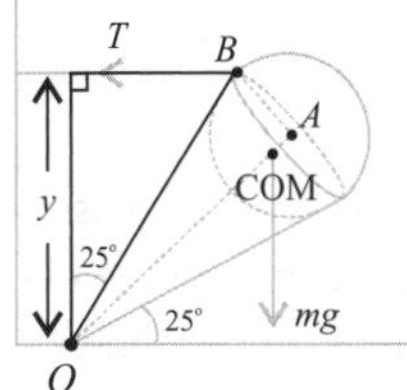

Before you can calculate y, you need to find the length OB:

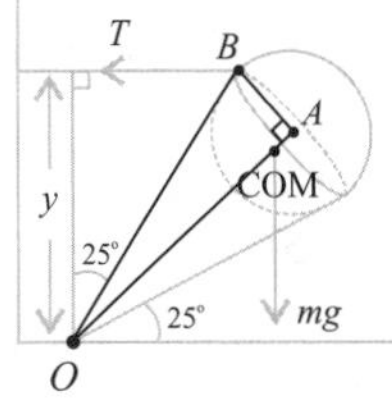

In triangle OAB, OA = 12 cm and

$\angle AOB = [90° - (25° + 25°)] \div 2 = 20°$ ***[1 mark]***

$\cos 20° = \frac{OA}{OB} \Rightarrow OB = \frac{12}{\cos 20°} = 12.770...$ cm ***[1 mark]***

Now using trig to find y:

$\cos 25° = \frac{y}{OB}$ ***[1 mark]***

$\Rightarrow y = 12.770... \times \cos 25° = 11.573...$ cm ***[1 mark]***

Now consider the horizontal distance from O to COM, marked x on the diagram:

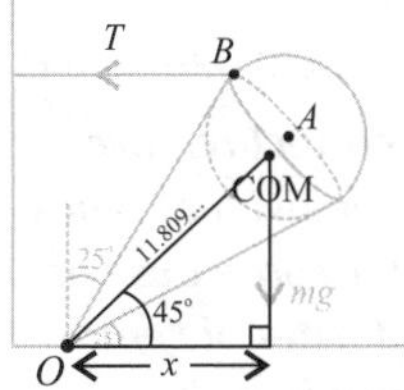

$\cos 45° = \frac{x}{11.809...}$ ***[1 mark]***

$\Rightarrow x = (11.809...)\cos 45° = 8.3505...$ ***[1 mark]***

The model is in equilibrium, so taking moments about O:

Moments clockwise = Moments anticlockwise

$mgx = Ty$

$\Rightarrow 2 \times 9.8 \times 8.3505... = T \times 11.573...$ ***[1 mark]***

$\Rightarrow T = 163.6716... \div 11.573... = 14.1417...$

So T = 14.1 N (3 s.f.) ***[1 mark]***

Well, that was a little bit tricky. The important thing is to decide whether resolving forces will make taking moments easier, or if, as in this case, calculating the distances straight off is the way to go. It's also a good idea to draw plenty of diagrams for these questions — that way you can picture exactly what's going on.

7 a) Consider motion vertically, taking up as positive:

$u = 10\sin 20°$, $a = -9.8$, $v = 0$.

Use $v^2 = u^2 + 2as$ ***[1 mark]***:

$0 = (10\sin 20°)^2 - 19.6s$ ***[1 mark]***

$\Rightarrow s = (10\sin 20°)^2 \div 19.6 = 0.597$ m.

The frisbee is thrown from 1 m above the ground, so the maximum height reached is 1 + 0.597 = 1.60 m (3 s.f.) ***[1 mark]***

b) Again consider vertical motion:

$u = 10\sin 20°$, $a = -9.8$, $s = -1$, $t = ?$.

Use $s = ut + \frac{1}{2}at^2$ ***[1 mark]***:

$-1 = (10\sin 20°)t - 4.9t^2$ ***[1 mark]***

$\Rightarrow 4.9t^2 - (10\sin 20°)t - 1 = 0$.

Use the quadratic formula to find t:

$$t = \frac{10\sin 20 + \sqrt{(-10\sin 20)^2 + (4 \times 4.9 \times 1)}}{9.8}$$ ***[1 mark]***

$= 0.91986... = 0.920$ s (3 s.f.) ***[1 mark]***

You don't need to worry about the other value of t that the formula gives you as it will be negative, and you can't have a negative time.

c) You need to know the time that the second stone is in the air. It is thrown when the first stone is at its highest point. Considering the vertical motion of the first stone:

$u = 10\sin 20°$, $a = -9.8$, $v = 0$, $t = ?$

Use $v = u + at$:

$0 = 10\sin 20° - 9.8t$ ***[1 mark]***

$\Rightarrow t = 10\sin 20° \div 9.8 = 0.3490...$ ***[1 mark]***

The first stone lands after 0.9198... seconds, so the second stone is in the air for:

0.9198... – 0.3490... = 0.5708... seconds ***[1 mark]***

Now considering the vertical motion of the second stone:

$u = u_y$, $a = -9.8$, $s = -1$, $t = 0.5708...$

Use $s = ut + \frac{1}{2}at^2$:

$-1 = (0.5708...)u_y - 4.9(0.5708...)^2$ ***[1 mark]***

$\Rightarrow u_y = 1.0454...$ ***[1 mark]***

Now considering the horizontal motion of the second stone:

$u = u_x$, $a = 0$, $t = 0.5708...$, $s = 9$

Use $s = ut + \frac{1}{2}at^2$:

$9 = (0.5708...)u_x$ ***[1 mark]***

$\Rightarrow u_x = 15.7656...$ ***[1 mark]***

You can now use Pythagoras and trig to find the initial speed and angle of projection:

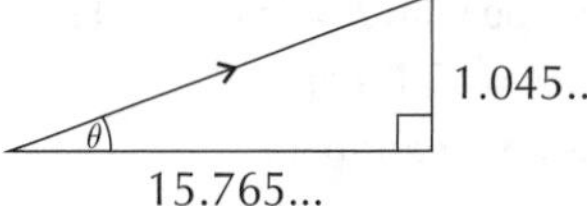

speed = $\sqrt{(15.765...)^2 + (1.045...)^2} = 15.8$ ms^{-1} (3 s.f.)

[1 mark]

$\tan\theta = \frac{1.045...}{15.765...} \Rightarrow \theta = 3.79°$ (3 s.f.) ***[1 mark]***

Answers

M2 — Practice Exam Two

1 First calculate the speed of the ball immediately before it hits the ground, taking down as positive:
$u = 0$; $a = 9.8$; $s = 5$; $v = ?$
Use $v^2 = u^2 + 2as$:
$v^2 = 0 + (2 \times 9.8 \times 5) = 98$ ***[1 mark]***
$\Rightarrow v = \sqrt{98}$. ***[1 mark]***
Now use the formula for the coefficient of restitution for a collision with a smooth plane surface:

$$e = \frac{\text{speed of rebound}}{\text{speed of approach}}$$

So: $0.7 = \frac{\text{speed of rebound}}{\sqrt{98}}$ ***[1 mark]***
$\Rightarrow$ speed of rebound $= 0.7\sqrt{98} = 6.93 \text{ ms}^{-1}$ (3 s.f.) ***[1 mark]***.

2 Friction is the only external force doing work on the particle, so the work-energy principle gives:
W.D. by friction = change in K.E. + change in P.E. ***[1 mark]***
Change in K.E. $= \frac{1}{2}m(v^2 - u^2)$ ***[1 mark]***
$= \frac{1}{2} \times 9 \times (0^2 - 11^2) = -544.5$ J ***[1 mark]***
Change in P.E. $= mgh$ ***[1 mark]***
$= 9 \times 9.8 \times 8\sin 30° = 352.8$ J ***[1 mark]***
So, W.D. by friction $= -544.5 + 352.8$
$= -192$ J (3 s.f.) ***[1 mark]***

Don't worry, you haven't broken maths — the work done by friction is supposed to be negative, because it's being done in the opposite direction to how the particle is moving. Phew.

3 a) Bus is travelling at constant speed, so resolve horizontally with $F = ma$ to find the driving force of the engine, T:
$T - 4500 = 0 \Rightarrow T = 4500$ N ***[1 mark]***
Power of engine = Driving force × velocity ***[1 mark]***
$= 4500 \times 14 = 63$ kW ***[1 mark]***

b) Call the new driving force of the engine T':

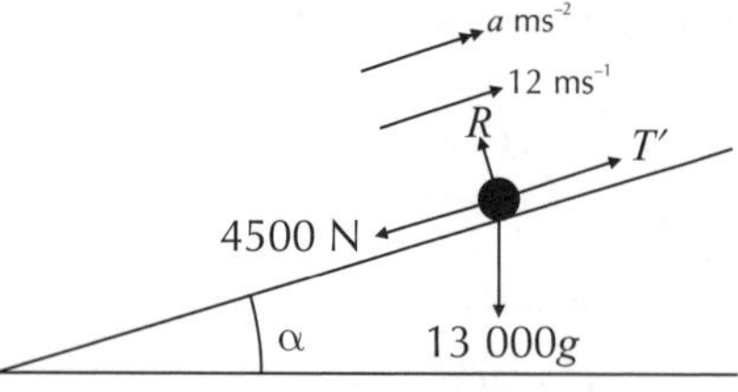

Use Power $= Fv$ to find T':
$72\,000 = T' \times 12 \Rightarrow T' = 6000$ N
Resolve parallel to the slope with $F = ma$ to find a:
$T' - (4500 + 13\,000g\sin\alpha) = 13\,000a$
Substitute known values and rearrange:
$a = \frac{6000 - 4500 - 3640}{13\,000} = -0.165 \text{ ms}^{-2}$ (3 s.f.)
[4 marks available — 1 mark for using Power = Fv, 1 mark for finding the new driving force of the engine, 1 mark for resolving parallel to the slope and 1 mark for correct final answer.]

4 a) Since both the circle and the rectangle are made from the same uniform material, their masses are in proportion to their areas:
Circle $m_1 = \pi r^2 = \pi \times 2^2 = 4\pi$
Rectangle $m_2 = 1.5 \times 1 = 1.5$
Taking the point P as the origin, the centre of mass of the circle, $(x_1, y_1) = (0, 0)$, since P is the centre of the circle.
The centre of mass of the rectangle is on both the horizontal and vertical lines of symmetry of the rectangle: $(x_2, y_2) = (0.75, 0.5)$.

Now use the formula to find the x- and y-coordinates of the centre of mass of the shape separately:
$m_1x_1 + m_2x_2 = \bar{x}(m_1 + m_2)$
$\Rightarrow (4\pi \times 0) + (1.5 \times 0.75) = \bar{x}(4\pi + 1.5)$
$\Rightarrow 1.125 = \bar{x} \times 14.066...$
$\Rightarrow \bar{x} = 0.0799...$
$m_1y_1 + m_2y_2 = \bar{y}(m_1 + m_2)$
$\Rightarrow (4\pi \times 0) + (1.5 \times 0.5) = \bar{y}(4\pi + 1.5)$
$\Rightarrow 0.75 = \bar{y} \times 14.066...$
$\Rightarrow \bar{y} = 0.0533...$

The <u>distance</u> of the COM from P can be found using Pythagoras:

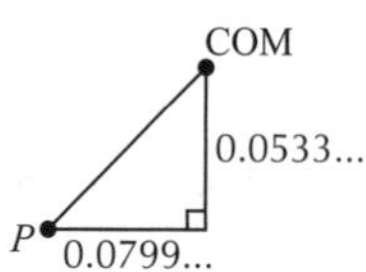

Distance $= \sqrt{0.0799...^2 + 0.0533...^2} = 0.0961$ cm (3 s.f.)
[5 marks available — 1 mark for correct relative masses of both shapes, 1 mark for individual centre of mass for both shapes, 1 mark for correct use of formula, 1 mark for correct coordinates of centre of mass, 1 mark for correct distance from P]

b) The shape is being hung from Q. Drawing a sketch will make it easier to see what's going on:

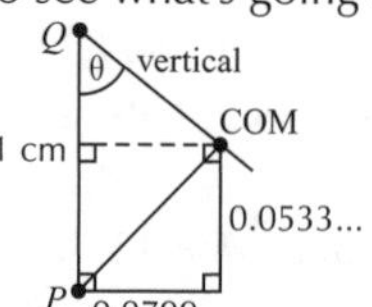

θ is the angle that PQ makes with the vertical.
Using basic trigonometry:
$\theta = \tan^{-1}\left(\frac{0.0799...}{1 - 0.0533...}\right) = 4.83°$ (3 s.f.)
[3 marks available — 1 mark for correct sides of the right-angled triangle, 1 mark for correct working, 1 mark for correct final answer]

Answers

5 a)

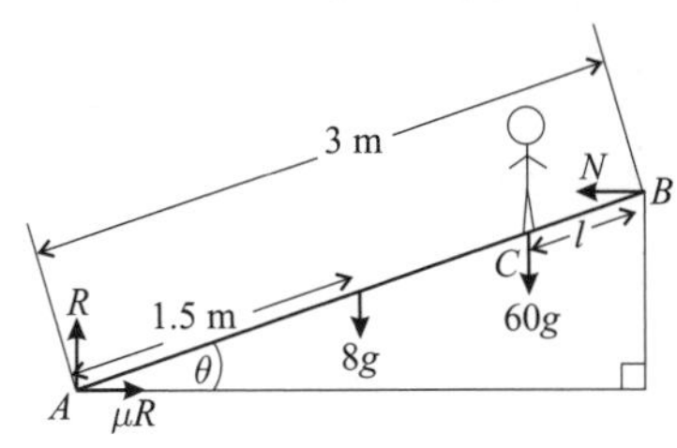

Resolving vertically:
$R = 8g + 60g = 68g$ ***[1 mark]***
Beam is in limiting equilibrium so $F = \mu R$:
$199 = \mu \times 68g$ ***[1 mark]***
$\mu = 0.298... = 0.3$ to 1 significant figure ***[1 mark]***

Drawing all the forces on the diagram is always the best way of starting one of these questions.

b) Resolving horizontally: $N = \mu R = 199$ N ***[1 mark]***
Taking moments about A:
$((3 - l) \times 60g\cos\theta) + (1.5 \times 8g\cos\theta)$ ***[1 mark]***
$= 3 \times 199\sin\theta$ ***[1 mark]***
Divide through by $\cos\theta$:
$((3 - l) \times 60g) + (1.5 \times 8g) = 3 \times 199\tan\theta$ ***[1 mark]***
$\Rightarrow 180g - 60gl + 12g = 597\tan\theta$

$\tan\theta = 0.45$ (from question),
so $180g + 12g - 268.65 = 60gl$
$l = 2.74$ m (3 s.f.) ***[1 mark]***

You could have taken moments about B instead. This'd mean one extra moment, but you wouldn't have had to resolve horizontally first. It's swings and roundabouts (or ramps and reactions).

6 a) Using the Law of Restitution for the collision between P and Q:

$e = \frac{v_Q - v_P}{u_P - u_Q} \Rightarrow 0.65 = \frac{v_Q - v_P}{5 - 0}$ ***[1 mark]***

$\Rightarrow v_Q - v_P = 5 \times 0.65 \Rightarrow v_Q - v_P = 3.25$ ...*[1]*.
Using conservation of momentum:
$m_P u_P + m_Q u_Q = m_P v_P + m_Q v_Q$

$(0.2 \times 5) + (0.6 \times 0) = (0.2 \times v_P) + (0.6 \times v_Q)$ ***[1 mark]***
$\Rightarrow 1 = 0.2v_P + 0.6v_Q \Rightarrow 5 = v_P + 3v_Q$ ...*[2]*.
Equation *[1]* + equation *[2]*:
$4v_Q = 8.25 \Rightarrow v_Q = 2.0625 = 2.06$ ms^{-1} to 3 s.f. ***[1 mark]***.
Substituting in equation *[2]*:
$5 = v_P + (3 \times 2.0625)$
$\Rightarrow v_P = 5 - (3 \times 2.0625) = -1.1875 = -1.19$ ms^{-1} to 3 s.f. ***[1 mark]***.

b) Loss of kinetic energy =
$(\frac{1}{2}m_P u_P^2 + \frac{1}{2}m_Q u_Q^2) - (\frac{1}{2}m_P v_P^2 + \frac{1}{2}m_Q v_Q^2)$
$= [(\frac{1}{2} \times 0.2 \times 5^2) + (\frac{1}{2} \times 0.6 \times 0^2)] -$
$[(\frac{1}{2} \times 0.2 \times 1.1875^2) + (\frac{1}{2} \times 0.6 \times 2.0625^2)]$ ***[1 mark]***
$= (2.5 + 0) - (0.14101... + 1.27617...)$
$= 1.0828... = 1.08$ J to 3 s.f. ***[1 mark]***.

c) Using conservation of momentum for the collision between Q and R: $m_Q u_Q + m_R u_R = m_Q v_Q + m_R v_R$

$(0.6 \times 2.0625) + (0.7 \times 0) = (0.6 \times 0) + (0.7 \times v_R)$ ***[1 mark]***
$\Rightarrow 1.2375 = 0.7v_R \Rightarrow v_R = 1.2375 \div 0.7 = 1.7678...$
[1 mark]

Using the Law of Restitution:
$e = \frac{v_R - v_Q}{u_Q - u_R} = \frac{1.7678... - 0}{2.0625 - 0}$ ***[1 mark]*** $= 0.8571...$
$= 0.857$ to 3 s.f. ***[1 mark]***.

7 a)

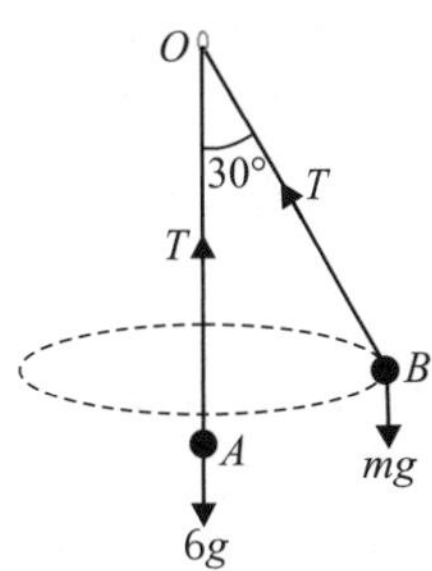

Resolving vertically for particle A:
$T = 6g$ ***[1 mark]***

Resolving vertically for particle B:
$T\cos 30° = mg \Rightarrow 6g\cos 30° = mg$ ***[1 mark]***
$\Rightarrow m = 6\cos 30° = 5.196... = 5.20$ kg (3 s.f.) ***[1 mark]***

b) Resolving horizontally for particle B, perpendicular to the direction of motion:

$6g\sin 30° = \frac{mv^2}{r}$ ***[1 mark]***

$3g = \frac{(5.196...)v^2}{0.3}$ ***[1 mark]***
$v^2 = 1.697...$
$v = 1.302... = 1.30$ ms^{-1} (3 s.f.) ***[1 mark]***

c) Here's a diagram of forces and angles:

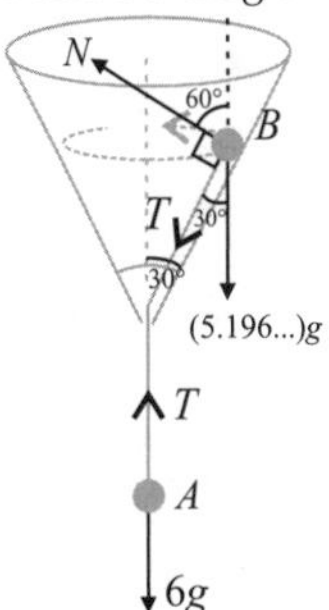

Here, N is the normal reaction of the conical shell on particle B and T is the tension in the string.
Resolving forces acting on A vertically:
$T = 6g$
Resolving forces acting on B vertically:
$(5.196... \times g) + T\cos 30° = N\cos 60°$ ***[1 mark]***

$\Rightarrow N = \frac{(5.196... \times 9.8) + (6 \times 9.8\cos 30°)}{\cos 60°}$ ***[1 mark]***

$= 203.689...$ N ***[1 mark]***

Answers

Now resolving forces acting on B horizontally and using $F = mr\omega^2$: ***[1 mark]***

$T\sin 30° + N\sin 60° = mr\omega^2$ ***[1 mark]***

$$\Rightarrow r = \frac{T\sin 30° + N\sin 60°}{m\omega^2}$$

$$r = \frac{(6 \times 9.8 \times \sin 30°) + (203.689... \times \sin 60°)}{5.196... \times (3\pi)^2}$$ ***[1 mark]***

$r = 0.446$ m (3 s.f.) ***[1 mark]***

That was fun.

8 a) Consider vertical motion, taking up as positive:

$a = -g$, $u = U\sin\alpha$, $v = 0$, $s = ?$:

Use $v^2 = u^2 + 2as$ ***[1 mark]***:

$0 = U^2\sin^2\alpha - 2gs$ ***[1 mark]***

$$\Rightarrow s = \frac{U^2\sin^2\alpha}{2g}$$ ***[1 mark]***.

The particle is initially 0.5 m above the ground, so the maximum height, h, it reaches is:

$$h = \frac{1}{2} + \frac{U^2\sin^2\alpha}{2g} = \frac{g + U^2\sin^2\alpha}{2g} \text{ m, as required}$$ ***[1 mark]***.

b) You first need to find the horizontal and vertical components of motion when the particle lands.

Vertically:

$u = U\sin\alpha$, $a = -g$, $s = -0.5$, $v = v_V$.

Use $v^2 = u^2 + 2as$ ***[1 mark]***:

$v_V^2 = U^2\sin^2\alpha + g$ ***[1 mark]***.

Horizontally, $v_H = u_H = U\cos\alpha$, as acceleration is zero ***[1 mark]***.

So, $V = \sqrt{v_V^2 + v_H^2} = \sqrt{U^2\sin^2\alpha + g + U^2\cos^2\alpha}$ ***[1 mark]***

$= \sqrt{U^2(\sin^2\alpha + \cos^2\alpha) + g}$

$= \sqrt{U^2 + g}$ ms^{-1}, as required ***[1 mark]***.

c) Resolving horizontally (taking right as +ve):

$u_x = U\cos 45° = \frac{U}{\sqrt{2}}$ $\quad a = 0$

$s = x$ $\quad t = t$

Using $s = ut + \frac{1}{2}at^2$:

$x = \frac{U}{\sqrt{2}} \times t$ ***[1 mark]***

Rearrange to make t the subject:

$t = \frac{\sqrt{2}x}{U}$ **— eqn 1**

Now resolving vertically (taking up as +ve):

$u_y = U\sin 45° = \frac{U}{\sqrt{2}}$ $\quad a = -g$

$s = y - \frac{1}{2}$ $\quad t = t$

Don't forget that the particle starts from 0.5 m above the ground — that's where $s = y - \frac{1}{2}$ comes from.

Using $s = ut + \frac{1}{2}at^2$:

$$y - \frac{1}{2} = \left(\frac{U}{\sqrt{2}} \times t\right) - \frac{1}{2}gt^2$$

$\Rightarrow y = \frac{Ut}{\sqrt{2}} - \frac{1}{2}gt^2 + \frac{1}{2}$ **— eqn 2** ***[1 mark]***

Now sub expression for t from **eqn 1** into **eqn 2**:

$$y = \frac{U\sqrt{2}x}{U\sqrt{2}} - \frac{2gx^2}{2U^2} + \frac{1}{2}$$ ***[1 mark]***

Which simplifies and rearranges to:

$y = \frac{1}{2} + x - \frac{gx^2}{U^2}$, as required. ***[1 mark]***

d) The point P has x-value $x = 0.5$ and y-value $y = 0$, so, using the expression from part c):

$$0 = \frac{1}{2} + \frac{1}{2} - \frac{g\left(\frac{1}{2}\right)^2}{U^2}$$ ***[1 mark]***

$$0 = 1 - \frac{g}{4U^2}$$ ***[1 mark]***

$$1 = \frac{g}{4U^2}$$

$U = \frac{\sqrt{g}}{2} = 1.57$ ms^{-1} (3 s.f.) ***[1 mark]***

Index

A

actual significance levels 122, 125
adding and subtracting fractions 46
adding vectors 82
addition formulas 18, 21
additive property of the Poisson distribution 96
algebraic
- division 47, 48
- fractions 46, 49, 50
- long division 47

alternative hypothesis (H_1) 121
angular speed 166, 167
approximating
- binomial distribution
  - by normal 112, 113, 115
  - by Poisson 98, 115
- Poisson distribution
  - by normal 114, 115
- roots 34
- using binomial expansions 61

arccosine x 15
arcsine x 15
arctangent x 15
areas under p.d.f.s 102-105
army of minions 18, 78
asymptotes 10, 11, 15, 16

B

bacteria 12
balance 181
bias 118
binomial distribution 98, 112, 113, 115, 125, 126
- hypothesis tests for parameter p 125, 126
- normal approximations 112, 113, 115
- Poisson approximation 98, 115
- tables 140-145

binomial expansions 58-61

C

Cartesian equations 53, 55
Central Limit Theorem 119
centres of mass 146-151, 155
centripetal force 166, 167
centroids 148
CGP Revolution 31
chain rule 24, 25, 28, 29, 64-67, 73
change in momentum 180
circular motion 166, 167
coefficient of restitution 182, 183
collisions 181-185
column vectors 83
combinations of transformations 7
common angles 18
common denominators 46
common factors 46
components
- of forces 156, 159
- of motion 162, 164

composite functions 2
composite shapes 149, 150
conical pendulums 167
conservation of momentum 181
constant of integration 30
continuity corrections 112, 114
continuous random variables 102-105
- mean 104
- median 105
- probability density functions (p.d.f.s) 102, 103
- shapes of distributions 105
- variance 104

convergent binomial expansions 60
conversion between sin and cos 21
$\cos^{-1} x$ 15
cosecant x 16, 65, 71
cotangent x 16, 65, 71
critical regions 122, 125
critical values
- in hypothesis tests 122
- normal table 109

D

definite integrals 31, 75
degree of a polynomial 47
déjà vu 74
difference of two squares 49
differential equations 78, 79
differentiation 24-29, 64-68
- e^x 25
- implicit 67, 68
- $\ln x$ 25
- parametric equations 66
- product rule 26
- quotient rule 27
- sin, cos and tan 64

discrete random variables 95, 96, 112-115
displacement vectors 83
divisor 47, 48
don't let the sun go down on me while I'm trying to catch my horse 259
domain 1-3, 11, 15
double angle formulas 19, 21, 55, 64, 74
driving force 175, 176

E

elastic collisions 182, 185
equating coefficients (partial fractions) 49
equilibrium 151, 154, 155, 157, 158
errors
- in hypothesis tests 122, 125
- percentage error in Simpson's rule 37

estimation 120
expected value
- continuous random variables 104
- Poisson distribution 95

exponentials (e^x) 10-12, 25, 30
- differentiation 25
- graphs 10, 11
- growth / decay problems 12
- integration 30

external forces 173

Index

F

factor formulas 21
finite binomial expansions 58, 60
forces 154, 170, 171, 173-176
French Revolution 31
friction 157, 158, 170
functions 1-5, 15, 16
  composite 2
  inverse 3, 10, 15
  many-to-one 1
  modulus 4, 5
  one-to-one 1, 3

G

general polynomials 48
general solutions of differential eqns 78
Godzilla 53
graphs
  exponential 10, 11
  inverse functions 3
  inverse trig functions 15
  modulus functions 4-6
  reciprocal trig functions 16
  transformations 7
gravitational potential energy 172, 173
gravity 170
groups of particles 146, 147

H

half-angle formulas 19
hiccups 73
Hugh Jackman 5, 75
hypothesis tests 121-127
  for binomial distributions 125, 126
  for normal distributions 123, 124
  for Poisson distributions 127

I

implicit differentiation 67, 68
improper algebraic fractions 50
impulse 180, 181, 185
Industrial Revolution 31
inelastic collisions 182
initial population 79
integrating trousers 103
integration 30, 31, 71-79
  $1/x$ 30
  by parts 76
  by substitution 30, 75
  e^x 30
  $f'(x)/f(x)$ 72
  $\ln x$ 76
  partial fractions 77
  to find probabilities 103
  trig functions 71, 72, 77
inverse
  functions 3, 10
  trig functions 15
iteration 34-36

J

juicy formulas 10
Jonny the horse 259

K

killing bunnies 79
kinetic energy 171, 174, 185

L

ladders 157
laminas 147-149, 151, 159
Law of Restitution 182, 183
limiting equilibrium 157
limits 75
line of action 154, 159
$\ln x$ 10, 11
  differentiation 25
  graph 10
  integration 76
  'log laws' 10, 11

M

magnitude of a vector 82, 84
many-to-one functions 1
mappings 1
maths club 26, 27
maximums 28
mean (expected value)
  continuous random variables 104
  estimate of population mean 120
  normal distributions 108, 110, 111
  Poisson distribution 95
mechanical energy 172-174
  principle of conservation 173
medians 148
minimums 28
modulus function 4
  sketching graphs 4
  solving equations 5, 6
  inequalities 6
moments 146, 154-159
momentum 180, 181, 183
morbid questions 79

N

natural log 10
non-uniform rods 155
normal approximation
  to binomial distribution 112, 113, 115
  to Poisson distribution 114, 115
normal distributions 108-111, 119
  and hypothesis tests 123, 124
  tables 139
  using tables 108-111

Index

normal reaction 157, 167
normals (straight lines) 28, 66
null hypothesis (H_0) 121
numerical integration 37

O

one-tailed hypothesis tests 121, 122
one-to-one functions 1, 3, 15

P

parallel vectors 82, 86
parameters 53
  and populations 120, 121
  Poisson distribution 95, 96
parametric equations 53-55
  differentiation 66
partial fractions 49, 50, 77
particular solutions of differential eqns 78
percentage error 37, 61
perfectly elastic collisions 182, 185
perpendicular vectors 86
pivot points 151
points of intersection (vectors) 85
Poisson distributions 95-99
  additive property 96
  approximating binomial 98
  hypothesis tests 127
  mean 95
  normal approximations 114, 115
  parameters of distribution 95, 96
  probability function 95
  tables 136-138
  the three conditions 96
  using tables 97
  variance 95
populations 118
position vectors 83, 85
power 175, 176
Premier League sticker album 172
probability density functions (p.d.f.s) 102-105
  finding probabilities 102, 103
  identifying 103
  sketching 102, 103, 105
product rule 26, 28, 65, 67
projectiles 162-164
proportion relations 78
Pythagoras' theorem 84

Q

quotients (algebraic division) 47, 48
quotient rule 27, 28, 65

R

rabbit traps 79
R addition formulas (trigonometry) 20
radial acceleration 166, 167
radians 166
random variables
  continuous 102-105
  discrete 95, 96
range (functions) 1-3
rate, average
  Poisson distribution 96
rates of change 28, 29
rational functions 46
reaction forces 156-158
reciprocals 16, 46, 65
reflections (graph transformations) 7
remainders (algebraic division) 47, 48
Remainder Theorem 48
removal method 149
resolving forces 154-157
restitution 182, 183
resultant
  forces 154-157, 171
  vectors 82
roots (finding by numerical methods) 34, 36

S

sampling 118
  bias 118
  distributions 118, 119, 121, 122
  sample means 119
scalar product 86-88
scalars 82
sectors of circles 148
secant x 16, 65, 71
significance levels 122
simple random sampling 118
simplifying expressions 46
Simpson's Rule 37
$\sin^{-1} x$ 15
skew lines (vectors) 85
standard deviation
  normal distributions 110, 111
  estimator of population standard deviations 120
standard normal distribution (Z) 108-111
standard unit vectors 83
starting conditions 79
statistical tables 136-145
statistics 118, 120
stretches (graph transformations) 7
substitution method (partial fractions) 49
symmetry 148, 150

Index

T

tables 136-145
- binomial tables 140-145
- normal tables 139
- Poisson tables 136-138
- using normal tables 108-111
- using Poisson tables 97

$\tan^{-1} x$ 15
tangents (straight lines) 28, 66
test statistics 121, 122
throwing up 164
thrust 156
tilting 151
transformations of graphs 7
translations (graph transformations) 7
trigonometry 15-21, 64, 71
- differentiation 64, 65
- identities 17-19, 55, 64, 74, 77
- integrals 71

two-tailed hypothesis tests 121, 122
Type I and Type II errors 122, 125

U

unbiased estimators 120
uniform
- rods 155
- shells 150
- solids 150

unit vectors 83, 84
upper and lower bounds (iteration) 35

V

validity of binomial expansions 60
variable resistive forces 176
variance
- continuous random variables 104
- estimator of population variance 120
- normal distributions 108, 110
- Poisson distribution 95

vectors 82-88
- 3D 83
- column 83
- displacement 83
- equations of lines 85
- magnitude 82-84
- parallel 82, 86
- perpendicular 86
- points of intersection 85
- position 83, 85
- resultant 82
- scalar product 86-88
- standard unit 83
- unit 83, 84

volumes of revolution 31

W

work done 170, 171, 173, 174
work-energy principle 173, 174
work rate 175

Z

Z (standard normal distribution) 108-111